2nd edition

PHILIP L. CARPENTER
PROFESSOR OF BACTERIOLOGY, UNIVERSITY OF RHODE ISLAND

W. B. SAUNDERS COMPANY
PHILADELPHIA AND LONDON,

MICROBIOLOGY

W. B. Saunders Company: West Washington Square,
Philadelphia, Pa.   19105

12 Dyott Street
London, W.C.1

Reprinted August, 1967, April, 1968, and September, 1968

Microbiology

PREFACE

The past few years have seen such extensive use of bacteria and other microorganisms as subjects for the study of cellular and subcellular biology that the nonmicrobiologist may forget that microorganisms are interesting biologic forms in their own right, and that they have been best known through the years for their helpful and harmful activities.

Most of those who started in the field before World War II were indoctrinated as bacteriologists, mycologists, protozoologists, etc., and had a minimum of contact with the other microorganisms. Nowadays it is increasingly necessary to be familiar with all groups, including algae and viruses. It is for this reason that there has been an attempt to provide some introduction to all microorganisms in this book. Obviously, however, it is possible only to scratch the surface in a one-semester course.

As in the first edition, the plan was to devote approximately equal space to: (1) a general survey of microorganisms; (2) a detailed study of the biology of bacteria—their metabolism, growth, death, and genetics; (3) the ecologic relationships and roles of microorganisms in natural or controlled environments such as soil, water, food and milk, and in industry; and (4) the interactions of pathogenic microorganisms and their animal or plant hosts. This treatment will orient the student within the micro-bial world, impress upon him the unity of vital processes, and point out the interplay among microscopic organisms and between them and macroscopic organisms.

There have been several major changes in the second edition. First is the inclusion of an early chapter on the history of microbiology, in which the development of microbiologic ideas and concepts is traced. Discussion of systematic bacteriology, including methods and classification, is also introduced near the beginning of the book, so that the student will be equipped to deal with organisms he may isolate early in the course. The chapter on bacterial metabolism, parts of which were rewritten by Dr. Norris P. Wood of the University of Rhode Island, reflects a more modern and perhaps more rigorous approach. Additional metabolic pathways and formulae of biologically active substances are included in order to provide an opportunity for the inquisitive student to visualize and gain insight into the complexity of biologic materials and processes. Major advances in microbial genetics within recent years necessitated complete revision of this chapter. Finally, the discussions of food and dairy microbiology are gathered together into a single chapter.

This book should provide a foundation for further study in the medical professions or in the various specialties such as pathogenic bacteriology and sanitary, soil, and industrial microbiology. It should also be suitable as the only experience in the field for students of home economics, agriculture, liberal arts, teacher education, pharmacy, and nursing.

I would like to thank all who helped in any way. Many offered suggestions for the revision, either to me directly or to the staff of the W. B. Saunders Company. These suggestions were very useful and most of them have been incorporated. Various individuals and companies kindly provided illustrative material, as noted. Finally, it is a special pleasure to thank my wife, Helen Carpenter, for patiently enduring the long silences necessary for study, and then as patiently transcribing my hieroglyphics into legible manuscript.

PHILIP L. CARPENTER
Kingston, Rhode Island

A LETTER TO STUDENTS

Before you read the first chapter I would like to welcome you to a new field of study and to wish you pleasure and profit from it. I would also like to give you a bird's-eye view of what is ahead and offer a few suggestions that may help you get the most from your study.

Microbiology is not just a book or a course in college. It is the study of small organisms, which have many of the same attributes as other forms of life. By learning from test tube experiments how microorganisms behave we can learn many things about how other organisms function.

No doubt you know that several kinds of organisms comprise the subject of this book: protozoa, algae, fungi, bacteria, and viruses. To begin, therefore, you will look at the various groups of microscopic organisms, both individually and as members of the plant or animal kingdom, concluding with a fairly detailed study of bacterial cells. Bacterial "anatomy," if you please, has been actively reinvestigated during the past fifteen or twenty years by new microscopic methods.

Next you will learn about the growth and death of bacteria and some of the metabolic processes that accompany growth and the search for energy. I hope you will be able to appreciate the simplicity and beauty of the schemes by which, one step at a time, living cells bring about seemingly complicated chemical changes. You will also learn that bacteria behave genetically like many other organisms; they undergo mutation, and some can apparently conjugate in a pseudosexual manner.

With the background you have at this point the section on applied microbiology will be a logical application of facts and principles already encountered. The kinds and numbers of microorganisms and their activities in natural and controlled environments can often be predicted from knowledge of their physiologic characteristics.

Lastly, you will make an excursion into pathogenic microbiology: infection, resistance and immunity, chemotherapy, and the ecology of infectious disease, with a few illustrations of bacterial, fungal, or viral infections of plants or animals.

When you study, get an overall picture of the subject first by skimming the subheadings within each chapter. Write a *brief* topic outline of a chapter or subject. Don't memorize a lot of details first; they never make sense by themselves, but if you know the general outline, the details fit into place without much conscious effort. Learning details without knowing how they are connected with one another is like looking at a large portrait only a few inches away; all you see is an eye or a foot, and your impression of the picture is distorted and incomplete until you back away and look at it as a whole.

Many of your fellow students approach microbiology with dread, expecting to be required to memorize long lists of names or other terms that seem to mean nothing. Naturally, there are unfamiliar terms in any new subject, but, as you read, hear, *and use* them, they soon become familiar. Moreover, the words do mean something, as you can learn with only a little trouble. You will note that there is no glossary in this book. Instead, the index contains boldface references to pages where terms are explained. It will be more work, but if you look up a term in the text and read a few sentences about it, the word will mean more to you, and you will remember it longer.

There are study questions after most chapters. Some are "fact" questions; some call for thought. If you cannot answer them, review the chapter and think about it, or look up some of the supplementary readings. Specific page references to the books listed at the end of each chapter have been omitted; decide from the comments which book contains the information you desire, and then use its table of contents or index.

If you are interested in still further information on some topic, there are many periodicals that publish the results of research. The *Journal of General Microbiology,* for example, is a British publication with excellent papers on the biologic activities of the various microorganisms. Its closest American counterpart is the *Journal of Bacteriology. Applied Microbiology* publishes papers on antibiotics, fermentations, enzymes, and the microbiology of manufactured products. The *Journal of Infectious Diseases* contains articles on the causes, pathogenesis, host response, and laboratory diagnosis of diseases caused by microorganisms. Papers surveying recent work on a topic are found in *Bacteriological Reviews.* Students who wish to try their facility in French will find interesting papers in the *Annales de l'Institut Pasteur,* which is similar to the *Journal of Infectious Diseases* but emphasizes immunization against bacterial and viral infections. The German equivalent is the *Zentralblatt für Bakteriologie, Parasitenkunde, Infektionskrankheiten und Hygiene.* A translation of the Russian *Mikrobiologiia* is now available, so it is not necessary to know this language in order to read some of the Russian literature.

Several chapters of this book were almost completely rewritten for the second edition because the advances in five years were so great. Doubtless some statements made today may not appear true tomorrow, but if you know what is *believed* today, you can better evaluate the discoveries of tomorrow.

PHILIP L. CARPENTER
Kingston, Rhode Island

CONTENTS

II BIOLOGY OF BACTERIA

III APPLIED MICROBIOLOGY

IV MICROORGANISMS AND DISEASE

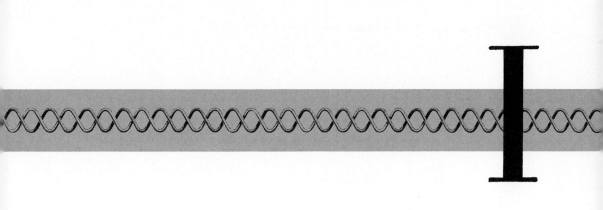

MICROORGANISMS

THE WORLD OF MICROORGANISMS

Bacteria, yeasts, molds, algae, protozoa, and viruses constitute a seemingly heterogeneous group of biologic entities, but they resemble one another in their small size and relative simplicity of structure and organization, and hence are called microorganisms or, as some authorities prefer, *protists* (Greek: *protista,* the very first). Study of them constitutes the science of microbiology.

Most microorganisms are unicellular, some consist of loose aggregates of independent cells showing little if any specialization of function, and some form long filaments containing several potentially independent vital units or protoplasts within a single cell wall (e.g., *coenocytic* molds and algae). Structural simplicity does not, however, necessarily imply physiologic simplicity. Microorganisms perform the same fundamental activities within their single cells as "higher" organisms do within their many-celled structures: utilization of food and energy, formation of new protoplasm, reproduction. It is important to remember that microorganisms are essentially the same biologically as other organisms.

Their small size makes it difficult to study the anatomy of individual cells, but the homogeneity of a population of microorganisms often permits an experimenter to investigate a particular phenomenon or chemical reaction (e.g., the metabolism of an amino acid) free from the complications introduced by the multicellularity of larger organisms. It is for this reason that microorganisms are favorite subjects of investigation by geneticists and cell physiologists. Moreover, the spectrum of forms comprised by the microbial world includes those on the border line between obviously living organisms and obviously nonliving matter. Study of these forms provides insight into the fundamental nature of life.

THE ORIGIN OF MICROORGANISMS

It is believed that about four and one-half billion years ago, after the

3

Earth had formed, oceans filled the depths between the mountains, and pools of water filled depressions in the rock. The atmosphere contained water vapor, methane, ammonia, and hydrogen but no oxygen or carbon dioxide.

Formation of Organic Compounds

The waters of the early Earth were salty with minerals dissolved from the rocks and became the repository of chemicals formed during a period of millions of years. Chance interactions of methane molecules gave rise to short carbon chains and later to longer ones, and eventually ring compounds, such as benzene, were formed. Further reactions of these hydrocarbons with water yielded sugars, glycerin and fatty acids. Union of ammonia with fatty acids produced amino acids. Some of these reactions occurred in the atmosphere, facilitated by electric discharges or by ultraviolet light that reached the Earth

from the sun unhampered by gaseous oxygen, which was absent at that time. The feasibility of forming amino acids by this kind of process was demonstrated in 1953 by Miller. He subjected a mixture of water vapor, methane, ammonia, and hydrogen to the electric discharge from an induction coil in a closed glass system and after a few hours detected glycine, α-alanine, and other amino acids (Fig. 1-1).

Another essential type of compound that formed before life appeared contains nitrogen as well as carbon within a ring structure. Purines and pyrimidines are the principal compounds of this type, and they are present in the nucleic acids of all living cells.

Ultimately these first organic compounds reacted with one another to form molecules of greater size and complexity. Polysaccharides were produced by the interactions of simple sugar molecules, fats were formed by the union of glycerin and fatty acids, and amino acids combined to yield proteins. These

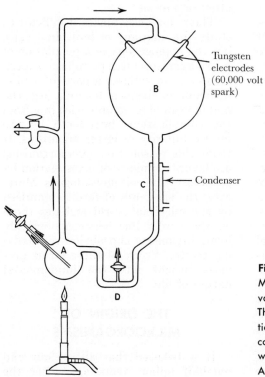

Tungsten electrodes (60,000 volt spark)

Condenser

Figure 1-1. Spark-discharge apparatus used by Miller to produce organic compounds from water vapor, hydrogen, methane, and ammonia gases. The water in flask A is boiled to promote circulation. Products formed by the discharge in B are condensed at C and return to A via U-tube, D, which prevents backflow. (Redrawn from Miller, Ann. New York Acad. Sci., 69:261, 1957.)

processes were slow, but time was not significant because there were no organisms to utilize and destroy the organic substances as they arose. Some compounds doubtless decomposed, but the steady input of solar energy promoted gradual accumulation of substances of increasing complexity, and the various reactions accelerated as the constituents were concentrated by evaporation of water in prehistoric pools or by adsorption to colloidal clay particles.

The development of proteins was important because many proteins, either alone or with the aid of certain metals, possess catalytic properties and can hasten certain chemical reactions. Catalysts of this sort are known as enzymes, and reactions controlled by enzymes are typical of living systems.

Nucleic Acids and the Beginning of "Life"

A somewhat more complicated structure resulted from the union of purines and pyrimidines with sugar and phosphate. These compounds, called nucleotides, are capable of joining each other, to form long chainlike supermolecules which commonly occur in the now familiar helical or coiled form (Fig. 1-2). These nucleic acids possess the remarkable ability to direct the formation of more nucleic acids of the same kind and also the formation of specific proteins. It is at this point that we can *begin* to think of inventing the word "life."

It must be understood that all these chemical reactions occurred very slowly and that probably two billion years elapsed before the first self-reproducing form appeared. At first, chance directed the union of one atom or compound with another atom or compound, and those products persisted that possessed greater stability than the separate components. The process was one of trial and error and displayed in rudimentary form features that later appeared in the evolutionary development of living organisms able to survive under conditions of biologic competition.

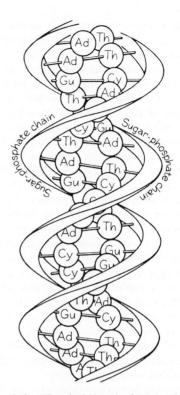

Figure 1-2. The double coil of DNA. The purines, adenine (Ad) and guanine (Gu), and the pyrimidines, thymine (Th) and cytosine (Cy), are joined in pairs, as shown, by hydrogen bonds, and hold the molecule in a rigid structure. (From Sussman: Animal Growth and Development. Englewood Cliffs, N. J., Prentice-Hall, Inc., 1960.)

CHARACTERISTICS OF LIVING SYSTEMS

After 1664, when Hooke observed that plants are composed of many smaller individual structures, it became recognized that the cell is the basic unit of life, whether plant or animal. Exactly what this basic unit comprises is largely a matter of definition. At the level of the higher plant or animal there is no disagreement: the cell is a discrete unit with common structural and chemical properties. It is bounded by a wall or membrane, which encloses cytoplasm containing proteins, deoxyribonucleic acid, and ribonucleic acid as necessary constituents. It has certain chemical activities known collectively as metabolism: the synthetic processes by which all its constituents are made from available ingredients and the transformations that convert energy from external sources into energy-rich bonds. Reproduction of the cell takes place by division, following the orderly increase in the amount of its chemical components.

At the level of the smallest microorganisms there has been some difference of opinion as to what constitutes a cell or even a living organism. Viruses consist of protein and deoxyribonucleic *or* ribonucleic acid, and in some cases (e.g., the myxoviruses) are apparently bounded by a membrane, but they lack the ability to perform metabolic activities or to replicate outside the proper environment (i.e., a host cell). They are, in fact, replicated only from and in the form of their genetic material; protein may be synthesized simultaneously but separately, and the two components are assembled at a later stage.

Bacteria are approximately the same size as the substructures or *organelles* of the cells of higher plants or animals that carry out various metabolic and reproductive activities, and electron microscopy reveals hardly any organelle in the bacterial cell that is structurally identical with a similar functional unit in the cells of larger organisms. Some authors therefore consider that bacteria are closer to the viruses than they are to "cells." However, bacteria possess both kinds of nucleic acid (DNA and RNA); all their components increase and the cells divide by a process of fission; and they possess many enzymes, some of which are active in converting the energy of foodstuffs into the high-energy chemical bonds essential for biologic syntheses.

The definition of life is essentially a philosophic matter that cannot be settled by argument, although discussion serves the useful purpose of focusing attention on the complexity of the problem. Without entering the realm of controversy we can note that every biologic form contains protein and deoxy-

ribonucleic acid or ribonucleic acid. Protein serves protective and catalytic functions, and in the latter role participates in energy transformation and transfer. Nucleic acids include the genetic material wherein is stored the information necessary to determine the chemical and physical behavior of the system. These ingredients and activities seem to constitute the irreducible minimum consistent with life.

The Primordial Form

The first living form was very simple by present standards. It probably consisted of little more than an aggregate of nucleic acids and proteins, perhaps surrounded by a layer of proteins and nutrient materials. This description sounds very much like that of what we call viruses today, and in fact the primordial form has been called a *protovirus* (Fig. 1-3). It should be remarked that this protovirus was capable of securing its constituents from the organic substances created by chance in prehistoric pools and oceans, whereas modern viruses secure their constituents only from the cells of living hosts: animal, plant, or microbial.

Some authors believe that modern viruses represent degenerate forms of higher microorganisms in which the parasitic state evolved as a consequence of the ready availability of nutrient substances within host cells. It is also postulated that viruses are direct descendants of the primordial protoviruses, or

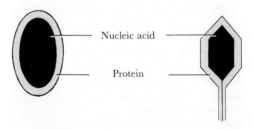

Figure 1-3. On the left is a sketch of a postulated "protovirus," the first living object. On the right is a sketch of a bacterial virus (T2 coliphage).

that they consist of nucleic acid and protein fragments originally derived from the cells of higher organisms. Whatever their origin, present day viruses are incapable of replicating in any nonliving nutrient solution so far devised. Conditions two or three billion years ago were undoubtedly much different from any yet produced in modern laboratories. Moreover, time was not a factor of importance; replication of the protovirus may have required one year, one hundred years, even one million years. Twentieth century investigators decide that their viruses are "dead" if they see no signs of reproduction within a few days; actual replication of the individual virus particle requires only a few minutes.

Development of Synthetic Activities

As early microbial forms multiplied, they utilized organic substances faster than these substances could be produced by chance chemical interaction. Eventually the available supply ran out, but ultimately the catalytic (that is, enzymatic) powers of primitive microorganisms developed to the extent that some forms could use simpler substances and perform increasingly complicated synthetic reactions. Synthesis requires energy, and at some early stage a mechanism became available for liberating energy from the chemical bonds of microbial nutrients by a process of rearrangement. Although this mechanism is not efficient in the absence of atmospheric oxygen, nevertheless it does provide some energy. Carbon dioxide may be a by-product.

Eventually organisms developed that possessed a pigment similar to chlorophyll and were able to secure energy from sunlight, using inorganic nutrients. Primitive plants resembling algae finally appeared. They produced carbohydrates and free oxygen from water and carbon dioxide. Thereafter types of life evolved that required oxygen and secured energy by direct oxidation; these included microorganisms that could oxidize and utilize plant carbohydrates.

For perhaps two billion years there was slow formation, evolution, and growth of microorganisms in the mud at the bottoms of pools, until about 600,000,000 years ago, when atmospheric oxygen had accumulated to about 1 per cent of the present level. According to a theory by Berkner and Marshall, this amount of oxygen shielded the oceans from lethal ultraviolet solar radiation and permitted an explosive multiplication and evolution of diverse forms of oceanic life (see Fig. 1-4). The oxygen level rose more rapidly, and about 400,000,000 years ago reached a concentration that permitted the emergence of life onto the land. An explosive evolution of terrestrial forms then followed, lush forests grew, and free oxygen levels may have reached ten times that of today. Atmospheric carbon dioxide, which insulates the Earth and prevents it from losing heat, was depleted and therefore the ice ages of 250,000,000 years ago took place. The oxygen level then decreased and has since fluctuated at or somewhat below the present value.

Cellular Evolution

Reproduction by means of particle or cell division restricted the size of the individual to dimensions that doubtless were chemically most efficient. Metabolic activity provided the energy for synthesis of components not immediately available in the environment.

Structural features that improved the survival powers of organisms were gradually added. Some of the most primitive microorganisms known today possess flagella and are independently motile. It is presumed that their extinct direct ancestors were also flagellate, but of course it is not known how many millions of years elapsed between the original protovirus and these ancestral flagellates. Independent locomotion provided a wider choice of food supply and enabled the progeny of a given par-

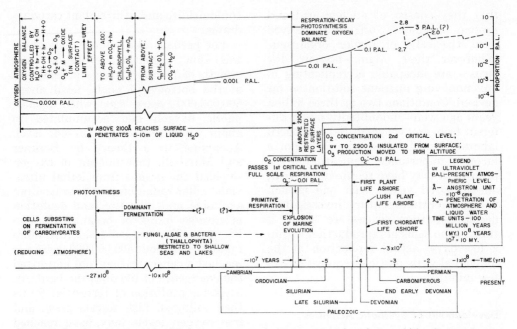

Figure 1-4. Postulated relationship between atmospheric oxygen and evolution of life. Oxygen (upper curve) is expressed as a fraction of the present atmospheric level (P.A.L.). (From Berkner and Marshall, J. Atmosph. Sci., 22:257, 1965.)

ent to migrate to a more favorable environment. Each evolutionary form might thus establish itself under those conditions best for its own survival.

A variety of microorganisms with differing morphologic and physiologic characteristics eventually appeared. However, the structural and behavioral properties of any organism are variable within a limited range. For example, most cells in a bacterial culture are killed or inhibited by a certain concentration of a disinfectant or an antibiotic; a few cells may be killed by a slightly smaller dose, whereas a few withstand a greater concentration. By subjecting the progeny of the latter to successively higher doses, stepwise increases in resistance are sometimes achieved. Morphologic and physiologic variations also occur among microorganisms; for example, nonmotile strains of species that usually are motile. The reverse variation is sometimes observed.

Series of related organisms can be found that differ only slightly from one type to the next. This phenomenon has

long been known among higher plants and animals, but microbiologists have only recently begun to appreciate the extent of intergrading among very small organisms. The living world can be pictured as a spectrum of forms varying almost imperceptibly from one to the next. Microorganisms constitute a small portion of this spectrum.

MICROORGANISMS IN THE PLANT AND ANIMAL KINGDOMS

Possible evolutionary relationships of microorganisms and higher plants and animals are shown in Figure 1-5. Structural development of the original protovirus through some early bacteria-like organisms may eventually have yielded the primitive flagellates from which most later forms of life arose.

Ancestral Flagellates

The ancestral flagellates are presumed to have possessed characteristics

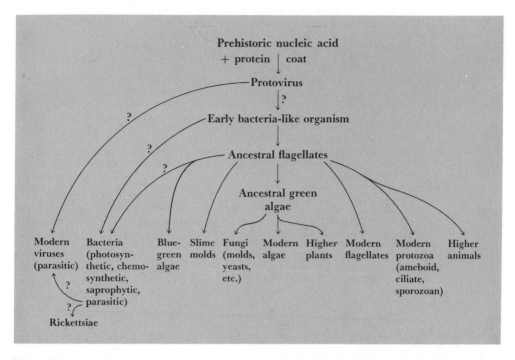

Figure 1-5. Postulated evolutionary development of modern plants, animals, and microorganisms from the original nucleic acid.

now associated with both plants and animals. Figure 1-6 shows the suggested basic structure of such an organism. It will be observed to be very similar to some modern flagellates. A definite cell structure called the nucleus is represented, and presumably the nucleic acid was concentrated within this organ. Chloroplasts contained the photosynthetic pigment by which light energy was utilized. A flagellum permitted motility and the active search for favorable conditions, including supplies of food.

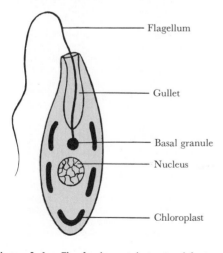

Figure 1-6. The fundamental structural features of a flagellate. Ancestral flagellates may have looked something like this.

Evolution of Animals

The evolution of animal-like forms was characterized by development of improved methods of locomotion and the use of preformed food materials. Evolution from the ancestral flagellates must have proceeded in several directions, perhaps simultaneously. One line led by direct descent to the modern flagellates (Fig. 1-7). A second line represented development of other modern protozoa: ameboid (Fig. 1-8), ciliate, and sporozoan. There are transitional forms in existence today that possess flagella but may also move in ameboid fashion by pseudopod formation. Ciliates (Fig. 1-9) lack flagella but instead

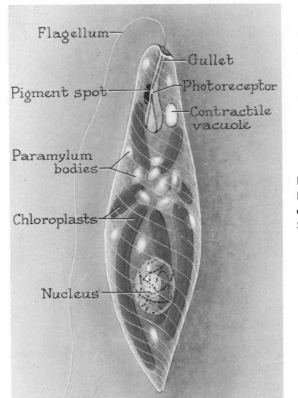

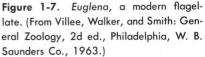

Figure 1-7. *Euglena,* a modern flagellate. (From Villee, Walker, and Smith: General Zoology, 2d ed., Philadelphia, W. B. Saunders Co., 1963.)

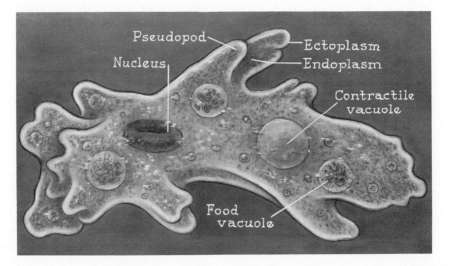

Figure 1-8. An ameba. Food vacuoles contain digesting material; the contractile vacuole contains waste products prior to discharge. This animal is moving toward the right. (From Villee, Walker, and Smith.)

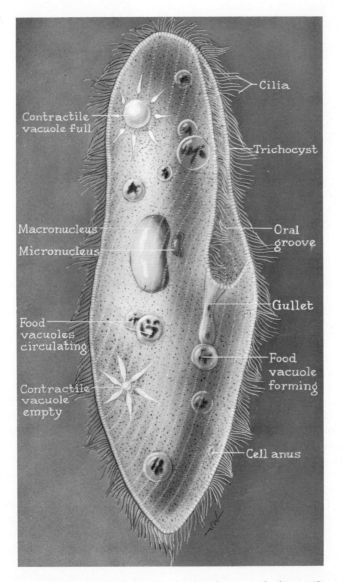

Figure 1-9.   Paramecium, a generalized drawing showing features of ciliates. (From Villee, Walker, and Smith.)

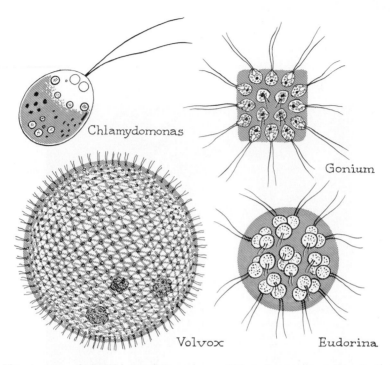

Figure 1-10. A series of plantlike flagellate protozoa. *Chlamydomonas* is single-celled, often called an alga; the others are multi-celled colonial organisms. Each individual cell in the colony feeds for itself. The colony as a whole is actively motile. *Volvox* is about $1/100$ inch in diameter; the other organisms are smaller. (From Villee, Walker, and Smith.)

move by means of many short hairlike cilia; these structures may also help to propel food toward the gullet. Sporozoa possess an added feature with survival value, a spore or resistant stage in their life cycle. Most protozoa are single-celled, but there are some colonial types (Fig. 1-10). Higher animals may have evolved from such a multicellular form, or perhaps they evolved independently as an offshoot from the line that culminated in modern protozoa.

Evolution of Lower Plants

Ancestral green algae were presumably intermediate between the early flagellates and modern algae and other organisms. Modern algae (Fig. 1-11) include green, brown, red, and other species in which the various pigments determine the wavelengths of light that can be utilized by the plant chlorophyll. Some algae are multicellular, and the

evolution of a multicellular habit of growth doubtless led to the development of higher plants. Fungi, including yeasts (Fig. 1-12) and molds (Fig. 1-13), do not possess chlorophyll and hence are unable to utilize light energy or to synthesize their constituents solely from simple nutrient substances. They are dependent on previously formed organic matter.

The slime molds are interesting but poorly understood organisms possessing protozoa-like and fungus-like phases. Their life cycle is illustrated in Figure 1-14. Flagellate cells similar to protozoan flagellates later lose their flagella and become ameboid. The ameboid cells clump together when they come into contact with one another, and in some species the cell membranes dissolve. A large mass of protoplasm known as a plasmodium then forms. This is multinucleate and may be as much as 1 foot in diameter. It flows in ameboid fashion

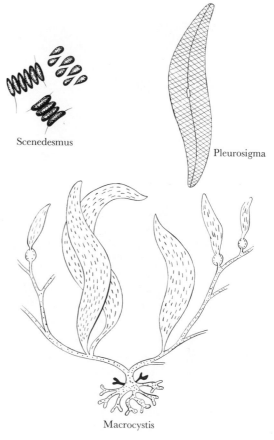

Scenedesmus

Pleurosigma

Macrocystis

Figure 1-11. Two small single-celled algae and one large multicellular alga. Each individual of the green alga, *Scenedesmus,* is about $\frac{1}{2500}$ inch long. The diatom, *Pleurosigma,* is $\frac{1}{250}$ inch in length. *Macrocystis,* a brown alga, may be 150 feet long and anchor in 60 feet of water; it is found on the Pacific coast of the United States.

over the substrate (decaying wood or other plant material), ingesting microorganisms and other organic substances. One or more upright stalks grow from this protoplasmic mass, and the tips develop into fruiting bodies within which numerous spores form. These spores may be released and transformed into single flagellate cells in suitable environments. The flagellate and ameboid stages are obviously animal-like; the fruiting body and spore stages resemble similar stages in the life of certain fungi.

Figure 1-12. The common bread yeast, *Saccharomyces cerevisiae,* showing budding, its principal method of reproduction. Enlarged 1500X. (From Sarles et al.: Microbiology. New York, Harper & Brothers, 1956.)

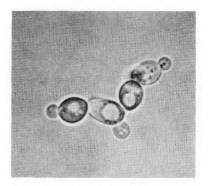

Figure 1-13. Photomicrograph of *Rhizopus nigricans*, a common bread mold. Enlarged about 200X. (From Sarles et al.)

Bacteria and Blue-green Algae

Modern bacteria and the blue-green algae are closely related. Most representatives of both groups are relatively small. Their cytoplasm contains no conspicuous vacuoles and is quite immobile, in contrast to that of many larger organisms in which more or less violent activity can be seen. The chlorophyll of the blue-green algae is not contained within chloroplasts, as it is in other algae and higher plants; rather, it is located within simpler bodies known as chromatophores. Similarly, the photosynthetic pigments of the few species of photosynthetic bacteria are found in chromatophores. Finally, the cell walls of blue-green algae and bacteria contain a strengthening mucopeptide composed of muramic acid and either diaminopimelic acid or lysine. The mucopeptide is absent from the cells of higher algae, protozoa, fungi, plants, and animals. Many blue-green algae and bacteria resemble one another morphologically

(Fig. 1-15), the principal difference being the presence or absence of chlorophyll. It seems likely that the two groups of organisms evolved from common ancestors.

Nutritional Types of Bacteria

The earliest of the modern bacteria may well have been of a photosynthetic type. As it lost its pigment and acquired the ability to secure energy by oxidation, it developed into a chemosynthetic organism. Increasing dependence upon preformed organic matter yielded saprophytes, and some that associated with living plants or animals acquired parasitic properties.

Parasites: Rickettsiae and Viruses

Extension of the parasitic habit led first to partial and ultimately to complete loss of the ability to live independently. Various cell structures were no longer formed. Eventually rickettsiae (Fig. 1-16), pleuropneumonia and pleuropneumonia-like organisms (Fig. 1-17), and the still smaller and less differentiated viruses (Fig. 1-18) appeared. It is argued, as previously mentioned, that modern parasitic viruses evolved directly from the original protovirus or that they represent nucleic acid and protein fragments derived originally from the genetic materials of the cells of higher organisms—that they are, in other words, "wild genes," which have escaped from the control of the host cell, become somewhat altered, and can now enter other similar host cells and pervert their synthetic machinery so that it manufactures virus materials instead of host materials.

Microorganisms: Plant or Animal?

The difficulty encountered in attempting to assign a microorganism to its proper category can now be appreciated. It is often difficult even to decide whether a given organism is a plant or an animal. Some forms have been described that have both plantlike and

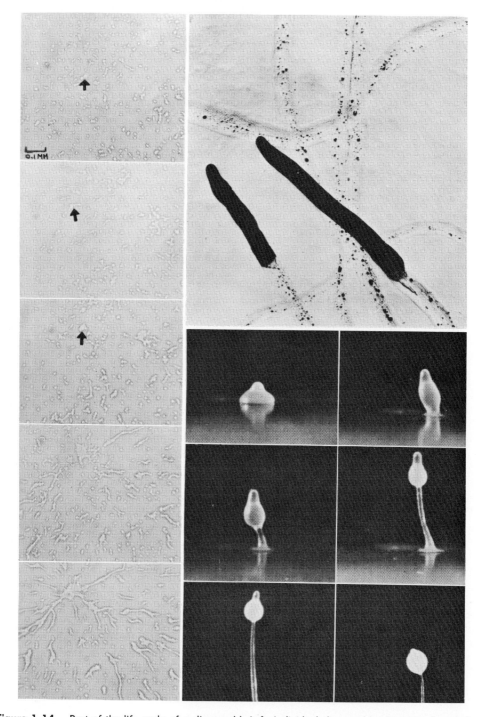

Figure 1-14. Part of the life cycle of a slime mold. *Left,* Individual slime mold cells gather by ameba-like migration. *Top right,* The slug that is formed continues migration. *Bottom,* Eventually the slug stops and forms a fruiting body; spores are contained within the structure on top of the stalk, which is only 1 to 2 mm. tall. (From Sussman: Animal Growth and Development. Englewood Cliffs, N. J., Prentice-Hall, Inc., 1960.)

BLUE-GREEN ALGAE   BACTERIA

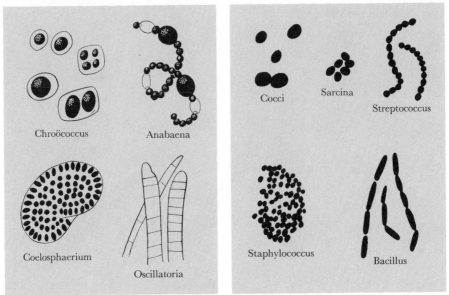

Figure 1-15. Blue-green algae and bacteria. The algae contain chlorophyll and are photosynthetic plants; the bacteria do not contain chlorophyll.

animal-like stages in their life cycles. Moreover, certain protozoa and algae are morphologically identical and differ only in the presence or absence of chlorophyll. The familiar organism *Euglena* is a chlorophyll-containing flagellate and is sometimes classified as an alga (Fig. 1-7). A protozoan form, *Astasia,* does not possess chlorophyll but is otherwise identical with *Euglena*. Cultivation of *Euglena* in the presence of penicillin suppresses chloroplast formation and produces a form indistinguishable from *Astasia*. Numerous other examples might be cited.

Gross observations of large animals and plants usually suffice to assign them to their proper kingdom. Classification of some of the smaller forms, however, requires critical analysis of the differences between plants and animals and perhaps even arbitrary decision as to what constitute plant and animal characteristics.

Plant and Animal Characteristics

Plant cells usually possess rigid outer walls of cellulose, which surround the living protoplasm and maintain the cell shapes; most animal cells do not have rigid outer walls and are therefore somewhat flexible. Certain plant cells, however, lack cellulose walls and some animal cells possess them.

Animals are usually capable of independent locomotion, and most plants are either attached to one spot by their roots or are transported by their environment (e.g., liquids in which they are suspended). Flagellate algae, however, are plantlike cells with powers of independent movement.

Higher plants secure much of their energy from photosynthesis, catalyzed by chlorophyll, whereas animals, lacking chlorophyll, derive energy from organic materials. The principal reserve food substance stored by plants is starch, whereas that of animals is either glycogen or fat.

Holophytic vs. Holozoic Nutrition

An important difference between animals and plants is their method of securing nutrients. Plants take their foods

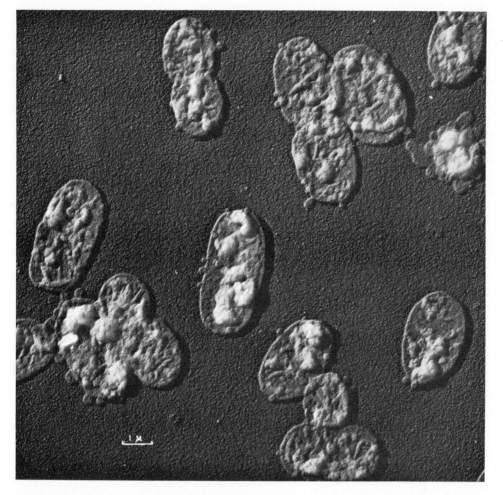

Figure 1-16. Electron photomicrograph of *Rickettsia nuseum,* shadowed to show surface structure. (Courtesy of the U. S. Armed Forces Institute of Pathology.)

Figure 1-17. Electron photomicrograph of a pleuropneumonia-like organism (PPLO) from the human female genital tract. The cells from an agar colony were shadowed with chromium. PPLO are spheroidal to ellipsoidal, lack a rigid cell wall, and are very fragile. (From Morton et al., J. Bact., 68:707, 1954.)

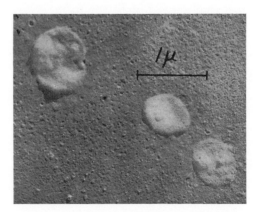

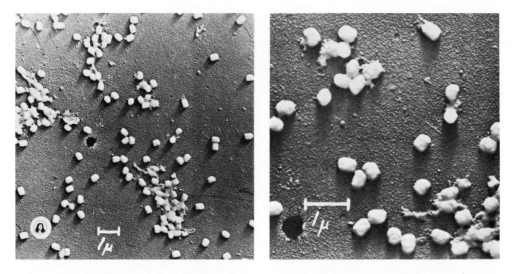

Figure 1-18. Electron photomicrographs of the vaccinia virus, shadowed with gold. The picture at the right is an enlargement of the one at the left. The rectangular or brick-shaped appearance of some of the particles is obvious. (Photograph by G. G. Sharp; A.S.M. LS-142.)

as dissolved salts, which they absorb in solution through their roots or secure as a gas (CO_2) through their leaves. This is *holophytic* nutrition. Animals, on the contrary, utilize organic matter secured in sizable chunks from plants or other animals, alive or dead. Food particles or masses are ingested or engulfed and are later digested within the animal body. The resulting fragments (molecules) are then resynthesized into animal protoplasm. This is *holozoic* nutrition.

Among the microorganisms, only protozoa are predominantly animal-like in their manner of nutrition. Most algae are readily assigned to the plant kingdom on the basis of their nutrient habits. Slime molds resemble protozoa at certain stages of their development and pose some problems of classification. Fungi and bacteria utilize only soluble foods and thus exhibit holophytic nutrition. These organisms have therefore traditionally been assigned to the plant kingdom and are still classified as plants by most investigators. Linnaeus in the eighteenth century temporarily solved the problem by assigning bacteria to the group Chaos! Haeckel in 1866 proposed

establishment of a third kingdom, *Protista,* to include bacteria and the other *relatively simple* organisms, such as protozoa, fungi, and algae. These are unicellular or coenocytic or, if multicellular, are not differentiated into separate and distinct tissue regions as are higher plants and animals.

Stanier and his collaborators in 1957 revived use of the term *protist,* and later described the cellular features that distinguish bacteria and blue-green algae from other algae, fungi, protozoa, and all higher plants and animals. The least developed cell type is that of bacteria and blue-green algae, the *lower protists.* It was originally designated *procaryotic,* but subsequently called *protocaryotic* (Greek: *protos,* primitive + *karyo,* nucleus), a more appropriate term. The more highly evolved cell type, *eucaryotic,* is typical of all other forms. Protists constructed of eucaryotic cells (i.e., protozoa, fungi, and most algae) are called *higher protists.*

Protocaryotic and eucaryotic cells differ principally in nuclear organization and division, cytoplasmic organization and the structure of the energy-transforming organelles, and the nature of the organs of locomotion (when present). In general, the subunits in which various functions of eucaryotic cells take place are surrounded by individual membranes, whereas in protocaryotic cells there are no equivalent separate structural subunits. For example, the eucaryotic nucleus is enclosed within a membrane, as are the mitochondria and chloroplasts, the organelles that contain, respectively, the enzymes and other apparatus necessary for respiration and those necessary for photosynthesis. The protocaryotic nucleus, on the contrary, is not bounded by a membrane; nuclear division consists of DNA replication and simple splitting; and several nuclear divisions may occur before the cell divides, with the result that multinucleate cells are found in rapidly growing cultures. Eucaryotic nuclei divide mitotically. Photosynthesis and respiration in protocaryotic organisms are not associated with definite and separable structural subunits. Photosynthesis in blue-green algae appears to be performed in paired leaf-like plates called *lamellae* distributed in a complex system throughout the cytoplasm; in some bacteria it is accomplished in small vesicular cytoplasmic bodies. Neither of these types of structure is organized into a membrane-bounded organelle, and the photosynthetic function depends upon the structural integrity of the intact cell. Similarly, the respiratory activity of the protocaryotic cell is dependent upon the cell in its entirety and apparently involves the cytoplasmic membrane—the sole membrane found in such cells.

The contractile organelles responsible for the locomotion of eucaryotic protists always consist of 11 fibrils (nine fibrils arranged around two central fibrils) surrounded by cytoplasmic membrane material (see Fig. 4-25). A true bacterial flagellum is the size of a single central eucaryotic fibril, and is not enclosed in the cytoplasmic membrane. Other locomotor mechanisms occur, but those of eucaryotic cells are different from those of protocaryotic cells.

THE WORLD OF MICROORGANISMS

SUMMARY

Microorganisms are for the most part too small to see with the naked eye: protozoa, algae, fungi, bacteria, viruses. These organisms differ in such characteristics as mode of nutrition, structure, size, and chemical composition, but presumably all arose from a common ancestor of two to three billion years ago.

The first living organism was probably nothing but nucleic acid and protein that had been formed by chance in the waters of the prehistoric Earth. This original "protovirus" developed into a simple flagellate during a period of several hundred million years. The ancestral flagellate gave rise to various evolutionary lines, culminating at one extreme in photosynthetic organisms, algae and higher plants, and at the other extreme in protozoa and higher animals. Other lines of development led to fungi and to the blue-green algae, the most primitive photosynthetic plants in existence today. Bacteria probably appeared about the same time as a result of parallel evolution.

Plants and animals are differentiated best by their modes of nutrition. Plants require only inorganic nutrients, which they secure in soluble form; their energy is derived from light. Animals rearrange preformed organic matter into their own characteristic protoplasmic constituents and secure energy by oxidation of organic compounds. With the exception of some protozoa, most microorganisms have a plantlike type of nutrition. They are therefore usually classified in the plant kingdom. There is, however, growing use of a third kingdom designation, *Protista,* to include all microorganisms.

STUDY QUESTIONS

1. In what ways are microorganisms simpler than "higher" organisms?
2. Discuss current views of the origin of life.
3. What characteristics of present microorganisms did the earliest living form probably possess?
4. How do modern viruses resemble and how do they differ from the postulated early protovirus?
5. Which were probably formed earlier: primitive algae or primitive protozoa? Explain.
6. What advantages does independent locomotion confer on a microorganism?
7. Describe two microorganisms that appear to be on the border line between the plant and animal kingdoms.
8. In what ways are blue-green algae closely related to bacteria?
9. List the principal groups of microorganisms and tabulate their important distinguishing characteristics.
10. Discuss the advantages and disadvantages of establishing a separate kingdom to include all microorganisms.
11. Distinguish protocaryotic from eucaryotic cells.

SUPPLEMENTARY READING

Wald reviews the spontaneous generation controversy and then discusses Miller's experiment and its implications with reference to the origin of life. Oparin's book on this subject is a classic. He develops the thesis that life came into being some two billion years ago as a result of the slow formation of organic compounds in the warm pools of the prehistoric Earth. Blum, in *Time's Arrow and Evolution,* shows that the evolutionary processes leading to the beginning of life were essentially irreversible—an expression of the second law of thermodynamics. Stanier and van Niel attempt to define what a microbiologist means when he—often intuitively—designates a given organism as a bacterium. Dr. and Mrs. Calvin discuss the attributes a molecular system must have in order to be called "alive," and then consider the processes of chemical and social evolution.

Blum, H. F.: *Time's Arrow and Evolution,* 2d ed. Princeton, N. J., Princeton University Press, 1954.
Calvin, M., and Calvin, G. J.: Atom to Adam. *Amer. Scientist, 52:* 163–186, 1964.
Oparin, A. I.: *The Origin of Life on the Earth,* 3d ed. New York, Academic Press, 1957.
Stanier, R. Y., and van Niel, C. B.: The Concept of a Bacterium. *Archiv für Mikrobiol., 42:* 17–35, 1962.
Wald, G.: The Origin of Life. *Scientific American, 191*(8):44–53, August, 1954.

EARLY DEVELOPMENT
OF MICROBIOLOGY

Microbiology, like most other sciences, had its origin in curiosity. As soon as instruments, however crude or imperfect, were devised for producing magnified images of objects too small to be seen with the naked eye, they were used to examine the previously unsuspected minute organisms that populate soil, water, natural foods, body surfaces and secretions, and indeed nearly everything on Earth. At first they appeared to be of little importance and were considered merely objects for speculation: How could such small organisms live, breathe, reproduce? Where did they come from? Much later it was found that they may bring about useful or undesirable chemical changes in their environment and that some produce disease. This knowledge stimulated a tremendous burst of investigation, so the great growth of microbiology was directed along practical lines. More recently, the fact that microorganisms are excellent objects for the study of biologic phenomena in general has come to be appreciated, and microbiology is now recognized as an important branch of biology.

DISCOVERY OF MICROORGANISMS

The discovery of microorganisms had to await the invention of the microscope. Suitable instruments were developed during the seventeenth century by Janssen, Malpighi, Hooke, Leeuwenhoek, and others (see Fig. 2-1). Early microscopes were simple instruments, often just a glass bead in some kind of holder.

As early as 1665, Hooke published a book, *Micrographia,* containing descriptions and illustrations based upon his microscopic examination of higher organisms and of filamentous fungi including molds and rusts.

Anton van Leeuwenhoek (1632–1723) was a versatile and intelligent dry goods merchant of Delft, Holland (see Fig. 2-2). He was also "Chamberlain of the Council Chamber of the Worshipful Sheriffs of Delft," city surveyor, and

21

Figure 2-1. An early compound microscope. Christopher Cook of London made these instruments about 1665 after the design of Robert Hooke. The light source is at the right with a lens for focusing the light on the specimen. (From Stanier, Doudoroff, and Adelberg: The Microbial World. Englewood Cliffs, N. J., Prentice-Hall, Inc., 1957.)

official wine taster. These various positions paid enough to support his large family and still left time for a hobby. His hobby was lens grinding and the production and use of microscopes. His simple microscopes consisted of a single biconvex lens mounted between two pieces of metal (see Fig. 2-3). Attachments were provided for focusing and for mounting insects or other large objects or drops of liquid.

Leeuwenhoek's lenses were so perfectly ground that magnifications of approximately 200 times could be obtained. With them, he found protozoa in canal and ditch water and bacteria in rain water that had been allowed to stand in a bowl for several days. Pepper infusions swarmed with bacteria. Scrapings from his teeth contained millions of "animalcules" (Fig. 2-4), which horrified

him until he found that all people had similar bacteria in their mouths. Some microscopic organisms were obviously alive, as was evident from their active motility, but others merely vibrated in place, exhibiting brownian movement. Leeuwenhoek also discovered that bacteria treated with vinegar or heated to a sufficiently high temperature "fell dead forthwith."

Leeuwenhoek's observations were recorded in more than 200 letters written to the Royal Society of London from 1673 until the time of his death. He apparently first saw bacteria about 1676.

The existence of viruses was not demonstrated until more than two centuries later, and photomicrography by electron microscopy was not possible for over 250 years.

Figure 2-2. Anton van Leeuwenhoek at the age of 54. He had discovered bacteria only a few years earlier. (From Dobell: Antony van Leeuwenhoek and His "Little Animals." London, Staples Press, 1932.)

Figure 2-3. One of Leeuwenhoek's "microscopes." This was really a simple magnifying lens, but its quality and method of use permitted objects as small as bacteria to be seen. The lens was mounted between two metal plates. The specimen was placed on the point of the short threaded rod; the various thumbscrews focused and positioned the object properly. (From Frobisher: Fundamentals of Microbiology, 7th. ed. Philadelphia, W. B. Saunders Co., 1962.)

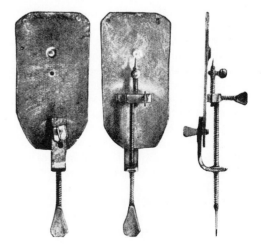

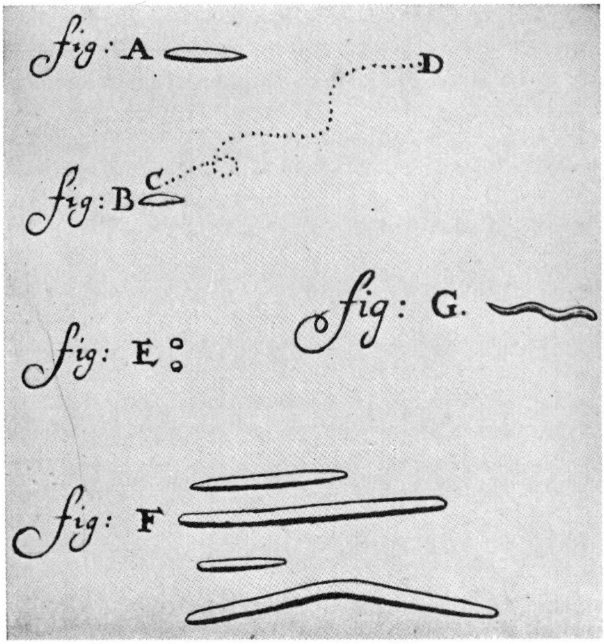

Figure 2-4. Leeuwenhoek's drawings of bacteria from the human mouth, from his letter of Sept. 17, 1683. Rods, cocci, and a spirochete are shown. The path of motion of a motile short rod form is indicated by the dotted line. (From Frobisher.)

SPONTANEOUS GENERATION CONTROVERSY

One would expect that the discovery of the first microorganisms would start an immediate, widespread further investigation of their nature and occurrence. Certainly this would happen in the twentieth century. However, communication was much slower in the seventeenth century; Leeuwenhoek's letters were presumably read at meetings of the Royal Society of London but were not widely distributed, and many years elapsed before much publicity was given them. Consequently, for many decades only a few persons studied bacteria. Then it required a controversy to incite interest and experimental investigation.

One of the first arguments about microscopic organisms has already been mentioned: the question of their origin. There were, of course, two schools of thought. One maintained that microorganisms arose spontaneously from decomposing organic materials; the other maintained that each organism was the progeny of an identical, pre-existing organism.

Needham in 1748 reported an experiment that seemed to prove that bacteria arose spontaneously where no living organisms had been before. He placed boiled mutton broth in flasks, tightly stoppered them with corks, and at intervals examined the broth with his microscope; bacteria appeared in large numbers. Certainly, he reasoned, boiling should destroy any living cells and those that appeared later must have arisen spontaneously. Needham postulated the existence of a vegetative force that was necessary to confer life upon the non-living ingredients of the liquid.

Spallanzani later (in 1765) repeated the experiments of Needham, but with modifications. Instead of closing the flasks with corks, Spallanzani sealed them hermetically in a flame, before heating the contents. He found that if he boiled the broth long enough, no bacteria ever appeared. The broth remained clear when observed with the naked eye and portions examined with the micro-

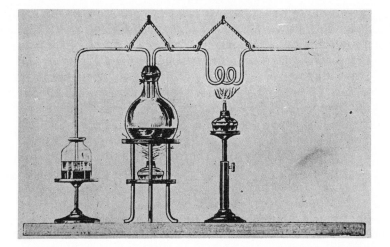

Figure 2-5. Schwann's experiment to disprove spontaneous generation. The flask of boiled broth, *center,* received only air that had passed through the heated glass coil. The broth remained sterile. (From Watson-Cheyne's Antiseptic Surgery, 1882.)

scope showed no sign of life. It appeared, therefore, that Needham might not have boiled his broth long enough. More importantly, however, the corks may not have been impervious to bacteria.

The fact that bacteria entered nutrient materials such as broth from the air was demonstrated by experiments performed by Schwann (1837). He arranged flasks so that a stream of air could be passed over the broth (Fig. 2-5). The air entering some flasks passed through a tube that was heated to redness, whereas that entering control flasks was unheated. Broth in the control flasks always became cloudy within a short time and showed microscopic

evidence of living organisms, whereas broth that was aerated with heated air remained free from microorganisms.

The proponents of spontaneous generation maintained that such drastic treatment destroyed the life-supporting property of air so that even though spontaneous generation might occur, the organisms generated would be unable to multiply. This argument was countered by Schroeder and von Dusch in 1854 when they introduced the use of cotton into microbiologic practice. They drew air into flasks of broth after passing it through cotton filters that had previously been baked in an oven (Fig. 2-6). The fact that the broth remained

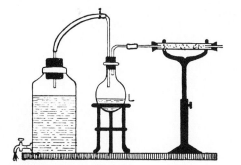

Figure 2-6. One of the experiments of Schroeder and von Dusch (1854) that showed that microorganisms could be removed from air by a cotton filter. The suction bottle at the left drew air through the sterilized tube of cotton-wool at the right and over the sterile broth in the round flask. The broth remained free from microorganisms. (From Burdon: Textbook of Microbiology. New York, The Macmillan Co., 1958.)

clear, whereas that in flasks that were not protected by cotton was promptly clouded with a heavy bacterial population, clearly demonstrated that the source of microbial life was the outside air. Schroeder and von Dusch further showed that flasks of broth were protected by a wad or plug of cotton wool in the mouth of the flask. If the flask was then boiled sufficiently, its contents remained sterile indefinitely. This is the origin of the familiar cotton plug of the bacteriology laboratory.

These experiments seemed conclusive, but Pasteur (Fig. 2-7) was starting his work on microbial fermentation at this time, and encountered opposition from the powerful school of chemists who maintained that fermentation and putrefaction were spontaneous chemical processes, and that any microbial activity was an effect rather than the cause of the observed changes. Pasteur realized that he must demonstrate conclu-

Figure 2-7. Louis Pasteur, 1822–1895.

sively the source of microorganisms in organic infusions. He became convinced that they floated in the air, perhaps upon dust particles, and that the likelihood of microbial contamination of an organic solution was greater in a dusty atmosphere than in clean air. He secured air samples in flasks of broth whose drawn-out necks had been sealed while the flasks were boiling so that upon cooling they contained a partial vacuum. A flask was opened wherever a sample was required, air was drawn in, and the flask was resealed. Then it was examined after incubation. Flasks opened in the streets of Paris always became turbid with bacteria, whereas similar flasks exposed to the dust-free air near the top of Mont Blanc rarely contained bacteria.

Pasteur also used flasks like those illustrated in Figure 2-8, to show that even filtration through cotton was not necessary to prevent contamination by microorganisms. A long, curving neck permitted interchange of air between the inside and outside of the vessel, but dust particles and bacteria were trapped along the moist walls of the neck. This was proved by tilting the flask so that broth washed the inside of the neck. The broth promptly became cloudy.

The final blow to the spontaneous generation doctrine was dealt by the English physicist, Tyndall, in 1877. He had discovered that air containing no dust particles was optically empty; that is, a beam of light passed through it could not be seen, whereas each particle in a dust-laden atmosphere was clearly visible. If Pasteur were correct, optically empty air should be free from microorganisms. Tyndall constructed a box like that illustrated in Figure 2-9. The inside of the box was coated with glycerine to which dust particles sooner or later adhered. When the box had become optically empty, Tyndall filled the test tubes with broth by means of a thistle tube and sterilized them by raising a pan of boiling brine underneath. The contents of the tubes remained in contact with the air, but as long as it

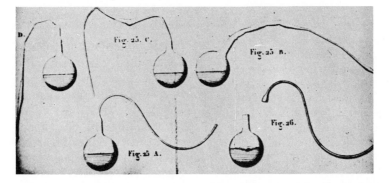

Figure 2-8. Pasteur's open flasks in which boiled broth remained free from microorganisms because dust particles carrying them were trapped in the bends of the necks. (From Pasteur, 1861.)

was free from dust, bacteria did not appear in the broth.

In the course of these investigations, Tyndall discovered a highly resistant bacterial structure, later known as a spore. He observed that infusions made by suspending hay in water were difficult to sterilize. Prolonged boiling was necessary or a process of intermittent

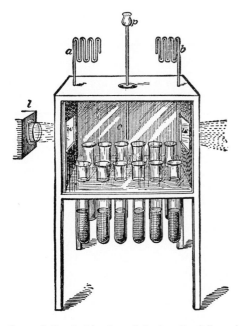

Figure 2-9. Inside view of the box Tyndall used to demonstrate that "optically empty" air contained no microorganisms. (From Krueger and Johansson: Principles of Microbiology, 2d ed., Philadelphia, W. B. Saunders Co., 1959.)

sterilization that subsequently became known as tyndallization. The solution was boiled for short periods on each of three successive days and was incubated at a temperature favorable to microbial growth during the intervening time.

The spontaneous generation controversy was important for various reasons. Before the study of microorganisms could be established upon a scientific basis it was necessary to demonstrate that they arose by an orderly process and not haphazardly, at the whim of uncontrollable environmental changes. When it was shown that each microorganism was identical with its predecessor, it became possible to study its properties and compare its activities with those of other organisms. These steps were necessary before the germ theories of fermentation, putrefaction, and disease could be demonstrated.

The spontaneous generation controversy stimulated research and the development of techniques of handling microorganisms. Any argument is likely to arouse the investigative spirit of the protagonists, and this argument was no exception.

GERM THEORY OF FERMENTATION

The souring of milk and the production of alcoholic beverages have been known throughout recorded history, but the fermentation processes concerned have been understood for only about a century. Berzelius, Liebig, Wöhler, and other distinguished and influential organic chemists of the last century interpreted the transformation of sugar into lactic acid or into ethyl alcohol and carbon dioxide as purely chemical phenomena. When it was pointed out that yeasts or other microorganisms are always present, they devised explanations other than the one which eventually proved to be true. Liebig, for example, noting how readily yeast is destroyed and decomposes, postulated that the process of decomposition was communicated in some way to sugar and other substances in contact with it. Berzelius interpreted fermentation as a contact phenomenon, and Mitscherlich saw in yeast globules a catalyst similar in behavior to spongy platinum in contact with hydrogen peroxide.

None of these investigators accepted the thesis, first proposed by Cagniard de Latour, Schwann, and Kützing between 1835 and 1838, that yeasts actively transform sugar into alcohol and carbon dioxide. They postulated that in other fermentations, various specific microorganisms formed characteristic end products during their growth.

Pasteur in 1857 observed the formation of lactic acid from sugar by several kinds of bacteria. He noted that a gray deposit in fermentation vessels consisted of microscopic, very short globules, occurring either singly or in small, irregular masses. These globules were much smaller than those of beer yeast. When they were transferred to a fresh nutrient solution containing sugar, yeast extract, and chalk, lactic acid was produced and the globules increased greatly in number. Pasteur demonstrated that the presence of the globules was a necessary prerequisite to lactic acid formation. He later showed that in alcoholic, acetic, butyric, and other fermentations, the typical end product appeared only when a specific microorganism was present.

A further discovery in connection with butyric fermentation was that the organisms responsible grow only in the absence of air. It was then found that alcoholic fermentation also occurs only in the absence of air, but yeast can grow in the presence of air and, in fact, grows more rapidly and abundantly with than without air. However, oxygen is toxic to the butyric bacterium. This was apparently the first indication that organisms could exist in the complete absence of oxygen—a revolutionary concept.

The germ theory of fermentation, stating that microorganisms bring about specific changes in their substrates, laid the foundation for important industrial developments. The research necessary to prove the germ theory of fermentation also demonstrated the necessity for strict control of the various factors associated with the fermentation processes: the composition of the fermenting solution, the identity and purity of the microbial population, and incubation conditions such as temperature and aeration.

GERM THEORY OF DISEASE

From the earliest times, disease was regarded as a mysterious or even supernatural phenomenon. Ancient Greek and Roman physicians suspected that invisible, minute particulate agents caused certain diseases and that they could be transmitted in some way or other from one individual to the next. Fracastoro in 1546 described three modes of transmission of infectious agents: direct contact, fomites (agents contaminated by the diseased individual and later handled by a healthy person), and contagion at a distance (e.g., through the air, as in the case of tuberculosis). Until the nineteenth century, however, there was no direct proof that microbes cause disease. The evidence upon which ancient authors and others through the Middle Ages postulated living, transmissible "seeds of disease" was purely epidemiologic.

The fact that certain bacteria produce disease was first clearly demonstrated by Robert Koch in 1876 (Fig. 2-10). He showed that a spore-forming organism, *Bacillus anthracis* (Fig. 2-11), was the cause of anthrax, which was then epidemic in sheep, cattle, and other domestic animals, and also occurred in man. A few years earlier (1863–1868) Davaine had demonstrated rod-shaped objects in the blood and organs of animals that had died of anthrax, and when material containing these objects was transmitted to healthy animals, the latter promptly died with symptoms characteristic of the disease. Koch passed these rodlike bodies through a long series of microscopic cultures in serum or aqueous humor and observed that they multiplied extensively in each successive culture. He therefore concluded that they were living bacilli. Moreover, although organisms from the last microculture in the series were obviously many generations removed from those in the diseased animal, experimental animals inoculated with them died showing typical symptoms of anthrax, and bacilli with the same characteristics were found in their blood and organs. This was clear-cut demonstration of the causal relationship between the organism and the disease.

Koch had followed four experimental steps, which he subsequently stated in the form of rules that have since been known as *Koch's postulates:*

1. Find the suspected organism in all cases of the disease and demonstrate its absence in healthy individuals.

2. Isolate the organism in pure culture.

3. Reproduce the same disease in suitable experimental animals.

4. Reisolate the same organism from the artificially infected animals.

Figure 2-10.   Robert Koch, 1843–1910. His last portrait. (From Bulloch: The History of Bacteriology. London, Oxford University Press, 1938.)

least a score were isolated within the last two decades of the nineteenth century.

EARLY TECHNICAL ADVANCES

Improved techniques for handling and studying bacteria were developed rapidly. One important problem was that of isolating pure cultures from the mixed flora usually encountered in natural specimens. Koch was fortunate in his early work because *Bacillus anthracis* grows more rapidly in the animal body than most other bacteria with which it may be mixed. Consequently, serial passage from one animal to another quickly yields a pure culture in the blood and spleen. Serial transfer on laboratory media is effective when the desired organism predominates or multiplies most rapidly under the culture conditions provided. However, a method of separating the bacteria in mixtures, even when the desired organism was in the minority, was obviously needed.

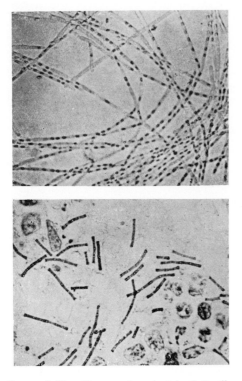

Figure 2-11. Photographs of stained *Bacillus anthracis* taken by Koch in 1877.

As early as 1872, Schroeter had observed the formation of distinctively colored growths or colonies on the cut surfaces of potatoes. Each colony proved to contain a single kind of organism. Inoculating potato slices with mixtures of microorganisms sometimes made it possible to separate the various components of the mixture, but some organisms did not grow on potato slices.

Brefeld added gelatin to a warm nutrient broth and poured the solution onto sterile glass plates, where it was allowed to cool and solidify. Mixtures of microorganisms were smeared on the surface of the solidified medium or added to the gelatin before it was poured. The plates were incubated in a sterilized box, and bits of the various colonies that developed were transferred to other media. Since gelatin liquefies readily when warmed, the temperature could not be allowed to rise above 20° C., lest the colonies run together. Moreover, many human and animal pathogens grow slowly, if at all, at 20° C. Further-

If carefully obeyed, these simple rules provide a logical basis for concluding that an organism produces a given disease (or any other characteristic change, for that matter). There are conditions under which all four rules cannot be observed. For example, apparently healthy individuals may be "carriers" of pathogenic microorganisms. Moreover, some infectious agents, such as certain viruses, have in the past been extremely difficult to isolate and cultivate outside the natural host. In these cases indirect evidence is sometimes necessary to establish the cause of an infectious process.

Koch's statement of these rules, together with technical procedures introduced by him and his colleagues, paved the way for an enthusiastic search for the causes of infectious disease, and at

more, some organisms digest and liquefy gelatin, whereupon their colonies mix.

These disadvantages of gelatin made the introduction of agar by Hesse in 1883 an important contribution. Hesse was a pupil of Koch, and his wife had friends in the Dutch East Indies who were familiar with the use of agar for solidifying jams and jellies. Agar is a polysaccharide extracted from various seaweeds. It is digested by very few microorganisms. It goes into solution only when heated to nearly 100° C. and remains liquid until cooled to about 42° C. It can therefore be inoculated with mixtures of microorganisms at 45° to 50° C., a temperature that most organisms can tolerate for a short time. The addition of 1.0 to 1.5 per cent agar to broth yields a satisfactory liquefiable solid culture medium.

Petri, another pupil of Koch, made what he called a minor modification of Koch's plating technique when he devised the familiar Petri dish, a flat-bottomed dish with a flat cover. The Petri dish is much more convenient to handle and use than the flat glass plates first used by Koch.

These technical advances were of greater importance than their simple nature would indicate, because they made it possible to isolate pure cultures conveniently and thus encouraged the widespread study of microorganisms.

It has been noted that Koch used the method of enrichment to isolate pathogenic bacteria by inoculating animals in which the pathogenic organisms would grow faster than other, contaminating microbes. Winogradsky and Beijerinck used selective enrichment to isolate various interesting soil bacteria, organisms that oxidize ammonia or nitrites, hydrogen sulfide or sulfur, or iron compounds. Winogradsky, for example, studied bacteria that do not grow in laboratory media containing organic compounds but can be cultivated in media containing only inorganic salts. When such a medium, with ammonium chloride as the only source of nitrogen and adjusted to pH 8.5, was inoculated

with garden soil and kept in the dark at 25° to 30° C. in the presence of air, the ammonium salt was gradually oxidized to nitrate. Later Winogradsky showed that the oxidation of ammonia occurred in two steps and that two principal kinds of bacteria were responsible: (1) *Nitrosomonas* species, which oxidized ammonia to nitrites, and (2) *Nitrobacter* species, which oxidized nitrites to nitrates. A selectively enriched culture of *Nitrobacter* was obtained by inoculating with soil a salt solution containing $NaNO_2$ at pH 8.5 and incubating it in air in a dark incubator at 25° to 30° C. Cultures of other soil bacteria may be selectively enriched by varying the composition of the medium and the conditions of incubation (Fig. 2-12).

The principle of selective enrichment by control of nutrients and culture conditions (temperature, air supply, light, pH, etc.) is most important. Thoughtfully applied, this method can assist in the isolation of practically any desired organism from natural sources.

Methods for the microscopic study of microorganisms also improved greatly during the last two decades of the nineteenth century. Koch devised better techniques of using the microscope and was especially skillful in photomicrography. His pictures of *Bacillus anthracis,* showing spores as well as vegetative cells, are excellent. Weigert introduced aniline dyes for staining tissues about 1875, and Koch used many of them to demonstrate the presence of bacteria. Gram devised a staining method in 1884 that distinguished certain bacteria from the tissues in which they were lodged. This technique, when later applied to pure cultures, revealed two great classes of organisms, which shortly became known as gram-positive and gram-negative, according to their ability to retain the dye gentian violet when the background was decolorized with alcohol. The Gram procedure is by far the most commonly used method of staining bacteria, and is almost always employed as a first step in identifying an unknown organism.

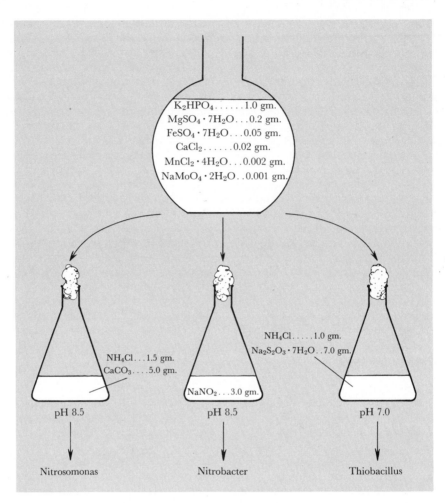

Figure 2-12. Selective enrichment of soil bacteria in synthetic media of differing composition. To portions of the basal medium from the large flask are added the ingredients indicated in the Erlenmeyer flasks, each of which is then inoculated with a soil sample and incubated aerobically in the dark. The added substances selectively enrich certain kinds of bacteria as indicated. (All amounts shown are in grams per liter.)

DISCOVERY OF VIRUSES

Pasteur suspected that the cause of hydrophobia was a submicroscopic organism that could not be cultivated outside the animal body, but the first disease clearly demonstrated to be produced by a submicroscopic agent was tobacco mosaic. This disease of tobacco plants is characterized by the appearance on the leaves of discolored spots in which the tissue dies and disintegrates, leaving holes. The disease can be transmitted by the sap of sick plants; when this fluid is spread on healthy leaves, they become diseased within two or three weeks. Iwanowski, a Russian, demonstrated in 1892 that the responsible agent passed through unglazed porcelain filters that would retain bacteria. The bacteria-free filtrate transmitted the disease as effectively as unfiltered plant sap, and the number of spots that appeared varied inversely with the extent of dilution of the filtrate. These facts made it appear that the cause of the disease was submicroscopic but particulate.

Beijerinck in 1899, apparently unaware of Iwanowski's work, made the same observations and then proceeded to demonstrate that the infectious agent could not multiply outside the host plant, although it survived for a considerable time. He showed also that it could withstand drying and precipitation by alcohol, but was inactivated at 90° C.

The first disease of animals attributed to a virus was foot-and-mouth disease of cattle. A German commission consisting of Loeffler and Frosch, appointed to study this disease, reported in 1898 that it was caused by a filterable agent that was too small to be seen under the microscope and could not be cultivated on ordinary media.

Not only plants and animals are subject to virus infections, but many bacteria are also parasitized by viruses. A British investigator, Twort, discovered the first such agent in 1915, but the clearest observations and those that were most thoroughly pursued were made by d'Herelle, in 1917. D'Herelle observed that the feces of a bacillary dysentery patient contained an agent that passed through a porcelain filter and that, when added to a broth culture of the dysentery organism, killed and apparently dissolved the bacteria within a period sometimes as short as a few hours. If a small amount of this lysed bacterial culture was added to a second bacterial culture, killing and lysis occurred again. In his first paper, d'Herelle reported passage of the lytic agent through 50 successive transfers. He further found that when a small amount of bacteria-free lytic filtrate was mixed with bacteria and spread upon an agar medium, the sheet of bacterial growth was punctuated by holes about 1 millimeter in diameter containing no bacteria. These represented colonies of the apparently particulate agent responsible for lysis (see Fig. 2-13). D'Herelle referred to the agent as *bacteriophage*. It was soon recognized that bacteriophages are viruses, and they are now commonly referred to as bacterial viruses.

A footnote to the discovery of viruses, one that was important in laying the foundation for the growing field of molecular biology, was the crystallization of tobacco mosaic virus by Stanley in 1935. This naturally stimulated contro-

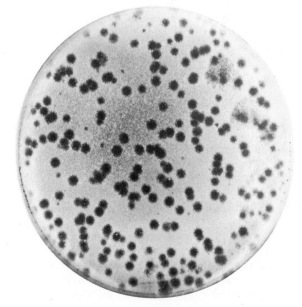

Figure 2-13. Bacteriophage plaques. The black, fuzzy-edged spots are "colonies" of bacterial virus growing on an agar plate culture of the proper host bacterium. (Photograph by J. Kleczkowska; A.S.M. LS-145.)

versy over the question: Is virus material living or dead? Some philosophers again proposed the doctrine of spontaneous generation, especially when it was found that virus particles consist of nothing more than nucleic acid and protein.

IMMUNITY

The treatment or prevention of infectious disease, that is, disease produced by microorganisms, has always been of interest. It was recognized in ancient times that some diseases occurred only once in an individual, and that thereafter he was immune. The ancient Chinese deliberately inoculated healthy persons with pustular material from the sores of patients with mild smallpox to produce a similarly mild disease that would induce lifelong immunity.

This practice, continued through the ages, spread to other parts of the world, and in the eighteenth century Lady Mary Wortley Montague attempted to introduce it into England on her return from the Near East. She encountered resistance, in part justified, because occasionally severe cases of smallpox resulted or concurrent infection with bacteria caused serious illness. Jenner, a British physician, developed an immunizing procedure known as vaccination. Observing that milkmaids who developed pocklike sores on their hands and arms after milking cows infected with cowpox never afterwards had smallpox, he deduced that there was a relationship between the two dieases. He transferred pustular material from infected cows to the skin of humans, who shortly displayed the typical sore that follows smallpox vaccination. Those who had this reaction became immune to smallpox, as was demonstrated by deliberate inoculation of a few individuals with virulent virus.

Pasteur in 1881 devised procedures for immunization against fowl cholera and anthrax. He used "attenuated vaccines," consisting of bacteria cultivated or treated so they lost most of their disease-producing power or virulence, and immunized animals by one or more injections of the weakened organisms. Fowl cholera bacteria were attenuated by aging cultures for a number of months. Chickens inoculated with them had mild infections from which they recovered, and thereafter they were immune to infection by fully virulent chicken cholera bacteria. The anthrax organism was attenuated by cultivation at an unusually high temperature, 42° to 43° C. Both types of vaccine stimulated satisfactory immunity, and they introduced a new method of controlling disease.

The period from 1880 to 1900 was marked by the discovery of various techniques for studying the so-called immune reactions, both *in vivo* and *in vitro*. It was also marked by controversy over the fundamental nature of immunity. Metchnikoff (Fig. 2-14) in 1884 proposed the cellular theory of immunity, based upon observations made in part on the transparent water flea *Daphnia*. These animals were subject to fatal infection by a yeast, but in some individuals ameboid cells engulfed and digested the infecting yeasts, whereupon the water fleas recovered. Metchnikoff named the ameboid cells phagocytes (Greek: *phagein,* to eat) and proposed that immunity to infectious disease is due to the action of similar cells. Such cells can readily be demonstrated in the blood and tissues of most animals.

The opposing doctrine, the humoral theory, maintained that soluble substances in the body fluids (e.g., the blood serum) are responsible for immunity. It was observed that cell-free serum of certain immune individuals was lethal to the bacteria to which they were immune. Moreover, serum from such immune individuals reacted with the corresponding bacteria in the test tube and caused them to clump together or "agglutinate." Serum from a patient with typhoid fever, for example, agglutinated typhoid bacteria but not cholera bacteria, and vice versa.

Figure 2-14.   Elie Metchnikoff, 1845–1916. (From Bulloch: The History of Bacteriology. London, Oxford University Press, 1938.)

Certain pathogenic bacteria produce poisons or toxins, which are responsible for the disease symptoms. Behring and Kitasato demonstrated in 1890 that the blood serum of an animal that had been immunized by the injection of diphtheria toxin contained a substance, *antitoxin,* that was capable of neutralizing the toxin. When administered to an animal before injection of the diphtheria organism or its toxin, antitoxin prevented the disease. If administered shortly after symptoms appeared, it prevented a fatal outcome. Behring and Kitasato simultaneously demonstrated the effectiveness of tetanus antitoxin.

A general term for an immune substance found in serum is *antibody.* Antibody is protein of the globulin type. The controversy between the cellular and humoral theories of immunity raged for several years and was finally resolved when Wright and Douglas showed that although antibody is not necessary for phagocytosis, it enhances the rate and extent of phagocytosis.

CHEMOTHERAPY

The modern era of chemotherapy began with Ehrlich's search for "magic bullets," beginning in the first decade of the twentieth century (Fig. 2-15). Perhaps his most outstanding success was the compound 606, or arsphenamine, used in the treatment of syphilis. Chemotherapy is an attempt to treat infectious disease by means of chemicals that will kill or interfere with the growth of the pathogenic microorganisms but not damage the host. Inasmuch as both are living agents, and often have similar chemical compositions and metabolic activities, the border line between toxicity to the parasite and to the host is often very thin. This is, of course, why 605 trials were unsuccessful before Ehrlich found a compound that was effective against syphilis.

Domagk, about 30 years later, tested the antibacterial activity of various chemicals of the sulfonamide type produced by the German dye industry and

Figure 2-15. Paul Ehrlich, 1854–1915. (From Bulloch: The History of Bacteriology. London, Oxford University Press, 1938.)

Another type of antibacterial agent is a natural product of cellular (usually microbial) activity. Antibiotics have been known for nearly a century but have been used only since about 1940. Fleming discovered penicillin in 1929 as the result of a common laboratory mishap: the appearance of a mold contaminant on a Petri dish culture of a staphylococcus. The significant feature of this mishap was that Fleming made note of the fact that staphylococcus colonies in the immediate vicinity of the contaminating penicillium dissolved and eventually disappeared (see Fig. 2-16). His keenness in making this observation was rewarded when he found that broth cultures of the mold contained a substance that was nontoxic to animals but inhibited staphylococci and certain other bacteria. Relatively little was done with penicillin until World War II, when its effectiveness as a chemotherapeutic agent was demonstrated and manufacture on a large scale was undertaken in the United States, because the British chemical industry was hampered by wartime difficulties.

At the same time Waksman at Rutgers University, and others, began to search for additional antibiotics. Streptomycin, one of the earliest and most important, was reported in 1943. Hundreds have since been found, but relatively few are manufactured commercially. Many are toxic; some are effective against only a few kinds of microorganisms; many are very expensive to manufacture; and to some antibiotics bacteria easily become resistant.

discovered that Prontosil was active against streptococcal infections in animals but was relatively nontoxic to them. The first human patient treated had a streptococcal septicemia that would otherwise have been fatal. Following other almost miraculous cures, a tremendous amount of research was directed toward the production of other even more effective and less toxic chemotherapeutic agents.

The mechanism of action of the sulfa drugs was deduced by Woods in 1940. He found that the action of sulfonamides was inhibited by p-aminobenzoic acid, a substance essential to the metabolism of certain bacteria. He concluded that sulfonamides inhibited the utilization of p-aminobenzoic acid, and thus the drugs interfered with a normal metabolic process and inhibited growth of the bacteria. Normal antibacterial body defenses then destroyed the organisms, permitting the patient to recover. The discovery that "competitive inhibition" is the mechanism by which these drugs operate started a search for other chemicals that behave in a similar manner— a search that is still in progress.

MICROBIAL PHYSIOLOGY AND GENETICS

Pasteur and his contemporaries studied microbial fermentations and learned that when various microorganisms attack a substrate like sugar, they form a variety of end products such as ethyl alcohol, lactic acid, succinic acid, acetic acid, butyric acid, and carbon dioxide.

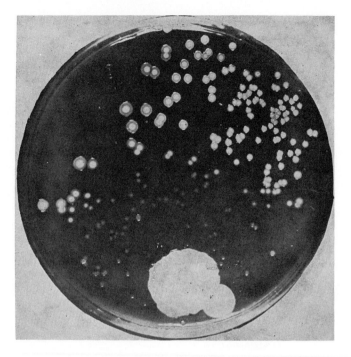

Figure 2-16. Fleming's original culture of staphylococci contaminated with *Penicillium notatum,* showing lysis of bacterial colonies in the vicinity of the mold. (From Fleming, Brit. J. Exp. Path., 10:228, 1929.)

During this period of discovery much information was amassed by direct observation. Later, early in the twentieth century, came a period of interpretation, when the experimental approach was used to determine the mechanisms by which various fermentation products are formed. Scientists in England, France, the Netherlands, Germany, the United States, and elsewhere undertook to learn the mechanisms of intermediary metabolism. It gradually appeared that the basic metabolic pathways of most organisms are similar. Moreover, cell metabolism in plants and animals markedly resembles that of microorganisms. This was recognized by Kluyver, Beijerinck's successor as chairman of microbiology at the technical university in Delft, Holland.

In a paper published in 1924, he pointed out the biochemical unity displayed by diverse organisms and expressed the belief that this would help to understand metabolism in higher organisms, a view since shown to be correct. Organisms differ with respect to the specific substrates they can utilize and the extent to which they employ oxidative or fermentative methods of attack, but the fundamental mechanisms by which energy is secured are few in number and common to all. They will be discussed in Chapter 12.

As microorganisms were studied more intensively, and physiologic as well as physical properties were determined, it became apparent that mutations occur among them as they do among higher organisms, but more rapidly because of their greater rate of reproduction. Just before the Second World War, Beadle and Tatum reported genetic studies of *Neurospora,* a mold that can be induced to mutate more rapidly than is normal by means of x-irradiation. Some of the mutants displayed metabolic or synthetic capabilities different from those of the parent organism. This means that they possessed different enzymes. Beadle and Tatum correlated the enzymatic differences with genetic differences and concluded that genes control enzyme activity. They introduced the expression "one gene—one enzyme" to indicate that in most cases a single gene controls one enzyme.

Tatum and one of his students, Joshua Lederberg, in 1946 found evidence for a sexual type of conjugation that occasionally occurs in certain bacteria, and other methods of inducing genetic change in bacteria were discovered by various other investigators. A common feature of all these methods was the participation of DNA. In every case, this substance was transferred by some mechanism from one organism to another, whereupon the recipient acquired certain characteristics of the donor.

The speed with which genetic changes can occur and be recognized in microorganisms makes them admirable subjects for genetic studies. Fruit flies, mice, grains, and other higher organisms were formerly used in most genetic studies, but great emphasis is now placed upon microbial genetics. A leading aim of research in molecular biology is to determine the exact relationship between chemical structure and genetic constitution. Much of this work is being done with microorganisms.

EARLY DEVELOPMENT OF MICROBIOLOGY

SUMMARY

The history of microbiology is a story of technical advance preceding knowledge about microorganisms. Leeuwenhoek could not see protozoa and bacteria until he had made a suitable microscope. Viruses could not be photographed until the electron microscope was invented. The study of pure cultures of microorganisms depended upon the development of methods for separating and cultivating the various individual species that make up the mixtures that usually occur in nature.

Not only were new techniques required, but also new concepts—or at least some old concepts had to be reexamined. The fact that single-celled organisms always arise from preexisting organisms of the same kind (as do higher forms), rather than by spontaneous generation, had to be proved before the science could progress. After this had been done, it was soon demonstrated that microorganisms produce a variety of chemical and other changes: fermentation, putrefaction, infectious disease, and so on.

The knowledge that microbial activities are important to man stimulated the development of methods to control them, either to promote useful activities or to prevent those that are harmful. Thus industrial microbiology, immunology, and chemotherapy evolved.

Finally, it was realized that microorganisms behave according to the same rules as multicellular organisms. Microorganisms are now used as tools in the search for knowledge of the molecular basis of life, because of the relative ease with which their biochemical and genetic properties can be studied.

STUDY QUESTIONS

1. Why was it important to disprove the doctrine of spontaneous generation?

2. Discuss the possibility that life could appear again on Earth as it presumably did at one time.
3. How did the experiments of Schroeder and von Dusch, Pasteur, and Tyndall help to disprove the belief in spontaneous generation?
4. How did the controversy over the germ theory of fermentation lay the foundation for modern industrial microbiology?
5. Describe a general approach to the problem of proving that an organism isolated from rotting wood is actually able to digest cellulose.
6. What desirable and undesirable characteristics does agar have as an ingredient of culture media?
7. Describe how one might secure a culture of soil organisms capable of utilizing carbolic acid.
8. Discuss arguments for and against considering viruses to be alive.
9. Why are there only a handful of useful antibiotics out of the thousands that have been discovered?
10. Discuss the advantages of using microorganisms as the subjects of research on the molecular basis of life.

SUPPLEMENTARY READING

Milestones in Microbiology is a well chosen collection of papers, translated into English where necessary, covering significant developments from 1546 to 1940; Brock has added pertinent explanatory comments. Bulloch's *History of Bacteriology* is a standard reference. Starting with ancient doctrines on the nature of contagion, it emphasizes the medical aspects of the science. Clark traces microbiology in America from its origins in Europe and its early emphasis on public hygiene along the Atlantic seaboard to its development in conjunction with agriculture and industry in the Midwest. DeKruif's *Microbe Hunters* is a well known popular account of a dozen early bacteriologists, written from the perspective of a bacteriologist turned writer. *Antony van Leeuwenhoek and His "Little Animals"* by Dobell is a delightful account of the life and achievements of the discoverer of bacteria; it also includes translations of some of his pertinent letters to the Royal Society of London. Lechevalier and Solotorovsky trace the evolution of microbiology, including bacteriology, virology, mycology, protozoology and chemotherapy, with a concluding section on genetics and the modern approach. Many extensive quotations from scientific papers introduce the reader to the personalities of the various scientists. Vallery-Radot's *Life of Pasteur* is one of the early accounts of the life and scientific work of this pioneer in microbiology.

Brock, T. D.: *Milestones in Microbiology.* Englewood Cliffs, N. J., Prentice-Hall, Inc., 1961.
Bulloch. W.: *The History of Bacteriology.* London, Oxford University Press, 1938.
Clark, P. F.: *Pioneer Microbiologists of America.* Madison, Wis., University of Wisconsin Press, 1961.
DeKruif, P.: *Microbe Hunters.* New York, Harcourt, Brace and Co., Inc., 1926.
Dobell, C.: *Antony van Leeuwenhoek and His "Little Animals."* New York, Staples Press, 1932.
Lechevalier, H. H., and Solotorovsky, M.: *Three Centuries of Microbiology.* New York, McGraw-Hill Book Co. Inc., 1965.
Vallery-Radot, R.: *The Life of Pasteur.* New York, Garden City Publishing Co., Inc., 1926.

THE TOOLS OF A MICROBIOLOGIST

Most of the equipment and materials used in microbiology are borrowed from chemistry and physics and the other biologic sciences. Some have been devised by microbiologists for their own purposes. Research often requires considerable ingenuity, and it may be said that a good laboratory investigator should also be handy in the machine shop. As shown in the preceding chapter, microbiology advanced at any one time only as far as the available equipment permitted; further progress had to wait for technical improvements.

THE MICROSCOPE

The Compound Microscope

Compound microscopes differ from simple microscopes like those of Leeuwenhoek in possessing two lenses or lens systems: an *objective* and an *ocular* (Fig. 3-1). The objective produces a magnified image of the object, which is further magnified by the ocular (eyepiece). The total magnification is the product of the magnifications produced by the two lenses individually.

It will be recalled that when a light ray passes at an angle from one medium to another of different density (e.g., from air to glass), the ray is bent or refracted. The direction of bending is toward a line perpendicular to the surface between the media when the ray is entering the medium of greater density, and away from the perpendicular when it is entering the medium of lesser density (see Fig. 3-2). The density of air is less than that of all other transparent substances. The intensity of refraction in any other medium is expressed by the *index of refraction,* which is obtained by dividing the angle of incidence in air by the angle of refraction in the second medium (e.g., i_1/r_1 in Fig. 3-2). The index of refraction of glass is about 1.52; it varies somewhat according to the composition of the glass.

Light passing from air into glass and out into air again is refracted twice, and if the two glass surfaces are parallel, the ray emerging into the air travels in

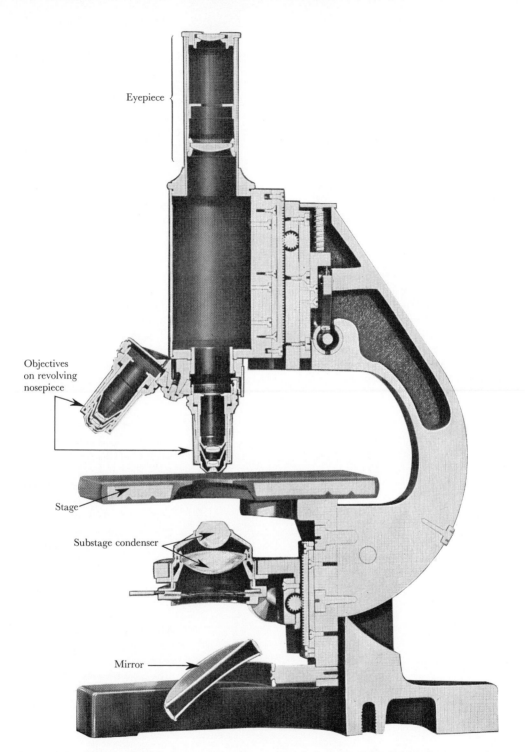

Eyepiece

Objectives
on revolving
nosepiece

Stage

Substage condenser

Mirror

Figure 3-1. Photograph of a cross section of a compound microscope showing interior construction. Light from the mirror is focused by the substage condenser on the object, placed upon the stage. The image produced by the objective is further magnified by the eyepiece. Some of the lenses of which the objectives are composed are important in reducing various aberrations (e.g., spherical and chromatic aberrations). (Courtesy Bausch and Lomb.)

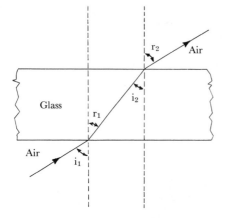

Figure 3-2. The path of a light ray showing refraction when it passes from air into glass and when it emerges into air again. The ray is refracted toward the perpendicular when entering a medium of greater density (that is, the angle of incidence, *i*, is greater than the angle of refraction, *r*) and away from the perpendicular when entering a medium of less density.

the same direction as the incident ray did before it entered the glass. However, if the two surfaces are not parallel, as in a biconvex lens, the emerging ray travels in a different direction, which depends in part upon the distance of its point of origin from the center of the lens (see Fig. 3-3). For each lens there is a distance from the center of the lens, designated the *focal length*, at which parallel rays entering the lens are brought to a focus; light originating at this point and traversing the lens emerges as parallel rays. Light originating from a source farther from the lens than this point is focused at some finite point when it emerges from the lens.

If, instead of a single point, the source of light is an area (e.g., an object like an illuminated bacterium), each point in that area will serve as the source of a ray which will be refracted by the lens in the same manner and focused to pro-

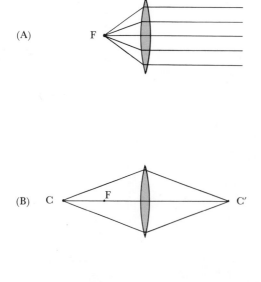

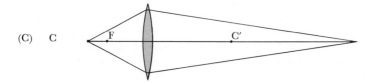

Figure 3-3. Paths of light through a biconvex lens. A, Parallel rays from the right are brought to a point (i.e., focused) at *F*, whose distance from the center of the lens is designated the *focal length* of the lens; conversely, a light ray originating at *F* is refracted into parallel rays upon emerging from the lens. B, A ray originating at a distance twice the focal length from the lens is brought to a focus at the same distance on the other side of the lens; *C* and *C'* are *conjugate foci*. C, A ray starting at a point between *F* and *C* is focused at some point between *C'* and infinity. This is the situation when the lens is used to produce a magnified image.

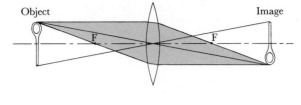

A

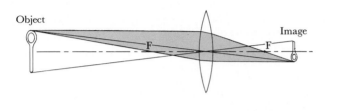

B

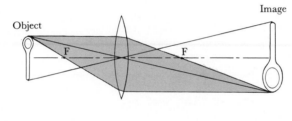

C

Figure 3-4.   Relationship between the size of the image and the position of the object relative to the lens. Note that the image is inverted.

duce an *image* on the opposite side of the lens. The image will be smaller than, the same size as, or larger than the object, depending upon the distance of the object from the lens (see Fig. 3-4).

Features of a Good Microscope

To be satisfactory, a microscope must provide adequate *magnifying power*. It should magnify the object sufficiently so that the finest details appear far enough separated to be visible to the eye. Magnification by each lens is usually indicated by markings (e.g., 10X, 43X, 97X on the objectives; 5X, 10X, 15X on the eye-pieces). A microscope should also produce a visible image of good *definition* and possess high *resolving power*.

Definition.   Definition is a matter of contrast and depends upon the quality of the lenses. Ordinary lenses suffer from defects known as spherical and chromatic aberrations. These result from the inability of optical glass to bring all light rays to a focus at a common point. Visible rays of different colors are refracted at different angles, the shorter wavelengths, such as blue, being refracted to a greater extent than the longer wavelengths. Spherical and chromatic aberrations can be partially corrected by the use of various glasses and the mineral fluorite. Ordinary or achromatic objectives are satisfactory for many routine purposes. Apochromatic objectives are more highly corrected and are used extensively for photomicrography because of their better color correction.

Resolving Power. Resolving power is the ability to produce separate images of small parts of an object that are only a short distance apart, that is, the ability to distinguish fine detail. Resolving power is measured by a quantity known as the *numerical aperture* (N.A.). The higher the numerical aperture of an objective, the greater is its resolving power. The numerical aperture of an objective varies directly with the refractive index of the medium between the object and the front lens of the objective, and with the angle of the light entering the objective.

The resolution or fineness of detail that can be distinguished also depends upon the wavelength of light used for illumination. Finest detail is observed with light of short wavelength (i.e., blue or blue-green in ordinary microscopy). The relationship between numerical aperture, wavelength of light, and resolving power is as follows:

$$\text{Limit of resolution} = \frac{0.61 \times \text{wavelength}}{\text{N.A. of objective}}$$

The units of measurement used in describing microorganisms and other microscopic or submicroscopic objects are the micron (μ), which is 0.001 millimeter; the millimicron (mμ), or 0.001 μ; and the Ångstrom (Å), which is 0.1 mμ or 0.0001 μ. The best objective on the usual student bacteriologic microscope

has a numerical aperture of 1.25, and if blue-green light at a wavelength of 500 mμ is used, the limit of resolution is

$$\frac{0.61 \times 500}{1.25} = 244 \text{ m}\mu$$

In other words, it is just barely possible to distinguish two objects as separate bodies if they are about 0.25 μ apart.

The Substage Condenser. Many improvements were made in the microscope during the three hundred years following its invention. Lens grinding became a science rather than an art, and greater magnification was obtained. Increased magnification necessitated better illumination. A rough comparison may be made with the common experience that newspaper headlines can easily be read by natural light late in the day, but artificial light must be used for reading fine print. Higher magnifications were made possible by a third lens system, which focused and concentrated light from the mirror or lamp upon the object. This lens system was called a *substage condenser* (Fig. 3-5). In the terminology of optics, the substage condenser provides a cone of light of sufficient angle to fill the aperture of the objective. This is not possible with the mirror alone when objectives of high magnifying power are employed. The Abbé condenser, named after its inventor, is found on most student microscopes in bacteriology.

Objective Lenses. Microscopes are usually equipped with a revolving nosepiece upon which are mounted at least three objectives (Table 3-1). The objective of lowest power ordinarily used provides magnification of ten times, and the

Table 3-1. Properties of Commonly Used Microscope Objectives

Objective Magnification	Equivalent Focal Length	Numerical Aperture	Working Distance	Total Magnification with 10X Eyepiece
10X	16 mm.	0.25	8.3 mm.	100X
43X	4 mm.	0.65	0.72 mm.	430X
97X	1.8 mm.	1.25 oil	0.14 mm.	970X

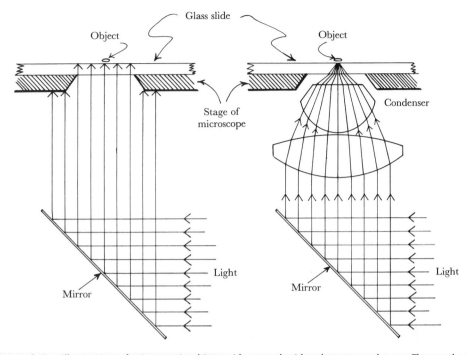

Figure 3-5. Illumination of microscopic object without and with substage condenser. The condenser focuses all the light from the mirror on the object.

intermediate objective magnifies 42 to 45 times. The objective of highest power magnifies about 97 times, and differs from the other two objectives in its manner of use. It is sometimes referred to as an *oil immersion* objective because it must always be immersed in cedar oil or some other medium having approximately the same index of refraction as glass (1.52). Substitutes containing mineral oil as the principal component are

often used and offer the advantage that they do not dry on prolonged exposure to air.

Light passing through a glass slide continues in a straight path through the immersion oil in contact with it and the front lens of the objective (see Fig. 3-6), whereas light emerging from a slide into air is refracted from the axis of the objective and toward the slide. Details of the observed image become fuzzy and

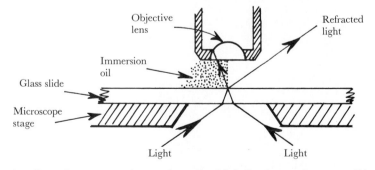

Figure 3-6. The effect of immersion oil upon the path of light leaving a microscope slide. In the left half of the sketch light passes in a straight line through the slide and oil and into the objective lens. In the right half, drawn without oil, part of the light is refracted away from the lens.

some light is lost; that is, part of the light passes by the objective and never enters it. Obviously, immersion oil enhances the resolving power of the objective so that finer details can be observed, and more of the incident light is utilized.

Ultraviolet Microscopy

It was noted previously that the resolving power of a microscope is determined in part by the wavelength of light employed and that resolution is improved with short wavelengths. Beyond the shortest visible light rays in the ultraviolet region is invisible light, which can be used for photography. A microscope for ultraviolet photography must be equipped with quartz lenses because glass absorbs ultraviolet light. Higher magnification is obtained than with visible light and resolution is approximately twice as great as with visible light; that is, objects about 0.1 μ apart can be distinguished. Focusing is obviously more difficult.

Darkfield Microscopy

The images produced by the darkfield microscope appear as luminous bodies against a black or nearly black background (Fig. 3-7). In the ordinary or brightfield microscope an object is visible if it absorbs or refracts some of the incident light and thereby creates contrast between it and the suspending medium; any object that does not absorb or refract light is difficult to see. In the darkfield microscope, such an object, illuminated by a strong beam of light so directed that none would normally enter the objective, reflects some of the incident light in all directions; part of the reflected light enters the objective and is seen through the eyepiece. The object therefore appears luminous.

The ordinary Abbé condenser fitted with an opaque disk or *dark ground stop* is used with the low power of the microscope (Fig. 3-8). The dark ground stop eliminates all light from the central portion of the condenser and permits only a thin cone of light to reach the object. Objectives of higher magnification require special condensers, which can be substituted for the Abbé condenser. Little or no other modification is required. Intense light is necessary, such as that provided by a carbon arc lamp or various research illuminators. Slides and coverglasses must be per-

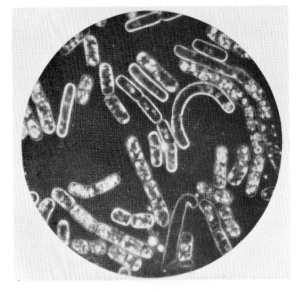

Figure 3-7. Photomicrograph of *Bacillus megaterium*, unstained, darkfield, by ultraviolet illumination (2500X). (From Topley and Wilson: Principles of Bacteriology and Immunology. Baltimore, Williams & Wilkins, 1946.)

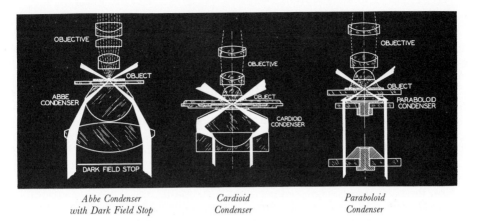

Abbe Condenser with Dark Field Stop   *Cardioid Condenser*   *Paraboloid Condenser*

Figure 3-8. Three forms of darkfield condenser. The Abbé condenser with darkfield stop can be used with low power objectives (10X or 20X); the paraboloid or cardioid condenser is required for higher power objectives. Note that the object is illuminated by peripheral light and only light reflected by the object (dotted lines) enters the objective lens. (Courtesy Bausch and Lomb.)

fectly clean and free from scratches because extraneous objects or marks also reflect light and produce a brighter background than desired.

The darkfield microscope is used to study very small or slender bacteria of low refractive index. *Treponema palli-dum,* the cause of syphilis (Fig. 3-9), can readily be detected in chancre fluid.

Fluorescence Microscopy

Microorganisms observed with the fluorescence microscope resemble those

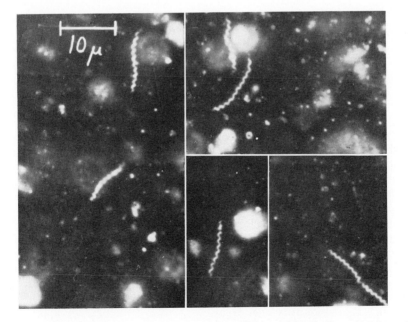

Figure 3-9. Darkfield photomicrograph of *Treponema pallidum.* The slender organisms reflect the oblique incident light and therefore appear bright against a dark background (1500X). (Photograph by Dr. Theodor Rosebury; A.S.M. LS-327.)

seen with the darkfield microscope: the cells are bright against a dark background. The principle of the microscope is quite different, however.

A source of intense light is used together with a filter that removes all except the ultraviolet and near ultraviolet rays. The specimen is stained with a yellow dye such as auramine O. A yellow filter is placed in the eyepiece of the microscope. The effect of the blue filter at the source of light and the yellow filter in the eyepiece is to produce a black field. Objects stained with the yellow dye fluoresce in the ultraviolet light and emit yellow light, which passes through the yellow eyepiece filter and readily reveals their presence and shape.

The fluorescence microscope is used to detect *Mycobacterium tuberculosis* in sputum. Lower magnification is required than with conventional methods of examination because the bright yellow organisms stand out clearly against the black background. The field observed is therefore larger, so the smear may be examined more quickly.

Immuno-fluorescence Microscopy

Immuno-fluorescence microscopy is a special extension and refinement of fluorescence microscopy. The stain consists of a particular type of blood serum protein known as an antibody (to be discussed in some detail in Chapter 21) to which fluorescein or rhodamine or some other fluorescent dye has been chemically coupled. An important property of antibodies is their ability to combine with certain other proteins or protein-polysaccharide complexes which may be part of bacteria or other cells. A fluorescent antibody can therefore be used to stain and hence to detect a specific chemical component of a cell. If this component is found in only a single kind of cell (for example, a hemolytic streptococcus), the fluorescent antibody stain can be used to identify this organism quickly (Figs. 3-10 and 3-11). Speed is often of importance in the diagnosis of disease caused by microorganisms.

In a modification of this procedure, known as the "sandwich" technique (Fig. 3-12), nonfluorescent antibody produced in a rabbit by immunization with the organism in question is placed on a smear in which the organism is presumed to be present. Excess (uncombined) antibody is washed off, and the preparation is treated with a fluorescent antibody capable of reacting with rabbit serum protein (and hence with the nonfluorescent antibody attached to the organisms). The antibody that reacts with rabbit protein is produced in an animal such as the sheep and then made fluorescent by coupling it with a fluorescent dye. This procedure makes it possible to use the fluorescence technique without preparing each specific fluorescent antibody.

Immunofluorescence microscopy is useful in determining the identity of microorganisms in mixtures (e.g., in a throat smear or fecal specimen), in ascertaining the location of certain organisms within the tissues or cells of an infected host animal or plant, and in studying the chemical structure of cells.

Phase Microscopy

The refraction that occurs when light passes from one medium into another of different density is utilized in the phase contrast microscope. An ordinary microscope can be adapted for phase microscopy by substitution of appropriate condensers and objectives.

Transparent cells in a transparent medium or transparent structures within the cells are indistinguishable by ordinary microscopy. If, however, the cells or structures differ from their surroundings in refractive index, even slightly, some of the light striking them is deviated. The phase microscope is so designed as to intensify slight differences in contrast produced by this deviation.

The condenser in a phase contrast microscope has a special diaphragm, which permits only a ring of light to strike the object (Fig. 3-13). In the back

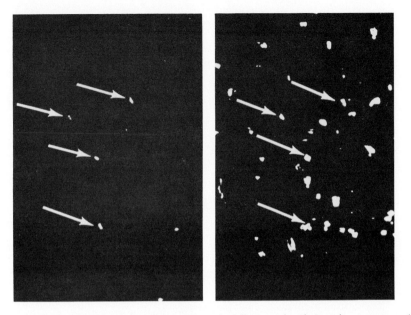

Figure 3-10. Specific staining of *Pseudomonas pseudomallei* mixed with *Pseudomonas aeruginosa* by means of fluorescein-labeled anti-*P. pseudomallei* globulin. The photograph on the left was taken by fluorescence microscopy; only cells of *P. pseudomallei* fluoresce. The photograph on the right is the same field taken with visible light and a darkfield condenser. Arrows point to *P. pseudomallei* cells; the others are *P. aeruginosa*. (From B. M. Thomason, M. D. Moody, and M. Goldman: J. Bact., 72:362, 1956; A.S.M. LS-361.)

focal plane of the objective is a transparent disk with a ring upon which light from the annular condenser aperture is focused. This ring alters by a quarter-wavelength the phase of light waves that pass through it, either advancing

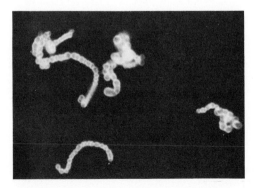

Figure 3-11. Smear of group A streptococci stained with homologous fluorescent antibody. (Photograph by M. D. Moody.)

or retarding them, according to its construction.

If each transparent particle in the object is considered individually, it will be apparent that when a single ray of light strikes a particle, two rays result. One is the direct continuation of the incident ray, which passes through the point and on to the phase-shifting ring, where it is either retarded or advanced. The other ray is refracted or deviated by the particle because of the difference in density between the particle and the material immediately adjacent to it. Since this ray has deviated, it does not strike the phase-shifting ring and hence its phase is unaffected. When both rays are again brought to a focus, the particle appears brighter on darker than the surrounding matter, depending on whether superposition of the two rays results in addition or subtraction of their intensities (Fig. 3-14). The object therefore appears either lighter than usual against a dark background (bright

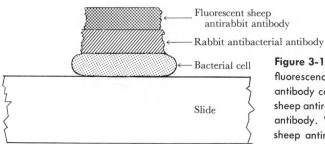

Fluorescent sheep antirabbit antibody

Rabbit antibacterial antibody

Bacterial cell

Slide

Figure 3-12. "Sandwich" technique of immuno-fluorescence microscopy. The rabbit antibacterial antibody combines with the bacterial cell, and the sheep antirabbit antibody combines with this rabbit antibody. When illuminated with ultraviolet, the sheep antirabbit antibody fluoresces and can be seen with the microscope.

contrast) or darker than usual against a bright background (dark contrast).

Phase microscopy is particularly useful in studying the internal structures of microorganisms because structures differing in refractive index from the surrounding protoplasm become visible, and their sizes and locations can be determined.

The Electron Microscope

It has been emphasized that a major factor limiting the resolution obtainable with a microscope is the wavelength of light used to illuminate the object. This limitation means that the smallest object that can be seen clearly with the ordinary microscope is about 0.2 μ in diameter and the best magnification

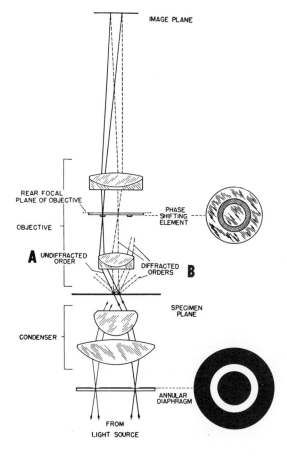

IMAGE PLANE

REAR FOCAL PLANE OF OBJECTIVE

OBJECTIVE

PHASE SHIFTING ELEMENT

A UNDIFFRACTED ORDER

DIFFRACTED ORDERS **B**

SPECIMEN PLANE

CONDENSER

ANNULAR DIAPHRAGM

FROM LIGHT SOURCE

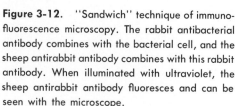

Figure 3-13. Path of light through the phase contrast microscope. Light enters through the annular diaphragm opening and illuminates the object. Part of the light, A (solid lines), is transmitted directly and focused on the phase-shifting ring at the rear focal plane of the objective, which advances or retards it by $\frac{1}{4}$ wavelength. The remainder of the light, B (broken lines), is diffracted by the object and scattered; most of it does not strike the phase-shifting ring. When undiffracted and diffracted rays (A and B) are finally focused to form an image, additive or subtractive superposition produces differences in brightness that are readily apparent. (Courtesy of Dr. J. R. Benford, Bausch and Lomb Scientific Bureau.)

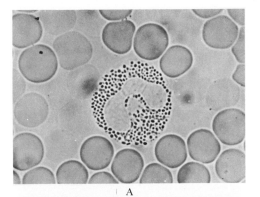

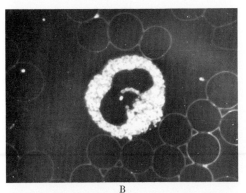

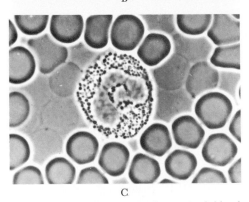

Figure 3-14. Appearance of unstained blood cells by A, ordinary, brightfield microscopy; B, darkfield microscopy; C, phase microscopy. A single eosinophilic leukocyte, surrounded by erythrocytes, magnified about 1250X. (From Scope, courtesy of the Upjohn Company.)

obtainable is not much more than 1000X. Ultraviolet light extends the range of useful magnifications to about 2000X.

A new form of microscopy became possible when it was discovered that cer-

tain radiations of much shorter wavelength can be focused by suitable electric or magnetic fields in somewhat the same way that glass lenses focus visible light. Radiations used for this purpose consist of electrons emitted by the cathode filament of an electron "gun" at a velocity of a few tens of thousands of volts.

A common type of electron microscope (Fig. 3-15) contains three or more ring-shaped electromagnets, which function as lenses. The first is a condenser which, like its counterpart in the light microscope, focuses the electron stream on the object. The second, the objective, produces a magnified intermediate image of the object. Finally, the projector magnifies a portion of the intermediate image to produce the final image, which is photographed or inspected visually on a fluorescent screen (Fig. 3-16).

Electrons are readily stopped by all forms of matter; therefore, electron microscopy must be carried out in a vacuum. This imposes a limitation on the types of specimens that can be studied. Living organisms cannot be examined because samples must be completely desiccated. Preparations must also be very thin (less than 0.5 μ) to reveal structural differentiation; biologic materials are often mounted on thin films of collodion or cellophane, supported on a metal grid.

Surface structural details are revealed by "shadowing" with a metal such as gold or chromium. The specimen is placed below and at one side of a tungsten filament charged with the desired heavy metal and is heated to vaporize the metal. The operation is carried out in a vacuum, and the metal atoms travel in straight lines in all directions from the filament. Some of the metal deposits on the sample, the thickness of the deposit being greatest on aspects of the surface tissue facing the oncoming atoms and thinnest in regions shaded by the specimen. The heavy metal is opaque to electrons, so an electron photomicrograph presents a

Figure 3-15. R.C.A. electron microscope. A human hair photographed with this instrument would appear as large as the Lincoln Tunnel.

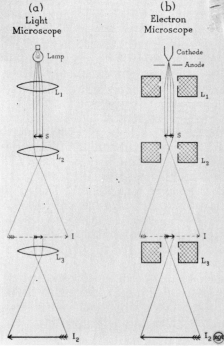

(a)
Light
Microscope

(b)
Electron
Microscope

Figure 3-16. The "optics" of the electron and light microscopes. In the light microscope (a) (shown inverted for better direct comparison) light is focused by condenser lens L_1 on the specimen, S; the objective lens, L_2, produces an image, I, which is further magnified by the eyepiece lens, L_3. The source of radiation in the electron microscope (b) is a cathode, which emits electrons accelerated by an electric potential of approximately 50,000 volts. A magnetic coil, L_1, serves as a condenser, deflecting the electrons and focusing them on the specimen, S; a second magnetic coil, L_2, functions like an objective lens, deflecting the electrons and producing an image magnified 100X to 200X, which is further magnified 200X to 250X by the projector coil, L_3, forming an image on a fluorescent screen for visual inspection or on a photographic plate. The total magnification is 20,000X to 50,000X, and the picture can be enlarged to 1,000,000X. (A.S.M. LS-31.)

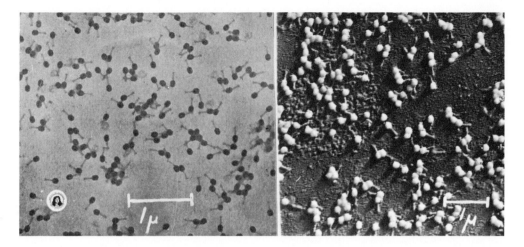

Figure 3-17. Electron photomicrographs of a bacterial virus (*Escherichia coli* bacteriophage gamma) showing the effect of shadowing with a heavy metal: *left,* unshadowed; *right,* shadowed. (Photographs by D. G. Sharp; A.S.M. LS-139.)

three dimensional appearance similar to that of a landscape seen from an airplane by the light of the early morning or late afternoon sun (Fig. 3-17).

Individual cells, even of bacteria, are too thick to show clearly details of internal structure in ordinary, unshadowed preparations. Ultrathin sectioning techniques have been developed, using glass or quartz knives and capable of yielding slices as thin as 20 mμ. These reveal that cells possess a complicated fine structure, and they present the opportunity to correlate structure with function.

Another technique that helps to demonstrate the internal structure of cells and even of virus particles is the use of heavy metal salts like phosphotungstate as "negative" stains. The background and any "hollow" region into which the salt penetrates become opaque to electrons, whereas areas occupied by cell material remain relatively transparent. Much greater structural detail is therefore shown (see Fig. 3-18).

The interpretation of electron photomicrographs is plagued by artefacts due to extraneous materials in the specimen or to faults in the technique of preparing and examining it. The identity of any newly detected structure has to be determined by correlating a variety of

methods of examination: light microscopy of stained preparations, phase microscopy, physiologic studies, and any other technique that the experimenter can devise.

The direct magnification theoretically obtainable with the electron microscope is as high as 100,000. Magnifications of 20,000 to 50,000 are common. Pictures obtained at lower magnifications are of sufficient sharpness that photographic enlargements of eight to

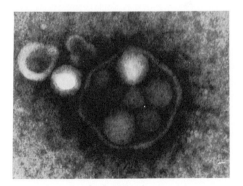

Figure 3-18. Use of negative staining with phosphotungstic acid and electron microscopy to demonstrate internal structures of cells: spherical bodies within a cell of *Mycoplasma hominis* (50,000X). (From Anderson et al., J. Bact., 90:189, 1965.)

ten times can be made with a resulting magnification of 1,000,000 or more.

MICROSCOPIC STUDY OF BACTERIA

Observation of Unstained Cells

Leeuwenhoek and all other microbiologists until the latter half of the nineteenth century had to be content with microscopic observation of unstained organisms. The advantages of direct study of living cells in their natural shape, arrangement, and size were counterbalanced by the fact that the refractive index of microbial protoplasm is so near that of water that the cells and their structures cannot be clearly differentiated from each other and from the mounting fluid.

The *wet mount* was a common type of preparation for observation of bacteria and is still used. A drop of broth culture is placed on a slide and a cover slip is carefully added. The living organisms can be examined by low power and high power dry (i.e., 43X) objectives. The diaphragm of the Abbé condenser must be partly closed to provide a narrow beam of light; otherwise the cells cannot be distinguished from the medium.

A *hanging drop* is preferred if prolonged study of living organisms is to be made (Fig. 3-19). A special slide with a hollow in one side is used. The culture is placed on a *clean* coverglass and inverted over the depression, sealed with water, oil, or petrolatum, and stud-

ied with the low power or high power dry objective. This type of mount is especially useful for continuous observation of bacterial motility or for watching the growth of individual cells in a microculture.

Bacterial Stains

Microscopic study of bacteria is greatly facilitated by treating them with dyes or stains. The shapes and relative sizes of stained organisms can be determined more easily, and staining also permits certain cellular structures to be recognized.

Chromophore and Auxochrome Radicals. Dyes are organic compounds containing color-producing *chromophore* radicals and salt-forming *auxochrome* groups. The nitro ($-NO_2$) and azo ($-N=N-$) groups are chromophores; the hydroxyl ($-OH$) and amino ($-NH_2$) radicals are auxochrome groups. Chromophores impart the property of color to a dye, and auxochrome groups permit the dye to unite with fibers or tissues. Most commercial dyes are salts, but are referred to as basic dyes if the colored portion behaves as a base or acidic dyes if it behaves as an acid. Basic dyes are usually available as chlorides and acidic dyes as sodium salts. Acidic dyes are used to stain basic material such as cytoplasm, whereas basic dyes stain nuclei, certain granules, and other acid substances.

Mechanism of Staining. Staining of cells and tissues is probably a combination of physical and chemical processes. The physical phenomena of adsorption,

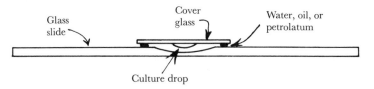

Figure 3-19. A "hanging drop" preparation. The drop of culture sealed in the small chamber by water, oil, or petrolatum may be observed for some time without drying.

absorption, capillarity, and osmosis play a part. On the other hand, the affinity of basic dyes for acidic tissues and of acidic dyes for basic tissues indicates that chemical reactions occur and lead to the formation of new compounds.

Preparation of Bacterial Smears for Staining

Before staining, bacteria are usually suspended in water or some other liquid on a *clean* microscope slide and are then spread in a thin, even film. The film is allowed to dry in air, and the organisms are "fixed" to the slide by chemical means or more commonly by gentle heat. The preparation is known as a *fixed smear.*

Simple Stains

A *simple stain* is a solution of a single dye, usually in alcohol or water. Most bacteria contain acidic material distributed more or less uniformly throughout the cell. They therefore stain intensely with basic dyes such as methylene blue, crystal violet, or carbol fuchsin (a solution of basic fuchsin in 5 per cent carbolic acid). The time required for staining varies with the dye solution: one to five minutes is necessary with methylene blue; 15 seconds usually suffices with crystal violet.

Stained smears are rinsed briefly with water to remove excess stain, dried in air, and are then ready for examination.

Simple stains are used to detect the shape, arrangement, and relative size of bacteria and are useful in helping to identify them. They do not, however, reveal details of internal structure.

Differential Stains

Differential staining procedures distinguish structures within a cell or distinguish one type of cell from another. Two dyes are usually employed, and certain structures or cell types appear in one color in the final preparation, with the remaining structures or cell types in the second color. The first dye applied is the *primary* stain. This is usually followed by *differentiation:* application of a solution that removes the primary stain from some cells or structures. The other dye, known as the *secondary* stain or *counterstain,* is then applied. Differential stains are widely employed in identifying bacteria.

Endospore Stain. The Bacillaceae, a large and important family, produce resistant bodies known as endospores at a particular stage in their life cycle. These structures are formed within the cell—hence the name, *endo*spore—and contain all the cell components necessary to maintain life. They resist harmful physical and chemical agents, and they also resist staining. Simple stains do not ordinarily appear to penetrate the spore wall, so a cell with its endospore (sporangium; Fig. 3-20) contains a colorless spherical or oval body when stained briefly with crystal violet or methylene blue.

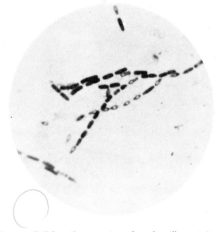

Figure 3-20. Sporangia of a bacillus stained with crystal violet. The endospores are the colorless oval bodies within some of the cells (approx. 1000X). (From Burrows: Textbook of Microbiology, 18th ed. Philadelphia, W. B. Saunders Co., 1963.)

Endospores may be stained by a drastic procedure. Strong dyes are allowed to remain in contact with the cells for a long time, or staining is facilitated by application of heat. The primary stain in the Schaeffer-Fulton procedure is malachite green; the smear is covered with dye and heated to steaming for 30 to 60 seconds. Differentiation is accomplished by washing with running water for 30 seconds. The green dye, which penetrates the endospores as well as the remainder of the cytoplasm, is thus removed from the vegetative portions of the sporangia but not appreciably from the endospores. A smear examined at this point reveals colorless cells containing green endospores, but the vegetative parts of the cells are difficult to distinguish. A counterstain of contrasting color, safranin, is then applied, and after brief rinsing and drying the preparation is ready to observe. It now consists of pink cells containing green endospores, and the position of the spores and their size in relation to that of the whole cells can readily be determined.

Endospore stains are useful in helping to identify the Bacillaceae, which are practically the only bacteria capable of producing endospores. The endospores of certain species are spherical, others are oval. Spores may be located in the center of the cell, slightly away from the center (excentrically), near the end of the cell (subterminally), or at the very end of the cell (terminally). The diameter of the spores may be less than, equal to, or greater than that of the sporangium. In the latter case, the sporangium bulges. The shape, position, and size of the endospore are fairly characteristic for a given species; hence these properties help to establish the species name of a previously unknown organism. This approach to the classification of bacteria resembles that employed with higher plants and with animals, which are usually identified by morphologic properties.

Acidfast Stain. The mycobacteria (e.g., *M. tuberculosis* and *M. leprae*), like endospores, are difficult to stain, but once stained they retain the dye tenaciously even when washed with dilute mineral acid.

In the Ziehl-Neelsen procedure the primary stain, carbolfuchsin, is heated to steaming for five minutes, after which the smear is decolorized briefly with dilute alcoholic H_2SO_4 or HCl and counterstained with methylene blue to reveal the presence of nonacidfast organisms. Acidfast bacteria retain the pink or red primary stain; all other organisms are decolorized by the acid and stain blue.

Acidfastness appears to be associated with the presence of large amounts of lipoid material, which may comprise as much as 40 per cent of the cell substance of *M. tuberculosis*. It has been postulated that the phenol-dye complex carbolfuchsin is more soluble in the lipoid cellular constituents than it is in the decolorizing agent and hence is retained by mycobacteria but not by organisms that lack a high lipid content.

Gram Stain. The Gram stain is the most widely used staining procedure in bacteriology. It divides bacteria into two great classes, *gram-positive* and *gram-negative;* moreover, the Gram reaction is correlated with certain other properties of an organism (Table 3-2).

The primary stain, crystal violet, is followed by an iodine solution that behaves as a mordant and helps fix the primary dye to gram-positive organisms. The smear is then decolorized, usually with 95 per cent alcohol, and counterstained with a contrasting dye such as safranin. Organisms that retain the purple primary stain are designated gram-positive; gram-negative cells lose the primary stain when decolorized with alcohol and stain with the relatively weak secondary pink dye, safranin.

Mechanism of the Gram Stain. Both chemical and cell wall permeability theories of the mechanism of Gram differentiation have held sway in the past. The present view is that the permeability of the cell walls of gram-positive and gram-negative bacteria differs under the conditions of the decolorizing step, and

Table 3-2. Some Differences between Gram-Positive and Gram-Negative Bacteria

Gram-Positive	Gram-Negative
Contain magnesium ribonucleate	Do not contain magnesium ribonucleate
Very sensitive to triphenylmethane dyes (e.g., crystal violet)	Less sensitive to triphenylmethane dyes
Sensitive to penicillin	Sensitive to streptomycin
Not dissolved by 1% KOH	Dissolved by 1% KOH
Apparent isoelectric point pH 2–3	Apparent isoelectric point pH 4–5
Sporeforming rods, many cocci (also *Lactobacillus* and *Corynebacterium* species)	Most nonsporeforming rods, spirals, some cocci
Toxins (if any): exotoxins	Toxins: endotoxins

that this is the factor that permits the loss of primary stain from the latter organisms. Protoplasmic constituents of both gram-positive and gram-negative cells combine with crystal violet by an ionic bond between their acidic groups and the basic groups of the dye. Iodine, in aqueous solution, enters the cells and reacts with the dye, either removing it from the cell protein or adding to the dye-protein complex.

It is believed that 95 per cent alcohol dehydrates the mordanted walls of gram-positive cells and forms a barrier, which traps the crystal violet-iodine complex. Such a barrier is not formed in gram-negative cells. It is known that the cell walls of these organisms contain a higher percentage of lipid than those of most gram-positive organisms, and hence the solubility of the surface lipids in alcohol may be a factor in the greater ease of decolorization of gram-negative cells. However, further study is necessary to clarify this point.

There is no sharp line of demarcation between gram-positive and gram-negative organisms; there is a continuous gradation from species that retain the primary stain even after decolorization for several hours, to species that decolorize within a few seconds. Aging cultures of many organisms that are normally considered gram-positive contain increasing numbers of gram-negative cells. Some species and even individual smears contain both gram-positive and gram-negative cells; such cultures are called *gram-variable*. The staining procedure must be carefully standardized to obtain consistent and reliable results, and control organisms of known Gram reaction should also be tested, particularly in critical work.

Nuclear (Chromatinic Body) Stain. The Feulgen reaction and numerous modifications of it are used to demonstrate "nuclear" material in bacteria. This reaction is actually a test for aldehyde, but is considered to indicate the presence of DNA. Smears fixed with osmic vapor are subjected to mild hydrolysis with 1N HCl (7–8 min. at 58° C.) and then treated with Schiff's reagent (fuchsin decolorized with SO_2). A light pink color indicates DNA. RNA is not stained after acid hydrolysis. The color produced by DNA is often not strong, but other stains have been used with success, such as dilute Giemsa stain, azure A, or thionin, following the hydrolysis step. Chromatinic bodies in the cells of *Escherichia coli* and two *Bacillus* species are shown in Figure 3-21.

Flagella Stain. The motility of a culture to be used for staining of flagella should be checked. Young cultures grown on fresh agar slants are gently washed with 2 to 3 ml. of sterile distilled water and the bacterial suspension is incubated a few minutes. Droplets are transferred by capillary pipette

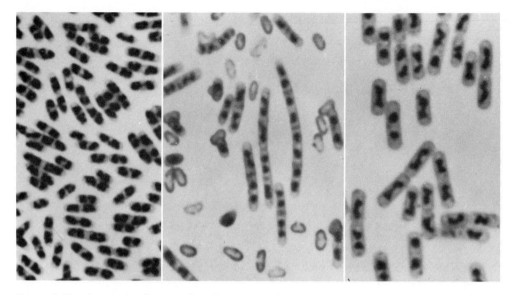

Figure 3-21. Bacterial cells stained to demonstrate chromatin bodies (nuclei). *Left, Escherichia coli,* 4000X; *middle, Bacillus mesentericus,* 4400X (note spores in various stages of germination, see page 94); *right, Bacillus cereus,* 4400X. (Photograph of *E. coli* by J. Hillier, S. Mudd, and A. G. Smith; A.S.M. LS-239; photographs of *B. mesentericus* and *B. cereus,* Committee on Materials for Visual Instruction; A.S.M. LS-266.)

from the top of the suspension, where motile cells are most numerous, to one end of a tilted, *scrupulously clean* microscope slide and allowed to run down the slide and dry in air without mechanical agitation that would break off the flagella. The Leifson stain contains potassium or ammonium aluminum sulfate and tannic acid as a mordant, and the dye basic fuchsin. Slides flooded with the solution are allowed to stand 10 minutes, washed, dried, and examined under oil. Flagella stain pink, their apparent diameter being greatly increased by the deposit of dye. Flagella staining requires very careful technique.

Cell Wall Stain. Cell walls may be stained by alcian blue, by crystal violet following tannic acid as a mordant, or by methyl green. Bisset and Hale's procedure consists of immersing thick smears in 1 per cent phosphomolybdic acid for 3 to 5 minutes and then in 1 per cent methyl green for the same interval. After washing and drying, the smear is examined under oil. Cell walls are dark

green or purple; cytoplasm is unstained. Cells of *Bacillus mycoides* stained by this method are shown in Figure 3-22. Complete cross walls are formed and divide the cells into several units.

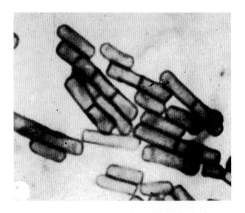

Figure 3-22. *Bacillus mycoides* stained with methyl green to demonstrate cell walls. Each bacillus may be divided into as many as four units by cross walls. (From Bisset et al., Exptl. Cell Res., 5:451, 1953.)

CULTIVATION OF MICROORGANISMS

Cultivation of microorganisms is accomplished by providing a favorable environment for their growth. This means that the necessary nutrients must be available in suitable form for use as building materials for new cells, a source of energy must be provided, and the pH, temperature, oxygen, and other conditions must be appropriate.

Definitions: Culture, Culture Medium

A *culture* is any growth or cultivation of microorganisms. The term is usually employed with reference to deliberate growth of microorganisms in the laboratory. A *pure culture* contains only a single kind of microorganism. Pure cultures are rarely found outside the laboratory because in nature microorganisms are usually associated with one another. In mixed populations one kind of organism may help, harm, or have no effect upon other microorganisms; their social behavior therefore resembles that of higher plants and animals, including man.

A *culture medium* is a substrate or nutrient solution upon which microorganisms are cultivated in the laboratory. Different microorganisms require different nutrient materials, and certain media are used for specific purposes (e.g., to determine the ability of an organism to digest proteins, carbohydrates, and so forth). The number of possible culture media is unlimited.

Infusions

The first solutions for cultivation of bacteria and other organisms consisted of natural materials. Leeuwenhoek employed the liquid obtained by soaking peppercorns in water. This fluid contained organic substances and minerals extracted from the plant tissue. Later investigators soaked other plant materials such as hay in water and obtained liquids in which microorganisms could be grown. Still others extracted animal tissues with water and obtained excellent substrates for the cultivation of bacteria. Tissue extracts are known as *infusions,* and until the latter half of the nineteenth century they were the only culture media for laboratory experimentation with bacteria. Their composition was not known exactly and they could not be reproduced with precision. However, they were usually sufficiently rich in organic materials and growth-promoting substances to favor the multiplication of many kinds of microorganisms and were satisfactory for the types of experiments performed at that time.

Chemically Defined or Synthetic Media

Pasteur was apparently the first to use culture media of known composition. He demonstrated that various microorganisms could be cultivated in solutions containing only sugar, a source of nitrogen such as an ammonium salt or a nitrate, and minerals. A medium of this kind is known as a *chemically defined* or *synthetic* medium. Chemically defined media can be reproduced exactly at any time and by workers in different laboratories because the chemical formulae of all their constituents are known exactly. They are essential for the study of nutritional requirements and are used in the manufacture of microbial products in which a minimum of extraneous organic material is desired.

Nonsynthetic Media

Some microorganisms like those studied by Pasteur grow satisfactorily with simple sources of carbon and nitrogen and a few mineral salts. Others require one or more vitamin-like substances or *growth factors.* Certain nutritionally fastidious organisms require a dozen or more of these accessory substances and are more conveniently cultivated on the traditional organic extract or infusion substrates, which are designated *non-*

synthetic media. Meat infusion broth, for example, is commonly employed for certain respiratory pathogens of man. It is prepared by soaking lean meat (e.g., ground beef) overnight in water, straining out the meat particles, boiling, filtering through paper and adding salt, peptone, and any other desired substances. Commercial peptones are manufactured by partially digesting native proteins (animal or plant) by means of enzymes; they furnish readily available amino acids and other nitrogen compounds.

Acidity or Alkalinity of Culture Media

Microbial culture media must possess a "reaction" (acidity or alkalinity) favorable for the organism to be cultivated. Before discovery of the relationship between hydrogen ion concentration and acidity it was customary to adjust culture media by adding alkali until the neutral point of phenolphthalein indicator was reached, and then adding a quantity of acid which previous experience indicated gave satisfactory growth. Discovery of the role of hydrogen ions and formulation of the pH scale revolution-

alized the adjustment of culture media.

pH. It will be recalled that pH is the negative logarithm of hydrogen ion concentration, and that the pH scale extends from 0 to 14 (Table 3-3). A solution of pH 0 contains hydrogen ions in a concentration of 10^0 or 1 normal. This solution is very acid. A solution of pH 1 is 10^{-1} or 1/10 normal with respect to hydrogen ions. A difference of one pH unit corresponds to a difference of ten times in the concentration of hydrogen ions. The upper limit of the pH scale, 14, represents a hydrogen ion concentration of 10^{-14} or 1/100,000,000,000,000 normal. Aqueous solutions also contain hydroxyl ions, and their concentration varies inversely with that of the hydrogen ions. Neutrality is represented by pH 7 and is the point at which the hydrogen ion concentration of a solution equals its hydroxyl ion concentration; this is the situation in pure water.

Many common bacteria like those found in and on the human body grow best at a reaction near neutrality, or from pH 6.5 to pH 7.5. Numerous pH indicators as well as electrical methods of determining pH are available. Adjustment of culture media by trial and error is relatively simple.

Table 3-3. pH and Hydrogen Ion Concentration

Hydrogen Ion Concentration		pH		Examples
N/1	$= 10^0$ N	0	↑	Gastric juice: pH 0.9
N/10	$= 10^{-1}$ N	1		
N/100	$= 10^{-2}$ N	2		Lemon juice: pH 2.3
N/1,000	$= 10^{-3}$ N	3		Pineapple juice: pH 3.5
N/10,000	$= 10^{-4}$ N	4		Tomato juice: pH 4.2
N/100,000	$= 10^{-5}$ N	5		Clam chowder: pH 5.7
N/1,000,000	$= 10^{-6}$ N	6	Acid	Milk: pH 6.6
N/10,000,000	$= 10^{-7}$ N	7	Neutral	Blood: pH 7.3
N/100,000,000	$= 10^{-8}$ N	8	Alkaline	Bile: pH 7.8–8.6
N/1,000,000,000	$= 10^{-9}$ N	9		Phenolphthalein color change: pH 9.2
N/10,000,000,000	$= 10^{-10}$ N	10		
N/100,000,000,000	$= 10^{-11}$ N	11		
N/1,000,000,000,000	$= 10^{-12}$ N	12		NH$_4$OH (N/1): pH 11.7
N/10,000,000,000,000	$= 10^{-13}$ N	13		Lime water: pH 12.3
N/100,000,000,000,000	$= 10^{-14}$ N	14	↓	NaOH (N/1): pH 14.0

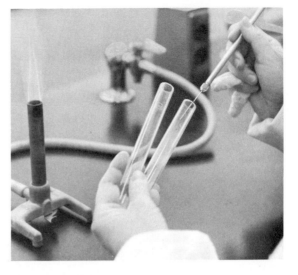

Figure 3-23. Method of transferring bacteria from one culture tube to another. The two tubes are supported firmly by the index, middle, and ring fingers and are held in position by the thumb. Plugs are grasped by the little and ring fingers of the other hand, which also holds the inoculating needle, as illustrated. Mouths of the test tubes and the needle are flamed, both before and after the transfer.

Figure 3-24. Flaming inoculating needle in the Bunsen flame. The needle is held as nearly vertical as possible so that its entire length reaches red heat rapidly.

Sterilization of Culture Media

Culture media are usually dispensed into test tubes, flasks or bottles, which are then plugged with nonabsorbent cotton or covered with screw caps or metal or plastic slip-on caps and sterilized. The usual sterilizing agent is steam at a temperature of 120° C. To secure this temperature, the steam must be under pressure (approximately 15 lb. per sq. in.); this is possible in a laboratory autoclave (see Fig. 15-3) or a home pressure cooker. Exposure for 15 to 30 minutes is sufficient to kill all organisms if the sterilizer is not loaded too heavily.

Sterilization of the mouths of test tubes and bottles to prevent contamination of media during subsequent operations (e.g., pouring Petri dishes, inoculating cultures) and sterilization of inoculating needles are effected by use of the Bunsen flame, as illustrated in Figures 3-23 and 3-24.

THE TOOLS OF A MICROBIOLOGIST

SUMMARY

Only a few years ago it seemed that the ultimate in microscopy had been attained with the brightfield, darkfield, and ultraviolet microscopes.

Since then, phase and electron microscopy and the use of fluorescent dyes and other histochemical methods have offered exciting new opportunities for the study of microbial structure.

Cultivation methods devised during the last third of the nineteenth century undergo minor modifications from time to time, but the principles are still essentially unchanged. Liquid or solid media containing the required nutrients and energy sources, at proper pH, sterile, and protected from outside contamination are necessary for work with pure cultures.

STUDY QUESTIONS

1. What is the importance of definition and of resolution in microscopy? What factors control these characteristics?
2. What is the function of immersion oil?
3. Of what advantage is ultraviolet illumination in using the microscope? What are some disadvantages?
4. Diagram the path of light through the darkfield microscope.
5. Explain the principle of fluorescence microscopy.
6. Compare the mode of operation of the electron microscope with that of the ordinary light microscope.
7. Explain how staining assists in the microscopic study of small organisms.
8. Tabulate the primary stains, decolorizers, and counterstains in the Gram, Schaeffer-Fulton, and Ziehl-Neelsen procedures.
9. Of what value is it to isolate pure cultures of microorganisms when they usually occur in nature as mixtures?
10. Is it possible to devise a single culture medium that will be suitable for all bacteria? Explain.
11. What are the comparative advantages and disadvantages of synthetic and nonsynthetic culture media?

SUPPLEMENTARY READING

The *Manual of Microbiological Methods* is not only a useful "cookbook" of basic procedures for the study of microorganisms; it also contains critical discussion of the methods and their relative advantages and disadvantages, and often recommends one. Conn's *The History of Staining* presents the facts and is occasionally enlivened by personal sidelights. Salle and Lamanna and Mallette have good chapters on microscopy and staining. Skerman's book contains keys to the genera of bacteria, based on the seventh edition of *Bergey's Manual of Determinative Bacteriology,* and these are supported by a complete list of the techniques necessary to identify bacteria by use of the keys: culture media, physiologic tests, staining procedures. Wyckoff's discussion of the theory and technique of electron microscopy is illustrated by excellent electron photomicrographs.

Committee on Bacteriological Technic, Society of American Bacteriologists: *Manual of Microbiological Methods.* New York, McGraw-Hill Book Co., Inc., 1957.

Conn, H. J.: *The History of Staining,* 2d ed. Geneva, N. Y., Biotech Publications, 1948.

Lamanna, C., and Mallette, M. F.: *Basic Bacteriology,* 3d ed. Baltimore, The Williams & Wilkins Co., 1965.

Salle, A. J.: *Fundamental Principles of Bacteriology,* 5th ed. New York, McGraw-Hill Book Co., Inc., 1960.

Skerman, V. B. D.: *A Guide to the Identification of the Genera of Bacteria.* Baltimore, The Williams & Wilkins Co., 1959.

Wyckoff, R. W. G.: *The World of the Electron Microscope.* New Haven, Yale University Press, 1958.

MORPHOLOGY AND STRUCTURE OF BACTERIA

Casual microscopic examination of bacteria, either unstained or stained with the reagents usually found in a diagnostic laboratory, shows little detail beyond the shape, arrangement, and size of the cells. There is no indication of internal structure. Special staining methods, like some of those described in Chapter 3, together with phase microscopy and electron microscopy, are necessary to reveal the internal architecture of the individual cell. These techniques show that bacterial cells are less highly organized than those of higher forms. Indeed, protocaryotic cells in general are structurally much simpler than eucaryotic cells.

Eucaryotic Versus Protocaryotic Cell Structure

One of the striking features of eucaryotic cells is their membranous nature, as revealed by electron photomicrographs. This is illustrated in Figure 4-1, which shows the ultrastructure of a pancreatic cell. Most of the cytoplasm is filled with a network of membranes, the *endoplasmic reticulum*. A double membrane encloses the nucleus and the cell is bounded by the plasma membrane. Minute granules throughout the cytoplasm are an important part of the cell's biosynthetic mechanism because they contain RNA, which assembles amino acids in the order required for the production of protein characteristic of the species. There are also larger discrete bodies bounded by double membranes, the *mitochondria,* which are the principal sites of respiratory activity (Fig. 4-2). The inner mitochondrial membrane is the origin of a series of thin internal membranes, which are the locations of enzymes that participate in the orderly transport of electrons from oxidizable substances to oxygen. Between these membranes are other enzymes involved in the oxidation of carbon compounds to carbon dioxide.

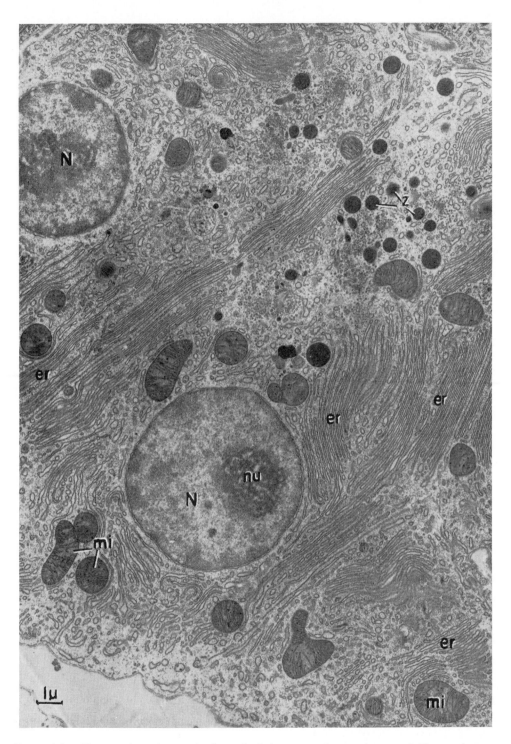

Figure 4-1. Electron photomicrograph of a cell of the eucaryotic type (pancreas). The membranous endoplasmic reticulum (*er*) is conspicuous, as is the nucleus (*N*), bounded by a double membrane and containing a nucleolus (*nu*). The mitochondria (*mi*) are also filled with thin membranes. Magnification: 7000X. (Courtesy of K. R. Porter, from DeRobertis, Nowinski and Saez: Cell Biology, 4th ed. W. B. Saunders Co., Philadelphia, 1965.)

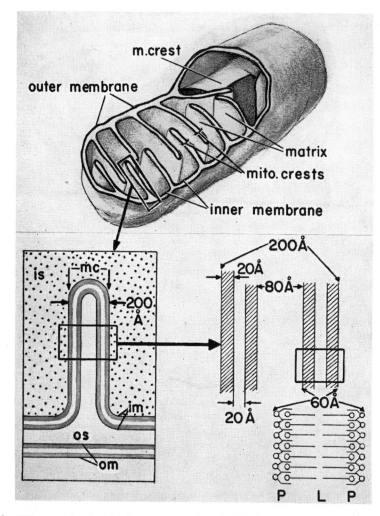

Figure 4-2. Diagrams showing the fine structure of a mitochondrion. *Top,* a three-dimensional diagram showing outer and inner membranes and *mitochondrial crests,* which are complex infoldings of the inner membrane. *Bottom left,* a higher magnification of a mitochondrial crest from the figure above. *Right,* higher magnification of a section through a mitochondrial crest from the left figure. *Below,* a further magnification indicating the molecular structure of a membrane. *im,* Inner membrane; *om,* outer membrane; *is,* inner space; *os,* outer space; *mc,* mitochondrial crest; *P,* protein; *L,* lipid. (From DeRobertis, Nowinski and Saez.)

In plant cells there are also *chloroplasts* in which photosynthesis occurs (Fig. 4-3). A chloroplast is composed of parallel layers of leaflike membranes or *lamellae,* not connected with the bounding membranes; they contain the chlorophyll and carotenoid photosynthetic pigments and the enzymes that convert light energy to chemical bond energy. Enzymes that assist in the formation of sugars from carbon dioxide are in the adjacent undifferentiated regions of the chloroplast.

It is thus obvious that eucaryotic cells, with their extensive internal surface areas that serve as sites for enzymatic activity, are highly organized units. In contrast, protocaryotic cells

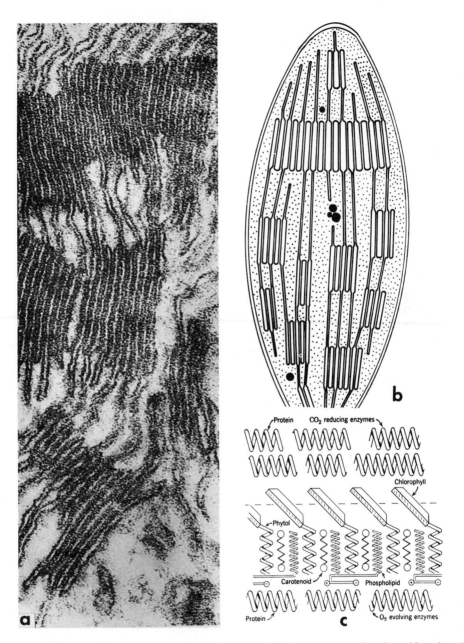

Figure 4-3. Electron photomicrograph (a) and diagrams of the fine structure of a plant chloroplast. Its membranous nature is obvious, and the internal organization is reconstructed diagrammatically in (b). The postulated molecular structure of the leaflike lamellae and adjacent, undifferentiated regions are sketched at (c). (Courtesy of P. Weiss, from Allen: The Molecular Control of Cellular Activity. McGraw-Hill, New York, 1962.)

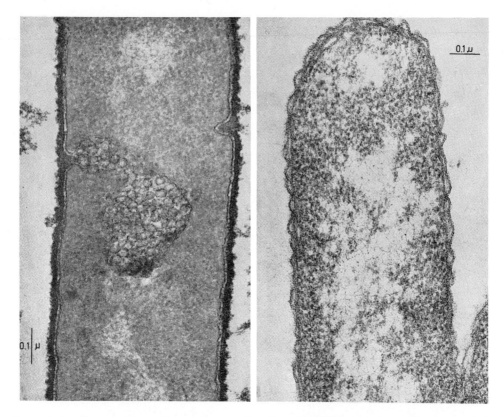

Figure 4-4.   Electron photomicrographs showing the relatively undifferentiated internal structure of thin sections of *Bacillus subtilis* (*left*) and *Escherichia coli* (*right*). The vesiculated organelle ("peripheral body" or "mesosome") in *B. subtilis* seems to participate in formation of the cross wall. Chromatin bodies are the less dense structures near the top and bottom. Chromatin material is scattered widely throughout *E. coli*. Note that the plasma membrane and cell wall are closely associated in *B. subtilis*, but are separate and distinct in *E. coli*. (From van Iterson, Bact. Rev., 29:299, 1965.)

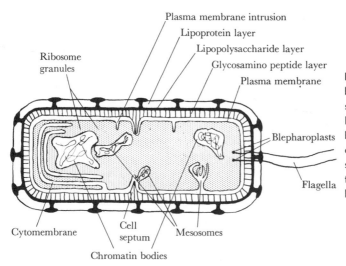

Figure 4-5.   Structures that may be found in various (but not necessarily all) bacterial cells. The layers outside the plasma membrane are considered part of the cell wall. Only a few of the many sites of lipopolysaccharide penetration through the lipoprotein layer are shown.

appear to be much simpler, structurally (Fig. 4-4). The major components of a bacterial cell are diagrammatically represented in Figure 4-5. The principal membrane is the plasma membrane, with various intrusions and *mesosomes* continuous with it (Fig. 4-6). The nucleus or *chromatin body* is not bounded by a membrane, and there are no mitochondria or chloroplasts. The cytoplasm is, however, packed with particles, the *ribosomes,* which have a characteristic fine structure (Fig. 4-7). They are nearly spherical, hollow, and often arranged

in rodlets; their function, as in eucaryotic cells, is to synthesize proteins. Respiratory activities are performed by enzymes situated in the plasma membrane and possibly in the mesosomes. In photosynthetic bacteria as much as 50 per cent of the cell may consist of discrete bodies known as *chromatophores* (Fig. 4-8), which contain the photosynthetic pigments and enzymes.

Vacuoles and other cell inclusions are common in eucaryotic organisms, and the cytoplasm is usually in a state of active movement; protoplasmic stream-

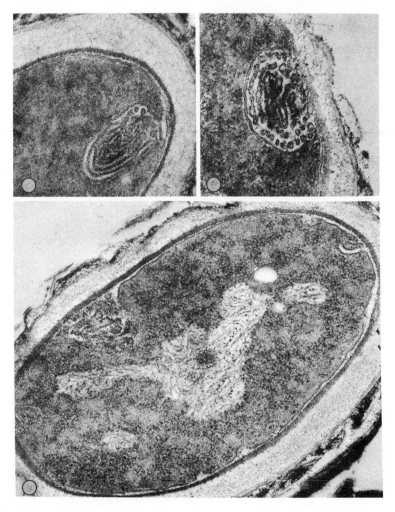

Figure 4-6. Electron photomicrographs of germinating spores of *Bacillus megaterium* showing several forms of mesosomes. A simple intrusion is found at the upper end of the bottom cell. *Top left,* 60,000X; *top right,* 80,000X; *bottom,* 60,000X. (Courtesy of C. F. Robinow and J. F. Marak, from Mazia and Taylor: The General Physiology of Cell Specialization. McGraw-Hill, New York, 1963.)

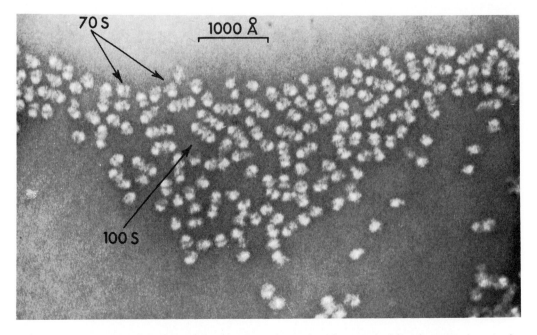

Figure 4-7. Electron photomicrograph of microsomal particles (ribosomes) of *E. coli* negatively stained with phosphotungstic acid. This is a mixture of two kinds of particles: (70S) monomers, containing two unequal subunits, and (100S) dimers, composed of two monomers joined at their smaller subunits (200,000X). (From Huxley and Zubay, J. Molec. Biol., 2:14, 1960.)

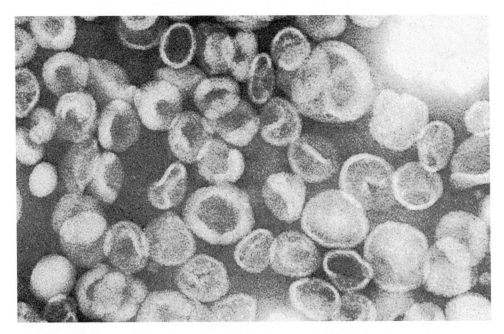

Figure 4-8. Electron photomicrographs of chromatophores of *Rhodospirillum rubrum*, a photosynthetic bacterium. (Photograph by D. Hickman and A. Frenkel, from Stanier, Doudoroff and Adelberg: The Microbial World, 2d ed. Prentice-Hall, Englewood Cliffs, N. J., 1963.)

ing is frequently observed in coenocytic fungi, for example. In contrast, the cytoplasm of protocaryotic organisms contains few if any vacuoles and is comparatively immobile.

SHAPES AND ARRANGEMENTS OF BACTERIA

Cocci, Rods, and Spirals

The three principal bacterial shapes are spheres, rods, and spirals (Fig. 4-9). A spherical bacterium is known as a *coccus* (plural, *cocci*). Cocci are not always perfect spheres; they are often flattened like a compressed rubber ball or elongated like a football (Figs. 4-10 and 4-11) and pass through a spherical stage during growth. They appear singly

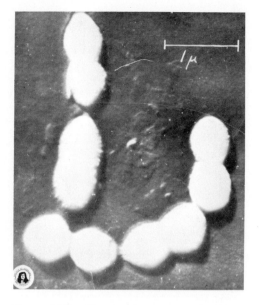

Figure 4-10. Electron photomicrograph of *Diplococcus pneumoniae,* type 2, shadowed with chromium. Several cells show the characteristic lancet shape. (Photograph by R. C. Williams; A.S.M. LS-162.)

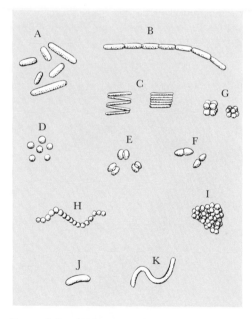

Figure 4-9. Shapes and arrangements of bacteria commonly encountered. *A,* Short and long rods occurring singly; *B,* rods in a chain; *C,* palisade arrangement of rods; *D,* single cocci (spheres); *E,* paired flattened cocci; *F,* paired elongate cocci; *G,* cubical packets of cocci (sarcina); *H,* a chain of cocci (streptococcus); *I,* an irregular cluster of cocci (staphylococcus); *J,* comma-shaped or bent rod; *K,* spiral rod.

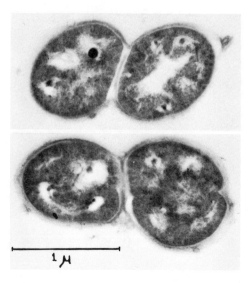

Figure 4-11. Electron photomicrograph of ultrathin section of *Neisseria catarrhalis.* (Photograph by G. B. Chapman.)

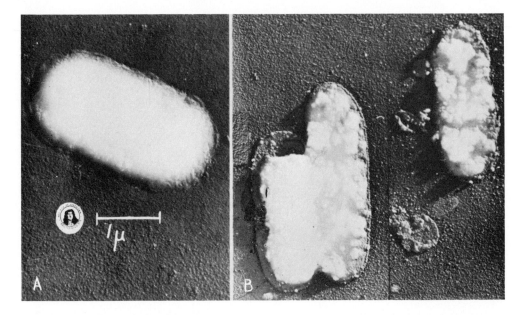

Figure 4-12. Electron photomicrographs of *Escherichia coli* shadowed with gold and manganin. These cells were from a one-hour broth culture. The cell at A is normal; those at B were heated in saline (0.85% NaCl) 10 minutes at 50° C. and show an interesting granulation of the cytoplasm caused by coagulation of some protoplasmic constituents. (Photographs by G. Hedén and R. W. G. Wyckoff; A.S.M. LS-290.)

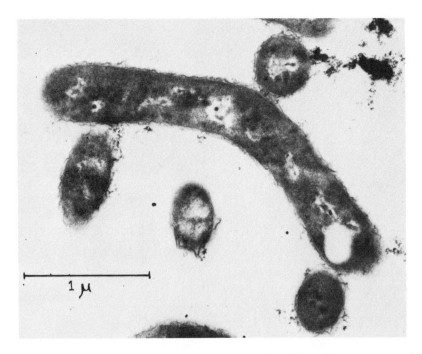

Figure 4-13. Electron photomicrograph of an ultrathin section of *Spirillum rubrum*. Part of a coil is shown. (Photograph by G. B. Chapman.)

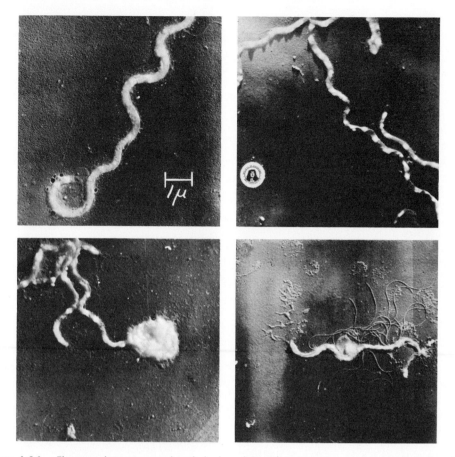

Figure 4-14. Electron photomicrographs of shadowed *Borrelia vincentii,* an oral spirochete found in cases of trenchmouth associated with a long, tapering rod-shaped bacterium. (Photographs by E. G. Hampp, D. B. Scott, and R. W. G. Wyckoff; A.S.M. LS-248.)

or in pairs (*diplococci*), chains (*streptococci*), irregular, grapelike clusters (*staphylococci*), or boxlike cubical packets (*sarcinae*).

Rodlike bacteria are straight and cylindrical or are long ellipsoids (Fig. 4-12); sometimes they appear slightly curved or wavy. They occur singly, in chains, or in a parallel (*palisade*) arrangement.

A spiral organism or *spirillum* (plural *spirilla*) is shaped like a corkscrew (Fig. 4-13). Some species consist of only part of a spiral turn and are called *vibrios,* some are composed of one or two loose turns, and others contain many close coils (Fig. 4-14). They are found as single cells or short chains.

The distinction between rodlike bacteria and cocci or spirilla cannot be defined accurately and is learned principally by experience. It is impossible to state the exact point at which a cell ceases to be considered a long coccus and becomes a short rod, or at which a rod is sufficiently twisted to be called a spirillum.

Morphologic Variation; Pleomorphic Forms

Most bacteria at some time display irregular or variant shapes known as *pleomorphic* forms. These variations may be either permanent or temporary. Permanent variations (mutations) are

Table 4-1. Sizes of Some Bacteria

Organism	Diameter (μ)	Length (μ)
Pasteurella tularensis	0.2	0.3– 0.7
Brucella melitensis	0.3	0.3– 1.0
Escherichia coli	0.4–0.7	1.0– 3.0
Bacillus anthracis	1.0–1.3	3.0–10.0
Staphylococcus aureus	0.8–1.0	
Streptococcus pyogenes	0.6–1.0	
Sarcina ventriculi	3.5–4.0	
Beggiatoa mirabilis	15.0–21.5	Several cm. Trichomes consisting of segments 5.0 to 13.0 μ long

for example, may appear less than one-third the size of living cells. Bacteria as commonly observed vary greatly in size; the range among species ordinarily encountered is twenty- to thirtyfold. A few representative and extreme figures are listed in Table 4-1.

It is worth emphasizing that the microscopic appearance of bacteria, including shape, arrangement, and size, depends greatly upon the age of the culture and other factors. Actively growing rod bacteria are usually several times longer than old, dormant, or dying bacteria, which are frequently almost spherical. Rapidly growing cocci may be 50 per cent longer than they are wide. Examination of cells from various growth phases (i.e., young as well as older cultures) is often needed before an unknown organism can be identified as a rod or a coccus.

the result of genetic alteration and are relatively stable and irreversible. Permanent loss of flagella or of the ability to produce endospores illustrates this type of morphologic variation. Temporary variations, such as changes in cell length or shape, occur during growth and division.

Involution Forms. Involution forms are degenerative cells of bizarre shape: filamentous or swollen. They are produced as a result of alterations in the osmotic pressure of the medium; the presence of metallic ions, antibiotics, or other chemicals; or the accumulation of waste products, and are particularly likely to appear as angular, budding, or branching forms during the death phase of a culture.

SIZE OF BACTERIA

Bacterial dimensions are difficult to determine with accuracy because considerable shrinkage occurs during the preparation of fixed and stained smears. Stained, dried cells of *Escherichia coli,*

CHEMICAL COMPOSITION OF BACTERIA

The chemical composition of bacteria is similar to that of other organisms. Although there is considerable variation between species, the approximate composition of a representative cell is as indicated in Table 4-2.

The DNA in *Escherichia coli* is a single molecule, 1100 to 1400 μ (1.1 to 1.4 mm.) in length. It has what is probably the highest molecular weight of

Table 4-2. Approximate Composition of a Bacterial Cell (after Pollard, 1965)

Water   70%
Dry weight   30%, composed of:
  DNA   3% (M.W. = 2,000,000,000)
  RNA   12%
  Protein   70%, found in:
    Ribosomes (10,000) (RNA-protein particles, M.W. = 3,000,000)
    Enzymes
    Surface structures
  Polysaccharides   5%
  Lipid   6%
  Phospholipid   4%

any material in nature and its weight amounts to about 10^{-14} gram per cell.

There are three kinds of RNA: messenger RNA (mRNA), with a molecular weight of 1,000,000; ribosomal RNA (rRNA), associated with protein in cytoplasmic granules, or *ribosomes,* which are the sites of protein synthesis; and transfer RNA (tRNA), sometimes called soluble RNA. For each kind of amino acid incorporated in a protein, a different transfer RNA is necessary. The molecules of tRNA are relatively small, being composed of 80 to 100 nucleotide units and having a molecular weight between 25,000 and 30,000. The amount of RNA in actively growing cells is almost double that in inactive cells.

Nearly all the amino acids have been detected in the proteins. A special amino acid, diaminopimelic acid (DAP), is found in almost all species of bacteria except gram-positive cocci and related organisms. It is also present in blue-green algae but is not found in other forms of life. It is part of a polypeptide attached to muramic acid (see Fig. 4-15).

Carbohydrates are present in the cell walls and capsules of bacteria. The capsules of some species are composed solely of polysaccharides. Cell walls of gram-positive bacteria contain 35 to 60 per cent carbohydrate; those of gram-negative bacteria contain 15 to 20 per cent carbohydrate. Glycogen and other polysaccharide granules are present in the cytoplasm.

Lipids are found in the cell wall and in the cytoplasmic membrane, which is a lipoprotein layer. Acidfast bacteria, such as the tuberculosis organism, contain unusually large amounts of lipid—

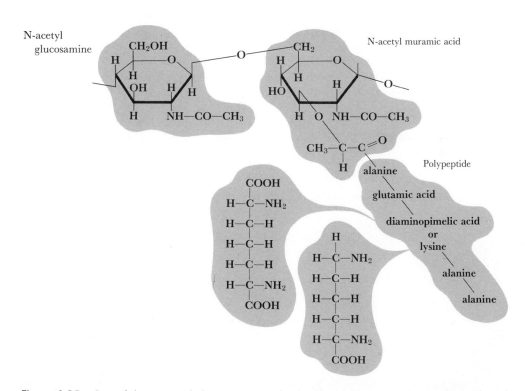

Figure 4-15. Part of the proposed glycosaminopeptide "backbone" that contributes to the rigidity of the bacterial cell wall. Diaminopimelic acid is found only in certain bacteria and blue-green algae.

as much as 40 per cent when they are grown in a medium containing a high percentage of glycerin.

In addition to the foregoing constituents there is a "pool" of organic substances of lower molecular weight readily available for use in metabolism, including sugars, organic acids, amino acids, nucleotides, phosphate esters, vitamins, and coenzymes. This reserve of metabolites consists of fewer than 10,000,000 molecules per cell (in *E. coli*), but amino acids and other substances are hundreds of times as concentrated as in the external medium.

BACTERIAL CELL STRUCTURE

Some of the structures of bacteria were indicated diagrammatically in Figure 4-5. The protoplasm is bounded by a discrete *plasma membrane,* which in turn is enclosed by the *cell wall.* Outside the wall is a *microcapsule,* a *capsule,* or *loose slime.* The protoplasm contains, in addition to thousands of ribosomes, a "nucleus" or *chromatin body* (*nucleoid* or *genophore* in recent terminology). Various species also possess granules of distinctive composition (e.g., iron, sulfur, or polysaccharide). Motile bacteria possess one or more *flagella,* and sporulating bacteria may contain *endospores.*

Cell Wall

The bacterial cell wall is a strong and rigid structure that protects and supports the weaker and biochemically more active parts of the cell. Its thickness varies from 10 to 25 mμ, according to the species of organism. In general, gram-negative bacteria possess thinner walls than gram-positive bacteria (see Fig. 4-4). Simple calculation indicates that the cell wall constitutes about 20 per cent of the total cell volume.

Cell walls can be removed and isolated by several methods, including mechanical disruption, enzymatic digestion, or sudden immersion in hot water. The inner protoplasm disintegrates readily, and the more resistant walls can be purified for chemical and physical study. Some of the constituents of cell walls are listed in Table 4-3. The cell walls of gram-positive bacteria differ from those of gram-negative species, particularly in their amino acid and lipid composition. The rigidity of bacterial walls is attributed to glycosaminopeptides (compounds containing amino sugars and amino acids). The basic structure consists of alternating residues of the amino sugars, N-acetyl muramic acid and N-acetyl glucosamine. The polypeptide chain is attached to muramic acid as shown in Figure 4-15. It may be remarked that the rigidity of

Table 4-3. Chemical Constituents of Cell Walls of Gram-Positive and Gram-Negative Bacteria

	Gram-Positive	Gram-Negative
Amino acids	Three or four principal amino acids, including alanine, glutamic acid, and lysine or diaminopimelic acid. No aromatic amino acids. No sulfur-containing amino acids.	Most amino acids found in ordinary proteins, including diaminopimelic acid.
Muramic acid	Present	Present
Lipids	0–2%	10–20%
Polysaccharides	35–60%	15–20%

Figure 4-16. Cell walls of bacteria. *Left,* Walls of *Streptococcus fecalis* prepared by grinding the cells; splitting permitted the cell contents to escape. Magnification, 12,000X. *Right,* A portion of the cell wall of *Spirillum rubrum* showing the regular pattern of the spherical bodies of which this wall is composed. Magnification, 42,000X. (Salton and Williams; Salton and Horne.)

the walls of blue-green algae, the other group of protocaryotic organisms, is also due to their glycosaminopeptide content. The walls of gram-positive bacteria are relatively amorphous, whereas those of gram-negative bacteria consist of several layers (see Figs. 4-4 and 4-5). Some walls are constructed in a regular hexagonal or rectangular pattern of macromolecular units 50 to 140 mμ in diameter (Fig. 4-16).

The wall maintains the characteristic shape of the cell and gives physical protection to the cytoplasm, in which most of the vital activites of the cell are performed. It plays little other role in the life of the cell; biochemical activity continues in cells from which the walls have been removed (protoplasts) if they are protected against osmotic lysis.

Microcapsule, Capsule, and Loose Slime

Outside the cell wall of most if not all bacteria is a layer of material designated according to its thickness, composition, and solubility as a microcapsule, capsule, or loose slime (Fig. 4-17).

A *microcapsule* is a relatively thin layer composed of protein, polysaccharide, and lipid. Microcapsules are found

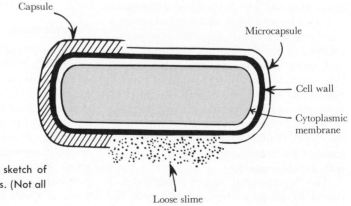

Capsule

Microcapsule

Cell wall

Cytoplasmic membrane

Loose slime

Figure 4-17. Diagrammatic sketch of surface layers of bacterial cells. (Not all bacteria possess all layers.)

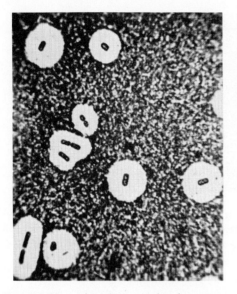

Figure 4-18. A heavily encapsulated streptococcus. The dark background is India ink. Magnification, 1500X. (Courtesy P. M. Borick, Wallace and Tiernan, Inc.)

on gram-negative bacteria and are also known as "somatic antigens" or "endotoxins" (see Chap. 20).

Capsules are thick, viscous, jelly-like structures surrounding the cells of certain species. Some capsules have definite structure; others appear to be amorphous. They stain poorly and are usually demonstrated by a "negative" staining procedure in which the background and cells are colored and the capsules remain colorless (Fig. 4-18).

Loose slime is similar to capsules but is more soluble in the suspending medium and has less structural integrity.

Capsules and loose slime are accumulated polymers of polysaccharide or polypeptide. The capsules of pneumococci and some streptococci are polysaccharide; each of the several score of pneumococcus "types" possesses a chemically different polysaccharide. Loose slimes of some gram-negative rods are also polysaccharide. Capsules and slime of some of the gram-positive spore-forming rods are polypeptide.

The "extramural" layer is not an integral or essential part of the cell. It can be removed without harm and is then replaced by the cell. The presence and amount of capsular and slime material are controlled by the genetic makeup of the organism and by the environment. Mutant forms may possess more or less of such material than normal forms. Capsule and slime formation are often favored by media containing appropriate sugars. Sucrose, for example, promotes the production of capsules or slime by certain organisms that can utilize the fructose portion of the molecule; the unused dextrose portion of the disaccharide polymerizes and a dextran of high molecular weight accumulates around the cells.

Slime layers and capsules protect bacterial cells against drying and other harmful agents. Encapsulated pathogenic bacteria, such as the pneumococcus, resist phagocytosis, a defensive process in which white blood cells or other tissue cells ingest and may digest foreign objects. Noncapsulated variants or organisms from which the capsules have been removed are readily ingested by phagocytic cells.

Bacterial slime and capsules are a cause of economic loss in the dairy and food industries. Milk, syrups, and other sugary solutions become "ropy" when contaminated by certain encapsulated bacteria. Some of the same organisms (e.g., *Leuconostoc* species) are used for commercial production of dextran, which has been used as a plasma "extender" in the treatment of shock caused by loss of blood.

The Protoplast

The protoplast is that portion of the cell that is within the cell wall. The wall can be removed from cells of some species by treatment with the enzyme lysozyme, derived from egg white, tears, or saliva. Lysozyme digests some of the complex polysaccharides in the cell wall. Certain organisms can also be made to grow without a wall in the presence of penicillin (which interferes with the formation of the glycosaminopeptide layer from its subunits), or by depriving them of diaminopimelic acid. A stabilizing agent such as 0.2 M sucrose must be present to prevent osmotic lysis. The resulting "naked" cells, which lack all traces of cell wall material, are called *protoplasts;* they are globular in shape and relatively stable (Fig. 4-19), although much more sensitive to environmental "discomforts" than intact cells. They are readily lysed by diluting with distilled water the stabilizing solution in which they are suspended.

Globular forms possessing partial or modified (e.g., by growth in penicillin or treatment with detergent) cell walls are known as *spheroplasts.*

Protoplasts perform most of the metabolic activities of whole cells, including energy-yielding respiratory processes, synthesis of proteins, enzymes, and nucleic acids. They do not synthesize cell wall material, whereas spheroplasts can do so. This seems to indicate that the wall contains its own synthetic

mechanism or that a "starter" or cell wall substance must be present before more can be laid down. Protoplasts can grow and divide, and protoplasts of spore-forming bacteria prepared from cells that have taken the first steps toward sporulation can complete the process of producing spores. Protoplasts of motile organisms may possess flagella but are not motile.

Plasma Membrane

Dilution with water lyses a suspension of protoplasts, releasing the cytoplasm and leaving "ghosts," delicate membranes with some granular material and debris. Protoplast (plasma) membranes are 5 to 8 mμ thick and constitute 10 to 20 per cent of the dry weight of the cells. They are composed largely of lipoprotein and also contain many enzymes, especially those concerned in biologic oxidations, by which the cell secures energy.

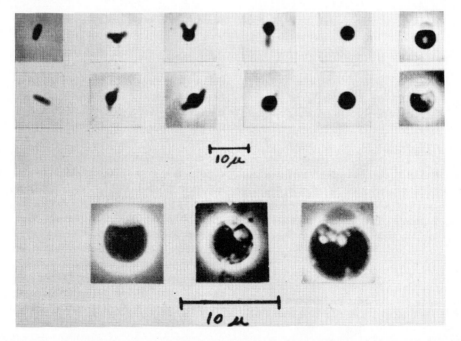

Figure 4-19. Phase contrast photomicrographs showing, in the horizontal rows above, successive stages in the formation of spherical protoplasts from typical rod-shaped cells of *Escherichia coli* by cultivation in penicillin sucrose broth for four hours. Below are three late stage protoplasts shown at higher magnification. (J. Lederberg and J. St. Clair, J. Bact., 75:143–160, 1958.)

The plasma membrane is a discrete, differentiated outer layer of the cytoplasm just beneath the cell wall (Fig. 4-20). It stains intensely with basic dyes and is said to form the highly reflective layer observed in darkfield preparations. Indirect evidence for the existence of a plasma membrane is derived from the shrinkage of the protoplasm of bacteria suspended in solutions of high osmotic pressure. Water passes outward through the cell wall, and the cytoplasm pulls away from the wall as though bounded by a separate membrane.

The plasma membrane is a membrane of the so-called *unit* type; that is, it is a three-layered structure consisting of a bimolecular "leaflet" of lipid between protein or other hydrophilic layers (Fig. 4-21). It regulates the passage of materials into and out of the cell. Certain substances of low molecular weight, such as urea, glycine, and glycerin, readily enter bacterial cells, whereas the electrolytes NaCl and KCl and larger organic molecules like glucose

and sucrose traverse the membrane very slowly. The membrane is essentially impermeable to polar organic substances because of its high lipid content. Enzymes called *permeases* transport particular materials or groups of materials by forming easily dissociable complexes with them. The plasma membrane, together with the membrane intrusions or mesosomes linked with it, comprises essentially a lipoprotein matrix upon which are organized most of the cytochromes (see Chap. 12), succinoxidase and related enzymes, and many other enzymes of the bacterial cell. It is such a vital organelle that Mitchell spoke of it as "not simply . . . an osmotic link between the media on either side of it, but . . . a chemical link."

Cytoplasmic Inclusions. Various granules or inclusions are present in the cells of an aging bacterial culture. Inclusions are nonliving bodies in the cytoplasm. Many seem to be reserve food materials because they accumulate during conditions of good nutrient supply and

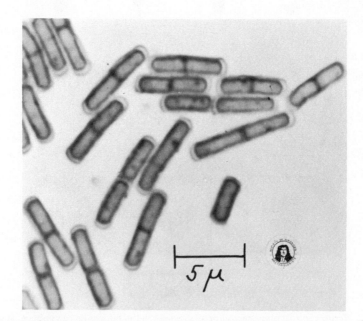

Figure 4-20. Photomicrograph of *Bacillus cereus*, a two-hour culture on agar, showing various stages in growth and cell division. Cell walls and plasma membranes can be distinguished because the cytoplasm has retracted from the walls. (Photograph by C. F. Robinow; A.S.M. LS-235.)

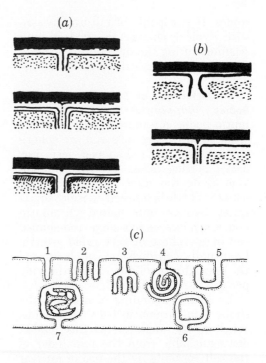

Figure 4-21. Diagrammatic sketches showing the plasma membrane of bacteria and its intrusions beneath a thick cell wall. (*a*) Three forms of "unit" membrane; (*b*) a single, dense layer, either apposed to the cell wall with a low-density layer on the cytoplasmic side (as in the micrococci) or with low-density layers on both sides; (*c*) various lamellated (1–4) and villous (5–7) mesosomes, originating from the plasma membrane. (Courtesy of R. G. E. Murray, from Mazia and Taylor: The General Physiology of Cell Specialization. McGraw-Hill, New York, 1963.)

decrease during starvation. The nature of the inclusions varies with the organism. Volutin granules, sometimes called metachromatic granules (Fig. 4-22), appear in various bacterial species and also in many fungi, algae, and protozoa;

they stain intensely with basic dyes and are composed of a polymerized phosphoric acid known as polyphosphate.

Polysaccharides may accumulate as glycogen or as a kind of starch. Lipid globules appear in various bacteria, particularly gram-positive organisms. Sulfur and iron are also found in certain species.

Chromatin Body or Nucleoid

The existence of nuclei in bacteria has long been debated. It has been stated (1) that bacteria contain no nucleus, (2) that bacteria contain definite and distinct nuclei, and (3) that bacteria contain a diffuse nucleus. No one questions the existence of some sort of structure containing DNA, which determines the genetic make-up of the cell. It does not, however, seem to conform in structure and mode of replication to the nuclei of higher (eucaryotic) organisms.

The nucleus in cells of higher plants and animals is an organelle of distinct character: a definite structure bounded by a membrane and containing chromo-

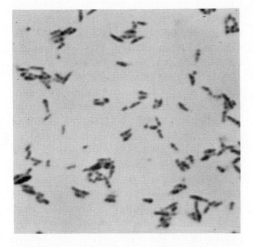

Figure 4-22. Metachromatic granules in *Corynebacterium diphtheriae*. The granules stain deeply, and each cell may contain one to five granules. The cells are often club-shaped (1000X). (Courtesy of G. L. Brown.)

somes. It is capable of mitotic division with typical changes in texture and staining during the division cycle. Only during mitosis does the membrane disappear.

Characteristics of Bacterial Chromatin Bodies. *Shape and Arrangement.* Chromatin bodies are more-or-less centrally situated in resting cells and are spherical or oval or rod-shaped (see Fig. 3-21). During active growth they divide along the same axis as the cell, usually a little before cell division; sometimes two to four paired chromatin bodies can be seen in a single rod-shaped cell in the phase of very rapid growth. Eventually cell divisions catch up and the normal ratio of one chromatin body per cell is reestablished.

Lacking a bounding membrane, the shape of a chromatin body is variable. It is, however, a definite structure, readily distinguishable from the remainder of the cell contents by the use of nuclear stains and recognizable by its characteristic relatively low density in electron microscopy. There are two general types: (1) solid structures forming bars or H, V, or butterfly shapes, shown particularly by staining, and (2) small granules enmeshed in fine strands, best seen in electron photomicrographs.

Size. Chromatin bodies vary in dimensions between species and within the same species at different ages. Resting cells of one species of *Staphylococcus* possess chromatin bodies about 0.4 μ in diameter, whereas in growing cells they enlarge to about 0.5 by 0.8 μ. This structure constitutes 5 to 16 per cent of the cell volume. Chromatin bodies of resting *E. coli* occupy 15 to 25 per cent of the protoplasmic space.

Structure and Replication of Chromatin Bodies. Bacterial chromatin bodies appear to be composed of fine fibrils of DNA or desoxyribonucleoprotein 0.3 to 0.4 mμ in diameter. In gram-negative bacteria like *E. coli* and *Salmonella typhimurium* these fibrils are arranged in a delicate but compact whorl, whereas in gram-positive bacteria, such as various cocci and bacilli, the dense fibers are aligned in an almost parallel pattern. The DNA constitutes a single chromosome, at least in the bacteria studied so far, and apparently a single two-stranded molecule about 1 mm. long carries all the genetic information of the cell. The chromosome is circular, and during replication it divides, but not by mitosis (Fig. 4-23). New strands of DNA form, complementary in the usual way to each of those in the parent chromosome. The process begins at a certain place in the chromosome and proceeds around the endless molecule. At the fork in the chain there is presumably a swivel, which permits the parent helix to uncoil as the new strand is formed.

Flagella

Bacterial flagella are slender, spirally coiled appendages found on most freely swimming bacteria. They are generally presumed to be organelles of locomotion.

Physical and Chemical Properties of Flagella. Bacterial flagella are extremely thin but may be very long. Their diameters vary between 0.01 and 0.05 μ, and they may be several times as long as the cell to which they are attached. Flagella more than 70 μ long have been reported. They are composed of an elastic fibrous protein, flagellin, similar to the actomyosin of skeletal muscle. Electron photomicrographs and x-ray diffraction patterns indicate that bacterial flagella consist of several fibrils, usually three (Fig. 4-24) surrounding a slender, nonprotein core, in contrast to the flagella of motile eucaryotic cells which are composed of nine pairs of fibrils around a core of two fibrils (Fig. 4-25).

Origin of Flagella. The fact that flagella arise from the cytoplasm was indicated by the observation that protoplasts of motile bacteria may still possess flagella. Their origin is apparently a granule or *blepharoplast* within the plasma membrane, as has been shown in numerous electron photomicrographs

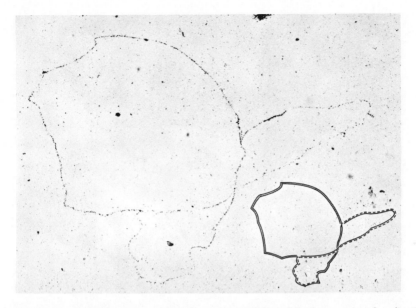

Figure 4-23. Autoradiograph of the circular chromosome of *E. coli* in the process of replicating. The DNA of the chromosome was labeled with radioactive hydrogen (H^3) by growing the organism in tritiated thymidine for two generations. The DNA was then extracted. A photographic plate was exposed to the radiation for two months, with the results shown. The insert is a diagram to explain the replication process. (Courtesy of J. Cairns, from Braun: Bacterial Genetics, 2d ed. W. B. Saunders Co., Philadelphia, 1965.)

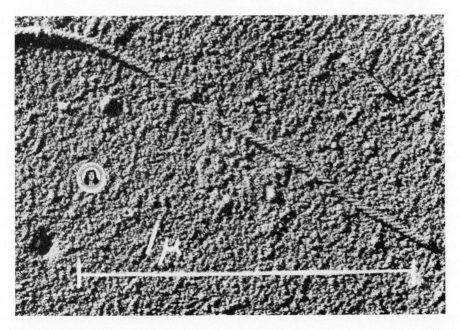

Figure 4-24. Electron photomicrograph of a shadowed bacterial flagellum at very high magnification. Its structure is that of a left-handed, triple-threaded screw. (Photograph by M. P. Starr and R. C. Williams; A.S.M. LS-300.)

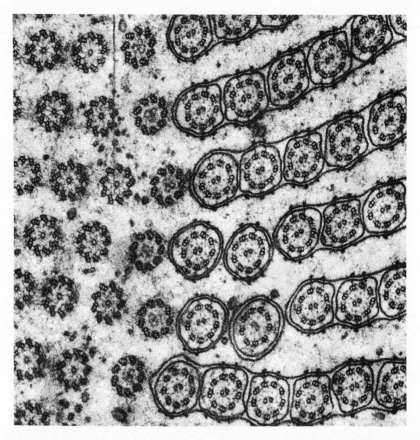

Figure 4-25. Electron photomicrograph of a cross section through protozoan cilia. Each cilium contains a ring of nine pairs of fibrils with two fibrils in the center. This pattern is found in cilia and flagella of all animals and plants. Bacteria and blue-green algae possess flagella consisting of a single fibril. (From P. Weiss, in Allen: The Molecular Control of Cellular Activity. McGraw-Hill, New York, 1962.)

(Fig. 4-26). Flagella grow rapidly, 0.5 μ per minute, and attain full length in 10 to 20 minutes.

Demonstration of Motility. Motility is usually accepted as presumptive evidence that bacteria possess flagella, although it gives no indication of the number or arrangement of the flagella. Motility is detected directly by microscopic examination of wet mounts or hanging drop preparations (see page 54), usually at a magnification of 400X to 500X. Stab cultures in soft agar (e.g., 0.5 per cent agar instead of the usual 1.5 per cent agar) can also be used (Fig. 4-27); nonmotile bacteria grow only along the line of inoculation, whereas motile organisms quickly grow throughout the medium.

Flagellation of Individual Cells. A single cell may possess from one to more than a hundred flagella. Their number and distribution over the bacterial surface are relatively constant for each species. There are two main groups of organisms: those with polar (terminal) and those with lateral (peritrichous) flagella. Polar flagellation is characteristic of *Pseudomonas, Spirillum,* and *Vibrio* species, whereas peritrichous flagella are found particularly on the Enterobacteriaceae (e.g., *Escherichia, Salmonella, Proteus*), and the spore-forming rods (*Bacillus* species). The length and frequency of the spiral turns vary more or less characteristically.

Leifson (1951) distinguished four types of flagellation (Fig. 4-28):

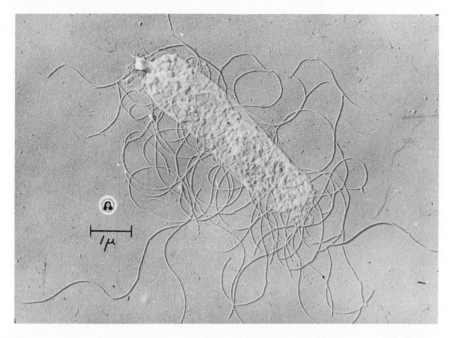

Figure 4-26. Electron photomicrograph of shadowed *Proteus vulgaris* demonstrating flagella. A few flagella appear to extend through the cell wall and to originate from a small mass of material within the cell. (Photograph by C. F. Robinow and W. van Iterson; A.S.M. LS-260.)

1. *Monotrichous:* a single flagellum at or near one or both ends of the cell; flagella have more than two curves (Fig. 4-29).

2. *Multitrichous:* more than one flagellum at or near one or both ends of the cell; these flagella also consist of more than two curves (Fig. 4-30).

3. *Lophotrichous:* ordinarily more than one flagellum at one or both ends of the cell; flagella consist of only one or two curves.

4. *Peritrichous:* flagella extending from all sides of the cell and possibly from the ends (Fig. 4-31).

It is probable that bipolar flagellation of a single cell is rare, and a cell that appears to bear flagella at both ends is in reality in the process of dividing. This might be demonstrated if it were possi-

Figure 4-27. Demonstration of bacterial motility in soft agar. A nonmotile organism grows only along the line of the stab inoculation (A); a motile organism spreads from the line of inoculation throughout the agar to the wall of the test tube, producing turbidity throughout the agar (B).

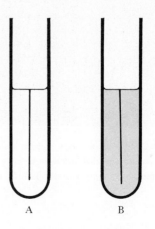

A   B

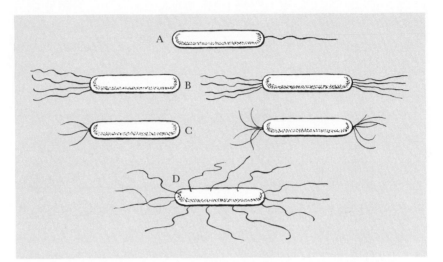

Figure 4-28. Types of flagellation: *A*, monotrichous; *B*, multitrichous; *C*, lophotrichous; *D*, peritrichous.

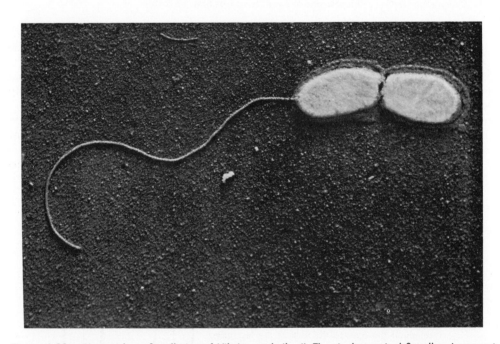

Figure 4-29. Monotrichous flagellation of *Vibrio metchnikovii*. The single terminal flagellum is present on only one of the dividing pair of cells (15,000X). (Shadowed electron photomicrograph by W. van Iterson, Biochim. Biophys. Acta, *1*:535, 1947.)

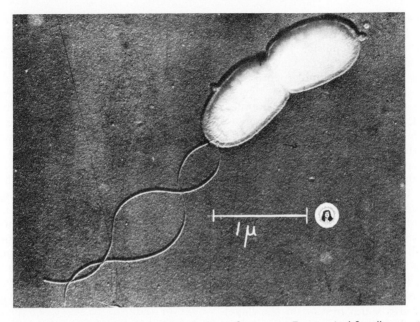

Figure 4-30. Multitrichous flagellation of *Pseudomonas fluorescens*. Two terminal flagella seem to arise in the cytoplasm and pass through the cell wall. (Shadowed electron photomicrograph by A. L. Houwink and W. van Iterson; A.S.M. LS-275.)

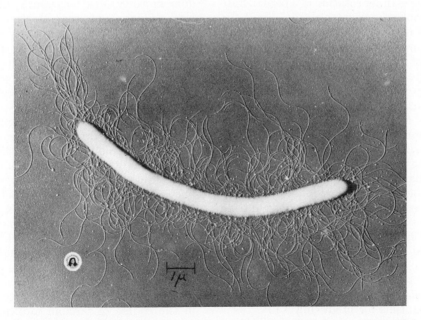

Figure 4-31. Peritrichous flagella on *Proteus vulgaris*. (Shadowed electron photomicrograph by C. F. Robinow and J. Hillier; A.S.M. LS-258.)

ble to stain the developing cell wall in such a bipolar flagellated organism.

Mechanism of Propulsion. The movement of flagella has been variously described as lashing, whiplike, rotary, or corkscrew-like. Lophotrichous flagella appear to rotate in a circular manner; when they are present at both ends of a cell, the forward group curves back toward the body and the posterior group curves out behind. This is observed particularly in certain spirilla; the organism seems to corkscrew itself through the medium. It can reverse its direction without turning around. The flagella of a peritrichous organism trail behind as the cell moves forward.

The driving force seems to be produced by a wave of contraction from the base to the tip of each flagellum; this causes spiral motion of the flagellum and opposite rotation of the bacterial cell. The flagella on a spiral organism rotate at about 40 revolutions per second, but the viscous resistance of the medium slows the rotation of the organism to almost exactly one-third of this rate. The rotary movement propels a spiral organism forward, and in a similar manner rotation of a peritrichate cell applies a torque to the flagellar helix and drives the cell. The speed of forward motion is very great in relation to the size of the cell, but rates of motility vary markedly. Average speeds of 25 μ per second have been recorded for peritrichous intestinal bacteria and a velocity as high as 200 μ per second for the monotrichous, comma-shaped *Vibrio cholerae.*

The energy necessary to maintain flagellar motion is presumably derived from adenosine triphosphate (ATP), a high energy compound formed during photosynthetic and respiratory activity (see Chap. 12). Aerobic bacteria remain motile only as long as they have sufficient oxygen to make ATP by oxidative processes, and the motility of other types of bacteria is correlated with their mechanisms for producing ATP.

Variations in Motility. Flagellar propulsion is the most common mechanism of motility among bacteria. It should be pointed out, however, that bacteria possessing flagella are not necessarily always motile, and loss of motility may occur without loss of flagella. Loss of motility may be caused by environmental changes or by mutation. Certain nonflagellate groups of bacteria are motile, notably some terrestrial forms which creep or glide by a mechanism that is not yet understood.

Ecologic Value of Motility. Motility may be looked upon as an adaptation that favors survival by enhancing the chance that an organism will encounter food and other favorable environmental agents, or avoid harmful substances and agents. Movement in response to environmental factors is called *taxis;* it is positive if the movement is toward the factor in question, negative if away from it. Whereas higher organisms can respond to a stimulus directly by turning or moving toward or away from it, bacteria apparently respond only by a "shock reaction," that is, reversal of direction of movement. This phenomenon is called *phobotaxis* (Greek: *phobos,* fear + *taxis,* influence). When the random motility of a bacterium brings it into a zone containing a stimulating agent that causes it to reverse direction, the response is called *negative* phobotaxis; i.e., the organism tends to leave the vicinity of the stimulus. A *positive* phobotactic response occurs when a bacterium, in the course of its random movement, starts to leave the source of stimulus. The stimulating agent thus serves as a trap, and many cells may accumulate within a small area.

Certain photosynthetic pigmented bacteria exhibit *phototactic* behavior; that is, their movements are influenced by light. If a culture is illuminated by a narrow beam of light, the bacteria will soon congregate in the lighted zone. This is an illustration of positive phobotaxis, and is explained as follows: Those organisms that enter the lighted area in the course of random motility give an immediate shock reaction when they start to swim into the dark portion of the culture; they reverse direction and hence remain in the light, which thus serves as a trap.

Protozoa and motile aerobic bacteria congregate in a region well supplied with oxygen (e.g., at the edges of a wet mount between a coverglass and a slide). Spirilla prefer a lower oxygen tension and will accumulate some distance from an air bubble or the edge of a wet mount. Anaerobic bacteria will congregate as far from a source of oxygen as possible.

Many other chemical agents exert some sort of *tactic* effect upon microorganisms, causing them to leave the source of the chemical or to be trapped and accumulate near it.

Adaptation is well illustrated by the type of flagellation on aquatic organisms as contrasted with terrestrial species. Terrestrial organisms are adapted to a moist rather than a wet environment and frequently have many peri-

trichous flagella; aquatic bacteria, on the other hand, usually possess only one or a few polar flagella.

Pili

Bacterial pili (Latin: *pilus,* hair) are morphologically distinct, nonflagellar appendages, found particularly on gram-negative bacteria freshly isolated from natural sources such as infected urine (see Fig. 4-32). Like flagella, they are too slender to be seen by ordinary light microscopy; most pili are 0.003 to 0.007 μ in diameter. They vary from 0.5 to 6 μ in length, and certain pili are as long as 20 μ. They are straight, and some appear to be rigid. One hundred to 400 are usually distributed over the cell surface. There are several types, which differ in size and structure. Mechanical agitation in a high-speed mixer removes them from the cell, and they can be purified by precipitation and centrifuga-

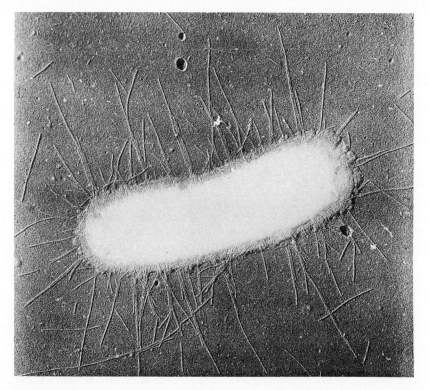

Figure 4-32. Electron photomicrograph of *E. coli* showing pili. (From Brinton, Trans. N. Y. Acad. Sci., II, 27:1005, 1965.)

tion to yield a protein, *pilin,* with a minimum molecular weight of about 17,000. A pilus is composed of pilin subunits arranged in a very precise helical structure to form a smooth tube around a longitudinal hole. Physical, chemical, and genetic study has shown that one type of pilus is intimately concerned in the process of sexual mating, and probably serves as the channel through which DNA from the donor (male) cell is transferred to the recipient (female) cell. Another type of pilus enhances growth when the oxygen supply is limited and the cell population is high, perhaps by mediating the transport of some metabolite. The functions of other pili are not known.

Endospores

Occurrence. Endospores are highly resistant bodies produced within the cells of certain bacteria. They are found in all species of the family Bacillaceae,

which is divided into two genera, *Bacillus* (aerobic spore-forming rods) and *Clostridium* (anaerobic spore-forming rods). One bacterial cell normally produces only a single endospore. Sporulation is therefore not considered to be a method of multiplication of bacteria as it is of yeasts and molds.

Physical and Physiologic Characteristics. Endospores are spherical to elliptical and may be situated anywhere within the parent cell or *sporangium* (Fig. 4-33). Their diameter may be less than, equal to, or greater than that of the rest of the sporangium. A cell with a greatly enlarged central endospore resembles a spindle and is called a *clostridium.* A *plectridium* (Fig. 4-34) is a sporangium containing an enlarged terminal endospore. The sizes of spores differ from one species to another; this property is of some use as a criterion for classification.

Unstained bacterial endospores are highly refractile when observed with

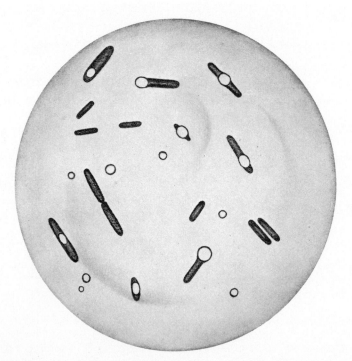

Figure 4-33. Various types of bacterial spores: terminal, subterminal, central, spherical, oval. Spores are sketched as though unstained, vegetative cells and portions of sporangia as though stained with methylene blue or crystal violet. (From Frobisher: Fundamentals of Microbiology, 7th ed. W. B. Saunders Co., Philadelphia, 1962.)

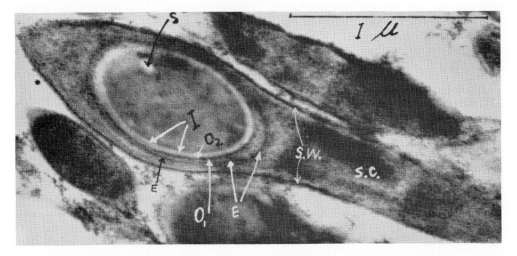

Figure 4-34. Electron photomicrograph of ultrathin section of *Clostridium sporogenes* showing a large, subterminal, elliptical endospore. *S.C.*, Sporangium cytoplasm; *S.W.*, sporangium wall; *E*, exosporium; O_1 and O_2, first and second outer membranes; *I*, inner membrane; *S*, spot of unknown nature. (Photograph by T. Hashimoto and H. B. Naylor, J. Bact., 75:647–653, 1958.)

the microscope. Ordinary simple staining methods color only the outer layer or spore coat. The inside of a spore can be stained if heat is applied. Apparently this treatment increases the permeability of the spore envelopes and permits strong dyes such as malachite green or carbolfuchsin to penetrate and stain the cytoplasm intensely. Stained endospores resist decolorization and are easily distinguished from vegetative cells or from other portions of sporangia.

The fine structure of endospores differs somewhat from one species to another. In general, however, there is a central core surrounded by a delicate membrane, the *spore wall.* In many species this will eventually transform into the cell wall of the future bacillus. Around the wall is a second layer, thicker and of relatively low density, the *cortex.* The cortex, in turn, is enclosed in one or two (depending on the species) *spore coats.* A spore coat may be smooth, grooved, or raised into ridges, sometimes in geometric (e.g., hexagonal) patterns. Lastly, the whole may be wrapped in an *exosporium,* which fits snugly at the sides but protrudes beyond the end of the spore.

Endospores are the most resistant of all living bodies to heat, desiccation and toxic chemicals, but there is great variation between species. Some endospores are killed within a few minutes at 80° to 90° C., whereas those of other species survive prolonged boiling. Spores of one bacillus resist 100° C. for over 20 hours. Variations occur among the endospores within a single culture; a few survive exposure to a lethal agent considerably longer than the majority.

The remarkable resistance of endospores implies that their chemical composition or physical structure must differ radically from that of the parent cells. Chemical analysis reveals that endospores contain DNA and RNA, proteins, lipids, carbohydrates, various enzymes, and minerals. Their water content is approximately 25 per cent less than that of vegetative cells. It has long been suggested that the ratio of "bound" to "free" water in spores is greater than in vegetative cells. In addition, spores contain more calcium. Some of the proteins are the same as those in vegetative cells, but proteins peculiar to endospores have been found. Formation of an endospore therefore appears to involve new synthesis as well as incorporation of vegetative cell constituents.

One of the most striking features of endospores is a compound, *dipicolinic acid,*

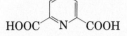

that is present in all the spores examined and absent from all vegetative cells. It makes up 5 to 15 per cent of the dry weight of the spore. Dipicolinic acid, a peptide, and other substances are released from germinating spores, and simultaneously the resistance of the spores is lost. It therefore appears that dipicolinic acid is partly responsible for spore resistance.

The metabolic activity of endospores is very low. They contain three or four active enzymes, but many others are present in a dormant or inactive state.

There is evidence that some of the enzymes and other normally thermolabile substances within spores are bound in the form of chemical complexes with dipicolinic acid and perhaps also peptide and calcium. Those complexes are highly resistant.

Other factors contribute to the resistance and low metabolic activity of spores. The impermeability of the spore coat undoubtedly prevents the entrance of lethal chemicals. The dehydrated endospore cytoplasm is unfavorable for any kind of chemical activity. This factor has been cited in partial explanation of the observation that intact spores cannot be stained.

Sporulation. Endospores are produced by healthy, well nourished cells growing under favorable conditions, normally just after the period of maximum multiplication rate. Sporulation occurs most frequently at a temperature favorable for vegetative growth and within a narrow range of pH, usually near neutrality but differing from species to species. It is inhibited by certain metabolic by-products such as straight-chain saturated organic acids of 10 to 14 carbon atoms, which may be derived from peptone or other ingredients of the culture medium. Aerobic spore-forming bacteria ordinarily do not produce endospores in the absence of oxygen nor do anaerobes sporulate in its presence.

It has been suggested that the exhaustion of nutrients is a factor in spore formation. Sporulation is favored by cultivation in dilute media; adequate food supplies promote vegetative growth and seem to delay the formation of spores. However, sporulation is also prevented by some substances that interfere with amino acid metabolism, and restored by appropriate amino acids. Spore formation therefore seems to depend upon the protein metabolism of the organism. It is envisaged either as a conversion of "vegetative proteins" into "spore proteins" or as a new formation of "spore proteins" from the culture medium. There is evidence favoring each hypothesis.

The first sign of spore formation usually detected is a faint elliptical envelope or clear patch in the granular cytoplasm at one end of the cell. This area gradually becomes more dense than the rest of the cytoplasm, and stains more intensely with basic dyes until the spore coverings form. This structure is the *spore primordium.* Local opacity and viscosity increase, and within a short time the spore wall, coat or coats, and cortex develop (Fig. 4-35). Dipicolinic acid is synthesized late in the process of spore formation, probably from diaminopimelic acid.

Nuclear changes demonstrable by appropriate stains both precede and accompany spore formation. Vegetative cells are more or less filled with chromatin in a granular filament or long bar. A short length of chromatin near the end of the cell moves to the tip, where it becomes deeply stainable and later evolves into a helical, twisted filament. In some species there is evidence of division and fusion of chromatin bodies. As the developing spore primordium elongates, the chromatin filament further twists into a figure eight or pretzel

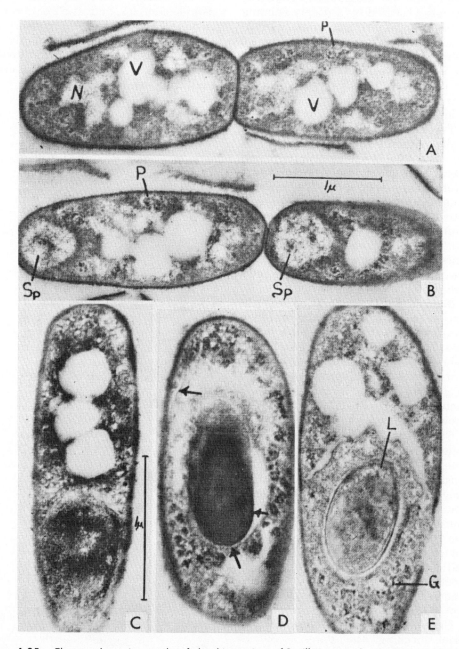

Figure 4-35. Electron photomicrographs of ultrathin sections of *Bacillus cereus* showing stages in sporulation. *A,* Dividing organism. *B,* Early stage of formation of spore primordia. *C,* The spore primordium has become more dense. *D,* The spore is forming; arrows point to sites where the three spore coats are visible. *E,* Further development of the spore and its coats. *N,* Nuclear element; *P,* peripheral body (see page 97); *G,* dense granule, *Sp.,* spore primordium; *V,* inclusions; *L,* low density particles. (From G. B. Chapman, J. Bact., 71:348–355, 1956.)

design and its stainability gradually becomes obscured by a deeply staining material, apparently not ordinary DNA. This process takes a half hour or so. Refractility increases, presumably as the cortex develops. Chromatin bodies are difficult to detect but seem to lie near the surface of the spore cytoplasm as interconnected strands or beads.

The endospore is now characteristically refractile and resistant to staining. The final stage, maturation and liberation of the endospore, may require several hours (Fig. 4-36). The sporangium is often alive and metabolically active for a short time after the endospore forms, but eventually autolysis sets the naked spore free. *Autolysis* is a process in which enzymes of a cell that has ceased to metabolize digest the cell's own protoplasm.

Germination of Endospores. The germination of endospores occurs within a very few hours after transfer to a favorable environment. This is true whether the spores have only recently been formed or have been dormant for a long time. Spores can survive for many years; bacteriology is so young that no one knows just how long.

Conditions that favor germination include the presence of water and nutrients, suitable temperature and oxygen tension, and the presence of certain "key" substances or germinating agents. For aerobic bacilli the latter include a source of nitrogen, a metabolizable carbon compound, and a nucleic acid precursor. An amino acid, such as l-alanine, and glucose and adenosine will usually meet the requirements. All these substances are important in the synthesis of protoplasm.

Germination may be hastened by "heat shocking" the spores at 80° to 85° C. for a few minutes. This temperature is too low to kill spores of most species but accelerates germination.

The first stage of germination is characterized by loss of heat resistance and refractility, and by increased stainability. A rapid breakdown of the structures that protect vital functions is followed

by the release of the dipicolinic acid-peptide complex, activation of dormant enzymes, and increased respiratory activity. Nuclear material is readily detected. The chromatin body divides twice and the resulting four bodies eventually appear in four vegetative cells.

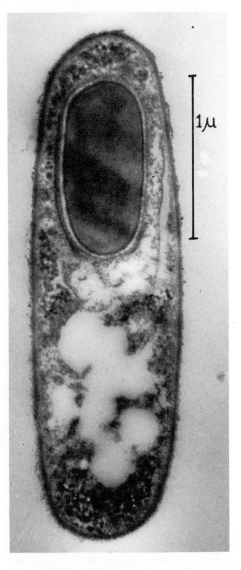

Figure 4-36. Nearly mature spore within a cell of *Bacillus cereus*. Three spore coats are clearly distinguishable. The large, white bodies in the lower end of the cell are vacuole-like inclusions. (Electron photomicrographs of ultrathin section by G. B. Chapman, J. Bact., 71:348–355, 1956.)

The imbibition of water and intake of salts and nutrients produce swelling, which bursts the spore coat or coats within an hour or so, either by equatorial splitting or by puncturing one end (Fig. 4-37). The elongating cell emerges and continues its growth as a vegetative cell. Divisions follow in the usual manner.

Significance of Endospores. The biologic significance of endospores is not known. Their great resistance to heat, drying, and chemicals tempts us to argue teleologically that spores are produced to permit survival under unfavorable conditions. However, the imminence of such conditions does not seem to be the trigger that initiates sporulation. Rather, spore formation occurs only in cultures that are adequately supplied with food and energy, under fairly restricted conditions of pH and temperature, and in the absence of "antisporulation factors," such as certain organic acids.

It has been mentioned that spore formation is not a method of multiplication in bacteria. Neither does it seem to be a means of rejuvenation by nuclear fusion or a sexual process. An endospore is clearly a resting stage in the life cycle. Its metabolic activity is low; it contains only small amounts of enzymes, less water than vegetative cells, and the unusual stabilizing agent dipicolinic acid. These properties evidently provide the remarkable resistance typical of spores. They are therefore adapted to survival, although it must be admitted that they can withstand conditions more rigorous than any likely to be encountered today except in rare circumstances (e.g., in hot springs).

It has long been believed that the resistance of spores is due to their marked dehydration, which can be expected to diminish greatly all chemical activity within the cytoplasm. Thimann pointed out that the volume of a spore is one-quarter to one-tenth that of the parent vegetative cell and that a large fraction of this is wall structure, so that

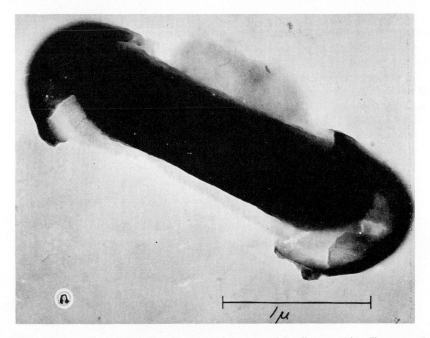

Figure 4-37. Electron photomicrograph of germinating spore of *Bacillus mycoides*. The vegetative cell still carries the two halves of the completely ruptured spore coats at its ends. The culture was grown on nutrient agar at 35° C. for 105 minutes. (Photograph by G. Knaysi, R. F. Baker, and J. Hillier; A.S.M. LS-204.)

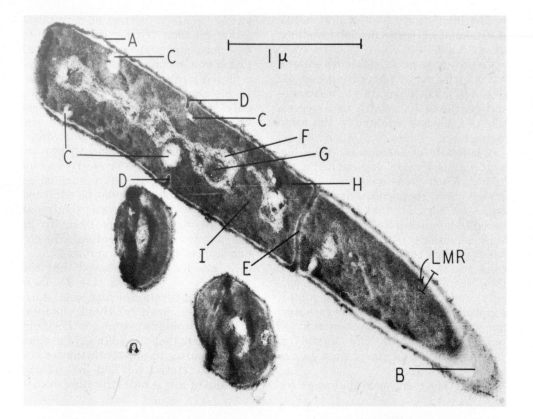

Figure 4-38. Vegetative reproduction of *Bacillus cereus*. Electron photomicrograph of an ultrathin section close to the median plane of one cell and passing obliquely through the next cell; cross sections of two other cells. A, Cell wall showing evidence of the shrinking of the cytoplasm. B, Very oblique section of the cell wall showing dense particles and the dense inner layer. C, Four peripheral bodies cut at different levels. D, Beginning of the centripetally growing transverse cell wall. E, Completed transverse cell wall before thickening. F, Low density fibrous component of nuclear apparatus. G, Dense body in nuclear apparatus that may be inclusion of cytoplasmic material. H, Small dense particles that appear to be main constituent of cytoplasm. I, Unidentified cytoplasmic inclusions. LMR, Scale indicating the limit of resolution of a light microscope using visible light. (Photograph by G. B. Chapman; A.S.M. LS-325.)

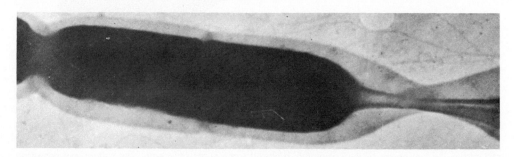

Figure 4-39. A plasmodesm (at right) connecting adjacent cells of *Bacillus cereus*. (Electron photomicrograph by F. H. Johnson; A.S.M. LS-58.)

the water content of the cytoplasm must be much less than that of vegetative cell cytoplasm. Therefore, the cytoplasm of a spore might contain protein in as high a concentration as 90 per cent, whereas in a vegetative cell its concentration is approximately 10 per cent. Obviously, it would be difficult to dehydrate spore protein further, either by desiccation at physiologic temperatures or by the use of heat. Moreover, the low moisture content greatly retards the action of chemical disinfectants. It appears, therefore, that the resistance of spores to desiccation, chemicals, and heat has a common basis, namely the lack of "free" water.

VEGETATIVE REPRODUCTION OF BACTERIA

Vegetative reproduction, as followed in a series of stained preparations studied at ordinary magnification, begins with the formation of new protoplasm and cell growth. Cells elongate, often to many times their original length, and nuclear division occurs. Cell division seems to be initiated by inward growth of the cytoplasmic membrane producing a cross-plate and forming two independent sister cells. A cross wall develops and splits this plate into two layers, and the sister cells may then separate.

Chapman and Hillier in 1953 examined ultrathin sections of *Bacillus cereus* with the electron microscope. Their reconstruction of the events in vegetative reproduction (Fig. 4-38) indicated that cell growth is accompanied by one or two nuclear divisions yielding two or four nuclei. Rings of six or eight "peripheral bodies" about .02 μ in diameter appear within the cytoplasm near the edge of the cell and approximately midway between the nuclei. The peripheral bodies are probably the structures later designated mesosomes (see Figs. 4-5, 4-6, and 4-21), which seem always to originate as plasma membrane intrusions. They also appear in other situations involving protoplast division, such

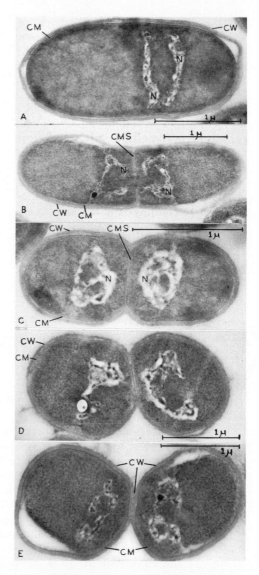

Figure 4-40. Electron photomicrographs of ultrathin sections of an unidentified bacterium showing various stages in cell division. *A,* Before cell division; the nuclear material is in the form of two bars through which a threadlike component extends. *B,* The nuclear material has divided and the cytoplasmic membrane nearly separates the cytoplasm into two portions. *C,* The cytoplasmic membrane septum is complete. *D,* Two layers of the cytoplasmic membrane septum can be distinguished; the cells are becoming rounded. *E,* The cell wall is complete between the daughter cells, which have nearly separated. (Photographs by G. B. Chapman; *A* and *C* are from J. Bact., 78: 96–104, 1959; *B, D,* and *E* are from J. Biophys. Biochem. Cytol., 6:221–224, 1959.)

as the formation of endospores. They gradually move toward the axis of the cell, and the cell wall grows inward like a slowly closing iris diaphragm. The inward-growing wall follows closely behind the peripheral bodies, and it is assumed that these bodies synthesize and secrete cell wall material. Cross wall formation is sometimes initiated before the adjacent nuclei have completely separated, and several cross walls may be in various stages of growth within a single cell. Occasionally a transverse wall is not completed and a small central hole remains, through which the cytoplasm of one cell is connected with that of the sister cell. The connecting link is called a *plasmodesm* (Fig. 4-39).

The completed transverse wall be-comes thicker; a less dense layer differentiates in the middle; and eventually the wall splits into two layers, one for each sister cell. These end walls are continuous with the lateral walls of the cells. Indentation occurs at the surface of the cell at the transverse wall, and the sister cells may separate. As the sister cells grow they set up turgor pressure, which pulls on their walls at regions of contact with adjacent cells so that separation begins at the outside and progresses toward the axis of the cells (Fig. 4-40). This is true of bacteria that characteristically appear as single cells. Chain-forming bacteria apparently possess tougher walls, which resist the tension produced by the growth of sister cells.

 # MORPHOLOGY AND STRUCTURE OF BACTERIA

SUMMARY

Bacterial and other protocaryotic cells are distinguished from eucaryotic cells by their comparatively unorganized internal structure. Their only obvious membranes are the plasma membrane and its associated mesosomes; the chromatin body or nucleoid is not enclosed within a membrane and there are no mitochondria or chloroplasts.

The bacterial cell wall is a strong protective coat, which owes its rigidity to a layer of glycosaminopeptides. The walls of gram-negative bacteria also contain lipopolysaccharide and lipoprotein layers. Within the wall, the plasma membrane serves as an osmotic barrier and link with the environment. It is composed of a lipid layer between two protein layers—the so-called unit membrane—and provides a matrix upon which many respiratory and other enzymes are organized.

A single chromosome contains the genetic material of the chromatin body. The double stranded DNA molecule is about 1000 μ long and appears to be circular. It divides amitotically. The cytoplasm is filled with ribonucleoprotein granules, the ribosomes, which are sites of synthetic activity.

The principal method of reproduction is simple fission, in which one or two cycles of DNA replication and division of the chromatin body are followed by the formation of septa and often by separation of the daughter cells. The formation of resting bodies known as endospores also occurs in a few genera under favorable conditions. Spores are resistant to desiccation, chemical disinfectants, and heat, and their resistance has been attributed to their great dehydration together with their possession of a characteristic substance, dipicolinic acid.

STUDY QUESTIONS

1. Describe the normal variation in shape of cocci and rod bacteria during the process of growth and division.
2. Describe how the manner of division of bacterial cells is correlated with their arrangement in clusters or other aggregates.
3. How are the various structures of bacterial cells demonstrated?
4. What is the function of the bacterial cell wall? Can a cell survive without its wall? What is such a cell called?
5. What is the composition of the bacterial cytoplasmic membrane? List some of its functions.
6. Describe the present view of the nature of the bacterial nucleus.
7. Compare the composition and structure of a bacterial flagellum with that of a protozoan flagellum.
8. To what is the great resistance of bacterial endospores attributed?
9. Is it correct to state that bacterial endospores are produced in response to unfavorable environmental conditions? Explain.
10. Describe the process of cell growth and division in an organism such as *B. cereus.*
11. Compare the cell walls of gram-positive and gram-negative bacteria.

SUPPLEMENTARY READING

The Bacterial Cell by Dubos presents a good general survey of bacterial cell structure and its relation to physiology and disease; an addendum by Robinow contains an illustrated discussion of the nuclear apparatus. A detailed treatment of the form, composition, and organization of the bacterial cell and its various structures is found in Knaysi's *Elements of Bacterial Cytology.* Bisset's *The Cytology and Life-History of Bacteria* is a short book with many excellent photographs. Spooner and Stocker are editors of a series of symposium papers with the title *Bacterial Anatomy.* An excellent work in this field is Volume I of *The Bacteria, A Treatise on Structure and Function,* edited by Gunsalus and Stanier. This book contains chapters by authorities on such topics as bacterial protoplasm, the internal structure of the cell, surface structures, spores, protoplasts, and bacterial viruses. Brieger makes liberal use of electron photomicrography to illustrate newer knowledge of the fine structure of microbial cells. Murray has a single chapter on bacterial organelles in the symposium volume edited by Mazia and Tyler, and DeRobertis, Nowinski, and Saez present an excellent discussion of various cell substructures in plants, animals, and microorganisms in the first few chapters of *Cell Biology.* Salton devotes an entire book to the bacterial cell wall with considerable discussion of its chemistry as well as its morphology. *Bacteriology Illustrated* is essentially an atlas, with many color photographs of bacterial cells and cultures. Brinton's paper is a detailed scientific account of several years of work on an interesting bacterial structure.

Bisset, K. A.: *The Cytology and Life-History of Bacteria,* 2d ed. Baltimore, The Williams & Wilkins Co., 1955.

Brieger, E. M.: *Structure and Ultrastructure of Microorganisms.* New York, Academic Press, 1963.

Brinton, C. C.: The Structure, Function, Synthesis and Genetic Control of Bacterial Pili and a Molecular Model for DNA and RNA Transport in Gram-negative Bacteria. *Trans. N. Y. Acad. Sci.* II, *27*:1003–1054, 1965.

DeRobertis, E. D. P., Nowinski, W. W., and Saez, F. A.: *Cell Biology,* 4th ed. Philadelphia, W. B. Saunders Company, 1965.

Dubos, R. J.: *The Bacterial Cell.* Cambridge, Mass., Harvard University Press, 1945.

Gillies, R. R., and Dodds, T. C.: *Bacteriology Illustrated.* Baltimore, The Williams & Wilkins Co., 1965.

Gunsalus, I. C., and Stanier, R. Y. (eds.): *The Bacteria, A Treatise on Structure and Function. Vol. I: Structure.* New York, Academic Press, Inc., 1960.

Knaysi, G.: *Elements of Bacterial Cytology,* 2d ed. Ithaca, N. Y., Comstock Publishing Co., Inc., 1951.

Murray, R. G. E.: The Organelles of Bacteria. In Mazia, D., and Tyler, A. (eds.): *The General Physiology of Cell Specialization.* New York, McGraw-Hill Book Company, Inc., 1963.

Salton, M. R. J.: *The Bacterial Cell Wall.* Amsterdam, Elsevier Publishing Company, 1964.

Spooner, E. T. C., and Stocker, B. A. D. (eds.): *Bacterial Anatomy,* Sixth Symposium of Society for General Microbiology. New York, Cambridge University Press, 1956.

THE SYSTEMATIC STUDY
OF BACTERIA

Systematics is the general study of organized nature, including the causes and historical background of observed phenomena. The branch of systematics that deals with the description, classification, and naming of plants, animals, and microorganisms is called *taxonomy* (from Greek: *taxis,* arrangement, + *nomos,* law). The classification of biologic forms into groups is based on their relationships with one another, that is, their greater or lesser similarity. There are various approaches to the problem of determining degrees of similarity and, it must be confessed, systematists do not agree on which is the best. In general, it seems that organisms should be assigned to groups (e.g., species) on the basis of the correlation of many characters, rather than the possession of only a few, so-called *key* characters. Useful characters include morphologic, physiologic, chemical, serologic, ecologic, pathologic, and other properties. The relative importance of various characters is a matter of debate. An experienced biologic taxonomist con-

sciously or unconsciously weights certain characters more heavily than others in his study of particular groups of organisms, whereas a *numerical* taxonomist considers each bit of information of equal value and even utilizes computer analysis to determine relationships. Groups are thus defined by possession of a majority of shared characters.

The ideal goal is a "natural" classification system based upon biologic relationships, and if possible also reflecting evolutionary (i.e., phylogenetic) trends. It should at the same time be practically useful in the identification of unknown specimens.

Natural Classification. Natural or *phylogenetic* classification indicates relationships between organisms on the basis of their probable origin; organisms with a common origin are grouped more closely together than those with diverse origins. The final picture resembles the structure of a tree: the trunk represents the main stream of evolution from its origin at the ground, the branches with

Figure 5-1. Electron photomicrograph of fossil bacteria in Gunflint chert sediments from southern Ontario. These precambrian rod-shaped bacteria were alive about 2,000,000,000 years ago. (From Schopf et al., Science *149*:1165, 1965.)

their twigs and shoots represent later stages in evolutionary development, and the outermost leaves indicate forms currently in existence.

Phylogenetic classification is possible if enough fossil remains of primitive and intermediate forms can be found to reconstruct the trunk and main branches. This is the reason why there is so much interest in so-called missing links. A reasonably complete reconstruction of the evolutionary stages in the develop-

ment of higher animals and plants has been possible, but unfortunately this is not yet the case with most microorganisms, particularly the bacteria.

Electron photomicrographs of two billion year old flint rock from southern Ontario have shown structures interpreted as bacteria (Fig. 5-1), but otherwise the only bacteria known are those in existence at the present; we see the leaves on the systematic tree but have little basis for connecting them in logical fashion to the main trunk. We may deduce that spherical bacteria are related to each other and came from some common ancestor and that spiral bacteria are derived from another common ancestor—but we find no trace of these ancestors.

Artificial Classification. The alternative to a phylogenetic system of classification is an *artificial* or *phenetic* system based upon easily recognized characteristics of known organisms. Such a scheme provides a practical guide that is useful for identifying unknown organisms; it also shows some relationships between these organisms. The nature of the relationships depends upon the criteria used to establish the classification system; these relationships are often not phylogenetic. Bacterial taxonomy has perforce had to develop along these lines.

GROUPS OF ORGANISMS

Although some authorities prefer to consider bacteria as members of a separate kingdom, Protista, including all microorganisms, they are classified at present in the plant kingdom and comprise the class Schizomycetes. The class is divided into orders, orders into families, families into genera, and genera into species. A genus is composed of "related" species, a family of "related" genera, and so forth. Decisions regarding the degree of relationship necessary to include a species in a given genus or a genus in a given family are made by experts in bacterial taxonomy. As in any situation influenced by opinion and judgment, there is occasional disagreement. Bacterial classification has so far always been in a state of change.

The Species Concept

The fundamental group upon which the taxonomic hierarchy rests is the *species*. There is in general good agreement regarding what constitutes a species. The definition of species has undergone considerable evolution with reference to higher plants and animals. A species is now often defined as a group of actually or potentially interbreeding forms that do not crossbreed with other groups. This definition presupposes a sexual mode of reproduction.

Bacterial Species. A few strains of *Escherichia coli* reproduce on rare occasions by a sexual method, but it cannot be said that their principal mode of reproduction is sexual. Moreover, sexual reproduction has not been demonstrated among bacteria generally. The definition of a species that applies to higher plants and animals therefore has no meaning with reference to bacteria or, in fact, to any organisms that reproduce principally by asexual means.

A species of bacteria may be defined as a *group of bacteria possessing the same genetic constitution.* For practical purposes, this definition is adequate in view of the necessity for using an artificial rather than a natural system of classification.

The genetic identity of two organisms is presumed to be demonstrated if they are shown to have the same morphology, physiologic behavior, pathogenicity, and other properties. Organisms that differ in one or more characteristics are genetically different. Whether these genetic differences are great enough to warrant classification in different species is left to the judgment of the investigator. This situation differs from that encountered with higher plants and animals, where the criterion is the ability of the two forms to interbreed—a matter in which the judgment of the investigator is not concerned.

The Type Culture. A newly discovered organism is described as completely as possible, and at the same time a typical culture is designated the *type culture.* This culture should be deposited in a central collection, such as the American Type Culture Collection in Washington, D. C., or the British equivalent, the National Collection of Type Cultures. The type culture is then available for any investigators who wish to compare other organisms with it. Indeed, some authorities define a bacterial species as the type culture or specimen and all other cultures or specimens regarded as sufficiently like the type to be grouped with it. This, it will be noted, is by implication the same as the definition stated earlier.

GROWTH OF BACTERIAL TAXONOMY

Bacteria were discovered by Leeuwenhoek in 1676, but few investigators possessed the interest, facilities, or know-how to study them for almost a century and a half. It is not surprising, therefore, that the famous naturalist Linnaeus, in 1767, included bacteria in his class Chaos, along with various other unrelated forms and ethereal substances. Mueller in 1773 listed two genera containing bacterial species: *Monas* consisted of spherical or ovoid forms; *Vibrio* contained longer rods but was composed largely of spiral organisms. Sixty-five years later, Ehrenberg (1838) added four genera: *Bacterium, Spirillum, Spirochaeta,* and *Spirodiscus.*

Serious attempts to classify bacteria began with the work of Cohn (1872), and for a score of years about one new classification scheme was proposed each year. New genera and species were added at an accelerating rate as bacteriologic research expanded into medical, agricultural, and industrial microbiology (Fig. 5-2).

Modern attempts to systematize the classification of bacteria began with the studies of Buchanan (1917), who proposed that the class Schizomycetes be divided into six orders. These and many other suggestions were included in the first edition of a *Manual of Determinative Bacteriology,* published in 1923 by a committee of the Society of American Bacteriologists of which the late Dr. D. H. Bergey was chairman. Thirteen families of bacteria were listed and a total of 88 genera.

The *Manual* has been revised at intervals. The seventh edition, published in 1957, includes 10 orders of bacteria in the class Schizomycetes. These are divided into 47 families, which are further subdivided into 190 genera. More than 1500 species are listed. Rickettsi-

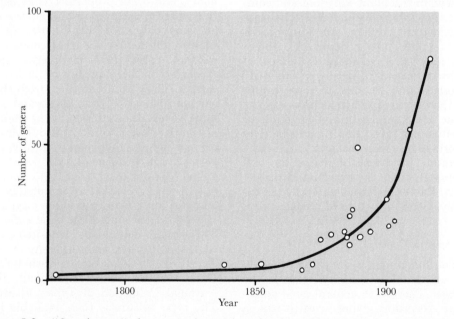

Figure 5-2. "Growth curve" of systematic bacteriology. Numbers of bacterial genera listed by various authors between 1773 and 1917.

ales and Virales are placed in a separate class, Microtatobiotes.

The growing number of categories for classifying bacteria reflects the discovery of previously undescribed organisms and changing opinions as to the taxonomic significance of forms already described. The latter consideration also dictates frequent rearrangements in the scheme as different investigators assist in the preparation of succeeding editions. The committee that edits *Bergey's Manual of Determinative Bacteriology* recognizes that it has shortcomings and welcomes suggestions for improvement and further revision. Nearly 100 specialists collaborated in writing the seventh edition, many of them from outside the United States. Their system of classification is gradually assuming a more international character and although not universally accepted, it is probably the best currently available.

NAMING OF BACTERIA

Scientific Names

Bacteria are named according to the *binomial* system proposed by Linnaeus in 1753. The *scientific name* of an organism consists of two words, genus and species. These names are written in a Latinized form and should be italicized (or underscored when written by hand or typewritten). The generic name is always capitalized, the species need never be capitalized even though derived from a proper noun. Words that are used both as generic names and as morphologic descriptions are capitalized when used to refer to the genus but not when used to indicate the morphologic type; for example, *Streptococcus* designates organisms of the genus, but streptococcus (uncapitalized) refers to spherical cells in a chain form.

A certain amount of abbreviation is permissible if the abbreviations are clearly understandable. Generic names may be abbreviated to the first initial or first few letters; species names are never abbreviated. The first time a scientific name is used in a paper or chapter (or examination) it should be written out in full; thereafter it may be abbreviated.

Colloquial Names

Many bacteria have been studied so much or are discussed so frequently that they have acquired common or *colloquial* names. These names have no scientific status and should not be used in scientific writing; it must be confessed, however, that they frequently appear. *Escherichia coli,* for example, is such a universal inhabitant of the large intestine that it is frequently called the colon bacillus.

Derivations of Bacterial Names

The beginning student frequently complains that there are too many bacterial names to learn and that they do not make sense. Actually, most bacterial names do make sense, but a little search is sometimes required to ascertain their derivation. The effort is rewarding because names are more easily remembered if their associations are known. Scientific names of bacteria usually indicate something distinctive about the organism such as its discoverer (*Escherichia,* by Escherich), its source or habitat (*coli,* the colon), morphology (*Spirillum,* spiral), pigmentation (*aureus,* golden), physiologic peculiarity (*aerogenes,* gas producing), pathogenicity (*typhosa,* typhoid fever), or cultural character (*mesentericus,* mesentery or membrane). Derivations are given in *Bergey's Manual.* Names should not be memorized by rote but should be understood and associated with other facts about the organism.

IDENTIFICATION OF BACTERIA

Identification of an organism is the process of determining its species. As many as possible of its characteristics are ascertained by appropriate observa-

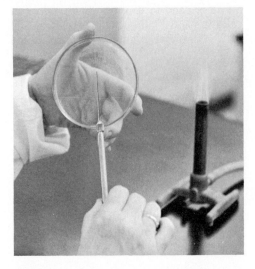

Figure 5-3. Streaking an agar plate. The inoculum on a straight wire needle is streaked rapidly and lightly back and forth across the medium, starting at the top as the plate is held in the position indicated. When the middle is reached, the plate is rotated 180° and streaking started again at the top. See the diagram in Fig. 5-4(a).

tions and tests, and the accumulated information is then compared with published descriptions of the various species. The organism is properly identified when a species description is found that is identical with the observed characteristics.

Isolation of Pure Cultures

Accurate identification of most bacteria can be made only with pure cultures because many characteristics used in classification depend upon the behavior of populations rather than individual cells. It is true that some bacterial properties change when the organisms are taken from the natural state and cultivated in the laboratory. However, classification schemes are ordinarily based on the properties of bacteria in laboratory cultures, so the net result is usually satisfactory.

Isolation of a pure culture is accomplished by securing the progeny of a single cell (or sometimes a group of identical cells, such as a streptococcus

chain). Various techniques are employed: single cell isolation by means of a mechanical micromanipulator, selective enrichment of the desired organism or inhibition of all undesired organisms, or "plating."

"Streak" or "Spread" Plates. Plating is the most widely used method for purifying cultures. "Streak" plates (Fig. 5-3) are prepared by streaking a small amount of the mixed bacterial specimen over the surface of a solid medium in a Petri dish with a platinum or a nichrome wire needle (Fig. 5-4). Each laboratory has its own favorite streaking procedure. It is essential to cover the agar thoroughly with the material so that the bacteria are well distributed (Fig. 5-5). The inoculum may also be spread with a sterilized, bent glass rod.

"Poured" Plates. "Poured" plates (Fig. 5-6), are prepared by diluting the bacterial mixture serially in tubes of

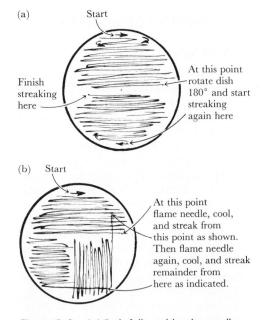

Figure 5-4. (a) Path followed by the needle on a well streaked agar plate. Fifty to 100 streaks should be made to ensure properly isolated colonies as illustrated in Fig. 5-5. This method works well with broth enrichment cultures or liquid suspensions. (b) An alternate method of streaking, particularly adapted to isolation of pure cultures from the mixed growth on solid media.

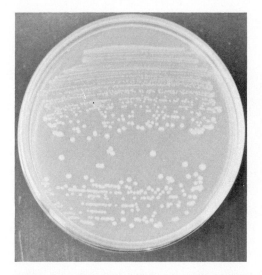

Figure 5-5. Petri dish streaked as in Fig. 5-4(a) showing well isolated colonies in the lower half.

melted and cooled (45° to 50° C.) agar medium which are then poured into sterile Petri dishes and allowed to solidify. Dilutions may be made with the inoculating loop or by pipette.

Poured plates contain subsurface (i.e., within the agar) as well as surface colonies. Subsurface colonies are

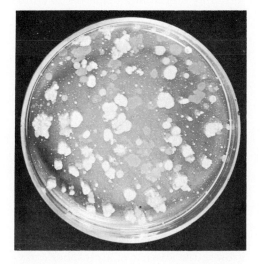

Figure 5-6. A "poured" plate with at least three different kinds of colonies: large, irregular; medium, smooth; pinpoint. Colonies were "picked" as illustrated in Fig. 5-7, and pure cultures were obtained on agar slants (Fig. 5-8).

smaller than surface colonies of the same species, and their shape is often different. Small, gram-negative rod bacteria, for example, form lens-shaped subsurface colonies, but their surface colonies are smooth, circular, and convex in cross section.

Colony Subculture. After incubation, some well separated colonies should appear on properly inoculated plates. Several such colonies are subcultured by transferring a small amount of each colony to broth or agar medium in test tubes (Figs. 5-7 and 5-8). It is assumed that each colony consists of the progeny of a single bacterium. This is not always true, because occasionally two bacteria stick to the agar so close together that their colonies merge. It is therefore desirable to replate a second or third time.

Special Isolation Methods. Special methods assist in the isolation of certain organisms. If it is desired to purify a spore-forming bacterium, for instance, a suspension containing spores mixed with vegetative cells of the same and other organisms may be heated to 85° C. for five minutes or treated with an appropriate disinfectant to kill all cells except the spores. Plating will then more readily yield a pure culture of the spore-former.

A method related to the foregoing consists of adding inhibitory or germicidal chemicals to culture media to suppress or kill unwanted types of bacteria while permitting the desired species to multiply. Basic dyes such as crystal violet and brilliant green inhibit gram-positive bacteria and aid in the isolation of gram-negative rod bacteria from mixed specimens (e.g., sewage).

Enrichment Cultures. The principle of selective enrichment has already been discussed (page 31). Applications of this method are limited chiefly by the ingenuity of the investigator. Lactose-fermenting bacteria, for example, are selectively enriched or stimulated in a medium containing this sugar, and even though they may occur as a minority in a mixed population (as in drinking

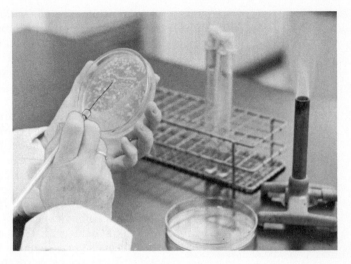

Figure 5-7. Picking or "fishing" a colony from a Petri dish culture. The plate is held so that the colony can be seen clearly, either by transmitted or by reflected light as circumstances dictate. The inoculating needle is held in such a manner as to give good control, and a small bit of the desired colony is removed.

water), within 24 to 48 hours they will predominate in a suitable lactose broth and can then easily be isolated.

Serial Dilution. An organism that predominates in a mixture can often be purified by dilution. Inasmuch as a single viable cell is sufficient to initiate growth in an appropriate medium, if the mixture is suitably diluted and aliquots of the dilution are subcultured the laws of probability dictate that some of the subcultures will consist of the desired organism in pure form.

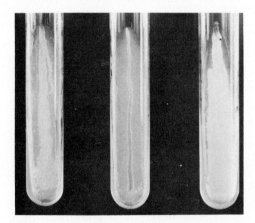

Figure 5-8. Growth of pure cultures obtained by inoculating agar slants with the three kinds of colonies shown in Fig. 5-6.

Single Cell Isolation. Single cells can be isolated with a micromanipulator, by which very fine glass pipettes can be manipulated mechanically in the field of the microscope. Droplets containing individual bacterial cells are deposited on a coverglass in a special chamber. The droplets are then transferred by sterile micropipettes to suitable nutrient media.

Growth Requirements

Conditions necessary to cultivate the organism must be determined, both for use in subsequent tests and because these conditions are frequently distinctive. Temperature requirements are ascertained by incubating cultures at a variety of temperatures. Various synthetic and nonsynthetic media are used to determine the nutrient requirements of the organism: whether it requires blood or serum, certain amino acids, or other growth factors. The ability to grow in the absence of atmospheric oxygen is of interest. A simple way to determine this is to inoculate uniformly a deep tube of melted and cooled agar medium, allow the medium to solidify, and then incubate it. Growth at the surface indicates an aerobic organism, growth in the depths of the medium indicates an anaerobe, and growth throughout is obtained with a facultatively anaerobic organism, that is, an aerobe that can grow anaerobically (Fig. 5-9).

Some bacteria grow in a layer a few millimeters below the surface; these have usually been called *microaerophiles,* because they were presumed to be inhibited by oxygen at normal atmospheric tension but not at reduced tension. This may be true in the case of a few bacteria that possess a vital enzyme that is partially sensitive to oxygen. Other organisms appear rather to be stimulated by carbon dioxide in greater than normal atmospheric concentration —a condition that might obtain within the agar after some metabolic activity has occurred.

Morphology

The shape and arrangement of the cells are determined by microscopic examination of wet mounts or hanging drop preparations and stained smears. Examination of the living organisms also reveals motility and gives presumptive evidence of the presence of flagella; nonmotile bacteria frequently display brownian movement, a vibratory motion caused by molecular activity in the fluid. The Gram stain indicates not only the shape and arrangement of the cells but also their Gram reaction; this is useful information. The acidfast stain, spore stain, capsule stain, and flagella stain are also frequently necessary and provide additional data.

It is important to remember that the morphology of a bacterium varies with the conditions under which it is cultivated. The age of the culture is also significant.

Cultural Characteristics

The gross appearance of bacterial cultures in various media frequently provides clues to the identity of the organism and should always be noted. Descriptions of colonies on agar plates should include size, shape, color, appearance by reflected and by transmitted light, and appearance when examined with the low power (100X) of the microscope (Fig. 5-10). Similar information can also be secured from agar slant cultures. Growth in broth may consist of uniform turbidity or cloudiness, a sediment at the bottom of

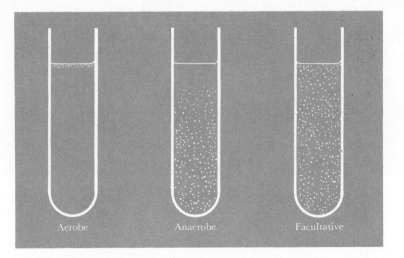

Aerobe   Anaerobe   Facultative

Figure 5-9. Growth of aerobic, anaerobic, and facultative bacteria in agar "shake" cultures. Deep tubes of a melted and cooled nutrient agar are inoculated, mixed, and allowed to harden. Colony growth occurs as indicated, according to the oxygen requirements of the organism.

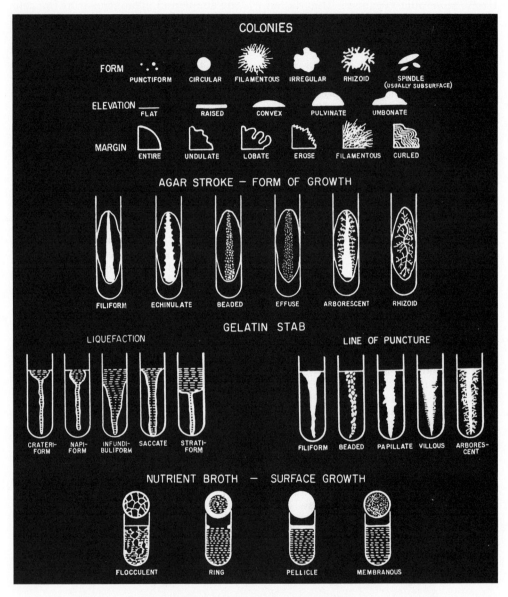

Figure 5-10. Cultural characteristics of bacteria.

Table 5-1.   Some Acid-Base Indicators Commonly Used in Microbiology

Indicator	pH Range	Acid Color	Basic Color
Bromcresol green	3.8– 5.4	Yellow	Blue
Methyl red	4.2– 6.3	Red	Yellow
Bromcresol purple	5.4– 7.0	Yellow	Purple
Litmus	4.5– 8.3	Red	Blue
Bromthymol blue	6.1– 7.7	Yellow	Blue
Phenol red	6.9– 8.5	Yellow	Red
Phenolphthalein	8.3–10.0	Colorless	Red

the culture, or a membrane or pellicle on the surface. These growth characteristics are frequently typical of certain species, although, as in the case of morphology, temporary variations sometimes occur under different cultural conditions.

Biochemical Characteristics

The general category of biochemical characteristics includes a variety of physiological properties.

Carbohydrate Dissimilation.   The ability of an organism to attack and break down various carbohydrates can be determined by the use of a suitable nutrient medium containing the carbohydrate and an acid-base indicator, such as bromcresol purple (see Table 5-1). A liquid medium is usually dispensed in Durham tubes which contain inverted vials to collect some of the gas that may be produced (Fig. 5-11). The formation of acid or of acid and gas is an indication that the carbohydrate is attacked. Chemical analysis of the acids, gases, and other products is not attempted in routine identification.

The metabolic processes by which the various products are formed in a Durham tube are largely anaerobic because the free oxygen is soon exhausted, especially within the inverted vial. Acid and gas formation under these conditions is called *fermentation*. Some bacteria dissimilate carbohydrates only aerobically. Special methods are required to demonstrate such oxidative formation of acid. Oxidative and fer-

mentative production of acid may often be distinguished in a carbohydrate medium made semisolid by the addition of 0.3 per cent agar. Two test tubes of medium are inoculated by stabbing, and the medium in one tube is covered with sterile petrolatum to exclude oxygen. Fermentative organisms produce acid throughout the medium in both tubes, whereas oxidative organisms produce acid in the unsealed tube only, first at the surface and then progressively toward the bottom.

Hydrolytic digestion of starch is demonstrated by the use of an agar medium containing 1 per cent starch. A Petri dish of starch agar is inoculated in a single spot, and after a large colony is formed the medium is flooded with iodine solution, which stains unhydro-

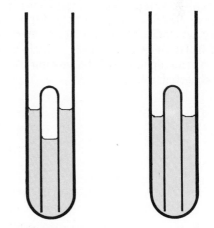

Figure 5-11.   Durham fermentation tubes. *Left,* With gas; *right,* without gas. (How are the inner vials filled with liquid?)

lyzed starch an intense blue-black. Colonies of bacteria that attack starch are surrounded by a colorless zone.

The digestion of cellulose can be demonstrated in a liquid medium to which strips of filter paper have been added before sterilization. Aerobic cellulolytic organisms visibly decompose the paper at the surface of the liquid, anaerobes at the bottom. Digestion by mesophilic organisms usually requires several weeks, whereas thermophilic decomposition is evident within a few days.

Proteolysis Tests. The ability of an organism to attack proteins can be determined in several ways. Blood serum coagulated in a slanting position in test tubes is digested and liquefied by certain proteolytic bacteria. Deep tubes of nutrient gelatin, which consists of nutrient broth solidified by addition of 10 per cent gelatin, are inoculated by stabbing with a straight wire needle. If these are incubated at 20° C., the undigested gelatin remains solid, and the zones of liquefaction are of characteristic shape (Fig. 5–10). Gelatin may also be incubated at a higher temperature and cooled just before making observations; gelatin that has been digested will no longer solidify below 20° C.

Hydrolysis of gelatin is also demonstrable on Petri dish cultures of Frazier gelatin-agar inoculated in the same manner as starch agar (page 111). After colony development, the medium is flooded with HCl-HgCl$_2$ solution, which produces an opaque, white precipitate of undigested gelatin.

Hydrogen Sulfide and Indole Production. A further indication of attack on protein breakdown products is provided by tests for hydrogen sulfide and indole.

Some organisms can produce H$_2$S by reduction of sulfur-containing amino acids such as cysteine. It is usually detected by adding a lead or iron salt to a medium containing protein or peptone and agar. Stab cultures are incubated, and the formation of black metallic sulfide along the line of inoculation indicates production of H$_2$S.

The ability of an organism to produce indole from tryptophan (Fig. 5-12) can be tested in almost any medium containing sufficient tryptophan. Nutrient broth is satisfactory, but tryptone or trypticase broth is generally used because it contains more tryptophan. Indole is detected after incubation by adding a solution containing p-dimethyl aminobenzaldehyde. Kovacs' solution contains this reagent together with amyl alcohol, which extracts the indole and brings it to the surface in a thin layer, where a red color appears.

Nitrate Reduction. Many bacteria utilize nitrates as hydrogen acceptors and reduce them to nitrites, free nitrogen, or ammonia. Nitrate reduction tests are usually performed in a liquid medium containing a small amount of peptone and sodium or potassium nitrate. Nitrite is detected by adding sulfanilic acid and α-naphthylamine; a pink to dark red color is the positive test. Nitrogen gas is collected in an inverted vial as in fermentation tests.

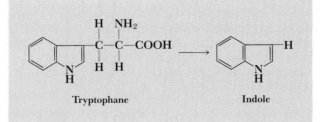

Figure 5-12. Production of indole from tryptophan by removal of the sidechain.

Ammonia can be detected by adding Nessler's reagent to a few drops of the culture in a spot plate; a yellow to orange color is produced.

Fermentation and Proteolysis of Milk. Milk cultures of certain bacteria provide much useful information. Dairy bacteriologists can often identify the organisms with which they are concerned almost entirely on the basis of their morphology and their behavior in milk.

Sterile skim milk containing an indicator such as litmus is a complete medium in which many species grow luxuriantly and in which a variety of physiologic characteristics can be determined. Milk contains lactose, casein and other proteins, and various minerals. Fermentation of the lactose produces an acid reaction; some organisms produce enough acid to curdle (solidify) the milk proteins. If the organism also produces gas, bubbles collect as foam at the top, or break or score the curd as they rise.

Digestion of the casein and other proteins produces a dirty brownish color, and the milk becomes watery; this appearance starts at the top, particularly with an aerobic organism, and gradually progresses downward until the entire contents of the tube are digested. The reaction often becomes alkaline as ammonia is liberated during proteolysis. Protein digestion is known as *peptonization.*

Decolorization or *reduction* of the indicator is characteristic of the behavior of certain bacteria in litmus milk. Litmus shares with some other dyes the property of behaving as an oxidation-reduction indicator as well as an acid-base indicator; that is, it accepts hydrogen from appropriate enzyme systems and is converted into a colorless form known as a leuko-dye. Bacteria that multiply and metabolize rapidly decolorize litmus vigorously; other bacteria decolorize it more slowly or not at all.

Rapid Biochemical Tests. It will be noted that the various biochemical tests described are simple and are quickly and easily performed after the required period of incubation. Simplicity and speed are virtues if combined with reliability because the investigator does not hesitate to use such tests freely.

The process of identifying bacteria can be shortened or simplified by various rapid tests currently under study. One procedure makes use of small amounts of concentrated medium inoculated with large numbers of bacteria; short incubation times are sufficient. Another procedure uses disks of filter paper impregnated with test substances such as carbohydrates. A nutrient agar containing an appropriate indicator is inoculated by streaking with the test organism, and the disks are placed upon the agar surface. The carbohydrates diffuse from the paper, and if acid is produced from a given carbohydrate the corresponding disk will be surrounded by a zone displaying the acid color of the indicator.

Biochemical Tests, Enzymes, and Genes. It is well to reemphasize that every physiologic test depends on one or more enzymes produced by the bacterium and that these enzymes are under genetic control. Bacterial genetics has not advanced to a point where all genes can be specifically located along chromosomes, but for practical purposes that information is not necessary. The important point is that physiologic studies, like other tests used to characterize bacteria, are fundamentally genetic studies.

Serologic Properties

Bacterial cells contain numerous antigenic substances, that is, substances that stimulate animals to produce antibodies capable of reacting specifically with the antigens. Antibodies are found in the sera of the inoculated animals; the sera therefore can be used as reagents to detect the corresponding antigens.

The agglutination test is most frequently used in identifying bacterial antigens. This test is not difficult and is performed routinely in diagnostic laboratories. A saline (e.g., 0.85 per cent NaCl) suspension of the bacteria is mixed with the test antisera; after appropriate incubation, the bacteria that contain antigens corresponding to the antibodies in the antiserum clump together in compact granules or in loose flocculent masses. A suitable set of test antisera provides a means of identifying species within a genus. Usually it is necessary to determine the genus on the basis of morphology and other characteristics. Antisera are available commercially for a few genera; laboratories conducting research in other genera prepare their own sera.

Pathogenicity

The value of pathogenicity in bacterial identification is limited because suitable means for testing are not always available, and because some organisms lose their pathogenicity after prolonged laboratory cultivation. It is used as a guide, however, in diagnostic medical bacteriology; for example, specimens from a patient suspected of having typhoid fever are examined for the presence of *Salmonella typhosa*. Pathogenicity can sometimes be tested in the laboratory by the inoculation of ani-

mals. Certain organisms are accurately identified only in this manner. The most conclusive test for *Corynebacterium diphtheriae* is the production of typical symptoms and death in a guinea pig, especially if the same symptoms are prevented in a second guinea pig by simultaneous administration of diphtheria antitoxin.

Identification by Means of a Key

Armed with as complete a description of the unknown organism as possible, the student or investigator identifying an unknown organism will search through a suitable key for an organism with the same characteristics. Most keys are so constructed as to present a series of dichotomies, and it is relatively simple to follow the path through the contrasting characteristics and ultimately arrive at the scientific name of the organism. Figure 5-13 is a diagram of such a key, and its use should be obvious. The keys in *Bergey's Manual* are similar, but alternate choices are indicated by single and double letters (A vs. AA, B vs. BB, etc.).

The keys in *Bergey's Manual* are intended for determinative use. They therefore emphasize diagnostic utility

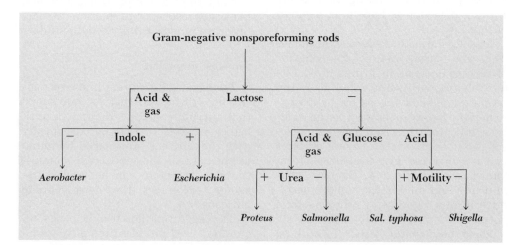

Figure 5-13. Diagram of a dichotomous key to some members of the Enterobacteriaceae.

and do not necessarily reflect phylogenetic relationships. Problems of identification can be solved by means of any readily determined characteristics. As new diagnostic tests are developed or old tests are modified or applied to different groups of organisms, and as more species are discovered, determinative keys are altered. These keys are tentative, in contrast to phylogenetic keys, which are based on the evolution of existing species from a common ancestor. As there is little likelihood that either the common ancestor or the intermediate stages in the evolution of most modern bacteria will ever be known, schemes for the identification of bacteria will probably always be subject to change according to diagnostic needs.

Occasionally, unknown organisms are encountered that cannot be identified by the keys. There are various reasons why this is so. Many bacteria have not yet been described in sufficient detail to justify their inclusion in a manual; other organisms have not been considered of sufficient importance. Keys constructed on the basis of the average or most common behavior of organisms do not take into account all the normal variations that occur. Finally, and perhaps most important, particularly for beginning investigators, the description of the unknown is sometimes at fault; a mistaken observation leads one down an erroneous path that may in fact come to a dead end. In such a case, unresolvable contradictions are encountered. Careful technique and a little practice in the use of keys are usually rewarded by increasing success and facility in the identification of unknown bacteria.

THE SYSTEMATIC STUDY OF BACTERIA

SUMMARY

Bacteria are classified according to an artificial system because their phylogenetic relationships are not known. The basis of classification is the type culture, a specimen deposited in a designated collection to serve as a continuing example of the characteristics that define a given species. Identification of an unknown organism consists of determining enough of its morphologic, physiologic, and other characteristics to demonstrate its identity with one or another type culture. The opinion of an expert is sometimes necessary to ascertain whether two organisms are sufficiently alike to be included in the same species or whether their differences are great enough to justify establishing a new species for one of them.

STUDY QUESTIONS

1. Why is it necessary to use an artificial rather than a natural system in classifying bacteria?
2. What does the word *species* mean with reference to plants and animals? Bacteria?
3. What is a *type culture*?
4. Contrast *classification* and *identification*.
5. Is it necessary to have a pure culture of a bacterium in order to identify it? Explain.

6. Are all microbial characteristics equally important in identification and classification? Explain.
7. Discuss the effect of normal variation of bacteria on the problem of identifying an unknown specimen.

SUPPLEMENTARY READING

Recommended methods that can be used to determine the characteristics of bacteria are described in detail in a volume published by the Committee on Bacteriological Technique of the Society of American Bacteriologists, the *Manual of Microbiological Methods,* which describes procedures for staining, preparation of media, maintenance of cultures, routine tests for identification of bacteria, serologic and pathogenicity studies, and virology. *Bergey's Manual of Determinative Bacteriology,* currently in its seventh edition, is the best available classification scheme for the bacteria. In addition to the keys to the various groups of bacteria, there is a valuable introductory chapter which describes how bacteria are named and identified. This chapter should be read by all serious students of bacteriology. *Taxonomic Biochemistry and Serology* is a collection of 47 papers presented at an international conference at the University of Kansas in 1962. There are sections on the principles of systematics, molecular taxonomy of bacteria, and the taxonomic biochemistry and serology of plants and animals. Skerman's book presents a detailed key to the bacteria, based upon *Bergey's Manual,* but in more workable form; it includes a complete list of techniques needed for identification of bacteria. The *Microbial Classification* symposium includes a score of papers on the background of and current approaches to the classification of algae, fungi, protozoa, bacteria, and viruses.

Ainsworth, G. C., and Sneath, P. H. A. (eds.): *Microbial Classification.* Twelfth Symposium of the Society for General Microbiology. New York, Cambridge University Press, 1962.
Breed, R. S., Murray, E. G. D., and Smith, N. R., (eds.): *Bergey's Manual of Determinative Bacteriology,* 7th ed. Baltimore, The Williams & Wilkins Co., 1957.
Leone, C. A. (ed.): *Taxonomic Biochemistry and Serology.* New York, The Ronald Press Co., 1964.
Skerman, V. B. D.: *A Guide to the Identification of the Genera of Bacteria.* Baltimore, The Williams & Wilkins Co., 1959.
Society of American Bacteriologists: *Manual of Microbiological Methods.* New York, McGraw-Hill Book Co., Inc., 1957.

MAJOR GROUPS OF BACTERIA

It was pointed out in Chapter 1 that some authorities prefer to classify bacteria and all other microorganisms in a separate kingdom, Protista. In this system bacteria and blue-green algae comprise the *lower protists* and the more fully developed algae, together with fungi and protozoa, are designated *higher protists*. But most systematists still recognize only two kingdoms, Plantae and Animalia, and place plantlike microorganisms (including bacteria, but not protozoa) in the first two divisions of the former, as shown in the following scheme:

DIVISION I. PROTOPHYTA. Primitive plants that are unicellular or occur in trichomes (chains or filaments of cells so closely associated with one another that they rarely live separately). They are generally too small to be distinguished by the naked eye. Little if any differentiation of cells is evident. Multiplication is usually by simple cell division (fission), but spores of various types may be produced by highly advanced forms.

CLASS I. SCHIZOPHYCEAE. Blue-green algae. They contain the photosynthetic pigment phycocyanin in addition to chlorophyll.

CLASS II. SCHIZOMYCETES. Bacteria. Cells reproduce by fission, are not normally filtrable, and usually do not contain photosynthetic pigments.

CLASS III. MICROTATOBIOTES. (Smallest living things.) Submicroscopic or barely microscopic forms that are obligately parasitic, that is, dependent upon other living organisms for growth and multiplication. There are two orders: Rickettsiales and Virales.

DIVISION II. THALLOPHYTA. Simple forms are unicellular; the plant body of higher forms is called a *thallus* and is not differentiated into roots, stems, and leaves.

SUBDIVISION I. ALGAE. Diatoms and the higher algae (green, red, brown, etc.). These organisms contain chlorophyll.

SUBDIVISION II. FUNGI. Yeasts, molds, mushrooms, etc.; organisms that do not contain chlorophyll.

CLASS I. MYXOMYCETES. The slime molds. Naked masses of protoplasm that occur on decaying vegetable matter and damp earth. They exhibit a slow, creeping motion.

CLASS II. PHYCOMYCETES. Alga-like fungi. The coenocytic plant body ranges from an undifferentiated protoplasmic mass to a highly branched filamentous structure. Vegetative filaments (concerned with securing food) are usually not divided by cross walls into definite cells. Multiplication is mainly by asexual spores, but sexual stages are also found.

CLASS III. ASCOMYCETES. The sac fungi. Unicellular fungi, the yeasts, and many groups of molds are included. Yeasts reproduce by budding, fission, asexual spore formation, and copulation. Some yeasts produce filamentous growths under certain conditions. Mold filaments are divided by cross walls into definite cells, and spores are produced in sacs (*asci*).

CLASS IV. BASIDIOMYCETES. The basidium fungi. Filaments are divided by cross walls into definite cells, and spores are borne on a stalklike structure (*basidium*). This class includes larger fungi: mushrooms, toadstools, puffballs, rusts, smuts, and bracket fungi.

CLASS V. FUNGI IMPERFECTI. Fungi for which a sexual reproductive stage has not been demonstrated. Organisms that cannot be placed in classes II, III, or IV are collected in this group; when a sexual stage is demonstrated, an organism is reassigned to its proper class.

SUBDIVISION III. LICHENS. Composite organisms consisting of a mold and an alga living together symbiotically.

DIVISION III. BRYOPHYTA. Liverworts and mosses. Green plants, somewhat differentiated into stems and leaves.

DIVISION IV. TRACHEOPHYTA. The vascular plants: club mosses, horsetails, ferns, coniferous and flowering seed plants. Roots, stems, and leaves are differentiated. This is the largest division in the plant kingdom.

SURVEY OF BACTERIAL GROUPS

The class Schizomycetes consists of small, unicellular plants that occur singly or in regular or irregular masses. The cells may be spherical, cylindrical, or spiral; they multiply typically by fission. They are distinguished from the Schizophyceae by their lack of phycocyanin. The ten orders and some of the families and genera included in this class will be described briefly. The groups discussed are of biological interest as causes of disease or because they produce desirable or undesirable changes in soil, water, food, and other materials.

Order I. Pseudomonadales

Some investigators believe that these are the most primitive bacteria still in existence. The cells are gram-negative and possess rigid walls, and most species are motile by means of polar flagella; a few are nonmotile. Coccoid forms, straight rods, and curved rods or spirals are found. One suborder comprises approximately 50 species containing a photosynthetic pigment, either bacteriochlorophyll or chlorobium chlorophyll; the former may also be accompanied by yellow and red carotenoid pigments with the result that the photosynthetic bacteria appear red, brown, purple, or green. The other suborder contains nearly 400 species. The Pseudomonadales are divided into 10 families with 72 genera. They are found principally in soil and water.

The photosynthetic bacteria are grouped in the first three families, Thiorhodaceae (red and purple sulfur bacteria), Athiorhodaceae (red, purple, and brown non-sulfur bacteria), and Chlorobacteriaceae (green sulfur bacteria).

The Thiorhodaceae are morphologically heterogeneous, including cocci and spindle-shaped, rod-shaped, spiral, and filamentous forms (Figs. 6-1 and 6-2). Their red or purple color is attributed to various combinations of the green bac-

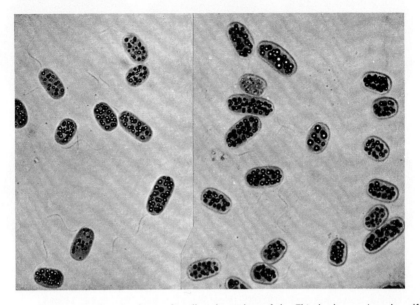

Figure 6-1. *Chromatium okenii,* a large, flagellated member of the Thiorhodaceae (purple sulfur bacteria) containing many sulfur granules (960X). (From Schlegel and Pfennig, Arch. Mikrobiol. *38:*4, 1961.)

teriochlorophyll and the red and yellow carotenoids. They develop only under anaerobic conditions in the presence of suitable hydrogen donors (i.e., substances readily oxidized by loss of hydrogen) such as H_2S or the lower fatty acids. When H_2S is oxidized, elemental sulfur is deposited within the cells. Light is, of course, necessary.

The Athiorhodaceae are spherical, rod-shaped, or spiral and contain bacteriochlorophyll and carotenoid pigments (Fig. 6-3). They grow anaerobically in the presence of suitable

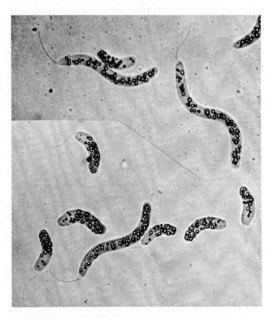

Figure 6-2. *Thiospirillum jenense,* a spiral member of the Thiorhodaceae. Numerous granules of sulfur are within the cells (960X). (From Schlegel and Pfennig, Arch. Mikrobiol. *38:*5, 1961.)

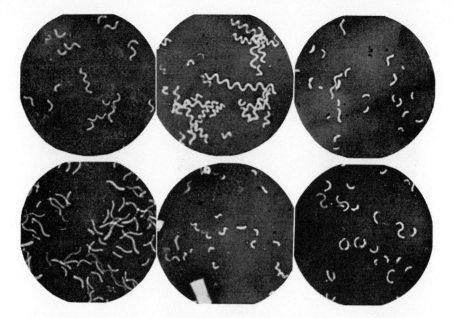

Figure 6-3. *Rhodospirillum rubrum,* a species of the Athiorhodaceae (purple non-sulfur bacteria), 7 day anaerobic cultures on various media (800X). (From van Niel, Bact. Rev. 8:24, 1944.)

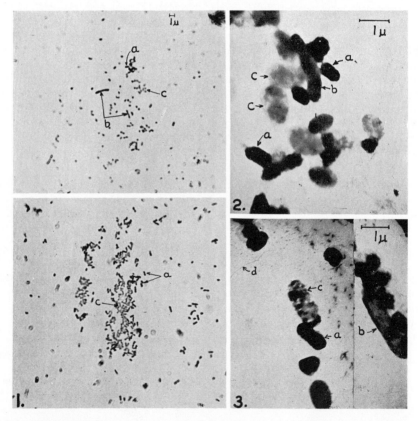

Figure 6-4. *Thiobacillus thiooxidans,* (1) stained, light microscopy, 1800X; (2, 3) unstained, electron microscopy, 12,000X. a, b, c, and d indicate cells of different size, staining, and electron opacity. (From Umbreit and Anderson, J. Bact. 44:318, 1942.)

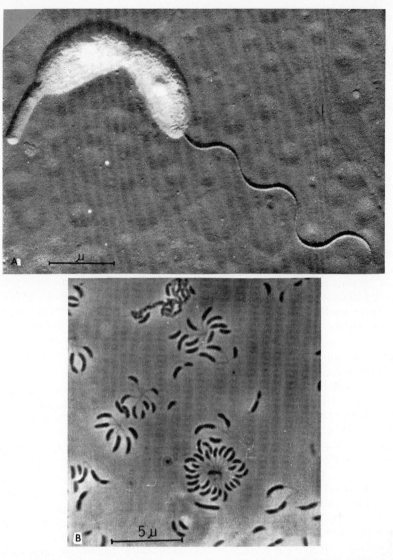

Figure 6-5. Stalked bacteria of the genus *Caulobacter*. *A,* Electron photomicrograph of a dividing cell, with flagellum at one pole and stalk at the other. *B,* Phase contrast photomicrograph showing rosettes formed when stalks of several cells adhere to each other's holdfasts. (From Poindexter, Bact. Rev. 28:231, 1964.)

hydrogen donors when exposed to light, but they do not oxidize H_2S and hence do not produce granules of sulfur. Some species can grow aerobically in the dark.

The Chlorobacteriaceae are spherical or rod-shaped organisms containing chlorobium chlorophyll, which differs from bacteriochlorophyll and plant chlorophyll, and a yellow carotenoid pigment. The green photosynthetic pigment is not masked by the yellow carotenoid, so the cells appear green. Under anaerobic conditions and when exposed to light they oxidize sulfide to sulfur, which is deposited outside the cells of almost all species.

Two families of the Pseudomonadales are obligately or facultatively autotrophic, that is, they may secure carbon from CO_2 and all other nutrients from inorganic sources. They are nonphotosynthetic, but derive energy from the oxidation of simple forms of nitrogen or sulfur. The Nitrobacteraceae, for example, secure energy by oxidation of ammonia or nitrite. These organisms are morphologically heterogeneous, including rods, cocci, and spirals. Those of *Nitrosomonas* and four other genera secure energy by oxidation of ammonia to nitrite, and *Nitrobacter* and *Nitrocystis* secure energy by the oxidation of nitrite to nitrate. The Thiobacteriaceae include five genera, predominantly rod-shaped but including coccoid and curved members, which derive energy from the oxidation of H_2S, sulfur, thiosulfates, or other sulfur compounds. They are known as the colorless sulfur bacteria. Some species produce elemental sulfur and some produce sulfate. *Thiobacillus thiooxidans*, for example, forms sulfuric acid and can tolerate a reaction as acid as pH 0 (Fig. 6-4).

The Pseudomonadaceae are a large family of small to medium sized nonspore-forming rods, generally motile by a single polar flagellum, highly aerobic, and capable of utilizing organic nutrients. The 12 genera are widely distributed in soil and water; many species are pathogenic for plants and some for animals. The genus *Pseudomonas* includes nearly 150 species; many are characterized by the production of water-soluble pigments, principally blue-green, that diffuse into the culture medium. *Pseudomonas aeruginosa* is an animal pathogen, found frequently in wound infections and other infections of man. The genus *Acetobacter* consists of bacteria that oxidize ethyl alcohol to acetic acid and are therefore used in the manufacture of vinegar. In laboratory cultures they are usually found to be small, gram-negative rods, but in mother of vinegar bizarre pleomorphic forms are produced.

The Caulobacteraceae are rod-shaped and normally attached to a solid substrate by a fine stalk. In the genus *Caulobacter*, the axis of the rod is the same as that of the stalk (Fig. 6-5), whereas in *Gallionella* the curved or kidney-shaped rod is at a right angle to the stalk (Fig. 6-6). The stalks of the latter genus are impregnated with ferric hydroxide,

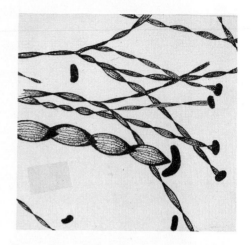

Figure 6-6. Gallionella; line drawing from a photomicrograph by Cholodny (1950X). Curved rods attach to the substrate by means of twisted stalks, which may be impregnated with iron. (From Dorff: *Die Eisenorganismen, Pflanzenforschung,* 1934. Courtesy of Gustav Fischer, Stuttgart, 1950.)

and for this reason the organisms are referred to as *iron bacteria.*

The Spirillaceae are bent or spiral rods, physiologically diverse, and include aerobic, anaerobic, and facultative species. *Desulfovibrio* reduces sulfates to H_2S, *Cellvibrio* attacks cellulose, and *Methanobacterium* reduces CO_2 to CH_4. Members of the genus *Vibrio* are typically comma-shaped, and include the organism that causes Asiatic cholera (Fig. 6-7). *Spirillum* species are corkscrew-shaped and mainly saprophytic.

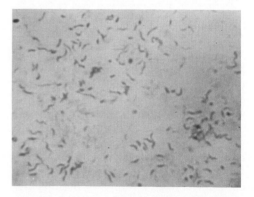

Figure 6-7. *Vibrio cholerae.* Both comma-shaped and spiral forms are shown (1000X). (Courtesy of G. L. Brown.)

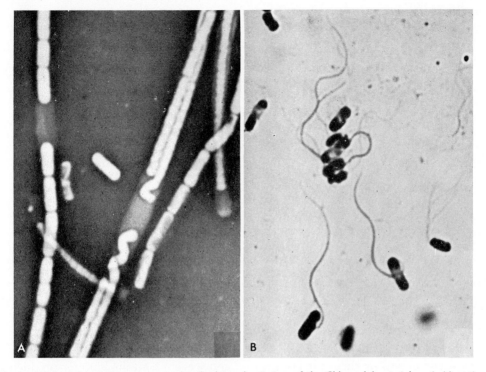

Figure 6-8. *Sphaerotilus natans,* a sheathed iron bacterium of the Chlamydobacteriales. *A,* Negative stain with nigrosin showing two strands of cells within a single sheath (2500X); *B,* tannic acid-fuchsin stain to show flagellated swarm cells that have emerged from their sheath (2700X). (From Stokes, J. Bact. 67:278, 1954.)

Order II. Chlamydobacteriales

Members of the Chlamydobacteriales characteristically occur in trichomes or filaments, which may be as long as 1 cm. and are often enclosed in a sheath of organic matter. In some species the sheath is encrusted with iron or manganese oxide, and these organisms are called *iron* or *manganese bacteria,* respectively (Fig. 6-8). False branching of the trichomes may occur because of displacement of the cells within the sheath. Reproduction is by transverse fission and, in some species, by the release of motile *swarm cells* or conidia from the trichome. The principal habitat of Chlamydobacteriales is fresh water.

Order III. Hyphomicrobiales

Bacteria of this order reproduce by budding, and some species also repro-duce by *longitudinal* fission. The cells, which are ovoid, pear-shaped, cylindrical, or spherical, are connected to neighboring cells by slender filaments (Fig. 6-9). Aggregates of several hundred cells may form and attach themselves to a surface or remain freely floating. They are widely distributed in soil and in the water and mud of fresh water ponds and streams.

Order IV. Eubacteriales

The Eubacteriales or "true bacteria" are a large order that includes many bacteria of direct concern to man. They are rods or cocci, gram-positive or gram-negative, and both motile and nonmotile forms are included. Flagellation of motile species is generally peritrichous. Reproduction is by transverse fission; among the cocci successive divisions

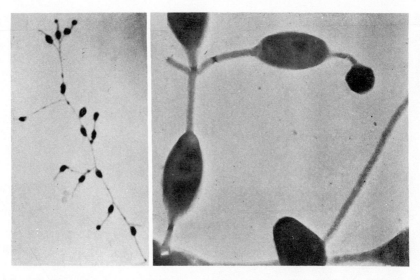

Figure 6-9. *Rhodomicrobium vannielii,* a member of the Hyphomicrobiales. *Left,* 1800X; *right,* electron photomicrograph, 10,000X. The cells are approximately 1.2 x 2.8 μ, and are connected by filaments 0.3 μ in diameter. A bud forms at the end of the filament, and this eventually becomes a new bacterial cell. (From Duchow et al., J. Bact. *58*:411, 1949.)

may occur in two or three planes, producing regular packets. Saprophytes, parasites, and pathogens of plants and animals are found among the members of this order, which are widely distributed in soil, fresh and salt water, the air, and on or in plants and animals. There are 13 families with 63 genera.

The family Azotobacteraceae consists of large, gram-negative rod or coccoid organisms that fix (i.e., utilize) atmospheric nitrogen (Fig. 6-10). They are aerobic, free-living soil bacteria and contribute in an important way to soil fertility.

The Rhizobiaceae are aerobic gram-negative rods, found in soil and often on plants. Species of the genus *Rhizobium* grow in a symbiotic relation with legumes. They invade the roots and produce nodules within which the bacteria multiply, utilizing atmospheric nitrogen from the soil and energy derived by oxidation of plant substances. Nitrogenous constituents of the bacteria ultimately become available to the plant, and its growth is greatly enhanced. The rhizobia are often called *symbiotic nitrogen-fixing* bacteria. Other genera of the Rhi-

zobiaceae contain tumor-producing plant pathogens and free-living soil and water organisms; some produce a characteristic violet pigment.

Most of the 10 genera of the Enterobacteriaceae are found in the human or animal intestine; a few are found primarily on plants. They are all gram-negative rods, and many species are motile. In general, they reduce nitrates to nitrites and attack (i.e., ferment) glu-

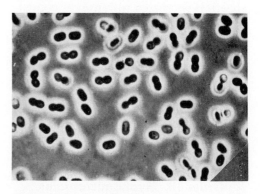

Figure 6-10. *Azotobacter vinelandii* showing typical paired coccoid cells; phase contrast (1000X). (From Jensen, Bact. Rev. *18*:214, 1954.)

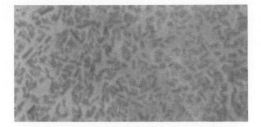

Figure 6-11. *Salmonella typhosa* showing variation from coccoid to long rods. This morphology is typical of gram-negative rod bacteria of the Enterobacteriaceae (1000X). (Courtesy of G. L. Brown.)

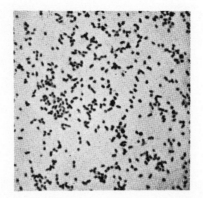

Figure 6-12. *Bordetella pertussis,* the whooping cough organism, showing minute, coccobacillary cells typical of the parvobacteria. (From D. T. Smith et al.: *Zinsser Microbiology,* 13th ed. New York, Appleton-Century-Crofts, 1964.)

cose anaerobically, producing acid and often gas ($CO_2 + H_2$). Many species also ferment other carbohydrates. *Escherichia coli* is usually prominent in the human intestine. *Salmonella* species (Fig. 6-11) produce typhoid fever, enteric fevers, and gastroenteritis, and *Shigella* species are the cause of bacillary dysentery.

The family Brucellaceae is composed principally of small, gram-negative coccobacillary (i.e., coccoid or short rod), parasitic organisms that require enriched media for laboratory cultivation. A number of species are pathogenic for man or for other warm-blooded animals. *Pasteurella* species cause hemorrhagic septicemia of domestic and other animals, bubonic plague, and tularemia. *Bordetella pertussis* is the cause of whooping cough. *Brucella* species are found in undulant fever in man and contagious abortion of cattle and various other animals. *Hemophilus* species are present in infant meningitis and other diseases of man and animals (Fig. 6-12).

The Micrococcaceae are spherical, gram-positive or gram-variable organisms, arranged singly or in regular or irregular clusters. Many possess yellow, orange, pink, or red pigment, and aerobic, facultative, and anaerobic species are found. They occur as part of the natural flora of the skin of vertebrates and also in water, soil, and air. Species of the genus *Staphylococcus* (Fig. 6-13) are prominent inhabitants of the skin and upper respiratory mucous membranes of man; they may be highly pathogenic when they invade the underlying tissues.

The Neisseriaceae are gram-negative diplococci; the individual cells that comprise the pairs are shaped like coffee beans and their flattened sides oppose each other. All species are parasitic, and some are also pathogenic. *Neisseria gonorrheae* (Fig. 6-14) is the cause of gonorrhea, and *N. meningitidis* produces cerebrospinal meningitis; *N. catarrhalis* is

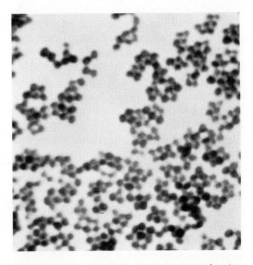

Figure 6-13. *Staphylococcus aureus* showing typical grapelike clusters (1000X). (Courtesy of G. L. Brown.)

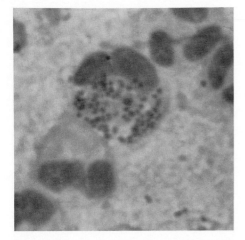

Figure 6-14.   *Neisseria gonorrheae* in a urethral smear from a patient with gonorrhea. The paired coffee bean–shaped cocci are situated principally within a pus cell (1000X). (Courtesy of G. L. Brown.)

frequently present in the normal nasopharynx, but may be associated with other organisms in upper respiratory infections.

The family Lactobacillaceae is composed of gram-positive rods and cocci that divide in a single plane, forming chains; they typically produce lactic acid as a by-product of sugar fermentation. Carbohydrates are necessary for good development, and many species require other enrichment. They are found in various infections, in the normal mouth and intestines of man and other animals, and in food and dairy products and fermenting vegetable matter. The principal species of the genus *Diplococcus* is *D. pneumoniae,* the major cause of lobar pneumonia. The genus *Streptococcus* contains species that digest red blood cells (hemolytic streptococci) and frequently produce serious disease; they can invade any part of the body. *Lactobacillus* species are common in the normal intestine and are active in fermenting dairy and plant products.

The Corynebacteriaceae are usually nonmotile rods, frequently club-shaped or otherwise irregular in form, and with deeply staining bands or beads known as metachromatic granules. They are generally gram-positive, but some species become gram-negative when they are older. The cells tend to divide by a snapping motion and fold like an accordion producing a parallel arrangement. Three genera consist of organisms that are primarily pathogenic for man or animals; the other three genera are saprophytic and live mainly on decomposing organic matter. The diphtheria organism is a member of the genus *Corynebacterium*.

Gram-positive spore-forming rods comprise the family Bacillaceae. The cells are generally large, sometimes arranged in long chains. In old cultures gram-negative cells are often found. There are two genera: *Bacillus* species are aerobic or facultative, *Clostridium* species are anaerobic. Most species are saprophytic soil organisms, a few are pathogenic for man or animals. Certain *Clostridium* species produce the most potent poisons known.

Order V. Actinomycetales

The Actinomycetales are more or less filamentous organisms that tend to produce a branching, mycelial type of growth. In the family Mycobacteriaceae the mycelium is rudimentary and spores are not formed. The other families display true branching and produce various kinds of spores (oidiospores, conidia, sporangiospores). The mycelium of Actinomyces later disintegrates into rods or cocci. Cells of the genus *Mycobacterium* are acidfast; both saprophytic and parasitic species occur, *Mycobacterium tuberculosis* being the best known of the latter. The Streptomycetaceae are principally soil organisms. Their vegetative mycelium does not break up into rod-shaped or coccoid forms, but reproductive conidia form in chains on special spore-bearing hyphae. Certain species are important sources of antibiotics (Fig. 6-15).

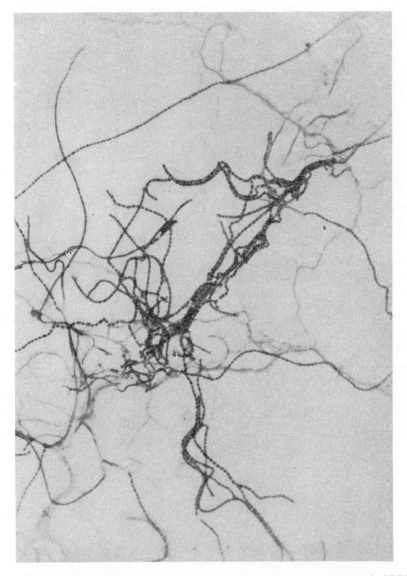

Figure 6-15. *Streptomyces venezuelae,* the organism that produces chloramphenicol (975X). Gram stain of branching mycelium and chains of oval spores. (Prepared by Littman, Armed Forces Institute of Pathology.)

Order VI. Caryophanales

The Caryophanales appear in the form of many-celled filaments or trichomes composed of cylindrical or discoid cells surrounded by a continuous wall rather than a sheath, as in the Chlamydobacteriales (Fig. 6-16). The individual cells contain a central ring-like nucleus, often in the form of a disc.

There are three families and six genera. They are found in soil, in the intestines of various animals, and in decomposing organic matter.

Order VII. Beggiatoales

Cells of the Beggiatoales also occur principally in trichomes (see Fig. 6-17).

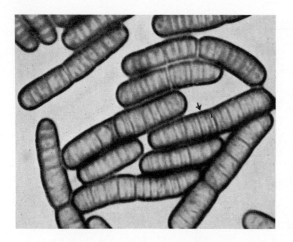

Figure 6-16.   *Caryophanon latum*, a large bacterium (2.5 to 3.2 μ x 10 to 30 μ) of unusual structural complexity; stained with tannic acid and crystal violet (2700X). Different stages in transverse fission are shown. Closely spaced surface striations are in focus in the cell indicated by the arrow, whereas unstained nuclear structures are in focus within other cells. (From Pringsheim et al., *J. Gen. Microbiol. 1:267,* 1947.)

The motile forms move by gliding over a solid surface or by a slow, rolling, jerky motion. They multiply by transverse fission of the individual cells in a trichome or of cells that occur singly. Sulfur globules form on or within the cells under favorable conditions. Species of *Beggiatoa* closely resemble the bluegreen algae of the genus *Oscillaria,* but do not produce a photosynthetic pigment. Beggiatoales are found in fresh water and marine habitats and in soil, where they can easily be mistaken for colorless members of the blue-green algae.

Order VIII. Myxobacterales

The Myxobacterales, unlike all the preceding groups of bacteria, are flexible organisms (Fig. 6-18). Their gliding motion over a solid substrate resembles that of the Beggiatoales. When inoculated upon a suitable medium, the rod-shaped cells divide transversely and a

Figure 6-17.   Filaments of *Beggiatoa*, which structurally resemble blue-green algae but are nonphotosynthetic. They obtain energy by oxidizing H$_2$S, and sulfur droplets accumulate within the filaments (1000X). (From Stanier et al.: *The Microbial World,* 2d ed. Englewood Cliffs, New Jersey, Prentice-Hall, Inc., 1963.)

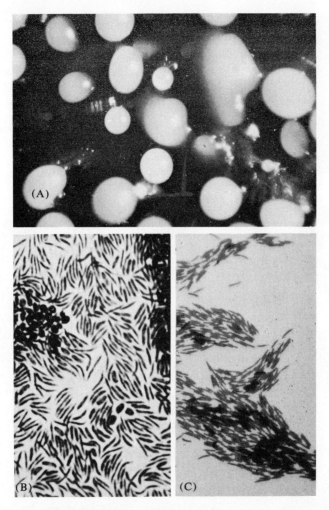

Figure 6-18. *Myxococcus,* a myxobacterium. (A) Fruiting bodies of the mature organism (30X), which is composed of spherical microcysts (see *B*) formed from long, thin, tapering rod-shaped vegetative cells (*B, C*) (1000X). (From Stanier et al.)

thin, rapidly spreading colony forms, supported by a layer of slime. Groups of several hundred actively motile cells at the edge of the colony produce tongue-like protrusions or separate islands. This appearance is typical of the order. Most members produce resting cells, which may consist of somewhat shortened vegetative cells or of thick-walled spherical or oval refractile bodies. The resting cells are generally borne in or on special structures, the fruiting bodies, which vary from a simple heap of resting cells to an elaborate aerial structure supported by a stalk. Fruiting bodies are often brightly colored and large enough to be seen by the naked eye. The Myxobacterales are found in soil, and grow especially well on dung. Some species are active in the decomposition of cellulose, chitin, and other insoluble organic materials.

Order IX. Spirochaetales

Cells of the Spirochaetales are also flexuous; they are slender spirals, and may be as long as 500 μ. All members of the order move by a rapid rotary motion,

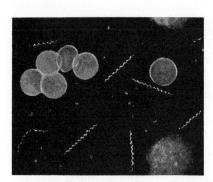

Figure 6-19. Darkfield preparation showing *Treponema pallidum* in serous exudate from a primary syphilitic chancre. Several red blood cells and parts of two leukocytes are also present (1000X). (From Gillies and Dodd: *Bacteriology Illustrated.* Baltimore, The Williams & Wilkins Co., 1965.)

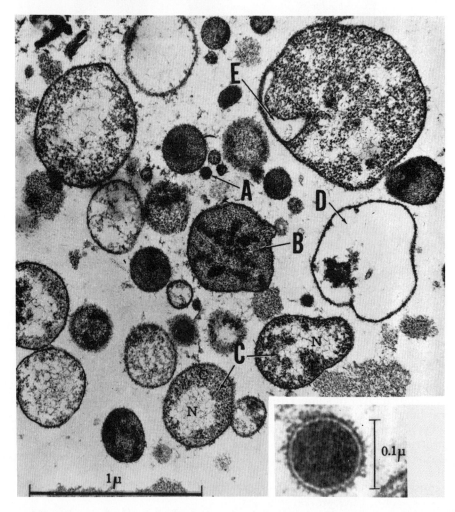

Figure 6-20. Electron photomicrograph of *Mycoplasma hominis,* a pleuropneumonia-like organism, grown in a broth of brain and heart infusion and horse serum and thin-sectioned to show internal structures. A variety of forms are apparent, ranging in size from about 0.1 μ (*A* and inset) to about 0.9 μ (*E*). Cell *B* has finely granular cytoplasm, cells *C* contain "nuclear" areas (*N*) with netlike strands and cytoplasm with ribosomelike granules, and *D* consists of an empty plasma membrane. (From Anderson et al., J. Bact. 90:181, 1965.)

which drives the cells forward or backward; they may also undergo violent bending movements. Some species have an axial filament or a lateral ridge or crista, and it has been suggested that these structures help in propelling the organism. The small spirochaetes, like *Treponema pallidum,* the cause of syphilis (Fig. 6-19), possess an index of refraction lower than that of other bacteria and are composed of a very fine protoplasmic thread about 0.25 μ in diameter. They can be seen under the microscope only by darkfield illumination or by special staining methods that increase the diameter of the cell. The family Treponemataceae includes a number of species pathogenic for man or lower animals. The Spirochaetaceae are very large organisms found principally in fresh or salt water.

Order X. Mycoplasmatales

The Mycoplasmatales are highly pleomorphic bacteria that lack a rigid cell wall and are hence highly plastic; they apparently reproduce by the breaking of more or less branching filaments into filterable, coccoid elementary bodies (Fig. 6-20). The soft cell bodies are very fragile and are frequently distorted or destroyed by the manipulations needed to prepare slides for microscope examination. The basic units or elementary bodies are 125 to 250 mμ in diameter, and the filaments from which they arise are 2 to 5 μ in length except in a very few species in which they are as long as 50 μ.

The Mycoplasmas grow on special serum-enriched agar media in the form of thin, flat colonies, rarely more than 0.5 mm. in diameter, and with a raised central portion, which gives the entire colony a "fried egg" appearance.

The first of these organisms to be studied were found in pleuropneumonia of cattle, and those that were later isolated, nearly all from human and animal sources, resembled them so closely that they were designated *pleuropneumonia-like organisms* (PPLO).

A hint of a possible relationship between bacteria of the pleuropneumonia group and true bacteria came from the discovery that many of the latter sometimes display filterable stages or "L forms" that closely resemble the PPLO in morphology and behavior. L forms appear naturally with a low frequency in certain Proteus and Salmonella cultures, but can be made to appear more frequently by cultivation of various bacteria in penicillin under conditions that protect the physical integrity of the cells, since the antibiotic interferes with normal cell wall formation. L forms sometimes revert to the normal true bacterial form when cultivated in medium free from penicillin. Mycoplasmas, however, have apparently not been made to assume a normal eubacterial morphology or structure by any cultivation method attempted, so the relationship between them and L forms is not clear.

RICKETTSIALES

According to present usage the Protophyta are divided into three classes of which the third, Microtatobiotes, consists of two orders, Rickettsiales and Virales. As stated earlier, both are parasitic and generally smaller than most organisms classified as bacteria. However, the Rickettsiales possess many characteristics found also in bacteria, and relatively few of their features, except small size and parasitic habit of life, are present in the Virales. The rickettsiae, for example, multiply by binary fission, contain *both* DNA and RNA, possess numerous enzymes, and are enclosed in rigid cell walls of a composition typical of bacteria. In these features they differ from viruses. There is a growing tendency to consider rickettsiae as bacteria, and they will therefore be discussed here.

Discovery

The first member of the rickettsiae was discovered in 1909 by Ricketts in

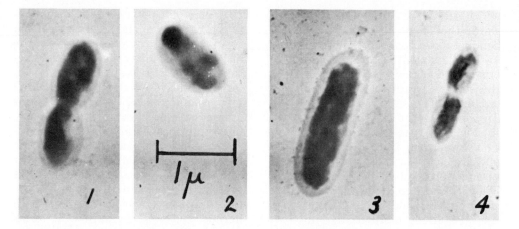

Figure 6-21. Electron photomicrographs of rickettsiae: *1*, epidemic typhus fever; *2*, endemic typhus fever; *3*, Rocky Mountain spotted fever; *4*, American Q fever. (Photographs by Plotz, Smadel, Anderson, and Chambers; A.S.M. LS-25.)

his investigation of Rocky Mountain spotted fever. The name *Rickettsia* was given by da Rocha Lima (1916) in honor of Ricketts, who died in 1910 of typhus fever, a disease caused by another species of the same genus.

Morphology of Rickettsiae

The rickettsiae are almost submicroscopic, spherical to rod-shaped organisms of highly parasitic nature (Fig. 6-21). They range from 0.2 to 0.5 μ in diameter and 0.3 to 1 μ in length. Al-

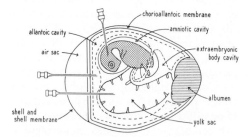

Figure 6-22. Section through a developing (10 to 12 day) chick embryo showing how inoculation can be made into the head of the embryo, the allantoic cavity, and the yolk sac. (From Burrows: Textbook of Microbiology, 18th ed., Philadelphia, W. B. Saunders Co., 1963.)

though they resemble true bacteria in structure and chemical composition, they stain poorly by ordinary procedures; however, satisfactory special methods of staining them have been devised.

Cultivation of Rickettsiae

Cultivation of rickettsiae presents certain problems, because of their obligately parasitic nature. Ordinary culture media are not sufficient; living host cells are necessary. Formerly only an appropriate host animal provided the requisite conditions, but later rickettsiae of many species were found to multiply in the developing chick embryo, particularly in the yolk sac (Fig. 6-22). Even more recently, cultivated animal cells have proved to be satisfactory, although the rate of multiplication of the parasites may be slow, e.g., one division in 16 hours.

Resistance of Rickettsiae

Rickettsiae are relatively susceptible to harmful environmental agents. Most species are easily killed by disinfectant chemicals, such as formaldehyde, phenol, or merthiolate. Rickettsiae are distinguished from viruses by their susceptibility to certain antibiotics: chlortetracycline, chloramphenicol, and oxytetracycline. They are killed within 30 minutes at 50° to 56° C. and, like viruses, are preserved best by quick freezing and storage at −75° C. *R. prowazeki* has been preserved longer than six years in a dry ice chamber.

Pathogenicity of Rickettsiae

Natural Hosts

The rickettsiae are established parasites of arthropods, such as lice, fleas, ticks, and mites. They are not ordinarily pathogenic for these insect vectors and even seem to be hereditary in certain insects, being present in the eggs and, consequently, in the next generation. Most rickettsiae are well adapted to certain animal species, particularly rodents, which constitute natural reservoirs of infection.

Pathogenicity for Man

Man is susceptible to many rickettsial diseases and usually acquires them by insect bites (Table 6-1). Pathogenicity for man is frequently very high. Two rickettsial diseases of considerable interest are typhus fever and Rocky Mountain spotted fever.

Typhus Fever. Epidemic or European typhus fever was first clearly described by Fracastorius in 1546. It apparently afflicted the Spanish army at the siege of Granada in 1489 and caused some 17,000 deaths—more than six times the number of soldiers killed by the Moors. The disease appeared intermittently thereafter, especially under overcrowded and filthy conditions in military camps and jails.

Typhus fever occurs in epidemic form, the number of cases at one time often being in the millions. The average mortality is about 20 per cent, but it may be as high as 70 per cent in severe epidemics. The causative organism, *Rickettsia prowazeki,* is transmitted by

Table 6-1. Some Rickettsial Diseases of Man

Group	Species	Disease	Vertebrate Reservoir	Arthropod Vector	Geographic Distribution
Typhus fever	*Rickettsia prowazeki*	Epidemic typhus fever	Man	Human louse	Europe, Asia, South America
	R. typhi	Murine typhus fever	Wild rats, field mice	Flea, rat louse	Worldwide
Spotted fever	*R. rickettsii*	Rocky Mountain Spotted Fever	Rabbits, small rodents, dogs, etc.	Ticks	North America
	R. conori	Boutonneuse fever	Dogs	Ticks	Mediterranean shores
Tsutsugamushi	*R. tsutsugamushi*	Tsutsugamushi disease	Wild rodents	Mites	Japan, Korea, China, India, Phillipines, Southeast Asia, North Australia
Miscellaneous	*Coxiella burnetii*	Q fever	Bandicoot, sheep, cattle, goats	Ticks	Worldwide

the body louse from man to man. The disease is more or less constantly present in Central Europe, Russia, and Poland; and it also occurs in Asia and South America. Milder forms are found in the United States.

Rocky Mountain Spotted Fever. Rocky Mountain spotted fever was first recognized in the Rocky Mountain region of the United States. The earliest published account (1899) called attention to the extensive skin eruptions that gave the disease its name. Rocky Mountain spotted fever occasioned unusual interest because mortality from the disease in the Bitter Root Valley of Montana was often as high as 90 per cent. For many years cases appeared to be confined to the mountainous areas of the northwestern states, but since 1930 outbreaks have been reported in nearly all

the states and in Canada. The total mortality averages about 20 per cent; the high mortality in the Bitter Root Valley seems to be associated with an unusually virulent strain of the organism.

Rodents and rabbits are important vertebrate reservoirs of the causative organism, *R. rickettsii*. It is acquired from them by ticks and then transmitted to man. The wood tick is the principal vector in western states and the dog tick in the eastern part of this country.

Rickettsiae, like viruses, seem to have evolved from organisms more completely endowed with the capacity for independent existence. It has been suggested that they were derived from bacterial species living in the intestines of insects, perhaps in a symbiotic relationship.

6 MAJOR GROUPS OF BACTERIA

SUMMARY

The Schizomycetes include a great variety of morphologic and physiologic types of organisms, but all possess the basic characters considered to define bacteria. They range from photosynthetic species to nonphotosynthetic types, autotrophs to heterotrophs, saprophytes to parasites; small, almost submicroscopic, to large, nearly macroscopic, forms; they may be spherical, rod-shaped, or spiral; without a well defined cell wall, with a flexible wall, or (like most species) with a rigid wall. The Rickettsiales are presently classified with the Virales in the class Microtatobiotes, but they actually resemble the bacteria more closely than they do the viruses.

STUDY QUESTIONS

1. What is a *scientific name?*
2. What are the derivations of the following words?
   a. Protophyta
   b. Schizophyceae
   c. Schizomycetes
   d. Thallophyta
   e. Microtatobiotes
   f. Phycomycetes
   g. Alga
   h. Phycocyanin

  i. Eubacteriales
  j. Actinomycetales
3. What are the usual hosts of rickettsiae?
4. How do rickettsiae resemble and how do they differ from viruses?
5. Why are rickettsiae considered to be bacteria?

SUPPLEMENTARY READING

Chapters 8, 9, and 10 in Weisz's textbook outline in graphic fashion some of the evolutionary and systematic relationships of microorganisms, plants, and animals. As far as bacteria are concerned, the most widely used guide is Bergey's Manual, now in its seventh edition. Skerman's book provides a useful key to the bacteria, which may be found somewhat more practical than that in Bergey's Manual.

Breed, R. S., Murray, E. G. D., Smith, N. R., *et al.: Bergey's Manual of Determinative Bacteriology,* 7th ed. Baltimore, The Williams & Wilkins Co., 1957.
Skerman, V. B. D.: *A Guide to the Identification of the Genera of Bacteria.* Baltimore, The Williams & Wilkins Co., 1959.
Weisz, P. B.: *Elements of Biology.* New York, McGraw-Hill Book Co., Inc., 1965.

PROTOZOA

Protozoa are the smallest of the animals. They range in size upward from something less than the diameter of a red blood corpuscle (about 7.5 μ). Most of them are invisible to the naked eye.

Apart from their role as parasites and causes of disease in animals of interest to man, protozoa are of concern as nuisances and as helpful organisms of decomposition. They are widespread in water and may affect its color, taste, or odor. Some species produce green or red colors; others liberate aromatic oils that cause fishy or cucumber odors, bitter or spicy tastes.

Protozoa are abundant in the soil and contribute to its fertility. One gram of garden soil may contain as many as 10,000 protozoa. They digest particles of insoluble organic matter and liberate soluble waste materials that can be utilized readily by plants or other microorganisms.

Protozoa also feed on bacteria and other microorganisms. This is probably an important means of natural control of microbial populations.

CLASSES OF PROTOZOA

The ancestral flagellate protozoa evolved into the present four classes, which include some 25,000 described species. These classes are defined principally in terms of their methods of locomotion (Figs. 7-1 and 7-2).

The Mastigophora retain flagella, and each cell possesses one or a few. In the Ciliophora flagella are replaced by cilia, which are shorter and much more numerous. Cilia move quickly and strongly in one direction and more slowly and feebly in the other, thus propelling the organism through a liquid medium. They may also assist in the process of feeding by directing food particles toward the gullet or other organ of ingestion.

The Sarcodina possess neither flagella nor cilia and move only by means of pseudopodia. Pseudopodia are protoplasmic extrusions that flow or creep forward from the main body of the cell. The rest of the organism flows into the pseudopodium, and the animal moves

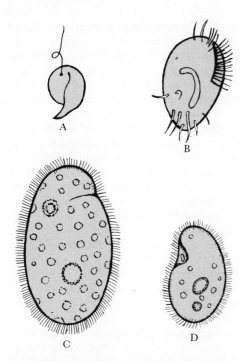

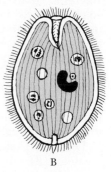

Figure 7-1. Fresh water protozoa: *A, Phacus,* a small flagellate, and three ciliates, *B, Euplotes; C, Nassula; D, Colpidium.* (Magnification: 250X.)

slowly from place to place. A similar type of locomotion is found in certain human and other animal phagocytes (e.g., white blood cells). Pseudopodia of Sarcodina species also surround and engulf food particles, which then become enclosed in a vacuole, where digestion occurs. The amebae are the most familiar members of this class.

Members of the fourth class, Sporozoa, possess no means of independent locomotion. They are distinguished by the production of minute resistant spores. All are parasitic, and many pathogens are included in this group. One of the most notorious is *Plasmodium,* species of which cause malaria.

CELL STRUCTURES OF PROTOZOA

Some protozoa, amebae for example, lack a definite external covering; other forms, such as *Paramecium,* possess a

Figure 7-2. Protozoa of the human body: *A, Entamoeba histolytica,* cause of amebic dysentery; *B, Balantidium coli,* an intestinal ciliate that sometimes produces a dysentery-like inflammation; *C, Giardia intestinalis,* a flagellate cause of tropical diarrhea; *D, Trichomonas vaginalis,* a flagellate of the vagina that may produce vaginitis. (Magnifications: *A* = 1200X, *B* = 450X, *C* = 900X, *D* = 1300X.)

distinct cuticle. Still others are surrounded by shells of material secreted
by the animal (chitin, calcium carbonate, or silica) or composed of foreign
particles (e.g., grains of sand).

The protoplasm of protozoa contains
one or more nuclei, various kinds of vacuoles, and frequently plastids. The
nucleus divides during binary fission as
in the cells of higher forms, half of the
nucleus going into each daughter cell.
Some of the vacuoles contain food in
various stages of digestion; others contain permanent globules of liquid; and
contractile vacuoles contain accumula-
tions of excretory products before their
release through the cell surface. Plastids
are bodies of starchy food substances or
are colored bodies (for example, the
chloroplasts of the photosynthetic alga-
like genus, *Euglena*).

PHYSIOLOGY OF PROTOZOA

Protozoa ingest solid food particles of
vegetable or animal origin (Fig. 7-3).
Bacteria, small algae, and other protozoa are favored foods. Some structure is
usually present that aids in the ingestion of food—a mouth or oral opening
toward which the flagella or cilia propel
food particles—and a food vacuole is
formed at the end of this structure. A
few protozoa are unable to ingest solid
particles; soluble materials enter by
diffusion through the cell membrane.

Digestion takes place within food
vacuoles. Enzymes secreted into them
by the surrounding protoplasm digest
and dissolve the food materials. Undigested matter is eliminated by some species through an anal opening. Digested
food passes from the vacuole into the
cytoplasm and is assimilated, that is,
synthesized into protoplasm.

Respiration of protozoa is similar to
that of higher animals. Oxygen passes
into the cell through the body wall and
is used in oxidative processes, which
yield carbon dioxide and other waste
products; these are then eliminated,
often first being collected in the contractile vacuole before being expelled.

Protozoa display several signs of irritability, one of the characteristics of life.
Irritability is responsiveness to external
stimuli. Certain protozoa are attracted
by weak light and repelled by intense
light. Temperature affects the rate of
motility and of various physiologic processes, but optimum temperatures vary
from one species to another. Protozoa
react violently to mechanical stimuli
such as contact with hard objects. An
ameba, for example, withdraws when
irritated by a sharp needle. Chemicals
attract or repel protozoa, depending
upon their potential usefulness as food.
Protozoa are aerobic and swim toward a
supply of gaseous oxygen.

REPRODUCTION

Binary fission is the most common
method of reproduction among protozoa. The nucleus and the remainder of

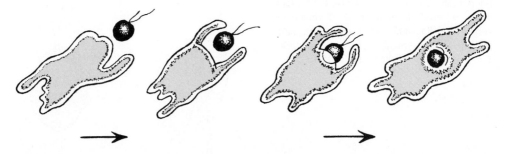

Figure 7-3.   An ameba feeding. It encounters a small flagellate and puts forth pseudopodia, which enclose
the smaller organism. A vacuole forms around the food particle, and enzymes digest it.

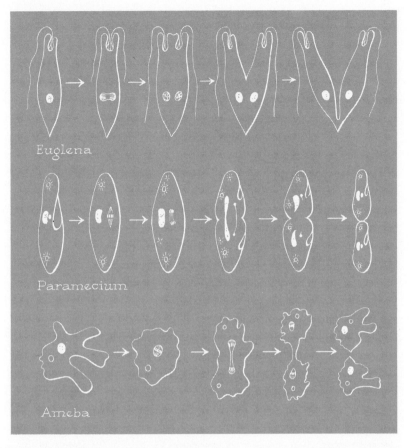

Figure 7-4. Asexual reproduction in three common protozoa. The nucleus divides mitotically; all other cell parts are then replicated, and finally cell division occurs. (From Villee, Walker, and Smith: General Zoology, 2d ed. Philadelphia, W. B. Saunders Co., 1963.)

the cell divide into two equal parts (Fig. 7-4). Division occurs longitudinally in flagellate forms such as *Euglena,* transversely in ciliates like *Paramecium.* The daughter cells separate and continue to perform their own life processes. The rate of binary fission depends upon the species and upon various environmental factors. It may take place several times a day or may require a few days. Binary fission is an asexual process.

A second form of reproduction is budding: a small part of the parent separates and develops into a new individual.

A third method of reproduction, spor-

ulation, is characteristic of the Sporozoa. Sometimes, as in the malaria parasites, there is a complicated life cycle involving more than one host (see page 142). Certain stages are performed in one host, the other stages only in a second host.

A sexual type of reproduction occurs in certain protozoa such as *Paramecium* (Fig. 7-5). These animals occasionally undergo conjugation. Each cell behaves as though it were both male and female, each fertilizing the other by nuclear exchange during temporary union. This process seems to result in retention of vigor. Genetic variation may also occur;

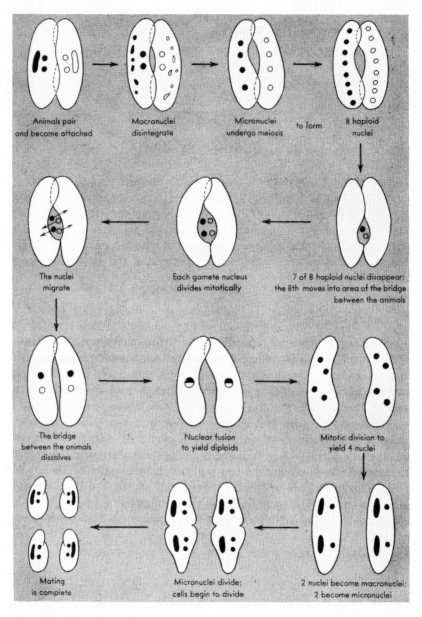

Animals pair
and become attached

Macronuclei
disintegrate

Micronuclei
undergo meiosis   to form   8 haploid
nuclei

The nuclei
migrate

Each gamete nucleus
divides mitotically

7 of 8 haploid nuclei disappear;
the 8th moves into area of the bridge
between the animals

The bridge
between the animals
dissolves

Nuclear fusion
to yield diploids

Mitotic division to
yield 4 nuclei

Mating
is complete

Micronuclei divide;
cells begin to divide

2 nuclei become macronuclei;
2 become micronuclei

Figure 7-5. Sexual reproduction by conjugation in *Paramecium.* (From Sussman: Animal Growth and Development. Englewood Cliffs, N. J., Prentice-Hall, Inc., 1960.)

binary fission after conjugation yields progeny that differ in some way from the two parent cells before conjugation.

SOCIAL BEHAVIOR OF PROTOZOA

It is a truism that most if not all forms of life are interdependent and affect one another in various ways. Some are seemingly indifferent to each other, but it may be questioned whether any individual is totally without effect on other individuals. A general term used to refer to the interrelationships between organisms is *symbiosis* (Greek: *syn,* with + *bios,* life). Symbiosis includes commensalism, mutualism, and parasitism. These are well illustrated by the relationships between various protozoa and other forms of life.

Commensalism

Some organisms live on or within other organisms but cause no obvious harm. These organisms are called *commensals*. Several species of protozoa live within the human intestine, where they secure food and favorable living conditions but do not cause disease. The only damage they can be said to do is to take some of the food from the intestinal tract; this may not be particularly harmful.

Mutualism

Mutualism is a symbiotic relationship in which each partner in the association receives some benefit from the other. It is illustrated by the relationship between *Paramecium bursaria* and the green alga *Zoochlorella*. The algae are ingested by the paramecium like any other particle of food but for some reason are not digested. They grow and multiply within the paramecium and are then passed on to the next generation when the protozoon divides, so the association continues indefinitely. The alga contributes to the partnership by taking carbon dioxide and other protozoan waste materials and by supplying oxygen and carbohydrates, both of which are products of photosynthesis carried out within the alga. The paramecium provides a protected environment for the plant, a constant supply of carbon dioxide, and transportation to areas of light where photosynthesis is possible.

Another well known example of mutualism is the relationship between termites and their intestinal flagellates. *Termopsis angusticollis* is a large species of termite that feeds on wood. Its intestine contains four different flagellate protozoa. The termite can be kept in an atmosphere of pure oxygen for 72 hours without harm, but its intestinal protozoa are destroyed by this treatment. The termite continues to eat wood after its return to a normal atmosphere but cannot digest the wood and dies of starvation within three to four weeks. Reinfection of such a termite from another termite restores its digestive powers. One of the four intestinal protozoa, *Leidyopsis,* is essential for digestion of wood within the termite; the other three protozoa contribute nothing vital. *Leidyopsis* is completely dependent on the termite and can live nowhere else.

Parasitism

Parasitism is an association in which one organism, the parasite, lives in or on and at the expense of another, the host. A completely parasitic organism derives essential nutrient or growth promoting substances from its living host and can multiply under no other conditions. The fact that the parasite utilizes host material suggests that it may damage the host to the extent of producing disease. This is often true, but disease is not a necessary consequence of parasitism; strictly speaking, parasitism is only a matter of nutrition.

Parasites often display striking host specificity; that is, a given parasite may inhabit only one species of host. Some parasites can utilize a few related hosts; others alternate between two hosts, passing part of their existence in one and completing their life cycle in the other.

All four classes of protozoa include parasitic species. Certain plants act as hosts, as do many species of animals in most subdivisions of the animal kingdom.

Plasmodium. The malaria *Plasmodium* is a notorious protozoan parasite whose reproductive cycle can be completed only by invasion of two hosts (Fig. 7-6). The infective stage, known as a *sporozoite,* is stored in the salivary glands of certain *Anopheles* mosquitoes. These spindle-shaped cells are about 0.01 mm. in length and are deposited in the blood stream of man when the mosquito feeds. The sporozoites develop in

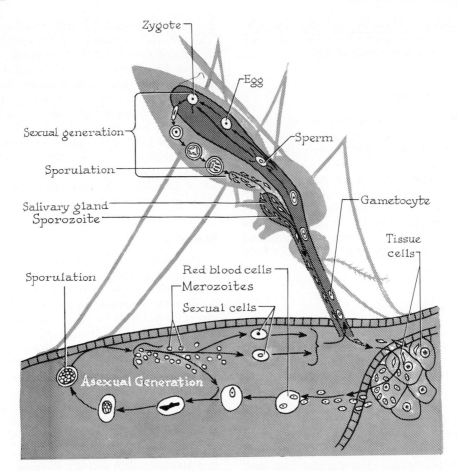

Zygote
Egg
Sexual generation
Sperm
Sporulation
Salivary gland
Sporozoite
Gametocyte
Tissue cells
Sporulation
Red blood cells
Merozoites
Sexual cells
Asexual Generation

Figure 7-6. The life cycle of *Plasmodium*, the malaria parasite. An infected mosquito injects sporozoites into the bloodstream of a human, where they reproduce asexually within the erythrocytes. If a second mosquito feeds on the patient after a few days, the sexual stage in the life cycle can be completed. (From Villee, Walker, and Smith: General Zoology, 2d ed. Philadelphia, W. B. Saunders Co., 1963.)

body cells for 10 days and then enter the red blood corpuscles, where they change into ameboid forms, eat the cell contents and grow to large size. Nuclear divisions occur, and 12 to 24 spores called *merozoites* form. The merozoites break out of the remains of the blood corpuscle, enter fresh red cells and repeat the asexual cycle. Chills and fever occur when a sufficient number of parasitized corpuscles break down simultaneously. The usual period of incubation in benign tertian malaria is about two weeks.

The sexual stage of *Plasmodium* reproduction begins after the infection has progressed for a few days. Some merozoites develop into sexual cells, male or female. If they are then ingested by another mosquito, further changes take place; otherwise they degenerate or are destroyed. Female cells are transformed into eggs within the stomach of the mosquito, and male cells produce flagella and become spermatozoa. Fertilization of the eggs occurs within the stomach. A fertilized egg soon becomes active and enters the stomach wall where its nucleus divides repeatedly until as many as 10,000 spindle-shaped sporozoites are formed. These escape into the body cavity, which is filled with fluid, and are carried to all parts of the body including the salivary glands. The life cycle of the *Plasmodium* is thus completed and the sporozoites are ready to be deposited in a fresh human host.

Colonial Protozoa

Certain protozoa exhibit another type of social relationship, a primitive kind of communal living. *Volvox* is a colonial form consisting of several thousand individual cells more or less intimately joined (see Fig. 1-10, page 12). It is a flagellate, closely related to *Eu-*glena, and illustrates an early stage in specialization or the acquisition of specific functions by certain cells. A colony is composed of a single layer of cells surrounding a cavity filled with fluid. Each cell possesses two flagella and a nucleus and is connected by bits of protoplasm with the six surrounding individuals. Most of the cells grow and multiply and assist in propelling the colony through the water. A special function has been acquired by a few individual cells, however, which develop into germ cells or sexual cells and bear the burden of reproducing new colonies.

PROTOZOA

SUMMARY

The protozoa, predominantly single-celled animals, are divided into four groups on the basis of their methods of locomotion or reproduction: (1) Mastigophora (flagellate), (2) Ciliophora (ciliate), (3) Sarcodina (ameboid), and (4) Sporozoa (spore-forming).

Most protozoa ingest solid food and digest it intracellularly. They are aerobic and derive energy by oxidation of organic nutrients in typical animal fashion. Reproduction is principally by asexual binary fission.

Various protozoa are partners or protagonists in commensal, mutualistic, or parasitic relationships and as such play important roles in agriculture and human and animal health.

STUDY QUESTIONS

1. Where in nature would one expect to find protozoa?
2. Protozoa often grow in hay infusions, i.e., water in which hay is soaked. Are they likely to be more abundant at the top of an infusion or near the bottom? Explain.
3. Describe an example of mutualism between a protozoon and an alga.
4. Is development of the parasitic habit completely beneficial for the parasite? Explain.
5. Describe what might take place if all the protozoa in soil were killed.

SUPPLEMENTARY READING

The beginner who has found some protozoa he wishes to identify may find help in Jahn's *How to Know the Protozoa*. This informal, short guide to common species contains brief descriptions and many good drawings. Kudo's *Protozoology* is an advanced text and gives an introduction to all phases of protozoology, including parasitic as well as free living species. The first few chapters of *Animals Without Backbones* by Buchsbaum are about protozoa; there are many excellent photographs and drawings. *Big Fleas Have Little Fleas,* by Hegner, consists largely of stories of parasitic protozoa, enlivened by imaginative cartoons and verses. Cheng's book contains four chapters on parasitic protozoa with detailed descriptions and many excellent drawings.

Buchsbaum, R.: *Animals Without Backbones,* Rev. ed. Chicago, University of Chicago Press, 1948.
Cheng, T. C.: *The Biology of Animal Parasites.* Philadelphia, W. B. Saunders Company, 1964.
Hegner, R.: *Big Fleas Have Little Fleas, or Who's Who Among the Protozoa.* Baltimore, The Williams & Wilkins Co., 1938.
Jahn, T. L.: *How to Know the Protozoa.* Dubuque, Iowa, W. C. Brown Co., 1949.
Kudo, R. R.: *Protozoology.* Springfield, Ill., Charles C Thomas, 1946.

ALGAE

Algae are the simplest chlorophyll-containing plants. It will be recalled that they apparently developed from ancestral flagellates and that this development was parallel with that of modern flagellates and other protozoa. One group, the blue-green algae, is believed to have evolved rather less completely, along with the bacteria, and these two groups are classified together in the Protophyta. Nevertheless, the blue-green algae will be considered with the more highly developed forms in this chapter.

OCCURRENCE

Algae can be found almost anywhere on Earth from the tropics to arctic regions. They are principally aquatic and hence occur in lakes and streams, seas and oceans. Some fresh water forms adapt to salt water and are found even in the salt lakes of the southwestern United States. Many species live in damp soil; some grow on rocks and aid in the slow decomposition by which rocks are eventually converted into soil; still others can be found on the north side of trees where they are protected from the midday sun. Some species are adapted to very cold climates and grow on snow and ice in polar and mountain regions. Others have become adapted to high temperature and flourish in hot springs at 85° to 90° C. (for example, in Yellowstone National Park).

MORPHOLOGY

Many species of algae are microscopic single cells. Their shapes vary from spheres to rods, clubs, spirals, and irregular forms. Multicellular species exhibit great variations in form and complexity. Some species are not truly multicellular but consist of simple aggregations of single, apparently identical cells held together by a slimy, gelatinous outer coat. Colonial forms, on the contrary, contain cells with special functions, such as reproduction, or rootlike holdfasts that anchor the plant to rocks or other solid surfaces. Some algae are motile by means of flagella, others (diatoms) by an unknown mechanism that may involve cytoplasmic streaming. Many algae are not independently motile but drift in the water. Some normally nonmotile species possess motile reproductive cells.

REPRODUCTION

Algae reproduce by a variety of methods. Sexual and asexual processes occur, and many species have complicated life cycles with both sexual and asexual stages.

Asexual reproduction includes simple cell division or fission in which a single cell enlarges and divides. Even cell fragments of some algae may suffice to initiate growth. Asexual spore formation also occurs; nonmotile spores or motile *zoospores* are produced by specialized cells called *sporangia*.

There are several types of sexual reproduction. One of the simplest is the fusion or conjugation of two sex cells that are indistinguishable from each other. A more advanced form is conjugation of cells that can be distinguished and are called male and female. Finally, some species produce large, nonmotile ova and small, motile sperm cells.

CLASSIFICATION OF ALGAE

Algae are classified according to the nature of the pigments they produce, the kinds of products they synthesize and store, and their methods of reproduction. Six major groups are described in Table 8-1.

Botanists maintain that the Euglenophyta are plants because they possess chlorophyll and are photosynthetic; zoologists consider them protozoa because they lack cell walls and are flexible like other protozoa. Microbiologists do not care into which kingdom they are placed and accept them as interesting,

unicellular, microscopic organisms with characteristics of both kingdoms. It has already been pointed out (page 16) that the only apparent difference between *Euglena* and the protozoon *Astasia* is possession of photosynthetic chloroplasts by the former.

The Cyanophyta or blue-green algae are considered the most primitive algae in existence today; they bear many resemblances to bacteria. The nuclear body of the blue-green algae, like that of bacteria, is not bounded by a definite membrane (Fig. 8-1). Similarly, photosynthetic activity in blue-green algae is not confined to membrane-enclosed structures or chloroplasts, as it is in higher plants. Instead, it takes place in a continuous leaflike lamellar system containing chlorophyll and carotenoid pigments (Fig. 8-2). It may be noted that photosynthetic bacteria differ from the blue-green algae in their possession of small, vesicular structures, the chromatophores, within which some photochemical activity occurs, but no fixation or reduction of carbon dioxide. Blue-green algae owe their color to the pigment phycocyanin, which is often sufficiently intense to mask the chlorophyll. Some species possess a red pigment in addition, and these forms appear reddish or purple. The product of photosynthesis that is stored is the animal-like polysaccharide, glycogen. Reproduction is by asexual fission, as in bacteria.

The Chlorophyta or green algae comprise a large and heterogeneous group with many characteristics similar to those of higher plants (Fig. 8-3). Colonial types are common, and the product of photosynthesis is starch. Reproduction is by asexual fission, formation of asexual zoospores, and also by primitive sexual fusion.

The Chrysophyta include diatoms, microscopic and mostly unicellular organisms with shells composed of silica (Fig. 8-4). These organisms are widely distributed in both fresh and salt water, even in arctic regions, and their shells have accumulated in certain places to depths as great as 3000 feet. This mate-

Table 8-1.   Major Groups of Algae

Group	Size, Structure, Etc.	Reproduction	Habitat
Euglenophyta (Euglena)	Microscopic, unicellular; store fat and paramylum	Longitudinal fission; simple sex cells	Fresh water
Cyanophyta (Blue-green algae)	Usually microscopic; multicellular or unicellular; store glycogen	Asexual fission	Fresh water and soil
Chlorophyta (Green algae)	Microscopic, a few macroscopic (e.g., a few inches); unicellular or multicellular; store starch	Asexual fission and zoospores; primitive sexual fusion	Fresh water, soil, tree bark
Chrysophyta (Diatoms, etc.)	Microscopic, mostly unicellular; store oils	Usually asexual	Fresh and salt water (some in arctic), soil, higher plants
Phaeophyta (Brown algae; seaweeds, kelp, etc.)	Multicellular, large (up to several hundred feet); store mannitol, laminarin (a polysaccharide)	Sexual; some asexual zoospores	Salt water (cool)
Rhodophyta (Red algae; seaweeds)	Multicellular, macroscopic (up to 4 feet); store flurodean starch	Sexual by well differentiated male and female germ cells; asexual by spores	Salt water (warm)

rial is known as diatomaceous earth; it is a filtering agent and also a very fine abrasive, and as such it is used in toothpaste. The chrysophytes produce and store oils and are believed to have been important sources of petroleum deposits.

The remaining two groups of algae, Phaeophyta (brown algae) (Fig. 8-5) and Rhodophyta (red algae) (Fig. 8-6), are large, multicellular organisms familiar as seaweeds, kelp, and the like. Their colors are attributed to brown, red, and other pigments, which mask their chlorophyll. They are marine forms, the brown algae preferring cool waters of higher latitudes; the red algae being favored by subtropical waters where

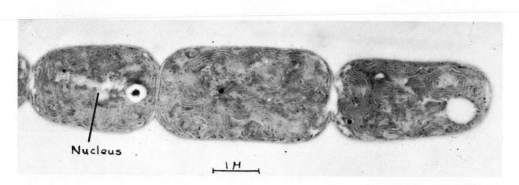

Nucleus

1 H

Figure 8-1.   *Anabaena*, a blue-green alga. The low density material is nuclear substance, but note the absence of a nuclear membrane. The membranous structures in the cytoplasm are the equivalents of chloroplasts. (Electron photomicrograph by G. B. Chapman.)

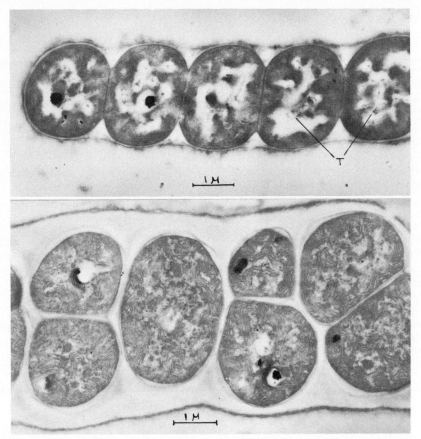

Figure 8-2. *Nostoc*, a blue-green alga. Low density nuclear material is abundant in the upper picture, and threadlike structures (*T*) are clearly shown in the nucleoplasm of the cells at the right. Membranous chloroplast equivalents almost fill the cells in the lower picture. (Electron photomicrographs by G. B. Chapman.)

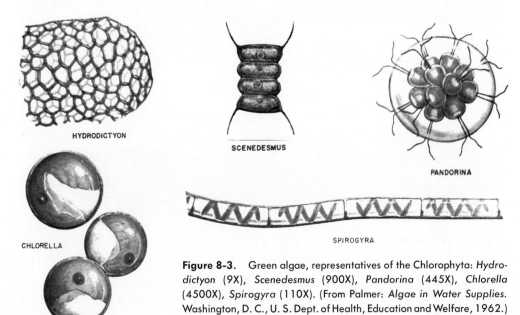

HYDRODICTYON

SCENEDESMUS

PANDORINA

CHLORELLA

SPIROGYRA

Figure 8-3. Green algae, representatives of the Chlorophyta: *Hydrodictyon* (9X), *Scenedesmus* (900X), *Pandorina* (445X), *Chlorella* (4500X), *Spirogyra* (110X). (From Palmer: *Algae in Water Supplies.* Washington, D. C., U. S. Dept. of Health, Education and Welfare, 1962.)

148

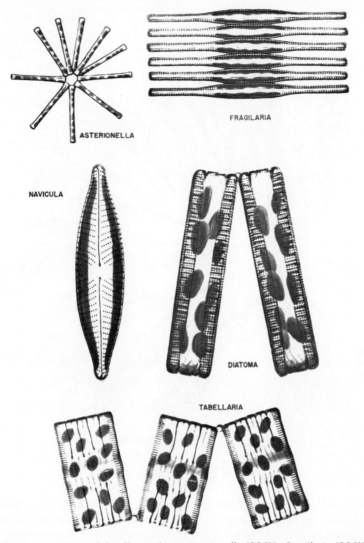

ASTERIONELLA

FRAGILARIA

NAVICULA

DIATOMA

TABELLARIA

Figure 8-4. Diatoms, members of the Chrysophyta: *Asterionella* (225X), *Fragilaria* (885X), *Tabellaria* (1350X), *Navicula* (1350X), *Diatoma* (1350X). (From Palmer: *Algae in Water Supplies.* Washington, D. C., U. S. Dept. of Health, Education and Welfare, 1962.)

Figure 8-5. *Fucus,* a brown alga, commonly found attached to rocks along the seashore. The bulbous structures along the leaflike body are air bladders. (Courtesy General Biological Supply House, Inc.)

Figure 8-6. A red alga, one of the Rhodophyta. These delicately branched, lacy forms occur in quiet, deep waters. The blue and violet rays of the sunlight can penetrate to the depths in which the Rhodophyta live and are utilized by the red pigment, phycoerythrin, characteristic of these algae. (From Villee: *Biology,* 5th ed. Philadelphia, W. B. Saunders Co., 1967.)

they may multiply to such an extent as to produce a red "bloom" that gives the water an almost bloody appearance. Sexual reproduction is well developed among them, but asexual reproduction by means of spores also occurs.

PHOTOSYNTHESIS BY ALGAE

Photosynthesis by algae is essentially the same as by any other plant. Light is absorbed by chlorophyll or by carotenoid or other pigments. In the latter cases the energy obtained from the light is transferred to chlorophyll within the plant. The chlorophyll is converted to an excited state and its extra energy then splits water:

$$2H_2O \longrightarrow 4H + O_2$$

The oxygen is released, but the hydrogen is passed along from one substance to another (temporary hydrogen "acceptors") until it participates in the carbon dioxide fixation cycle (Fig. 8-7).

Meanwhile a special phosphate-containing five-carbon carbohydrate, ribulose diphosphate, has reacted with the carbon dioxide and water to produce a three-carbon compound, phosphoglyceric acid. This substance accepts some of the hydrogen released from water by chlorophyll and then immediately rear-

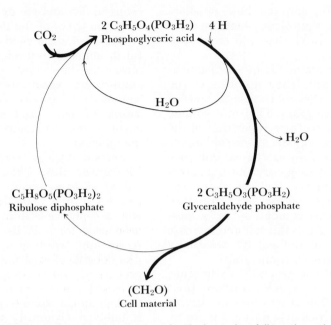

CO_2

$2\ C_3H_5O_4(PO_3H_2)$ 4 H
Phosphoglyceric acid

H_2O

H_2O

$C_5H_8O_5(PO_3H_2)_2$
Ribulose diphosphate

$2\ C_3H_5O_3(PO_3H_2)$
Glyceraldehyde phosphate

(CH_2O)
Cell material

Figure 8-7. Simplified form of the photosynthetic cycle. The heavy line follows the path of carbon from CO_2 to the product of synthesis.

ranges to produce water and phosphoglyceraldehyde, two molecules of which combine and eventually yield glucose; other phosphoglyceraldehyde molecules regenerate ribulose diphosphate, which participates in the same cycle all over again.

The combined reactions are summarized to show the raw materials and products as follows:

$$6CO_2 + 12H_2O \longrightarrow C_6H_{12}O_6 + 6O_2 + 6H_2O$$

SIGNIFICANCE OF ALGAE

Algae are present in great numbers in water, both fresh and salt. The brown and red seaweeds are familiar to anyone who has walked along the ocean shore. They contain useful chemicals, such as iodine, bromine, and potassium, and also considerable protein. In some countries millions of tons are used each year for fertilizer.

The microscopic, single-celled algae are very abundant in natural waters. The ocean may contain several hundred thousand individuals per cubic foot in the surface layers where sunlight can penetrate. Algae are important primary photosynthesizing organisms in this location, and without them all oceanic animal life would soon cease. Microscopic algae constitute the basic food material for aquatic animals. Even the mammoth blue whale, which may reach 100 feet in length, feeds upon algae indirectly; one of its principal sources of food is a crustacean, which in turn feeds upon algae, particularly diatoms.

The distribution of algae in water is limited by the penetration of light. In northern oceans algae are not usually found much below 180 feet, whereas in the clear water of southern latitudes they may be found as deep as 600 feet. The pigments of algae play an important role in their absorption of light. The red phycoerythrin permits red algae to live in deeper water than most other algae because it absorbs blue light particularly well, and the blue or short wavelengths of sunlight penetrate more deeply into water than the longer red wavelengths.

Algae are abundant in soil, particularly moist soil. Their numbers in the upper few inches reach several tens of thousands per gram. The total volume of algae may be three times that of the soil bacteria. Organisms as abundant as these necessarily exert great influence upon the soil chemistry. As photosynthetic organisms they increase the organic matter of the soil. Moreover, some species can combine or "fix" atmospheric nitrogen in the soil and increase the fertility of the soil by eventually releasing nitrogen compounds.

Algae are not generally pathogenic, although a few species produce toxic substances that reach man by way of shellfish, particularly during the warm, summer months (those whose names lack the letter R).

The oil droplets stored by diatoms are rich in vitamins A and D. These vitamins are transferred through crusta-

ceans to fish and are extracted by man from the livers of the fish.

Some red algae yield substances useful in industry and microbiology. Irish moss, an important thickening and emulsifying agent, is derived from species of *Chondrus. Gelidium* is the source of agar, used as a solidifying agent in many industries as well as in microbiology.

Certain algae are even used for food. The green alga, *Chlorella,* has been cultivated experimentally for this purpose for several years. It has not found wide acceptance as human food but has been used for animals. An interesting recent application of its biologic activities consists of experiments designed to provide oxygen to support human life in closed vehicles such as space ships. Carbon dioxide from human respiration is bubbled vigorously through illuminated tanks of *Chlorella* in a mineral salt solution. Photosynthesis by the algae produces the familiar reaction in which carbon dioxide is used and oxygen is set free.

 **8** **ALGAE**

SUMMARY

The algae display characteristics of several other diverse groups of organisms. The blue-green algae closely resemble bacteria. The Euglenophyta bridge the gap between the plant and animal kingdoms. Red and brown algae are large, multicellular, plantlike organisms—seaweeds, kelp, etc.

Reproduction varies from simple, asexual fission through primitive sexual conjugation to a well developed sexual process.

Algae are found in wet or at least moist habitats exposed to light, where they conduct photosynthetic reduction of carbon dioxide to various starchy substances. Their photosynthetic activity is probably more significant than that of all other plants combined.

STUDY QUESTIONS

1. From what sources might one cultivate algae? What nutrients and cultural conditions should be provided?

2. Of what significance are the blue, red, or other pigments which various algae possess in addition to chlorophyll?
3. What is the importance of algae in the ocean? In soil?
4. How does man secure the vitamins that algae manufacture?
5. Why are algae usually included in a balanced aquarium, that is, a closed vessel containing fish and other animals?
6. Discuss the evolutionary significance of organisms such as *Euglena*.

SUPPLEMENTARY READING

Many botany and biology textbooks offer chapters on algae. Among them are Weatherwax's *Botany* and Villee's *Biology. The Fresh-water Algae of the United States,* by Smith, and *Marine Algae of the Northeastern Coast of North America,* by Taylor, begin with a few introductory chapters describing algae in general and methods of studying them, and devote the remainder to detailed descriptions with illustrations. *Algae in Water Supplies* is a small, authoritative monograph, well illustrated with color plates and drawings.

Palmer, C. M.: *Algae in Water Supplies.* Washington, D. C., U. S. Department of Health, Education, and Welfare, 1962.
Smith, G. M.: *The Fresh-water Algae of the United States,* 2d ed. New York, McGraw-Hill Book Co., Inc., 1950.
Taylor, W. R.: *Marine Algae of the Northeastern Coast of North America,* rev. ed. Ann Arbor, Mich., The University of Michigan Press, 1957.
Villee, C. A.: *Biology,* 5th ed. Philadelphia, W. B. Saunders Co., 1967.
Weatherwax, P.: *Botany,* 3d ed. Philadelphia, W. B. Saunders Co., 1956.

MOLDS

The Thallophytes, which constitute the second division of the plant kingdom, are commonly subdivided into three groups: (1) algae, which have just been discussed, (2) fungi, and (3) lichens.

Fungi are frequently filamentous, at least in microscopic structure, but are sometimes single-celled (e.g., many of the yeasts). There are five classes: Myxomycetes, Phycomycetes, Ascomycetes, Basidiomycetes, and Fungi Imperfecti. The Myxomycetes, or slime molds, were described briefly in Chapter 1 (page 12). Basidiomycetes include mushrooms, puffballs, rusts, smuts, and other forms that have considerable economic importance but are of little interest to most microbiologists; these will not be discussed further. Molds and yeasts are found among the other three classes. The terms *mold* and *yeast* have no taxonomic significance; they are colloquial designations for forms that cannot be accurately defined. Molds will be discussed in this chapter, and yeasts in Chapter 10.

GROSS STRUCTURE OF MOLDS

Molds are usually described as filamentous, multicellular fungi in which the filaments, known as *hyphae,* branch and sometimes rejoin to form a tangled mass, any large portion of which may be referred to as *mycelium.* Two types of hypha can often be distinguished. *Vegetative* hyphae penetrate the substrate or lie along its surface and secure water and nutrients for the plant; they may also anchor the plant in place. *Fertile* hyphae usually extend into the air and bear the reproductive bodies or spores.

Many mold hyphae are divided by crosswalls or *septa* into definite cells, each containing one or more *nuclei.* Hyphae of other molds possess few septa and are essentially long tubes containing protoplasm with numerous nuclei scattered throughout. Active protoplasmic streaming can often be observed. These are *nonseptate* or *coenocytic* hyphae.

GROWTH AND
REPRODUCTION OF MOLDS

Cell Structure

Individual mold cells possess rigid
walls surrounding the protoplasm. The
cell walls are composed of chitin, the
substance that makes up the shells of
crabs and lobsters, or of a chitin–cellulose complex. The protoplasm is held
within a semipermeable cytoplasmic
membrane and contains one or more
small nuclei together with various vacuoles, granules, and droplets.

Mold cells are often cylindrical and
vary greatly in size. The diameters of
cells of some common molds range
from 2 to 5 μ, and they may be two to
four times as long as their diameter.
Mold nuclei are not easily demonstrated; special staining methods must
be employed.

Vegetative Growth of Molds

Mold growth is initiated by germination of a spore or enlargement of any
hyphal fragment that falls upon a suitable substrate under proper conditions
of temperature, moisture, and aeration.
Apical growth and extension occur, and
in a septate mold the terminal cells
increase in length and crosswalls form
to establish new cells. Developing hyphae branch repeatedly and produce a
tangled mycelial mass.

Growth is rapid under favorable conditions. An orange or lemon may be
completely covered by the bluish green
mycelium of *Penicillium* in a day or
two, and in the laboratory the same
mold will produce colonies an inch or
more in diameter on a suitable medium
within the same period. Some species
grow more slowly and require one or
two weeks to produce colonies one-half
inch in diameter. Certain molds grow
very luxuriantly, producing a cottony
mycelium that can fill any given container, such as a bread box, within a few
days.

Growth of mold mycelium can con-

tinue indefinitely *under favorable
conditions.* Older hyphae die and disintegrate, and new hyphae develop. Alexopoulos stated that colonies of fungi
have been known to continue growing
for over 400 years, and it is likely that
some mycelia (but not the individual
cells of which they are composed) are
thousands of years old.

Reproduction; Spore Formation

Molds reproduce by spore formation.
Sexual and asexual spores are produced.
Both types are formed by members
of the Phycomycetes and Ascomycetes;
only asexual spores are found in the
Fungi Imperfecti.

Asexual Spores. The spores most frequently observed are asexual. They are
produced by the mycelium without nuclear fusion. There are several kinds of
asexual spores, and the type of spore is
more or less characteristic of the species
of mold.

Sporangiospores. These are produced
within a swollen structure, the *sporangium,* on the end of the fertile hypha of
a nonseptate mold or Phycomycete
(Fig. 9-1). The tip of the hypha enlarges,
and a septum divides it from the remainder of the hypha; nuclear division
occurs repeatedly, bits of protoplasm
surround each nucleus, and spore walls
form. A fertile hypha bearing a sporangium is called a *sporangiophore;* its
rounded or club-shaped end, which supports and is partially surrounded by the
sporangium, is the *columella.*

A fully developed sporangium may
burst or be broken by mechanical contact and will then broadcast the thousands of spores it contains. These spores
are somewhat more resistant to drying
and other unfavorable conditions than
are vegetative cells and can survive for
some time while being blown about in
the air. They germinate when they encounter a suitable moist medium, and a
whole new plant may start from each
spore.

Conidia. The Ascomycetes and
many Fungi Imperfecti bear exposed or

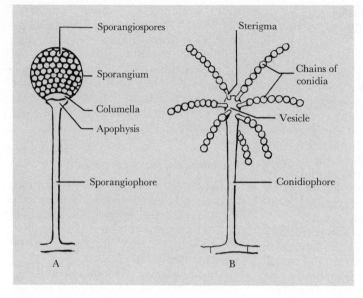

Figure 9-1. Fruiting bodies of *Rhizopus* (A) and *Aspergillus* (B).

unprotected spores, *conidia,* upon fertile hyphae called *conidiophores.* The tips of the conidiophores differentiate into special cells or swellings from which the conidia form. The cell that immediately supports the conidia is a *sterigma.* A sterigma pinches off a conidium and then repeats the process several times, pushing the preceding conidia ahead to form a chain with the oldest conidium at the end. In some molds a swelling or bud pinches off from the terminal conidium; the bud then becomes the terminal conidium and later it too produces a bud. In this case the conidium at the end of the chain is the youngest.

Chlamydospores. Two or three additional types of asexual spores are found (Fig. 9-2). *Chlamydospores* may be produced by all molds. A thick wall develops around any cell in the mycelium. This cell, containing reserve food, is fairly resistant to drying, can remain dormant for considerable periods, and will germinate to produce new growth when it encounters a favorable environment.

Oidia. Hyphae of certain septate molds break up or fragment under proper conditions into their component cells, which are then known as *oidia* or *arthrospores.* These cells do not seem to be reproductive bodies in the same sense as sporangiospores or conidia and possess little if any greater resistance to drying than any other mold fragment. However, they are capable of initiating new growth under favorable conditions and are considered to be a growth form of the organisms.

Asexual spores, particularly sporangiospores and conidia, are produced in thousands by each mold plant. Common household molds, such as *Aspergillus* and *Penicillium,* ordinarily begin to

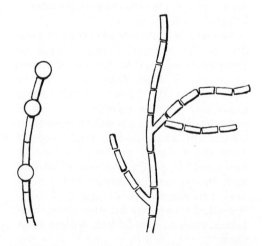

Figure 9-2. Chlamydospores and oidia of molds.

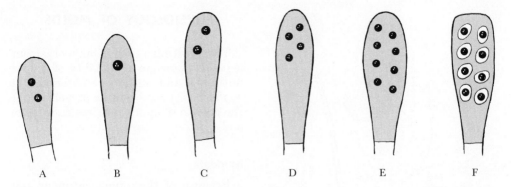

Figure 9-3. Ascospore formation in a mold. The cell shown in A was produced by fusion of two cells from the same or different mycelia. Its two nuclei unite and then divide repeatedly until eight nuclei have formed (E). In F, the spore walls have been produced. The cell containing the spores is called an ascus.

produce spores within a day or so after inoculation onto fresh culture medium. The spores are usually colored, often quite brilliantly. The striking colors of mold colonies are associated almost solely with the spores on the older mycelium. The edge of an actively growing colony is colorless or grayish white where vegetative growth is taking place.

Sexual Spores. These spores are produced following nuclear fusion. Their manner of formation is used as the principal basis for classification. Sexual spores are less frequently observed than asexual spores, and some particular habitat or environmental condition is often necessary to induce sporulation.

Ascospores. Sexual spores of Ascomycetes are known as *ascospores* (Fig. 9-3). Two neighboring cells, either from the same mycelium or from two separate mycelia, send out tubelike processes, which meet and fuse. The two nuclei unite, and the single nucleus that forms then divides to produce daughter nuclei. Two more divisions may occur, yielding eight nuclei. Each nucleus is surrounded by a layer of dense protoplasm and covered by a spore wall. The spores are retained within the original wall that resulted from the union of the two cells, which is now known as an *ascus* or sac.

Oospores. Some Phycomycetes produce *oospores* by the union of small male cells with large female cells formed on neighboring hyphae. Oospores possess thick walls and are very resistant to drying; they can remain dormant for considerable periods.

Zygospores. On other Phycomycetes, zygospores are formed by the union of two apparently identical cells from the same or different plants (Figs. 9-4 and 9-5). The two hyphae join, nuclear fusion occurs, and a thick wall surrounds the resulting zygospore. Zygospores, like oospores, can remain dormant for a long time.

Significance of Sexual and Asexual Sporulation. Both sexual and asexual spores are important to the survival of a species, but in different ways. Sexual reproduction is of great importance in the process of evolution because it permits the recombination of genes and the appearance of progeny with combinations of characteristics different from those of either parent. Selective environmental factors eliminate the least well adapted forms, and only those with great survival powers persist. Asexual spores, particularly conidia and sporangiospores, are especially significant in multiplication and distribution. Their somewhat increased resistance, together with their very great number, favor survival of the species during unfavorable conditions.

PHYSIOLOGY OF MOLDS

The multiplication of any organism depends upon the availability of proper nutrients and suitable environmental conditions. Promotion or prevention of the growth of molds requires knowledge and control of these factors.

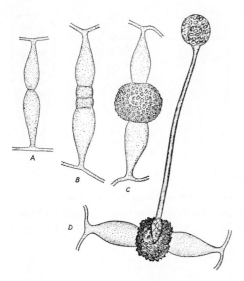

Figure 9-4. Zygospore formation in *Rhizopus*. Cells from the same or different mycelia meet (A) and produce special sex cells (B), which fuse and form a zygospore covered with a thick, black, protective wall (C). The zygospore remains dormant until proper conditions arise; it then germinates and produces a typical asexual fruiting body. (From Frobisher: Fundamentals of Microbiology, 7th ed. Philadelphia, W. B. Saunders Co., 1962.)

Nutrients

Because of their rigid chitinous cell walls, molds secure nutrients only by diffusion or transport of soluble matter and hence are limited to relatively simple foods. Most molds secure carbon and energy from carbohydrates, especially glucose, and some can utilize alcohols or organic acids. Carbon can also be secured from proteins or, in the absence of a more readily available supply, from products of protein digestion. Very few species utilize fats extensively.

Sources of nitrogen include organic compounds, such as peptones, peptides, and amino acids. Some species can utilize ammonia or nitrates.

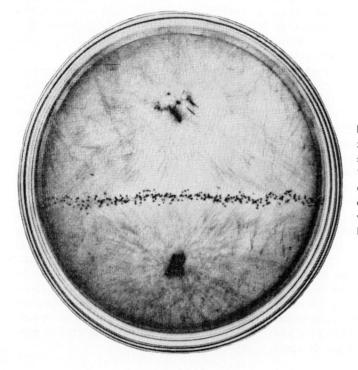

Figure 9-5. A row of black zygospores that formed where sexually different ("plus" and "minus") strains of *Phycomyces* came into contact. (From Milne and Milne: Plant Life. Englewood Cliffs, N. J., Prentice-Hall, Inc., 1959.)

Many molds can synthesize all the vitamins and other growth factors they require, but some must be supplied with preformed thiamin or biotin or their precursors.

Molds vary greatly in their ability to utilize complex materials. Some, such as *Penicillium* and *Aspergillus,* excrete digestive enzymes which enable them to grow on nearly any substrate that contains organic matter; they are found on jams and jellies, dates, tobacco, fabrics, and bicycle saddles, to mention only a few places. Others are parasitic and in nature may be restricted to a few host species or even a single species or variety. Some molds parasitize man and other animals. Many are parasites of plants, among which they cause serious epidemics, such as wheat rust.

The metabolic activity of molds yields energy, which is used in the synthesis of the proteins, polysaccharides, and lipids that comprise the various cell structures and protoplasmic constituents. Excess carbohydrate and lipid, stored in the form of glycogen and oil, are readily available whenever needed as sources of energy. By-products of mold metabolism include citric, oxalic, gluconic, glycolic, and other organic acids; various aldehydes and esters; cholines; alkaloids, hydroxylamine, and other nitrogenous compounds; pigments; and antibiotics.

Moisture and Osmotic Pressure

Mold growth is favored by a moist environment, but these organisms do not need as much water as do yeasts and bacteria, which require an almost completely aqueous medium. Growth upon such dry materials as dried fruits, grains, cloth, tanned leather, and furniture takes place only in a humid atmosphere. Mildew appears on books and shoes, for example, during prolonged periods of "muggy" weather or in damp climates.

The osmotic pressure of a solution varies with the molecular concentrations of dissolved substances and their degree of ionization. Distilled water has very low osmotic pressure, whereas a concentrated sugar or salt solution possesses high osmotic pressure. The osmotic requirements of different mold species vary widely. Some species are inhibited by 10 per cent salt or 15 to 20 per cent sugar; others grow luxuriantly in 50 or even 75 per cent sugar. Jams and jellies are readily spoiled by molds even though they are usually 50 to 60 per cent sugar.

pH

Molds tolerate changes in pH better than most other forms of life. Common species that grow on bread, citrus fruits, or milk can multiply between pH 2.2 and 9.6, although pH 5 to 6 is most favorable for many of these organisms. Certain unusual forms have been found growing in strong organic or inorganic acids, such as 1N acetic acid or even 2N sulfuric acid. The nutrients that support the growth of these organisms are impurities present in trace amounts in the acid solutions. The predilection of molds for acids explains why mold spoilage is so common in acid fruits and preserves, but their wide range of pH tolerance accounts in part for the universal observation that nearly any organic household object may develop mold growth at some time.

Temperature

Few mold species will grow at temperatures below 0° C. or above 42° C. Lowest, highest, and most favorable temperatures for growth of many common species are listed in Table 9-1.

Death occurs at any temperature above the maximum for growth, and the rate of killing accelerates as the temperature rises. Vegetative mycelium is, in general, easily killed; spores are more resistant, but there is wide variation between spores of different species. Almost all, however, are killed within 5 to 30 minutes at 60° to 63° C. For comparison, it may be noted that milk is commonly pasteurized by heating for 30 minutes at about 62° C.

Table 9-1. Temperature Relations of
Common Mold Species

Temperature to kill spores within 30 min.	60–63° C.
Maximum growth temperature	30–40° C.
Optimum growth temperature	22–32° C.
Minimum growth temperature	5–10° C.

Oxygen

Practically all molds are highly aerobic
and require abundant oxygen. Only a
few species, such as that used in Roquefort cheese, will grow satisfactorily under
conditions of reduced oxygen tension.
Even in this case, however, growth is
promoted by stabbing the cheese with
wires to provide air holes through the
ripening curd.

The necessity for oxygen limits mold
spoilage to the surfaces of materials.
Molds are found only on the top of the
preserves in an imperfectly sealed jar
or the jelly in a glass whose paraffin
covering has been disturbed so that
air can enter.

Despite the requirement for free oxygen, mold metabolism does not yield
solely oxidized products. Complete oxidation of glucose and other carbohydrates produces only carbon dioxide and
water; the acids and alcohols formed
by molds result from incomplete oxidation.

Knowledge of the types of nutrients
preferred by molds, together with their
pH, temperature, and oxygen requirements, explains most common instances
of mold spoilage. The same information,
intelligently applied, indicates how to
prevent undesired mold growth.

SOME COMMON MOLDS

Many mold genera are encountered
in household, agricultural, or industrial
situations. Three will be described briefly
because of their widespread distribution.

Rhizopus

Rhizopus nigricans is commonly
known as the bread mold because it so
frequently occurs on this food. It produces a cottony mycelium and grows
rapidly and luxuriantly. Its structure,
illustrated in Figure 9-6, resembles that

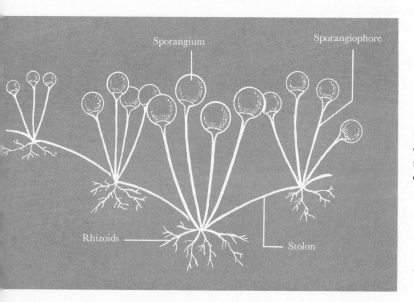

Figure 9-6. *Rhizopus nigricans.* The plant anchors to a
solid substrate by its rhizoids
and spreads by stolons.

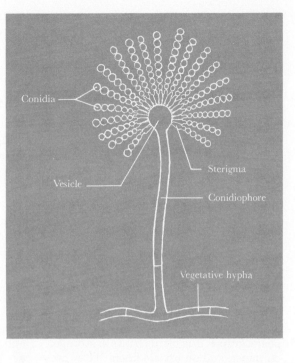

Conidia

Vesicle

Sterigma

Conidiophore

Vegetative hypha

Figure 9-7. *Aspergillus.* At intervals in the vegetative hypha a cell puts forth a fertile hypha, upon which conidia form.

of a strawberry plant. Rootlike *rhizoids* anchor the mold to the substrate and secure water and nutrients. One or more sporangiophores rise into the air and support sporangia filled with sporangiospores. A hypha similar to the runner or stolon of the strawberry plant burrows through or extends over the substrate and produces another rhizoid, from which more fertile hyphae arise. Growth through and over the substrate can continue almost indefinitely. The spores within the sporangium are gray or black and make the mature mycelium appear to the naked eye to be dotted with black specks.

Aspergillus

Aspergillus species are widely distributed and cause numerous kinds of spoilage. They rot figs and dates, decay tobacco and cigars, spoil nuts and bread, and grow on leather and clothing in humid weather. *Aspergillus* colonies are more limited in size that those of *Rhizopus:* colonies on malt extract or yeast glucose agar may be 40 to 50 mm. in

diameter. Mature colonies are velvety in texture and dark brown or black, the color being attributed to the conidia.

The microscopic structure of an *Aspergillus* is illustrated in Figure 9-7. Septate vegetative hyphae grow in or over the substrate. At intervals a cell branches and sends a fertile hypha or conidiophore into the air; the top of the conidiophore enlarges to form a *vesicle,* upon which numerous sterigmata are attached radially. Each sterigma supports a chain of conidia. Microscopic study of an undisturbed conidiophore shows only the hypha surmounted by an indistinct black body, because the conidia are so tightly packed and opaque en masse that the internal structure of the "fruiting body" cannot be discerned. The sterigmata and vesicle are seen in preparations that have been disturbed mechanically to remove the conidia.

Penicillium

Species of *Penicillium* are also widely distributed and occur on decaying or-

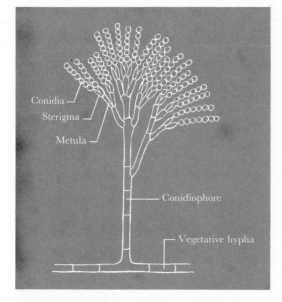

Conidia
Sterigma
Metula
Conidiophore
Vegetative hypha

Figure 9-8. *Penicillium.* The brushlike appearance of the parallel chains of conidia is characteristic of this genus.

ganic matter. They are found on apples, pears, grapes, and citrus fruits in storage, on paper, and on textile fibers. They are used in the manufacture of Camembert and Roquefort cheese. The colonies are velvety and greenish or blue-green and may be 30 to 40 mm. in diameter on laboratory media.

The microscopic structure of *Penicillium* is somewhat similar to that of *Aspergillus.* Septate vegetative hyphae penetrate or grow over the substrate, and septate fertile aerial hyphae arise at intervals. These are sometimes branched and support the conidia, which pinch off from sterigmata. The sterigmata in turn arise from metulae. Several parallel chains of conidia are formed and superficially resemble the bristles of a brush (Figs. 9-8 and 9-9). (The name *Penicillium* is derived from a Latin word meaning *little brush.*)

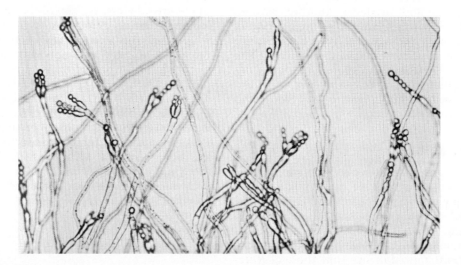

Figure 9-9. Photomicrograph of a *Penicillium* showing twisted, branching hyphae and a few chains of conidia. (From Frazier: Food Microbiology. New York, McGraw-Hill Book Co., Inc., 1958.)

SIGNIFICANCE OF MOLDS

The widespread distribution and nutritional versatility of molds fit them well for a role as spoilage agents, and it is this activity that is probably of most popular concern. Molds are, however, increasingly valuable for the commercial production of chemicals. Citric acid is produced by strains of *Aspergillus niger;* this same organism can be used to produce oxalic acid. Gluconic, lactic, and other acids are also produced by certain molds. Industrially valuable enzymes (e.g., amylase, which hydrolyzes starch) are secured from various molds, and certain species are used in the manufacture of cheeses and other foods.

Penicillin is probably the most widely known commercially manufactured mold product. Originally produced by *Penicillium notatum,* it is now manufactured by use of *P. chrysogenum,* and annual production is about 1000 tons in the United States, with a market value of approximately $100,000,000. Growth of the industry over a period of only 18 years is indicated in Table 9-2. The 180-fold increase in production since 1945 has been accompanied by a drop in the cost per pound to less than $1/70$ of its earlier figure.

Another, quite different but equally significant use of molds is illustrated by the use of various species of *Neurospora* in the study of biochemical genetics. *Neurospora,* commonly known as red bread mold, is an ascomycete. Its vegetative growth resembles that of most filamentous fungi; the mycelium

Table 9-2. Production and Value of Penicillin in the United States Since 1945.

Year	Production (Tons)	Market Value per Pound
1945	6	$3870
1950	215	266
1955	284	117
1960	430	84
1963	831	56

consists of branching, multinucleate hyphae, and asexual conidia form at the ends of aerial conidiophores. Sexual spores are produced in asci after interaction of the two mating types, *A* and *a*. The fruiting body or perithecium contains numerous asci, which are elongated sacs, each containing a linear array of eight ascospores derived equally from the parental strains. Fertilization of the female element can be accomplished by almost any hyphal element of the male strain, including a conidium.

The usefulness of *Neurospora* in genetic research derives partly from the fact that mutations can be induced by irradiating conidia with x-rays and then using the treated spores to fertilize normal material of the opposite mating type. The sexual spores thus produced are separated by micromanipulation, germinated, and tested for mutation-induced characteristics.

Normal, "wild-type" *Neurospora* will grow on a simple "minimal" medium containing mineral salts, sugar, and biotin. Various mutants produced as just described cannot grow on the minimal medium until it has been fortified by other vitamins, amino acids, purines, or pyrimidines. These are biochemical mutants, and by appropriate crossing with the normal or wild-type strain they can be used to study the genetic basis of the mutations.

Some molds are pathogenic for plants, animals, or man. Human infections are of two principal types: superficial and deep-seated. Superficial infections often involve the hair, skin, and nails (e.g., ringworm, athlete's foot) and are comparatively mild. Deep-seated infections of internal organs, such as the lungs, run a prolonged course and are often difficult if not impossible to cure.

Relatively few of the thousands of species of molds are pathogenic, particularly in temperate climates. Almost all of the common spoilage molds are harmless and could be eaten without danger. It is a reflection of human inconsistency that *Penicillium roqueforti* and *P. camemberti* are eaten with relish when they occur upon Roquefort and Camembert cheeses, but most people consider the same molds undesirable on other foods and discard the moldy portions. The chief danger from moldy food is that unsatisfactory methods of preservation or storage may have permitted harmful microorganisms as well as molds to enter or survive.

Under natural conditions, molds are kept in check to some extent by the bacteria with which they are associated. Many kinds of bacteria grow more rapidly than molds and produce waste materials that inhibit the multiplication of molds; suppression or destruction of the bacteria therefore permits the molds to grow. This phenomenon is illustrated by the incidental results of treating humans with antibiotics. The bacterial flora of the intestine can be almost completely eliminated by suitable antibiotics, but when this occurs various fungi (e.g., *Monilia*) replace the bacteria, and the physical characteristics of the intestinal contents change markedly.

 **MOLDS**

SUMMARY

Molds comprise those fungi that are predominantly multicellular and filamentous; yeasts, on the other hand, are usually single-celled. Inasmuch as the fungi are classified partly on the basis of their methods of sexual reproduction, and molds and yeasts may reproduce in the same manner, the systematic distinction between these two groups is very unsatisfactory.

Molds grow by a vegetative process of cell enlargement and division, particularly at the end of a hypha. Sexual and asexual processes yield thousands of spores from which new mold plants can arise. The spores are somewhat more resistant than vegetative cells.

Molds grow under a wide variety of conditions. They are favored by acidity, require damp but not necessarily wet substrates, and need abundant oxygen. Although commonly associated with spoilage, they are also important sources of chemicals and antibiotics. Some species are pathogenic for man, others for plants.

STUDY QUESTIONS

1. What *different* functions are performed by sexual and asexual spores of fungi?
2. From what source might one expect to isolate molds?
3. What cultural conditions favor growth of molds?
4. Indicate procedures or conditions that might be expected to prevent growth of molds on book bindings, citrus fruits, jams and jellies, etc.
5. What kinds of useful products are manufactured by molds?

SUPPLEMENTARY READING

One of the best known general books on molds and yeasts is *Henrici's Molds, Yeasts, and Actinomycetes,* rewritten after his death by Skinner, Emmons, and Tsuchiya. It includes both pathogenic and nonpathogenic species. Two authoritative books on special groups are those on the Aspergilli and the Penicillia by Raper and colleagues. Each begins with a few general introductory chapters and continues with detailed descriptions of the various species. The book on *Aspergillus* is especially well illustrated; it also contains a chapter on pathogenicity. Funder's *Practical Mycology* is a small book, illustrated with many drawings. It is intended as an introduction for beginners and others without special botanical knowledge and as a guide to identification of the most common forms. Alexopoulos's book is much more complete and detailed. The volume edited by Ainsworth and Sussman is the first of a series of three volumes summarizing modern knowledge of the fungi: physical and chemical structure, metabolism, nutrition and growth, genetics. In this volume, fungi are treated at the cellular level, Volume II will be concerned with the entire fungus organism, and Volume III with fungal populations.

Ainsworth, G. C., and Sussman, A. S. (Eds.): *The Fungi; an Advanced Treatise.* Vol. 1, *The Fungal Cell.* New York, Academic Press, Inc., 1965.
Alexopoulos, C. J.: *Introductory Mycology,* 2d ed. New York, John Wiley & Sons, Inc., 1962.
Funder, S.: *Practical Mycology. Manual for Identification of Fungi,* 2d ed. Oslo, A. W. Brøggers Boktrykkeri A/S, 1961.
Raper, K. B., and Fennell, D. I.: *The Genus Aspergillus.* Baltimore, The Williams & Wilkins Co., 1965.
Raper, K. B., and Thom, C.: *A Manual of the Penicillia.* Baltimore, The Williams & Wilkins Co., 1949.
Skinner, C. E., Emmons, C. W., and Tsuchiya, H. M.: *Henrici's Molds, Yeasts, and Actinomycetes,* 2d ed. New York, John Wiley & Sons, Inc., 1947.

YEASTS

There is no clear-cut distinction between yeasts and molds. Yeasts have been defined as fungi whose usual and dominant growth form is unicellular. This is perhaps as good a definition as can be stated. The close relationship between yeasts and molds is indicated by the observation that large colonies of many yeast species develop hyphal filaments upon a suitable medium and under certain cultural conditions. Moreover, many yeasts produce sexual spores (ascospores) by a process similar to that of various molds.

MORPHOLOGY OF YEASTS

Shape and Size

Yeast cells are spherical, elliptical, or cylindrical. Their sizes are highly variable. Cells of *Saccharomyces cerevisiae* range from 2 to 8 μ in diameter by 3 to 15 μ in length. Cells of some species attain a length of 100 μ.

Cell Structures

The protoplasm of a yeast cell is enclosed by a cell wall and cytoplasmic membrane, and contains a nucleus, a large vacuole, and numerous granules and fat globules (Fig. 10-1). No flagella or other organs of locomotion are present. Recent electron photomicrographs indicate that the cell wall is composed of an outer dense layer about 0.05 μ thick and a less dense layer of about 0.2 μ. The inner part of the wall may in turn be subdivided into about three layers. The cell wall is composed of polymers of glucose and mannose with smaller amounts of protein, lipid, and chitin.

The nucleus is less than 1 μ in diameter; practically nothing is known of its internal structure. The protoplasm of young, actively growing cells is fairly free from granules and globules of reserve substances, but large numbers accumulate later as growth ceases. Fat globules gradually coalesce and may form one large globule. Carbohydrate granules, principally glycogen, appear in yeasts as in more complex fungi. They stain deep reddish brown with iodine. Fine granules of protein have also been demonstrated within yeast protoplasm.

The large vacuole near the nucleus

Figure 10-1. Sketch showing structures of a ''typical'' yeast, such as *Saccharomyces cerevisiae*. The vacuole is prominent in unstained yeast preparations; the nucleus and lipid globules are demonstrated by special staining or by electron micrography of ultrathin sections.

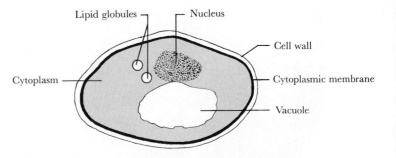

contains a solution or suspension of *volutin,* also found in higher fungi and in bacteria. Volutin is a complex material consisting of RNA, polyphosphates (polymers of phosphate), and lipoprotein. It may be absent from very young cultures, is abundant in old cultures, and disappears during spore formation.

REPRODUCTION OF YEASTS

Budding

Yeasts characteristically multiply by budding, although a few organisms clas-

sified as yeasts multiply by other methods. Budding is an asexual process and is well illustrated in the series of electron photomicrographs in Figure 10-2. A small bulge develops in the cell wall and gradually enlarges. The cytoplasm of the mother and daughter cells remains continuous for some time, but eventually the opening between the two cells closes. A double crosswall forms, whereupon the two cells are physiologically distinct and may separate. A convex bud scar remains on the mother cell after the daughter has separated, and the daughter cell retains a correspond-

Figure 10-2. Successive stages in budding of the yeast, *Saccharomyces cerevisiae.* A small bulge (1) marks the site of future bud formation. The bulge enlarges (2) and eventually reaches the size of the mother cell (3); the cytoplasm of the two cells is still continuous. Formation of cell wall material (4) makes possible independent existence of the two cells. (From H. P. Agar and H. C. Douglas, J. Bact., 70:427–434, 1955.)

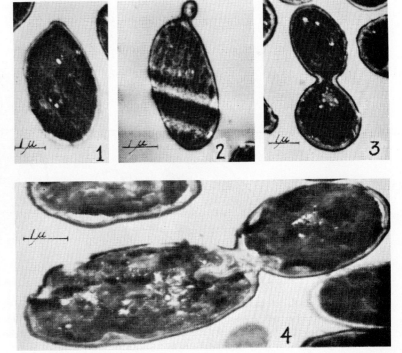

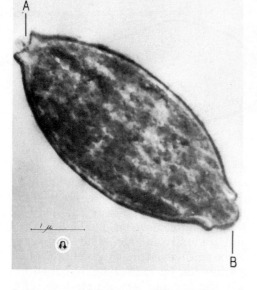

Figure 10-3. Birth scar (A) and bud scar (B) on a cell of *Saccharomyces cerevisiae*. (Photograph by H. D. Agar and H. C. Douglas; A.S.M. LS-336.)

ing concave birth scar (Figs. 10-3 and 10-4). Nuclear division presumably preceded or accompanied development of the bud (Fig. 10-5).

Daughter cells do not always separate immediately but may remain attached while one or more additional buds form on the mother cell (Fig. 10-6). Moreover, daughter cells themselves may undergo budding while still attached. The result is a pseudomycelial mass composed of as many as 64 connected cells.

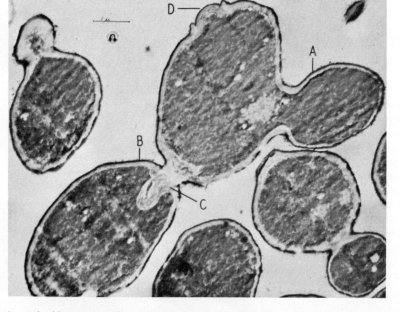

Figure 10-4. A budding yeast cell. A young bud is shown at A; its cytoplasm is still connected to that of the mother cell. B is an older bud, now physiologically separated from the mother cell by cell wall substance (C). The mother cell has budded previously, as indicated by the bud scar (D). (Photograph by H. D. Agar and H. C. Douglas; A.S.M. LS-335.)

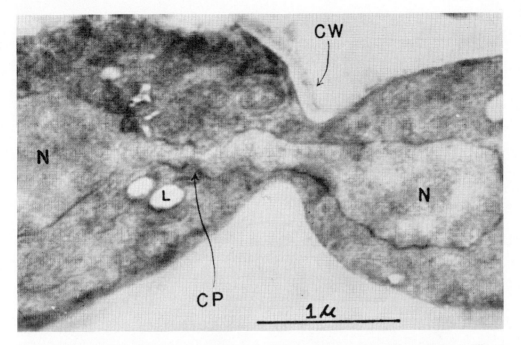

Figure 10-5. An advanced stage of budding of *Saccharomyces cerevisiae*. The nuclei are still not separated. N, nucleus; CW; cell wall; L, lipid granule; CP, constriction point, where the two nuclei will eventually separate. (From Hashimoto, Conti, and Naylor: J. Bact., 77:344–354, 1959.)

Binary Fission

Binary fission is another form of asexual reproduction that occurs in a few yeast genera. This process is similar to that in bacteria and consists of elongation of the cell followed by formation of a crosswall and possible separation of the two cells.

Sexual Reproduction of Yeasts

Sexual reproduction of some yeasts is associated with ascospore formation. At least two methods of spore formation are known. In the first method, vegetative yeast cells in a colony fuse and their nuclei unite; nuclear division follows and is repeated once or twice so that several bits of nucleus are formed. Essential protoplasmic materials surround each nucleus, and spore walls develop. The spores (ascospores) may remain within the ascus where they developed. Subsequent germination is followed by division and formation of the usual vegetative cells.

Another method of spore formation begins with nuclear division within a cell or ascus and formation of four spores, each containing half the usual number of chromosomes. These spores fuse directly, two by two, or else germinate, bud, and then fuse (Fig. 10-7). The cells produced possess the normal number of chromosomes and can then multiply vegetatively by budding until conditions again favor sporulation. This form of reproduction occurs in some yeasts of industrial importance, such as *Saccharomyces cerevisiae*.

Yeasts are divided naturally into two groups on the basis of their methods of reproduction. One group reproduces by both budding and spore formation; the other reproduces only by budding. The spore-forming group is classified with the Ascomycetes and may represent a primitive form of this class. Yeasts that reproduce by budding only are included in the Fungi Imperfecti, because they lack a sexual phase. A third small group of yeasts is related to the Basidiomycetes.

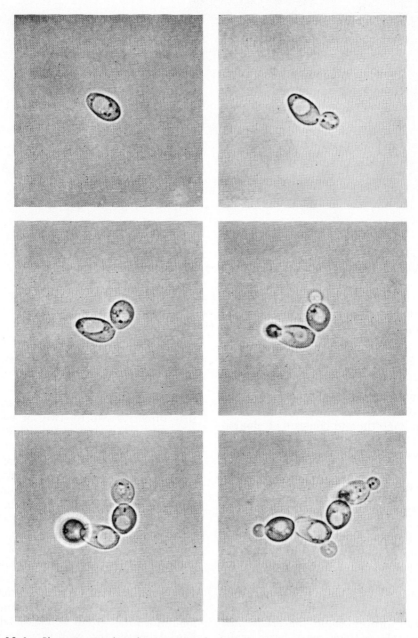

Figure 10-6. Photomicrographs taken at intervals during a period of four hours to show successive budding of rapidly growing *Saccharomyces cerevisiae*. The original cell increased to eight cells. (From Sarles et al.: Microbiology. New York, Harper & Brothers, 1956.)

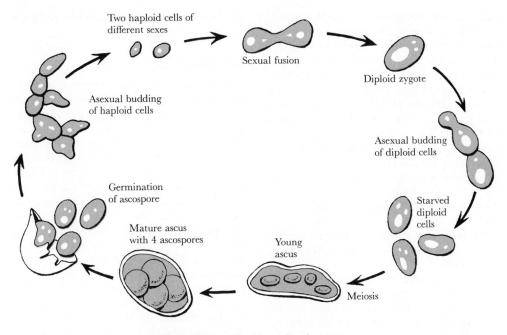

Two haploid cells of
different sexes

Sexual fusion

Diploid zygote

Asexual budding
of haploid cells

Asexual budding
of diploid cells

Germination
of ascospore

Starved
diploid
cells

Mature ascus
with 4 ascospores

Young
ascus

Meiosis

Figure 10-7. The life cycle of a yeast.

Hybridization of Yeasts

An interesting outgrowth of theoretical studies of sexual reproduction by yeasts is the development of hybrids. Single spores are dissected from an ascus using microtools and a micromanipulator. Individual spores are allowed to germinate, and the characteristics of their progeny are determined. Two spore cultures, each possessing one or more characteristics desired for a certain process, such as brewing, are mixed and allowed to grow together. A form of sexual copulation occurs and a zygote forms. The progeny may possess the desired qualities from both parent spore cultures. This method might be used, for instance, to secure strains that produce a particular flavor and aroma together with increased yield of alcohol.

PHYSIOLOGY OF YEASTS

Nutrient Requirements

Yeasts require the same chemical elements as other forms of life: carbon, hydrogen, oxygen, nitrogen, phosphorus, potassium, sulfur, magnesium, iron, zinc, manganese, copper, and molybdenum. The last five metallic elements listed are required in minute quantities as components or activators of enzymes. They are often present in sufficient amounts as impurities in the water or other ingredients of culture media.

Carbon is ordinarily secured from sugars, organic acids, aldehydes, or glycerin. Part of the carbon is utilized in the synthesis of protoplasmic constituents, but the greater portion is oxidized with the release of energy for synthetic and other vital processes. Nitrogen is secured from products of protein hydrolysis, such as proteoses, peptones, amino acids, and ammonia, or from urea or amides. Ammonium sulfate, phosphate or chloride is often used as a source of nitrogen in culture media and in industrial processes. Phosphorus is essential for growth and plays an important part in carbohydrate metabolism; it is usually supplied as a phosphate salt.

Growth Factors. Yeasts require certain vitamin-like *growth factors*. As early as 1901, Wildiers noted that small inocula did not grow in simple, chemically defined media in which large inocula multiplied rapidly and luxuriantly. When large amounts of culture were transferred, sufficient growth-promoting substance was carried over from the original culture to initiate growth, but this did not occur when small amounts were used. The addition of a little yeast extract permitted multiplication of the organisms in small inocula; after growth was under way, the yeast manufactured its own growth-promoting substance. The unknown factor was called "bios" and was later found to consist of at least six substances: thiamine, biotin, pyridoxine, inositol, pantothenic acid, and niacin.

These growth factors are active in extremely low concentrations. For example, a yeast that fails to grow in the absence of biotin may grow maximally when biotin in a concentration of only $1:1,000,000,000$ to $1:1,000,000$ is provided. Inositol is much less active than biotin, but it stimulates the growth of yeasts when it is present in concentrations of $1:100,000$ to $1:20,000$. Biotin is significant in nitrogen metabolism; pyridoxine, thiamin, and niacin are precursors of certain coenzymes (substances that permit the activity of enzymes); and inositol is apparently built into the cell structure.

Water

In general yeasts require somewhat more water than molds but less than most bacteria. It should be emphasized, however, that great variation exists among yeasts; some species grow in media containing as little as 40 per cent water, for example, honey and jellies or jams. Organisms that grow in solutions of such high osmotic pressure are called *osmophilic*.

pH

Yeasts grow over a wide range of pH, although their requirements are more restricted than those of molds. Many species can multiply in solutions as acid as pH 3 and as alkaline as pH 7.5. The optimum reaction is usually between pH 4.5 and 5.0.

Temperature

Growth cannot be expected at temperatures much below freezing, nor does it occur above 47° C.; maximum temperatures for some species are lower. The most favorable temperature is usually between 20° and 30° C. Incubation at 30° C. is generally satisfactory. Highest yields of cells or of ethyl alcohol are obtained at somewhat lower temperatures, because the inhibitory effect of the toxic waste products that accumulate in the medium increases with temperature. This factor is of concern in the commercial manufacture of yeast.

Yeast spores are resistant to low temperatures; they can survive through the winter, frozen in the soil. Laboratory tests indicate that there is rapid death early during freezing, but the number of viable spores soon levels off and remains relatively constant. Yeasts have been found alive after storage for 160 weeks at $-13°$ to $-15°$ C.

Vegetative cells of most species are killed within five to ten minutes at 52° to 58° C. Spores are more resistant but are killed within a few minutes at 60° to 62° C. The medium in which the organisms are suspended affects the sterilization time and temperature; survival is often better in solutions containing high concentrations of sugar or salt.

Oxygen

Yeasts were the first organisms found to grow in the absence of atmospheric oxygen. Pasteur was greatly impressed by this fact, and he observed that anaerobic utilization of sugar yielded principally alcohol and carbon dioxide, whereas aerobic products were carbon dioxide and water. Yeast multiplication is more rapid and the yield of cells is greater under aerobic than under anaerobic conditions; an abundance of oxygen is therefore provided in the manufacture of commercial yeast, but oxygen is excluded when the desired product is alcohol (e.g., in brewing or wine making).

These observations are most readily understood by reference to the equations that express empirically the over-all reactions of complete oxidation and of alcoholic fermentation of a simple sugar:

$$(1)\ C_6H_{12}O_6 + 6O_2 \longrightarrow$$
$$6CO_2 + 6H_2O + 688{,}000\ cal.$$
$$(2)\ C_6H_{12}O_6 \longrightarrow$$
$$2C_2H_5OH + 2CO_2 + 54{,}000\ cal.$$

These show that complete, aerobic oxidation of a sugar such as glucose can be expected to yield a theoretical maximum of 688,000 calories of energy, whereas anaerobic fermentation of the same sugar to alcohol and CO_2 makes available no more than 54,000 calories of energy. Since the manufacture of protoplasmic constituents and structures, budding, and all other vital activities require energy, it is obvious that aerobic conditions favor more rapid and extensive cell growth.

CLASSIFICATION OF YEASTS

Yeasts are divided into two groups on the basis of their ability to produce ascospores. Those that form ascospores are assigned to the class Ascomycetes and are sometimes colloquially designated "true yeasts." Yeasts that do not produce ascospores but reproduce chiefly by budding are classified among the Fungi Imperfecti and are sometimes called "false yeasts" or *torulae*. The name torula in this connection does not have taxonomic significance.

There are about 30 genera of yeasts. The best known and the most important industrially is *Saccharomyces*. *S. cerevisiae* is the species used in brewing and baking. The *ellipsoideus* variety of *S. cerevisiae* is commonly used in the manufacture of wine.

False yeasts appear in the white or grayish scum that develops on acid foods like pickles left in an opened container. Some species utilize the organic acid, which normally acts as a preserva-tive, oxidizing it to carbon dioxide and water, thus paving the way for further spoilage.

Classification by Physiologic Characteristics

Protozoa, algae, and molds are classified principally on the basis of their morphology. Organisms as small as yeasts display so few distinctive morphologic features that additional characteristics must be found if fine subdivision is considered desirable. The same situation will be noted among bacteria. Properties useful in subdividing morphologically similar groups are based upon physiologic behavior, that is, what the organisms do rather than how they appear. Such characteristics are useful if they are distinctive and stable.

Physiologic classification is illustrated by three species of *Saccharomyces*: *S. cerevisiae*, *S. carlsbergensis*, another beer yeast, and *S. fragilis*, found in various fermented milks. These organisms produce oval cells and resemble one another morphologically; moreover, all ferment the simple sugar glucose ($C_6H_{12}O_6$) and produce large quantities of gas (CO_2). They can be distinguished, however, by their behavior in culture media containing two other carbohydrates, the disaccharides lactose and melibiose (Table 10-1). These compounds have the empirical formula $C_{12}H_{22}O_{11}$, but their monosaccharide components are joined differently. *S. cerevisiae* ferments neither lactose nor melibiose, *S. carlsbergensis* ferments melibiose, and *S. fragilis* ferments lactose. Characteristics like these

Table 10-1. Fermentation of Sugars by Three Common Species of Yeast

Species	Glucose	Lactose	Melibiose
Saccharomyces cerevisiae	+	−	−
Saccharomyces carlsbergensis	+	−	+
Saccharomyces fragilis	+	+	−

are used in classifying yeasts and, as will be found later, bacteria.

IMPORTANCE OF YEASTS

Spoilage

Yeasts are almost universally present in soil and from this source are widely disseminated by insects; they also travel on dust particles in the air. Yeast spores are not as resistant as spores of bacteria and molds, but in the dried state they are known to survive at least four years. Hence, it is obvious that they may easily find access to substances capable of supporting their growth.

Yeasts have a particular predilection for acid foods that contain sugar, from which they produce ethyl alcohol and a large quantity of gas. Fruits are especially subject to this type of spoilage; untreated fruit juices are almost certain to undergo alcoholic fermentation. It is believed that insects inoculate fruits with yeasts that are commonly present in or upon their bodies. Since yeasts, unlike molds, can grow in the absence of oxygen, sealing a food container does not prevent spoilage. However, even moderate heat (e.g., 60° C. for a few minutes) destroys yeasts and provides practical preservation.

Fermentation

Yeasts are very important in industry. Alcoholic fermentation has been practiced on a trial and error basis for thousands of years; scientific principles have been applied only within the past 80 to 90 years. Strains of *S. cerevisiae* are used to make beer and ale; this organism produces 4 to 6 per cent alcohol. "Bottom yeasts" are usually employed in making beer; they get their name because they gradually settle to the bottom of the fermenting solution. "Top yeasts" are used in making ale; they rise to the top of a fermentation tank, swept upward by the rapid evolution of gas. Strains of *S. cerevisiae,* var. *ellipsoideus,* are commonly present on grapes and other fruits and produce as much as 16 per cent alcohol in wine fermentation. Yeasts are found in fermented milks such as kefir, koumiss, or matzoon, beverages that are popular in eastern European countries. The alcoholic fermentation is a necessary preliminary to the manufacture of vinegar, in which bacteria of the genus *Acetobacter* oxidize alcohol to acetic acid. Yeasts also participate in the production of certain cheeses.

Commercial manufacture of ethyl alcohol is a large industry. Numerous by-products are formed, including carbon dioxide, which can be compressed into solid form as dry ice. Before World War I, it was discovered that sodium bisulfite modified the yeast fermentation so that glycerin was formed; the Germans used this procedure during the war to produce glycerin for explosives. An American process employs alkali for a similar purpose. Compressed yeast is used not only in baking but also as a source of vitamins and of enzymes useful in the manufacture of syrups and confectionery products.

A few yeasts are pathogenic, some producing superficial infections of man, others causing deep-seated infections. *Candida albicans* is the cause of thrush, and *Cryptococcus neoformans* produces one type of blastomycosis. Yeast infections present problems similar to those of mold infections.

 YEASTS

SUMMARY

Yeasts are large microscopic organisms. Their characteristic method of multiplication is budding, but various species also reproduce by fission, and by sexual and/or asexual spore formation.

Yeasts grow in acid and slightly alkaline media at moderate temperatures. They can grow without oxygen but their rate of multiplication is greater in its presence. Growth is favored by sugar, and in fact yeasts are noted for their ability to ferment large quantities of sugar. The products of anaerobic fermentation are ethyl alcohol and carbon dioxide; aerobic respiration yields only carbon dioxide and water. Yeasts are classified in part according to the sugars that they can attack.

Industry makes great use of yeasts in the manufacture of alcohol, alcoholic beverages, and certain other chemicals, and in bread making. These organisms also cause spoilage, particularly of materials containing sugars.

STUDY QUESTIONS

1. Describe similarities between yeasts and molds.
2. What are *growth factors?*
3. What nutrient and cultural conditions favor yeast growth (and spoilage)?
4. What differences does the absence of air make in the growth and activity of yeasts?
5. Describe the bases for classification of yeasts.

SUPPLEMENTARY READING

There are several good chapters on yeasts in *Henrici's Molds, Yeasts, and Actinomycetes,* by Skinner, Emmons, and Tsuchiya. *The Yeasts, A Taxonomic Study,* by Lodder and Kreger-van Rij, is a large and technical volume. Introductory chapters of a general nature are followed by detailed descriptions of many species. Ingram's *An Introduction to the Biology of Yeasts* offers a fairly detailed description of the morphology, composition, growth, reproduction, fermentative activity, genetics, and ecology of yeasts. The book by Cook includes a large section on metabolism as well as chapters on classification, ecology, life history, and genetics of yeast.

Cook, A. H. (Ed.): *The Chemistry and Biology of Yeasts.* New York, Academic Press, Inc., 1958.

Ingram, M.: *An Introduction to the Biology of Yeasts.* London, Sir Isaac Pitman and Sons, Ltd., 1955.

Lodder, J., and Kreger-van Rij, N. J. W.: *The Yeasts, A Taxonomic Study.* New York, Interscience Publishers, Inc., 1952.

Skinner, C. E., Emmons, C. W., and Tsuchiya, H. M.: *Henrici's Molds, Yeasts, and Actinomycetes,* 2d ed. New York, John Wiley & Sons, Inc., 1947.

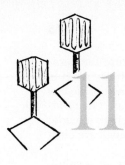

VIRUSES

VIRUSES AND PARASITISM

Viruses are usually placed at one end or the other of the evolutionary series that embraces all living organisms, past and present. It was pointed out in Chapter 1 that the primordial form probably consisted of nucleic acids and protein, and these turn out to be the essential and in many cases the only components of modern viruses. Some people therefore believe that present viruses are direct descendants of the prehistoric protovirus, and that no great evolutionary development was necessary.

The protovirus secured its chemical components from the supply of organic compounds that had formed by chance during the preceding billions of years in the pools and oceans of the early Earth. Twentieth century viruses are made in the living cells of animals, plants, or bacteria, where their proteins and nucleic acids are assembled. Thousands or even millions of years were probably required to replicate a protovirus; a few minutes suffice for a modern virus.

Most authorities believe that today's viruses are the culmination of a long series of evolutionary transformations —first, through forms of increasing efficiency in the activities associated with independent life, and later through forms of increasing dependence as the parasitic habit developed. Whether the independent intermediate organisms resembled bacteria as we know them now or were some long extinct direct or indirect ancestors of present bacteria will never be known.

The path from the postulated intermediates to modern viruses is a trail along which the capacity to live independently was lost by disuse because the intracellular habitat provided preformed protoplasmic constituents, energy, a stable environment, and other favorable conditions. Structural and chemical components disappeared as they were no longer used; the final form may be hardly larger than a macromolecule. The organism retains only the ability to direct its own reproduction or replication; it is completely dependent upon the living cells within which it resides.

CULTIVATION OF VIRUSES

Host Specificity

Routine cultivation of viruses requires the continuous availability of suitable living cells. The word *suitable* is used deliberately, because host specificity is a significant characteristic of viruses; that is, a given virus ordinarily grows in only one or a very few host species. For plant viruses, this usually means the appropriate specific host plant or sometimes certain closely related plants. Early workers with animal viruses formerly needed a constant supply of susceptible animals. A laboratory had to be equipped with several kinds of animals in order to work with a variety of viruses.

Chick Embryos

The discovery that many viruses could be cultivated in the developing chick embryo was an important advance. The chick embryo provides a suitable culture medium in its own "test tube" and is easily secured in large numbers. In addition to permitting rapid diagnosis of numerous virus infections, the chick embryo is also used for mass cultivation of viruses in the production of immunizing vaccines and for large scale research.

Cell Cultures

Another method of propagating viruses arose out of the earlier development of techniques for cultivating human and animal tissue cells *in vitro* (i.e., in test tubes or flasks). Susceptible tissues are grown in a suitable nutrient medium and inoculated with virus; upon continued incubation the virus infects and multiplies in the cultivated cells. Monkey kidney cells are used to propagate the poliomyelitis virus in the manufacture of Salk vaccine; the virus is harvested when a satisfactory concentration has been attained and is then inactivated with formalin.

Tissue cells can be made to grow on agar in a layer only one cell thick; in such a culture many human and animal viruses produce characteristic plaques or areas of cell destruction readily visible to the naked eye (Fig. 11-1).

Bacterial Viruses

Bacterial viruses also exhibit host specificity; a given virus lyses and multiplies within a certain species of bacterium, or perhaps a few closely related species. Some viruses attack only particular strains of a species. Bacterial viruses are cultivated upon the appropriate bacteria growing on agar or in broth.

A young broth culture of an organism such as *Escherichia coli* inoculated with coliphage becomes increasingly turbid for two to four hours and then clears completely within 10 to 15 minutes. The culture may contain as many as 10 billion virus particles per milliliter. Turbidity sometimes gradually reappears during continued incubation, and the secondary bacterial growth is resistant to the virus. A normally susceptible bacterial culture contains about one resistant cell for every 1,000,000 to 100,000,000 susceptible cells. The susceptible cells are lysed by the virus, but the resistant cells multiply freely and their progeny are thereafter resistant.

The particulate nature of bacteriophage is shown by the formation of plaques in the growth on agar media. The solid sheet of bacterial growth on a heavily inoculated nutrient agar plate, upon which a small amount of bacterial virus lytic filtrate has also been spread, becomes riddled with holes where no bacteria can be found. The number of these plaques is proportional to the amount of lytic filtrate spread upon the agar. A bit of material from one of these plaques produces typical lysis when

Figure 11-1. Plaques of type III polio-virus (1) and type 6 ECHO virus (2) in a thin layer of monkey epithelial cells growing on a special nutrient medium solidified with agar. The plaques resemble those of the bacterial virus shown in Figure 2-13. (Photos courtesy of Drs. G. D. Hsuing and J. L. Melnick; from Virology, 1955, Vol. 1.)

transferred to a young broth culture of the same bacterium. It therefore represents a colony of the bacteriophage.

PURIFICATION OF VIRUSES

The usual sources of viruses are infected plant or animal tissues, body fluids, secretions, feces, sewage, and so forth. All are crude mixtures containing bacteria and other microorganisms as well as the virus, tissue cells, and debris. Moreover, more than one virus may be present.

Filtration

Partial purification of viruses in tissue extracts, fecal suspensions, sewage, etc., can be effected by the method used by Iwanowski and other early investigators, that is, filtration to remove bacteria and other large particles. Filters are made of unglazed porcelain, diato-

maceous earth, asbestos, paper, sintered glass, or collodion (Figs. 11-2 and 11-3). The effective pore size of most filters can be determined indirectly with a fair degree of accuracy, and collodion filters of predetermined pore size can be made. In addition to removing bacteria and other large particles, filters have been used to estimate the dimensions of viruses. Early rough approximations have been confirmed in many instances by electron microscopy and by ultracentrifugation.

Ultracentrifugation

The ultracentrifuge is a machine that whirls test tubes or other containers at very high speed (e.g., 70,000 revolutions per minute). Particles suspended in a liquid are thrown outward from the axis of rotation at a velocity that varies with the size and density of the particles relative to the density of the suspending medium, the speed of rotation, and

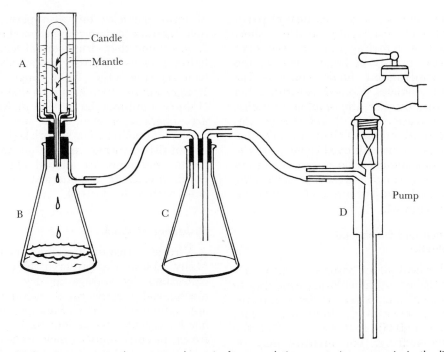

Figure 11-2. Apparatus used to remove bacteria from a solution; most viruses remain in the liquid after filtration. The solution in the mantle at A passes through the diatomaceous earth or unglazed porcelain candle and collects in the filter flask, B; C is a flask to trap water that might accidentally be sucked over from pump, D. Two other filters are shown in Figure 11-3.

Figure 11-3. Various filters. *Left,* A sintered glass filter. The filter disk is made of finely powdered glass that has been heated just enough to fuse together. Filters of different porosities can be made. *Center,* A diatomaceous earth filter. *Right,* A Seitz filter. The filtering agent is an asbestos pad clamped tightly between the upper and lower portions of the unit.

other factors. Large (i.e., heavy) particles travel most rapidly, so after a short period of centrifugation the sediment consists mainly of large particles, and the supernatant liquid contains the small particles. Longer centrifugation deposits smaller and smaller particles. The ultracentrifuge therefore separates viruses according to their sizes. Optical devices can be employed to measure the rate of sedimentation during operation of the centrifuge and from such data the sizes and relative purity of viruses can be calculated.

Dilution and Enrichment; Antibiotics

Purification of viruses is often accomplished by inoculating appropriate hosts, chick embryos, or tissue cultures with a series of dilutions (e.g., 1:10, 1:100, 1:1000, 1:10,000, . . .) of the crude mixture. The mixture may be treated with streptomycin or other antibiotics to inhibit bacteria. If the desired virus predominates in the mixture, it should theoretically appear in pure form in one or more of the higher dilutions. Serial passage of virus-containing material from one individual host or chick embryo to another is sometimes used to enrich the virus; after several transfers it can be isolated in a pure state.

Plaque Formation

Isolation of bacterial viruses from plaques on solid media has been mentioned. The same method can be used with animal viruses that produce plaques on tissue cultures. Some plant viruses form leaf spots or other localized lesions and can be purified by a similar procedure.

PHYSICAL AND CHEMICAL PROPERTIES OF VIRUSES

Morphology of Viruses

The electron microscope not only made possible accurate measurements of virus particles but also permitted investigators to determine their shapes. It was found that viruses are at least as heterogeneous in gross appearance as bacteria (Fig. 11-4). They range from 10 mμ to more than 300 mμ in diameter (1 mμ = 1 millimicron = 0.001 μ). Many are spherical or oval; some are long, narrow cylinders; a few are brick-shaped or consist of other regular geometric forms; and some are shaped like tadpoles, possessing a spherical or oval head with a slender tail.

Resistance of Viruses

Viruses withstand freezing very well. Many laboratories preserve their virus collections by storage in dry ice or mechancially refrigerated cabinets at approximately −75° C. Smallpox virus has been kept alive as long as 15 years frozen in chick embryo membranes.

Viruses are about as resistant to heat as many nonsporulating bacteria; most species are inactivated or killed within 30 minutes at 53° to 56° C.

Certain viruses (e.g., poliomyelitis) possess considerable resistance to phenol, cresol, and ether, withstand a wide range of pH, and survive indefinitely in 50 per cent glycerin. The infectious hepatitis virus survives about three times the concentration of chlorine necessary to kill pathogenic intestinal bacteria; a dosage of one part per million is required to ensure its destruction in water.

Composition of Viruses

Viruses vary in chemical composition from those of small particle size, which contain only nucleic acid and protein, to the large vaccinia (cowpox) virus, with several distinct proteins (including nucleoprotein), lipid, carbohydrate, copper, and one or two vitamin-like substances. Even this complex form does not carry on independent metabolism in the absence of living susceptible host cells.

Nucleic Acids of Viruses. The nucleic

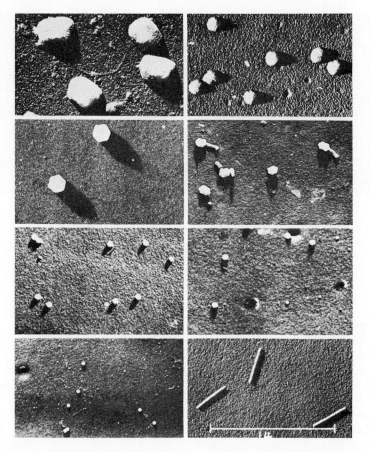

Figure 11-4. Electron photomicrographs showing the variation in size and shape of animal, plant, and bacterial viruses. From top to bottom:

Left	*Right*
Vaccinia	Influenza
Tipula iridescens	T2 bacteriophage
T3 bacteriophage	Rabbit papilloma
Poliomyelitis	Tobacco mosaic

(From Fraenkel-Conrat: Design and Function at the Threshold of Life: The Viruses. New York, Academic Press, 1962.)

acids that carry genetic information are the most vital constituents of any organism. In nearly all plants, animals, and microbes, as previously noted, these are of the DNA type and are found only in cell nuclei. RNA may also be present in nuclei, but is consistently found in cytoplasm, usually associated with granules where protein synthesis is most active. RNA therefore translates the information from nuclear DNA into proper structural terms as proteins (which include enzymes) are made.

The nucleic acid of bacterial viruses is DNA. Most animal viruses also contain DNA, but some of the smaller viruses (e.g., poliomyelitis and influenza) contain RNA and no DNA. RNA is the only nucleic acid in plant viruses.

Microstructure of Viruses. X-ray diffraction studies and electron microscopy have revealed that viruses display

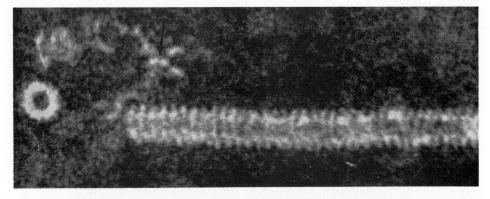

Figure 11-5. Electron photomicrograph of negatively stained tobacco mosaic virus showing helical symmetry (700,000X). The cross-section at the left shows the central hollow. The long, rod-shaped virion is composed of 2200 capsomeres helically arranged around the central core, as shown by the model in Figure 11-6. (From Horne et al., Virology, 15:348, 1961.)

remarkable symmetry in their microstructure. A virus particle or *virion* is composed of numerous small *capsomeres* comprising the protein coat or shell (*capsid*), which surrounds the nucleic acid *core*. Capsomeres and other viral components are arranged in regular helical, cubic, or complex patterns. Helical symmetry is illustrated by the arrangement of the capsids in a long coil around the core of the tobacco mosaic virus (Figs. 11-5 and 11-6). Cubic symmetry is characteristic of many viruses, both large and small. The capsomeres forming the outer, protein shell are closely packed in triangular, pentagonal, hexagonal, or other arrangement or combination of arrangements as illustrated in the electron photomicrograph and model of adenovirus in Figure 11-7. Vaccinia, contagious pustular dermatitis, and certain other large bacterial viruses illustrate complex symmetry (Fig. 11-8).

The tobacco mosaic virus (Fig. 11-5) consists of a spiral coil of protein 18 mμ in diameter and 300 mμ long. It has a hollow core 4 mμ in diameter, which contains the RNA. Stanley crystallized this virus in 1935 and found that the crystalline material was highly infectious (Fig. 11-9). Fraenkel-Conrat separated the protein from the RNA and found, in 1956, that the RNA alone is infectious, although its infective effi-

ciency is only about one two-hundredth that of the intact virus. The RNA induces the plant to produce not only RNA but also the protein "coat"; thus a complete tobacco mosaic virus is formed.

An *E. coli* bacteriophage is a tadpole-shaped particle 220 to 280 mμ long with

Figure 11-6. Model of tobacco mosaic virus showing a portion of the helical array of protein capsomeres that comprise the capsid of the virion. The RNA helix near the core of the virion is also shown. (From Klug et al., Adv. Virus Research, 7:225, 1960.)

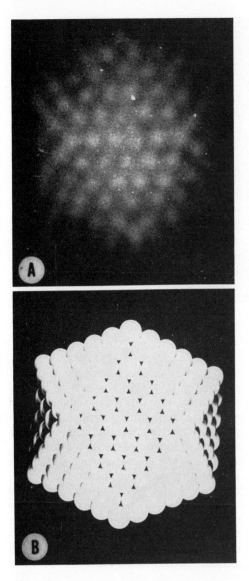

Figure 11-7. A, Electron photomicrograph of negatively stained type 5 adenovirus showing cubic symmetry (850,000X). B, Photograph of a model of an icosahedron with 252 surface spheres oriented in the same way as the virus capsomeres. (From Horne et al., J. Molec. Biol., 1:84, 1959.)

Figure 11-8. Complex symmetry shown in electron photomicrograph of negatively stained contagious pustular dermatitis virus (143,000X). (From Nagington et al., Virology, 16:248, 1962.)

Figure 11-9. Crystals of tobacco mosaic virus (675X). (From Stanley, Am. J. Botany, 24:59–68, 1937.)

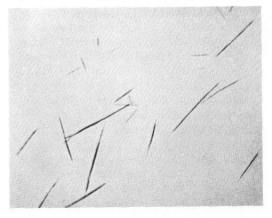

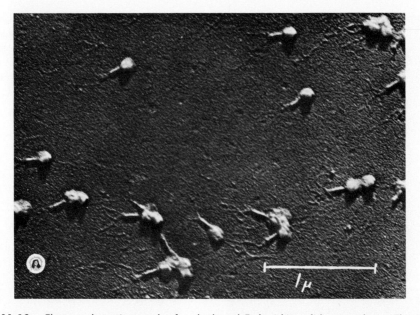

Figure 11-10. Electron photomicrograph of a shadowed *Escherichia coli* bacteriophage. The "head" is about 130 x 100 mμ; the "tail" is about 6 x 150 mμ. (Photograph by T. F. Anderson; A.S.M. LS-138.)

a "head" that is hexagonal in cross-section and a long, slender "tail" (Fig. 11-10). The tail and the outer part of the head are composed of protein; the core of the head is DNA.

REPRODUCTION OF VIRUSES

Bacterial Virus Reproduction

Virus multiplication is a complex process, divisible for descriptive purposes into four phases: (1) infection: adsorption and entry of virus into the host cell; (2) intracellular synthesis of virus components; (3) assembly of new virus particles; (4) liberation of virus. Reproduction has been most thoroughly investigated in bacterial viruses such as coliphage T2 and it is their reproduction that will be described; it should be understood that the multiplication of animal and plant viruses differs in various details from that described here.

A virus alone is unable to replicate *in vitro;* it must first enter a susceptible host cell. When a virus encounters an appropriate receptor site on such a cell,

union and adsorption occur *immediately* (Fig. 11-11). In the case of T2 bacteriophage, the tail fibers attach to cell wall receptors, and a viral enzyme apparently starts digesting the muramic acid–peptide complex that confers rigidity on the bacterial cell wall. The elastic protein tail sheath contracts, and the viral DNA is injected into the bacterium. The protein coat remains outside, having performed its function of protecting the virus during its extracellular existence (Fig. 11-12). Plant and animal viruses gain entrance to their respective host cells by somewhat different and perhaps less dramatic mechanisms, but the basic steps are the same: specific adsorption, penetration, shedding of the protein coat.

A period of "eclipse" then follows, during which the virus disappears as an independent infective agent. This is the interval when virus components are being formed. The metabolism of the host bacterium suddenly changes and production of bacterial-type DNA, RNA, and protein ceases. In fact, microscopic evidence indicates that the chromatin body of the bacterium, which

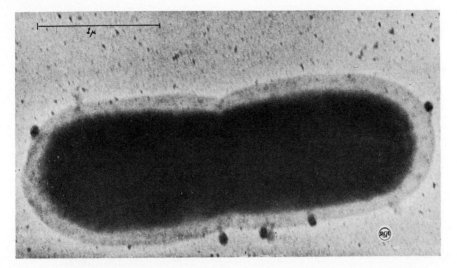

Figure 11-11. Electron photomicrograph showing five particles of bacteriophage attached to the cell wall of *Escherichia coli*. (Photograph by S. E. Luria, M. Delbrück, and T. F. Anderson; A.S.M. LS-37.)

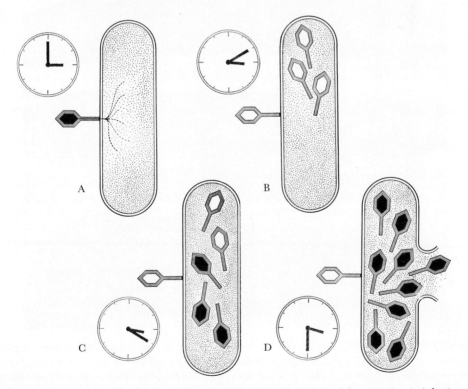

Figure 11-12. Reproduction of bacterial virus (coliphage T2) consists of four stages: A, Infection, in which the virus attaches to the host bacterium by the "tail," and the nucleic acid core is emptied into the bacterial cell; B, the "dark" period during which virus nucleic acid begins to multiply and induces formation of new protein "coats;" C, the "rise" period when nucleic acid appears within the protein coats; and D, the burst, when some 200 new virus particles are released. The bacterium lyses and disappears. (From Stent, Scientific American, *188*(5):36, May 1953.)

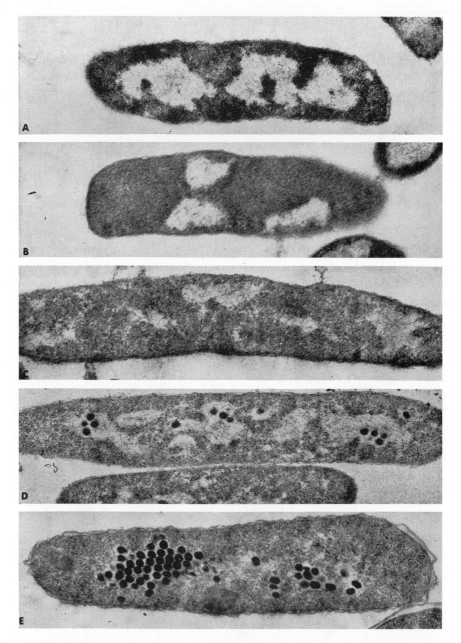

Figure 11-13. Electron photomicrographs of ultrathin sections of *Escherichia coli* at various stages in the growth of infecting T2 bacteriophage. *A,* A normal cell at the moment of infection showing typical electron-transparent chromatin bodies. *B,* A cell two to four minutes after infection; the chromatin bodies have changed in shape and migrated toward the cell wall. *C,* Ten minutes after infection the chromatin bodies have disappeared and have been replaced by vacuoles filled with fibrillar phage DNA. *D,* The first polyhedral condensates of phage DNA appear 14 minutes after infection. *E,* Forty minutes after infection many condensates and phage heads are present. (Photomicrographs by Kellenberger, from Jacob and Wollman, Scientific American, 204(6):92, June 1961.)

contains the cellular DNA, disintegrates and its contents are dispersed within the first minute after infection (Fig. 11-13B). Pools of virus-type DNA precursors and protein precursors accumulate. Part of these materials is derived from the breakdown of host components and part from the external medium.

After the eclipse period, virus DNA is removed from the pool for incorporation into progeny phage. The rate of formation of phage is approximately the same as the rate of synthesis of phage DNA, and the precursor DNA pool contains the equivalent of 50 to 100 phage units throughout the remainder of the latent period.

The protein pool is derived almost entirely from the external medium instead of from the host cell. Synthesis of the internal protein components of the virus begins within two or three minutes, but the polypeptides of the head and tail proteins are not formed until several minutes later.

Assembly of an infective phage unit —that is, enclosure of the nucleic acid in a protein coat and addition of the protein tail—begins about 10 minutes after infection with *condensation* of a single viral DNA macromolecule from the vegetative precursor pool into a polyhedral body that can be detected by electron microscopy (Fig. 11-13D–E). This body is stabilized by its internal protein, and the protein head membrane forms around it by aggregation of a thousand or more identical units from the protein pool. The tail is added and finally the virus particle attains maturity when its various components "set" sufficiently to remain intact after being liberated by lysis of the host cell. Lysis may be the result of continuation of the enzymatic process which enabled the infecting phage to inject its DNA into the host. The various stages in the development of a coliphage are diagramed in Figure 11-14.

Normally, 100 to 300 virus particles form within an infected bacterium.

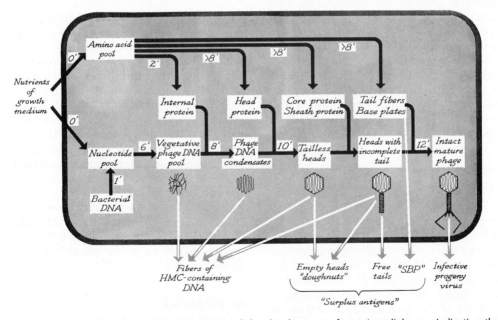

Figure 11-14. Diagrammatic representation of the development of certain coliphages, indicating the timing of the successive intracellular events. The origin of various phage constituents is indicated in the lower part of the diagram. HMC-containing DNA is phage DNA, which possesses the unusual pyrimidine, 5-hydroxymethylcytosine, whereas bacterial DNA contains cytosine. "Surplus antigens" are incompletely assembled phage proteins. (From Stent, Molecular Biology of Bacterial Viruses. San Francisco, W. H. Freeman & Co., 1963.)

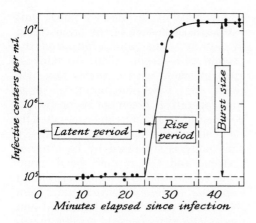

Figure 11-15. One-step growth curve of a coli-phage. Each infective center represents one or more phage particles assayed by formation of a single plaque. (From Doermann, J. Gen. Physiol., 35:645, 1952.)

These are suddenly released when lysis occurs. This is known as the "burst" and is shown graphically in Figure 11-15, which presents the results of a *one-step growth* experiment. In this experiment, the infective phage units in broth cultures of appropriate bacteria were counted at short intervals. All the units were situated within bacterial cells during the first 24 minutes, which is called the *latent period*. During the *rise period* of 12 minutes which followed, 100 phage particles were released for every one that had initially infected a bacterial cell.

Lysogeny

The events just described, which occur after infection of a bacterium by a bacterial virus, can be considered the consequence of partial replacement of one system of genetic information by another. The new genetic mechanism so completely dominates the physiologic activity of the host cell that the latter is destroyed in fulfilling the mission of the former. There are bacterial strains and phage strains, however, that can exist compatibly together. The DNA of such a *temperate* phage becomes incor-

porated in the DNA of the host organism and replicates at the same rate as the remainder of the host DNA and the cell itself. The bacterium is said to be *lysogenic,* because an appropriate external stimulus can induce active replication of the virus and subsequent death and lysis of the cell. Temperate phage or *prophage* within the bacterium, replicating at the same rate as the bacterial DNA, is in an essentially commensal relationship with the host cell. Prophage per se is not infective, but it endows the cell with the ability to form infective phage without the entrance of phage from outside. Effective inducing agents include ultraviolet light, x-rays, hydrogen peroxide, and nitrogen mustard. Only temperate phages can give the lysogenic response; virulent phages do not, and they do not occur as prophages in lysogenic bacteria.

VIRAL INFECTIONS

Plant Viruses

More than 400 plant viruses have been described and named since 1898. The number of diseases they cause has not been determined. Symptoms of viral disease of plants include stunted growth, distortion, other abnormalities that reduce the yield or quality of the plant, necrosis, and death. Mosaic diseases are the most common. They are so named because the leaves and stems are mottled in characteristic colored patterns. Many plant species are affected (Table 11-1).

A given plant species may be susceptible to many different viruses. At least 25 viruses are known to infect potatoes, and a dozen or more infect tobacco plants.

Animal Viruses

At least 500 animal viruses have been isolated. As mentioned previously, they display considerable host specificity and, in fact, many viruses invade only certain types of tissue. *Neuro-*

Table 11-1. A Few Plant Viruses

Type	Representative Plant Hosts
Mosaic	Tobacco
	Orchids
	Beans
	Turnips
	Alfalfa
	Potatoes
	Tomatoes
	Cucumbers
Yellows	Aster
Leaf curl	Tobacco
	Cotton
	Sugar beets

tropic viruses, for example, multiply in the brain, spinal cord, and peripheral nerves; *respiratory* viruses infect cells of the respiratory tract; *enteric* viruses are associated with the gastrointestinal tract; and *viscerotropic* viruses attack the abdominal viscera, especially the liver, or produce generalized infection.

Animal viruses are classified according to the nucleic acid (RNA or DNA) they contain, their size, sensitivity to ether, presence or absence of an envelope, type of symmetry displayed by their capsids, and the number of capsomeres in each capsid. Size can be determined by use of the electron microscope, but for practical purposes it is often sufficient to estimate it roughly by attempting to pass the virus through

filters of known pore size. Ether, a lipid solvent, greatly reduces the infectivity of certain viruses but has little effect on others, which either lack lipid or contain lipid that is not essential for infectivity or is not extractable by ether. The *nucleocapsids* (nucleic acid–protein particles) of certain viruses are "naked," those of others are enclosed within a membrane or envelope, partly derived from the nuclear or cytoplasmic membrane of the host cell and partly composed of virus protein.

It is obvious from Table 11-2 that animal viruses vary greatly in physical characteristics. The range of size is nearly 20-fold, and the actual structures of the smallest have not yet been determined with certainty. There are eight principal groups, divided according to the characteristics just listed.

The *picornaviruses* (Spanish: *pico,* small quantity + RNA) are the smallest animal viruses known. They exhibit cubic symmetry, but their small size makes it difficult to determine the number of capsomeres in each virion. There are more than 140 viruses in this group, including enteroviruses of man and lower animals (polio, Coxsackie, ECHO, foot and mouth disease), over 60 rhinoviruses (common cold), and several encephalomyelitis and encephalomyocarditis viruses of lower animals. The ECHO viruses (**E**nteric, **C**ytopathogenic, **H**uman, **O**rphan) were originally isolated from the feces of supposedly normal persons, and were detected by

Table 11-2. Distinguishing Characteristics of Major Groups of Animal Viruses

Group	Nucleic Acid	Size (mμ)	Ether Sensitivity	Presence of Envelope	Capsid Symmetry	Number of Capsomeres
Picornavirus	RNA	17–30	−	−	Cubic	
Reovirus	RNA	74	−	−	Cubic	92 or 180
Arbovirus	RNA	20–100	+	?	?	
Myxovirus	RNA	80–200	+	+	Helical	
Papovavirus	DNA	40–55	−	−	Cubic	42 or 72
Adenovirus	DNA	65–85	−	−	Cubic	252
Herpesvirus	DNA	120–180	+	+	Cubic	162
Poxvirus	DNA	150–300	+ or −	+	Helical	

their destructive effect (cytopathogenicity) on tissue cultures; they were called orphan viruses because they had not been shown to produce disease.

Reoviruses are found in the respiratory and enteric tracts of animals and man, and are orphan viruses. Unlike that of other RNA viruses, their RNA is double-stranded and is present in very high amount. So far, these viruses are of primarily academic interest as biologic oddities.

The *arboviruses* (**ar**thropod-**bo**rne) are a large group composed of 200 to 250 types classified in three principal subgroups and many smaller subgroups. They are transmitted to mammals and birds by blood-sucking insects and replicate in the arthropods as well as in the vertebrate hosts. Important members of the group are various encephalitis viruses and the yellow fever virus.

The *myxovirus* group (Greek: *myxa,* mucus) is named because of the affinity of its members for mucoproteins. Both spherical and filamentous forms are found: characteristic features include a helical internal ribonucleoprotein and a lipoprotein envelope with radial projections. Many members of this group react with erythrocytes of one or more species and may cause them to clump together (agglutinate). Myxoviruses include the etiologic agents of human and swine influenza, mumps, measles, distemper, and a number of other animal diseases.

The *papovaviruses* comprise a group of small, DNA viruses that induce tumor formation. The name was coined from the first two letters of the names of three viruses: **pa**pilloma, **po**lyoma, and **va**cuolating agent. A virus of interest to man is the human papilloma (wart) virus.

There are many types of *adenovirus* (Greek: *adenos,* gland). They are medium-sized, ether resistant, of uniform icosahedral structure, immunologically (i.e., chemically) related, and found in man, monkeys, and certain other animals. Some are associated with epidemic or sporadic cases of respiratory disease, others have been isolated from tonsils and adenoids and from fecal specimens. Pathogenicity of some types has not yet been demonstrated.

Members of the *herpesvirus* group are moderately large DNA viruses enclosed in an envelope consisting of host cell material. The 10 viruses include herpes simplex, found in cold sores, and the varicella-zoster virus, which occurs in chickenpox and in herpes zoster or shingles. There are also several animal pathogens.

The *poxviruses* are large, brick-shaped DNA viruses that infect a variety of species and produce typical skin lesions. Among the twenty-odd poxviruses are variola (smallpox), vaccinia (used to immunize men against smallpox), and poxes of a dozen or more animals. Several tumor viruses of lower animals are also included in this group. The poxviruses are about the size of rickettsiae and other small bacteria, and approach them in chemical organization. However, they possess only a single type of nucleic acid and their manner of replication is virus-like rather than bacteria-like. They are therefore considered to be the most complex viruses.

Modification of Viruses.   Tissue specificities are not absolute and unchangeable. Initial invasion of the customary susceptible tissue may be followed by spread to other tissues. Moreover, the tissue affinity of certain viruses can be altered deliberately. Viscerotropic strains of yellow fever virus become neurotropic after repeated inoculation into the brains of mice, and will produce fatal encephalitis in suitable experimental animals.

The modification of viruses by passage through an unnatural tissue or host is important to an understanding of the natural history of disease and the evolution of microorganisms. It illustrates processes that doubtless occur constantly in nature. In a normal infection with a given virus the customary tissues are affected, and ordinarily the virus in its usual form passes to the next host. An unusually large infecting dose or overwhelming multiplication in a highly susceptible individual may be followed by invasion of tissues not ordinarily affected. This provides opportunity for a transformation in the virus (more properly, selection of a mutant virus) and the appearance of a modified parasite capable of producing a new disease, as is illustrated by the yellow fever virus. Host specificity may also be altered in a similar manner.

VIRUSES

SUMMARY

Viruses are obligately parasitic entities composed essentially of a single nucleic acid (RNA or DNA) and protein. They can ordinarily invade cells of only one type (e.g., plant, animal, bacterial), often of only one species or even of a certain tissue. The viral nucleic acid combines with or replaces part of that of the host cell, whereupon the host thereafter produces viral nucleic acid and protein, normally at the expense of its own nucleic acid and protein. Virus replication within the host cell is followed by lysis of the host or liberation of virus progeny as a "burst" consisting of as many as 300 new virions, or both.

More than 400 plant viruses, 500 animal viruses, and hundreds of bacterial viruses have been isolated. They vary greatly in size and complexity, but display remarkable structural symmetry. They are composed of protein–nucleic acid units or *capsomeres,* arranged in a cubic, helical, or complex pattern to form a *capsid.* Animal viruses are classified according to their size, structure, and composition. At present eight major groups are recognized.

STUDY QUESTIONS

1. What is the derivation of the word *bacteriophage?* Is this an appropriate name for a bacterial virus?
2. Are viruses soluble or particulate agents? Describe how to demonstrate this.
3. Why would one expect viruses to require *specific* hosts or tissues, whereas most other microorganisms can multiply in or on a variety of substrates?
4. Describe how to secure a pure culture of an *Escherichia coli* bacteriophage from sewage.
5. Do viruses constitute a sharply defined class of organisms? Explain.
6. Describe the process of replication of a bacterial virus.
7. What sorts of organisms are subject to infection by viruses?
8. Are all viruses pathogenic? Explain.
9. What seems to be the essential chemical component of viruses? Do viruses differ in this regard from other organisms?
10. Would you expect an RNA virus to be lysogenic in its host cell? Explain.

SUPPLEMENTARY READING

Viral and Rickettsial Infections of Man, edited by Horsfall and Tamm, contains a wealth of material. It begins with general chapters on techniques, and proceeds to chapters on individual viruses and rickettsiae and the diseases they produce. Burnet's *Principles of Animal Virology* offers a biologic slant typical of the author's approach in all his writing. He reviews the properties of host cells and viruses, and then discusses the effects of viruses on host cells, immunity, latent infection, and the ecology, genetics, and evolution of viruses. *The Viruses,* edited by Burnet and Stanley, is a complete account by specialists in the field. Stent presents a valuable discussion of the nature of bacteriophage, its replication, and its significance in genetic studies, with over 700 references. The Stanley and Valens book is a readable, popular account of the nature and significance of viruses. *Scientific American* frequently has interesting short articles on viruses.

Burnet, F. M.: *Principles of Animal Virology,* 2d ed. New York, Academic Press, 1960.
Burnet, F. M., and Stanley, W. M. (Eds.): *The Viruses.* New York, Academic Press, 1959.
Horsfall, F. L., Jr., and Tamm, I. (Eds.): *Viral and Rickettsial Infections of Man,* 4th ed. Philadelphia, J. B. Lippincott Co., 1965.
Knight, C. A., and Fraser, D.: The Mutation of Viruses. *Scientific American, 193*(1): 74–78, July, 1955.
Luria, S. E.: The T2 Mystery. *Scientific American, 192*(4): 92–98, April, 1955.
Pollard, E. C.: The Physics of Viruses. *Scientific American, 191*(6): 62–70, December, 1954.
Stanley, W. M., and Valens, E. G.: *Viruses and the Nature of Life.* New York, E. P. Dutton and Co., Inc., 1961.
Stent, G. S.: *Molecular Biology of Bacterial Viruses.* San Francisco, W. H. Freeman and Co., 1963.

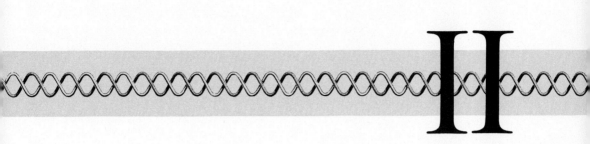

II

BIOLOGY OF BACTERIA

BACTERIAL METABOLISM

MICROBIAL NUTRITION

Nutrients

Nutrients (foods) are extracellular substances that, on entering a cell after passing across the cell membrane, can be used by the cell for building material or for obtaining energy.

Practically any material on Earth can nourish one microbe or another. An astounding list of materials can be compiled, ranging from the usual growth substances—proteins, sugars, purines, and pyrimidines—to the unusual, such as rubber, paper, leather, oil, turpentine, carbon monoxide, iron, and elemental sulfur. No one organism is capable of utilizing all nutrients, and some nutrients can be used by only a small number of species. Many cannot attack native proteins but grow luxuriantly when supplied with products resulting from partial digestion of proteins. Most organisms use several carbohydrates, but a few do not use any.

Differences in the ability to utilize nutrients constitute a part of the basis for the identification of microorganisms. Nearly all species, and in some instances genera, are classified according to the compounds they utilize and the products formed from them. The ability to oxidize thiosulfate separates autotrophs that oxidize ferrous iron to ferric iron, at low pH, into two genera—*Thiobacillus* (thiosulfate is oxidized) and *Ferrobacillus* (thiosulfate is not oxidized). Among heterotrophs, the genus *Staphylococcus* ferments glucose, whereas the related genus *Micrococcus* does not.

Except for viruses and holozoic protozoa (see p. 18), microorganisms are holophytic in their nutrition. These latter organisms can transport molecules of low molecular weight across the cell membrane but not the large molecules of proteins, fats, and starch. In most natural environments there are bacteria that can secrete enzymes which hydrolyze large particles (predigestion) to substances of lower molecular weight. These extracellular enzymes diffuse away from the organisms and into the surrounding environment. Their activity furnishes nutrients not only for their own organisms, but for neighboring organisms as well. Extracellular enzymes are specific in their action; for example, chitinase acts on chitin and cellulase hydrolyzes cellulose.

Hydrolysis of Complex Foods. Hydrolysis is a process by which proteins, polysaccharides, fats, and other large structural components are converted into their constituent parts by the introduction of water at points of cleavage of the large molecules, liberating the constituent molecules (Fig. 12-1). The removal of water during the synthetic process by which the complex food was made is usually accomplished by a mechanism that differs from the hydrolytic reaction. The hydrolysis of proteins yields the consecutively smaller proteoses, peptones, peptides, and amino acids. Proteoses are large fragments that can be precipitated by ammonium sulfate. Peptides are smaller fragments of two or more amino acids united through the carboxyl group of one and the amino group of the next. These fragments differ according to the protein from which they are derived and the method of digestion that produced

them. The hydrolysis of polysaccharides such as starch or cellulose yields disaccharides and monosaccharides; glycerin and fatty acids are the products of fat digestion.

Penetration of Nutrients. The selection and transport of nutrients is the function of the cell membrane. The bacterial wall appears to play a minor part, that of excluding large molecules. Some compounds enter the cell by diffusion, but in most instances the nutrients are transported across the cell membrane by a process called *active transport.* Active transport refers to the ability of an organism to accumulate substances within the cell in high concentration from an external environment in which the substances are in low concentration (movement against the concentration gradient). The transport process requires energy and is catalyzed by enzymes called *permeases.* Some permeases are produced only when the substrate (the substance upon which the enzyme acts) is present. Such is the case in certain strains of *Escherichia coli* that do not readily metabolize lactose. The organism cannot transport lactose until the cell has produced the permease (enzyme induction). After the lactose crosses the cell membrane, the organism may have to synthesize the enzymes to metabolize it. Thus the inability of an organism to metabolize a nutrient may reflect its inability to transport the nutrient; on the other hand, the organism may have a trans-

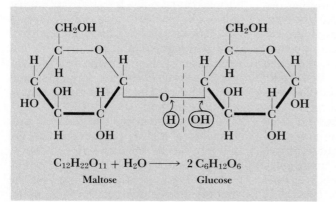

$$C_{12}H_{22}O_{11} + H_2O \longrightarrow 2\,C_6H_{12}O_6$$
Maltose   Glucose

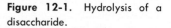

Figure 12-1. Hydrolysis of a disaccharide.

Table 12-1. Nutritional Types

Type	Oxidizable Substrate (Hydrogen Donor)	Energy Source	Carbon Source	Organisms
Photosynthetic autotroph[1]	Inorganic	Light	CO_2	Chlorobacteriaceae (green sulfur bacteria) Thiorhodaceae (purple sulfur bacteria) [Also green plants]
Chemosynthetic autotroph[2]	Inorganic	Oxidation–reduction reactions	CO_2	*Hydrogenomonas* *Thiobacillus* *Beggiatoa* *Nitrosomonas* *Nitrobacter*
Photosynthetic heterotroph[3]	Organic	Light	CO_2 and organic	Athiorhodaceae (nonsulfur purple bacteria)
Chemosynthetic heterotroph[4]	Organic	Oxidation–reduction reactions	Organic	Most microorganisms except algae [Also animals]

Notes: Also referred to by the following names, which have not yet been universally accepted:

1. Photolithotroph
2. Chemolithotroph
3. Photoorganotroph
4. Chemoorganotroph

port mechanism but lack the necessary metabolic enzymes. *E. coli* has a mechanism for metabolizing citrate, but it is unable to transport it into the cell. An organism of this type is often described as *cryptic* to citrate.

Nutritional Types of Bacteria

Bacteria can be divided into four categories according to their carbon source and manner of securing energy (Table 12-1).

Autotrophic bacteria live on a strictly inorganic diet. Their carbon is derived from carbon dioxide; the hydrogen needed to reduce this to organic form comes from inorganic sources such as hydrogen in the atmosphere, hydrogen sulfide, ammonia, or water. Energy is supplied in the form of light in the case of *photosynthetic* organisms and by the oxidation of inorganic compounds

in the case of *chemosynthetic* organisms. For example, thiobacilli can obtain energy through the oxidation of thiosulfate (Table 12-2). *Thiobacillus thiooxidans* can oxidize elemental sulfur to sulfuric acid and grow in an environment of 5 per cent sulfuric acid. *Nitrosomonas* species can oxidize ammonia to nitrite; *Nitrobacter* species oxidize nitrite to nitrate; and species of *Hydrogenomonas* oxidize hydrogen to

Table 12-2. Medium for Cultivation of Thiobacilli

Constituent	Amount per Liter
Sodium thiosulfate	5.0 gm.
Ammonium sulfate	0.4 gm.
Monopotassium phosphate	4.0 gm.
Calcium chloride	0.25 gm.
Magnesium sulfate	0.5 gm.
Ferrous sulfate	0.01 gm.

water. In each organism a mechanism exists for capturing energy during the oxidation process.

Occasionally an organism is found that exhibits an autotrophic way of life except that it requires a cofactor or vitamin. An organism of this type is considered by many bacteriologists to be essentially an autotroph. Such instances, among many others, demonstrate that there is no sharp line of demarcation between the autotrophs and heterotrophs.

Our knowledge and techniques of cultivating autotrophs stem from the pioneer work of Beijerinck, Winogradsky, Kluyver, and van Niel. The classical reports by Serge Winogradsky on the sulfur bacteria (1889) and the nitrifying organisms (1890) should be read by all students.

Heterotrophic bacteria require complex organic compounds for their main carbon source, although they may use carbon dioxide to a lesser extent. The energy source may be photosynthetic or chemosynthetic. *Photosynthetic heterotrophs* consist of one family—the Athiorhodaceae (the nonsulfur purple bacteria). These organisms can use organic compounds as their carbon source and hydrogen donor. They require vitamins (e.g., *p*-aminobenzoic acid), and some will grow aerobically in the dark by oxidizing organic compounds (*facultative phototrophs*).

Chemosynthetic heterotrophs constitute the vast majority of bacteria commonly studied or dealt with in general or applied microbiology. A type organism is *Escherichia coli*. This species has the ability to grow on inorganic salts and glucose; the ammonium ion serves as the nitrogen source. *E. coli* can also use preformed materials such as amino acids, vitamins, purines, and pyrimidines. A second type organism is *Streptococcus faecalis* (various *Lactobacillus* species are of the same type). This organism does not have the ability to grow on a glucose-salt medium but requires vitamins, amino acids, purines, pyrimidines, and peptides as well. Some-

times the amino acids are supplied as peptides to facilitate transport across the cell membrane and to prevent decarboxylation of essential amino acids (e.g., tyrosine). *S. faecalis* will grow well on the relatively complicated medium illustrated in Table 12-3. This is a complete medium for the growth of *S. faecalis,* but it is not complete enough to elict all the capabilities of the organism. In this medium *S. faecalis* will not oxidize pyruvate (an intermediate in sugar metabolism), because the vitamin (coenzyme) lipoic acid is omitted. *S. faecalis* does, however, produce the protein (apoenzyme) to which lipoic acid can attach, and thus when lipoic acid is added to the cells the complete active enzyme is formed. In this manner cells containing the apoenzyme can be used to assay food for lipoic acid content.

Microorganisms require of a growth

Table 12-3. Semisynthetic Medium for Lipoic Acid Assay*

Constituent	Amount per Liter	
Acid-hydrolyzed casein (H$_2$SO$_4$)	10	gm.
Enzymatic casein hydrolyzate	7.5	gm.
Glucose	3	gm.
Dipotassium phosphate	5	gm.
Sodium thioglycolate	100	mg.
DL-tryptophan	200	mg.
L-cystine	200	mg.
Adenine, guanine, uracil (each)	25	mg.
Nicotinic acid	5	mg.
Riboflavin	1	mg.
Pyridoxine (HCl)	1	mg.
Thiamine (HCl)	1	mg.
Calcium pantothenate	1	mg.
Folic acid	10	μg.
Biotin	1	μg.
Salts B†	5	ml.

° Final pH 7.0 to 7.3; autoclave for 15 minutes at 121° C.

† Salts B, per 250 ml.: 10 gm. of MgSO$_4$ · 7H$_2$O; 0.5 gm. of NaCl; 0.5 gm. of FeSO$_4$ · 7H$_2$O; 0.5 gm. of MnSO$_4$ · 4H$_2$O; and 0.5 gm. of ascorbic acid.
From I. C. Gunsalus, and W. E. Razell: *In* S. P. Colowick and N. O. Kaplan (Eds.): *Methods in Enzymology,* 3d ed. New York, Academic Press, Inc., 1957, p. 941.

medium a source of carbon, nitrogen, energy, and inorganic ions. The inorganic needs of most bacteria can be met by the addition of K^+, Mg^{++}, Mn^{++}, Fe^{++}, $PO_4^{\equiv}$, and $SO_4^=$ to a synthetic medium. A requirement can be demonstrated for these ions, but others (Zn^{++}, Cu^{++}, molybdate) are needed in such small amounts that a requirement is difficult to establish, mainly because these ions are contaminants of glassware and the chemicals used in the medium. For example, many bacteria synthesize vitamin B_{12}, which contains cobalt, but no quantitative requirement for cobalt has been demonstrated.

All organisms can utilize ammonia for the synthesis of nitrogen compounds, but some require additional nitrogenous growth factors. Some can convert nitrate or nitrite to ammonia or degrade organic nitrogenous compounds to ammonia. A few (*Azotobacter, Rhizobium,* and *Clostridium pasteurianum*) are able to utilize nitrogen for growth (see p. 124 and Chap. 17).

The requirement for sulfur is met for most organisms by supplying them with the sulfate ion. These organisms reduce sulfur to the sulfhydryl (—SH) form and attach it to amino acids to form cystine, methionine, glutathione, etc. Some bacteria have lost their ability to reduce sulfate and require sulfur in the reduced form—hydrogen sulfide, cysteine, methionine, etc.

The requirement for amino acids, vitamins, purines, and pyrimidines, as well as for a miscellaneous group of organic compounds needed for growth, represents a loss in the ability of a microorganism to synthesize or transport these compounds. This in turn reflects the genetic capabilities of the organism. The microbiologist has learned to make the genetic apparatus of organisms defective for the purpose of producing a mutant requiring a growth substance; this is done by subjecting bacteria to ultraviolet light. The nutritional mutant produced is termed an *auxotroph,* the parent organism a *prototroph* (see Chap. 16).

SOURCES OF ENERGY AND METHODS OF SECURING ENERGY

Energy transformation is one of the central activities of life. Every individual is continually securing energy and utilizing it to maintain and produce protoplasmic substances.

Energy can be demonstrated in various ways, and any one form of energy can be converted into any of the others. Energy in the form of light (e.g., from the sun) is incorporated into chemical bonds by photochemical processes such as photosynthesis. Chemical bond energy is converted to the energy of motion when a protozoon or a bacterium moves its flagella; it may be transmuted into the energy of new chemical bonds when protoplasm is manufactured.

Energy is always transferred to a lower level. In biologic systems, however, the energy level of a compound can be raised by transferring to it certain types of chemical groups, but energy is lost or wasted in the process. Some chemical bonds possess more energy than others, and although the displacement of their electrons provides large quantities of energy, only under certain conditions can biologic systems make use of this energy. In energy-yielding systems, these bonds are mainly phosphate bonds which serve to activate compounds in the building of protoplasm. These bonds are referred to as "high-energy phosphate" bonds, symbolized as $(\sim PO_3H_2)$ or $(\sim P)$. The types of phosphate bond that can be used for transferring energy and compounds in which they are found include:

$$P\sim N-\overset{\|}{C}-\begin{cases} \text{phosphoarginine} \\ \text{phosphocreatine} \end{cases}$$

$$P\sim O-\overset{\|}{C}-\begin{cases} \text{phosphoenol pyruvate} \\ \text{acetyl phosphate} \\ \text{1,3-diphosphoglycerate} \end{cases}$$

$$P\sim O-\overset{|}{\underset{\|}{P}}-\begin{cases} \text{adenosine triphosphate} \\ \text{and similar compounds} \end{cases}$$

The addition of phosphate to an organic compound is known as *phosphorylation.*

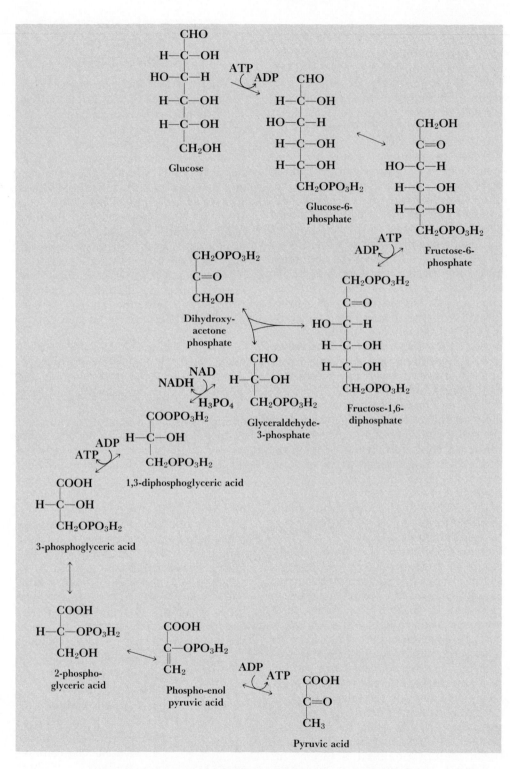

Figure 12-2. The Meyerhof-Embden system of glucose dissimilation.

Substrate Phosphorylation

When *Streptococcus faecalis* is grown on a complex medium containing glucose, complete with all the amino acids, purines, pyrimidines, and vitamins needed by the organism for building protoplasm, glucose is converted (99 per cent) to lactic acid. It can be demonstrated that less than 5 per cent of the cell carbon comes from glucose; nevertheless the glucose molecule furnishes energy for building cell material by the polymerization of preformed materials (i.e., proteins from amino acids, and nucleic acids from purines and pyrimidines). The conversion of glucose to lactic acid in a medium containing preformed cell constituents provides enough energy to produce 20 gm. of cells (dry weight) per mole of glucose metabolized. As will be shown (p. 202), when glucose is fermented, two biologic units of transfer energy (high energy phosphate) are obtained from one molecule of glucose. Compounds that produce one high-energy phosphate provide enough energy for only 10 gm. of cells per mole of substrate. From the growth yields of a microorganism supplied with various energy sources, it is possible to determine the numbers of high-energy phosphates available in the different substrates.

The sequence of events in glycolysis (the conversion of glucose to pyruvate) is given in Figure 12-2. The key to the energy-yielding process is the type of phosphate bonding to carbon. Hydrolysis of a phosphate bond like that in glucose-6-phosphate yields 2000 to 3000 calories, but hydrolysis of the phosphate on the first carbon of 1,3-diphosphoglyceric acid and the phosphate of phosphoenol pyruvate yields 8000 to 10,000 calories per mole. These are the bonds referred to as high-energy phosphate bonds.

All biologic systems are able to transfer energy through high-energy phosphate bonds and through certain carbon-sulfur bonds (acetyl-coenzyme A) (Fig. 12-3). Therefore, the object in energy-yielding systems is to rearrange molecules to provide high-energy phosphate or other bonding. In glycolysis, low-energy phosphate bonds are brought to the high-energy level at the glyceraldehyde-3-phosphate stage by adding inorganic phosphate to the carbon 1 (the aldehyde carbon) of the molecule and removing a pair of hydrogen atoms to form 1,3-diphosphoglycerate. At the 2-phosphoglycerate stage, the phosphate is brought to a high-energy state by removing water to produce 2-phosphoenol pyruvate. When the phosphate is at the high-energy level, it can be transferred to adenosine diphos-

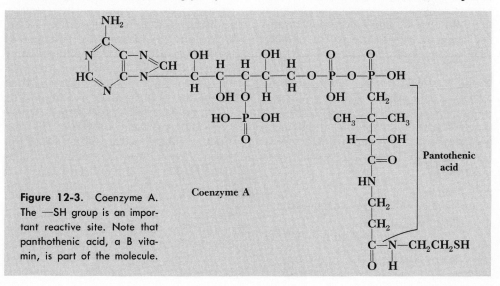

Figure 12-3. Coenzyme A. The —SH group is an important reactive site. Note that panthothenic acid, a B vitamin, is part of the molecule.

Coenzyme A

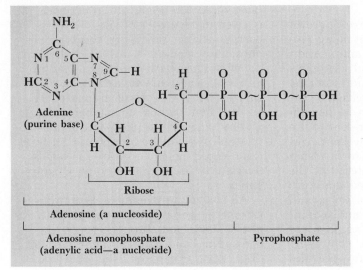

Figure 12-4. Adenosine triphosphate (ATP). The phosphate attached to ribose is low-energy phosphate. The high-energy phosphates may be removed one at a time to form adenosine diphosphate (ADP) and adenosine monophosphate (AMP), or two may be removed together to form AMP and pyrophosphate (P—P).

phate (ADP) or adenosine monophosphate (AMP) to form, respectively, adenosine triphosphate (ATP) or ADP (Fig. 12-4). ATP is then used in synthetic reactions to activate molecules for the building process.

In order to convert glucose for energy release, ATP was needed to make the molecule sufficiently reactive. By using ATP to form glucose-6-phosphate and later fructose-1,6-diphosphate, the electronic balance within the molecule was modified to the extent that fructose-1,-6-diphosphate could be split. Although two high-energy phosphates were used, four were eventually recovered, giving a net gain of two high-energy phosphates per molecule of glucose in the conversion of glucose to lactate.

In the polymerization process by which proteins, nucleic acids, polysaccharides, cell walls, etc., are formed, monomers are activated by ATP to a reactive state. For example, amino acids are first activated and transferred to RNA and coded into a protein (see p. 280):

ATP + amino acid $\longrightarrow$
  amino acid-AMP + PP (pyrophosphate)

n AMP-amino acid $\longrightarrow$
  $(\text{amino acid})_n$ + n AMP

Glucose-6-phosphate is converted to glucose-1-phosphate, which can poly-

merize to a polysaccharide, thereby releasing inorganic phosphate:

n glucose-1-phosphate $\longrightarrow$
  $(\text{glucosyl})_n$ + nP_i

Oxidative Phosphorylation

In oxidative phosphorylation, ATP is generated by an electron transport system. The mechanism is incompletely understood, but high-energy phosphate is produced from inorganic phosphate during the transfer of electrons to a terminal hydrogen acceptor such as oxygen. An example is the electron transport system in most aerobes—electrons and hydrogen are transported from substrate to nicotinamide adenine dinucleotide (NAD) and then to a flavin (Fig. 12-5). The electrons are then passed to cytochromes b and c (Fig. 12-6) and finally to cytochrome a, where they and hydrogen ions from the medium combine with oxygen to form water. A quinone (ubiquinone or coenzyme Q; Fig. 12-7) has been implicated in the conversion of inorganic phosphate to high-energy phosphate, but the mechanism is not understood completely. For each pair of hydrogen atoms converted to water in oxidative phosphorylation, as many as three ATP are generated. The maximum amount of

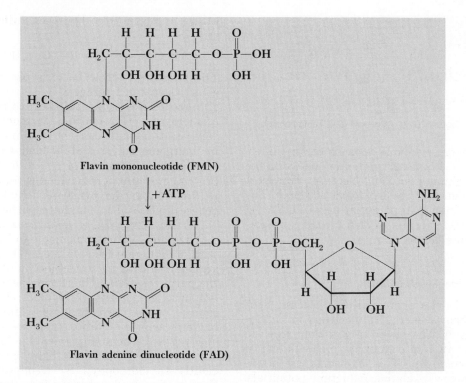

Figure 12-5. Oxidized forms of flavin mononucleotide (FMN) and flavin adenine dinucleotide (FAD).

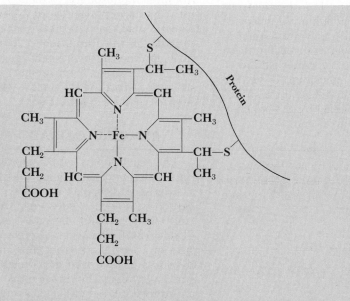

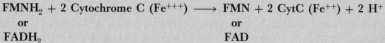

$$FMNH_2 + 2 \text{ Cytochrome C (Fe}^{+++}) \longrightarrow FMN + 2 \text{ CytC (Fe}^{++}) + 2 H^+$$

or   or

$FADH_2$ FAD

Figure 12-6. Cytochrome C.

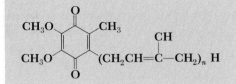

Figure 12-7.   Coenzyme Q (ubiquinone).

energy available depends on the difference in electric potential between the beginning of an electron transport chain and the hydrogen acceptor. The difference in potential between NADH (-0.28 v.) and oxygen ($+0.81$ v.) represents 25,000 calories.

Photophosphorylation

In the photosynthetic process, light imparts energy to electrons in chlorophyll. The electrons are then received by an iron-containing molecule called *ferredoxin*. This molecule is active at low oxidation-reduction potentials. Chromatium ferredoxin operates at -0.49 volt, spinach ferredoxin at -0.43 volt. Ferredoxin transfers the electrons to nicotinamide adenine dinucleotide phosphate (NADP) and subsequently through an electron transport system to generate ATP in a manner similar to that in oxidative phosphorylation. In green plants the photoreduction of ferredoxin is accompanied by the stoichiometric evolution of oxygen:

$$4Fd_{ox} + 2H_2O \xrightarrow{h\nu} 4Fd_{red} + O_2 + 4H^+$$

ATP is also produced by the ferredoxin-dependent (noncyclic) photophosphorylation reaction; water is the hydrogen and electron donor:

$$4Fd_{ox} + 2ADP + 2P_i + 2H_2O \xrightarrow{h\nu}$$

$$4Fd_{red} + 2ATP + O_2 + 4H^+$$

Bacteria do not use water as a hydrogen and electron donor; instead they use inorganic and organic hydrogen-containing compounds. For example, the green and purple sulfur bacteria can utilize hydrogen from hydrogen sulfide (H_2S):

$$2H_2S + CO_2 \longrightarrow 2S + (CH_2O) + H_2O$$

The nonsulfur purple bacteria use organic sources of hydrogen.

Ferredoxin is a molecule new to microbiologists. Chromatium ferredoxin contains three molecules of iron linked by inorganic sulfur and bonded to a low-molecular-weight (M.W. = 6000) protein. Initially, ferredoxin was found to function in the pyruvate dehydrogenase system of a nonphotosynthetic bacterium, *Clostridium pasteurianum*.

The photosynthetic pigments in bacteria are different from chlorophyll and are referred to as bacteriochlorophyll in the purple bacteria (Thiorhodaceae and Athiorhodaceae) and chlorobium chlorophyll in the green bacteria (Chlorobacteriaceae). In addition there are red and yellow carotenoid pigments, which are reported to transfer light inefficiently to chlorophyll by resonation. Carbon dioxide absorbed during photosynthesis is coupled to a 5-carbon sugar, ribulose diphosphate, which is then split into two molecules of 3-phosphoglyceric acid. An alternate mechanism consists in the formation of pyruvate through the pyruvate-dehydrogenase-ferredoxin system. By reversing glycolysis and adding ATP, glucose (688,000 calories) can be synthesized.

BIOLOGIC OXIDATIONS

The reactions by which most bacteria secure energy are oxidations. When a substance becomes oxidized it loses electrons; another substance receives the electrons and becomes reduced (Table 12-4). Oxidation therefore consists in a loss of electrons accompanied by a loss of hydrogen or a gain of oxygen. Every oxidation is accompanied by an equivalent reduction of some other substance, and no oxidation occurs in the absence of reduction. In speaking of an oxidation or a reduction reaction, the complete term *oxidation-reduction* is preferable. For convenience, however,

Table 12-4. Mechanism of Oxidation and Reduction

Oxidation		Reduction
Loss	Electrons	Gain
Loss or Gain	Hydrogen	Gain or Loss
	Oxygen	

the two aspects of oxidation-reduction will be referred to separately, particularly when attention is focused upon one or the other reactant.

Hydrogen (and Electron) Transfer

In the majority of biologic oxidations, hydrogen atoms are transferred from a substrate molecule, designated the *hydrogen donor,* and eventually passed to another substance, the *hydrogen acceptor.* Between the donor and ultimate acceptor there may be several *hydrogen carriers,* substances that readily accept and release hydrogen (FAD, FMN, NAD, NADP).

Fermentation. In fermentation, organic substances serve as both hydrogen donor and hydrogen acceptor; indeed different parts of the same molecule often fill these roles (Table 12-5). Since the products contain considerable amounts of energy, the yield in available energy during fermentation is low.

Glycolysis. The best known pathway by which energy is obtained from glucose anaerobically is by glycolysis, otherwise known as the Meyerhof-Embden pathway (Fig. 12-2). In homolactic bacteria (bacteria producing mainly lactic acid), glucose is metabolized to lactic acid, although traces of other products may form. These may increase in amount with a change of pH. With yeast, pyruvate is not converted to lactate, but instead to ethanol and carbon dioxide. In either case a net gain of two ATP is obtained.

Hexosemonophosphate Pathways. In heterolactic fermentation, only parts of the Meyerhof-Embden pathway may function because of the absence of certain enzymes. The organisms use a different pathway; the hexose monophosphate pathway, which has a number of variations and is found in a variety of microorganisms: *Escherichia coli, Pseudomonas fluorescens, Azotobacter vinelandii, Bacillus subtilis, Streptococcus faecalis.* In some bacteria both the glycolytic and monophosphate pathways are present but function under different conditions.

Leuconostoc mesenteroides oxidizes glucose-6-phosphate to 6-phosphogluconate, which is then decarboxylated. The resulting pentose-phosphate splits into a three-carbon and a two-carbon unit. The final products are lactate and ethanol (Fig. 12-8). A net gain of one ATP is obtained from this reaction, but the growth yield is one-third rather than one-half of the amount obtained from glycolysis:

$$\text{glucose} \longrightarrow \text{lactate} + \text{ethanol} + CO_2$$

Entner-Doudoroff Pathway. Pseudomonas lindneri converts 6-phosphogluconate to 2-keto-3-deoxy-6-phosphogluconate and then splits this to form glyceraldehyde-3-phosphate, which is processed through the Meyerhof-Embden pathway to pyruvate, eventually producing ethanol. A net gain of one ATP is produced in the process:

$$\text{glucose} \longrightarrow 2CO_2 + 2 \text{ ethanol}$$

Respiration. Biologic oxidation in

Table 12-5. Energy-Yielding Reactions

Type	Example
Respiration	$C_6H_{12}O_6 + 6O_2 \rightarrow 6CO_2 + 6H_2O + 688,000$ cal.
Anaerobic respiration	$C_6H_{12}O_6 + 12KNO_3 \rightarrow 6CO_2 + 6H_2O + 12KNO_2 + 429,000$ cal.
Fermentation	$C_6H_{12}O_6 \rightarrow 2CO_2 + 2C_2H_5OH + 54,000$ cal.

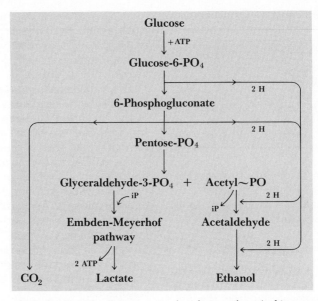

Figure 12-8. Heterolactic fermentation (hexose monophosphate pathway) of *Leuconostoc mesenteroides.*

which molecular oxygen is the ultimate hydrogen acceptor is called respiration —sometimes more specifically designated *aerobic respiration* (Table 12-5). The product, carbon dioxide, is the most highly oxidized form of carbon, and thus the greatest possible yield of energy is obtained. Chemosynthetic autotrophs secure energy by oxidizing inorganic substances: hydrogen gas, hydrogen sulfide, elemental sulfur, iron, thiosulfate, ammonia, and nitrite (Table 12-6). Energy is obtained by oxidative phos-

phorylation. For some heterotrophs, glucose is converted to pyruvic acid by glycolysis and then to carbon dioxide and water by processes outlined in the tricarboxylic acid cycle (Krebs citric acid cycle). At present there are only two well established mechanisms by which microorganisms oxidize foodstuffs to carbon dioxide and water. These are the tricarboxylic acid cycle and the oxidative pentose phosphate cycle (a hexose monophosphate pathway).

Table 12-6.   Respiration by Oxidation of Inorganic Substrates

Organism	Reaction
Hydrogenomonas	$6H_2 + 2O_2 + CO_2 \rightarrow 5H_2O + (CH_2O)$ cell material
Beggiatoa	$2H_2S + CO_2 \rightarrow 2S + (CH_2O) + H_2O$ (S stored cell material in cells) or, in absence of H_2S: $2S + 5H_2O + 3CO_2 \rightarrow 2SO_2^= + 3(CH_2O) + 4H^+$ cell material
Thiobacillus	$S_2O_3^= + H_2O + 2O_2 \rightarrow 2SO_4^= + 2H^+$
Nitrosomonas	$2NH_3 + 3O_2 \rightarrow 2NO_2^- + 2H^+ + 2H_2O$
Nitrobacter	$2NO_2^- + O_2 \rightarrow 2NO_3^-$

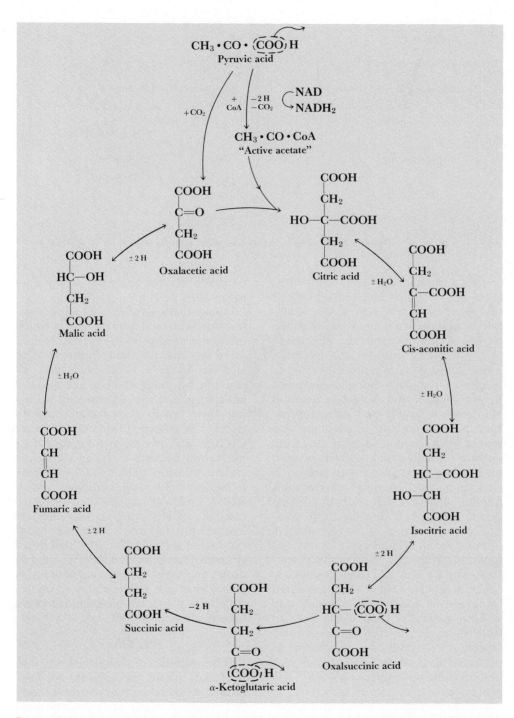

Figure 12-9. The Krebs cycle (abridged); aerobic oxidation of pyruvic acid. Oxalacetic acid formed by carboxylation of pyruvic acid is joined with "active acetate"; two carbon atoms are lost by oxidation to CO_2, and oxalacetic acid is regenerated. Succinyl-CoA is an intermediate between α-ketoglutaric acid and succinic acid, and during its formation two hydrogen atoms are transferred to FAD.

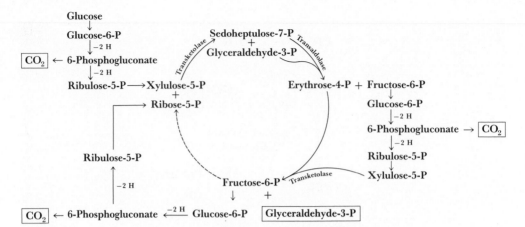

Figure 12-10. The oxidative phosphate pentose cycle.

Krebs Citric Acid Cycle. The most thoroughly studied and best known of the respiration processes is the oxidation of acetyl-coenzyme A (acetyl-CoA) by the Krebs tricarboxylic acid cycle (Fig. 12-9). In respiration, pyruvate formed from glucose is not converted to lactate as in glycolysis but is converted to acetyl-coenzyme A (active acetate) by decarboxylation and dehydrogenation. A small amount of pyruvate also reacts with carbon dioxide to form oxalacetic acid, which condenses with acetyl-CoA to produce the tricarboxylic acid, citric acid. A series of reactions follows, some of which release hydrogen atoms and carbon dioxide, until eventually oxalacetic acid is regenerated.

Four pairs of hydrogen atoms are removed from the intermediate substrates by DPN or FAD and appropriate enzymes and are ultimately transported to oxygen by the cytochrome pathway to form water. For each acetyl-CoA fed into the cycle, 12 ATP are generated. During the conversion of glucose to pyruvate by glycolysis and then to carbon dioxide and water, 38 ATP are generated.

Oxidative Pentose Phosphate Cycle. The oxidation of glucose by successive dehydrogenation, decarboxylation, and group transfer produces carbon dioxide and water. Energy is generated by oxidative phosphorylation. This cycle can

be demonstrated in many microorganisms (Fig. 12-10).

Anaerobic Respiration. Anaerobic respiration is an oxidative process in which inorganic substances other than oxygen serve as the terminal hydrogen and electron acceptor. Some organisms oxidize glucose completely in the absence of atmospheric oxygen when an oxidizing agent such as potassium nitrate (KNO_3) is present (Table 12-5). Other electron and hydrogen acceptors used by certain bacteria include sulfate and carbon dioxide (Table 12-7). Sulfate reduction may yield hydrogen sulfide (H_2S), and various bacteria produce methane (CH_4) from carbon dioxide. The energy formed from these oxidations is considered to be generated by an electron transport system. The mechanisms by which these reactions take place, although not completely understood, are presently receiving intensive investigation.

ENZYMES

The activities of living cells, whether bacterial, plant, or animal, are performed with the help of enzymes. Each cell possesses many enzymes, the kind and number depending on the genetic capabilities of the organism. Enzymes are proteins and are produced only by living cells. They can be extracted from cells and studied *in vitro*.

Table 12-7.   Anaerobic Respirations

Organism	Reaction
Many species	$NO_3^- \xrightarrow{H} NO_2^- \begin{smallmatrix} \xrightarrow{H} N_2\uparrow \\ \searrow^{H} NH_4^+ \end{smallmatrix}$
Desulfovibrio	"Sulfate reduction" $CH_3COOH + SO_4^= \rightarrow 2CO_2 + H_2S + 2OH^-$
Various species	"Methane fermentation" Organic cmpds. $\xrightarrow{\text{(anaerobic)}} CO_2 + CH_4 + (CH_2O)$ cell material
Methanobacterium omelianskii	$2C_2H_5OH + CO_2 \rightarrow 2CH_3COOH + CH_4$
Various species	$4H_2 + CO_2 \rightarrow CH_4 + 2H_2O$
Various species	$CH_3COOH \rightarrow CH_4 + CO_2$
Clostridium aceticum	$4H_2 + 2CO_2 \rightarrow CH_3COOH + 2H_2O$

The Nature of Enzymes

An enzyme is an organic catalyst that alters the rate of a chemical reaction and yet remains unchanged at the end of the reaction. The enzyme has a special site which is specific for a certain chemical grouping. It performs the function of bringing together and orienting substrates so that they can react in close proximity. In addition, the enzyme forms a complex with the substrate, which brings about an energy redistribution within the substrate, and thus lesser amounts of energy are required for the reaction to take place. The energy used to initiate a reaction is called the energy of activation. After forming the complex, the products dissociate from the enzyme, leaving it unchanged.

In addition to protein, some enzymes contain an organic component of low molecular weight, either tightly bound

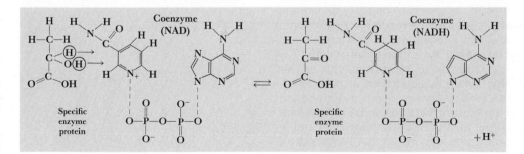

Figure 12-11.   Diagrammatic illustration of the behavior of enzyme and coenzyme (NAD) in the dehydrogenation of lactic acid to pyruvic acid. Hydrogen goes from lactic acid to the nicotinamide of NAD while the two molecules are held close together by the enzyme. NADH may then dissociate and transfer its extra hydrogen to another acceptor. Nicotinamide adenine dinucleotide phosphate (NADP) is similar to NAD except that the ribose (not shown) between adenine and the diphosphate bears another phosphate radical.

(prosthetic group) or loosely bound (coenzyme). A metallic ion, such as magnesium, zinc, copper, iron, or manganese (cofactor), may be necessary for enzyme activity. Both cofactors and coenzymes may modify the structure or surface forces of the substrate or of the enzyme so that a better "fit" or stronger reaction is obtained.

A diagrammatic representation of the foregoing description is presented in Figure 12-11. The substrate molecule, lactic acid ($CH_3 \cdot CHOH \cdot COOH$), adsorbs to the enzyme protein at a region where it fits, and the coenzyme adsorbs to a neighboring region. Two electrons and hydrogen ions from the lactic acid are transferred to the coenzyme (see p. 213); pyruvic acid remains and dissociates from the enzyme protein. The reduced coenzyme also dissociates and will be adsorbed by another enzyme, which has previously adsorbed some other substrate, and the electrons and hydrogen ions will be transferred to the new substrate.

Factors Affecting Enzyme Action

Enzyme action is affected by physical or chemical agents that modify the properties of proteins.

Temperature.   High temperature produces a poorly understood change in proteins known as *denaturation*. Presumably certain unstable bonds are broken, atoms or radicals rearrange slightly into an irregular configuration, and new bonds form. Most enzymes are inactivated very quickly above 70° C.; low temperature retards enzyme action (Fig. 12-12). Each enzyme displays maximum activity at some intermediate temperature. Enzyme activity decreases below the optimum temperature and is practically nil at 0° C. Temperature therefore affects enzyme activity in two ways: (1) as the temperature rises from a point below the optimum temperature, enzyme action accelerates, just as the rate of most other chemical reactions is greater at higher temperatures; (2) above the optimum temperature,

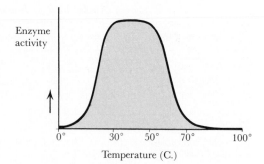

Figure 12-12.   Effect of temperature on the activity of common enzymes.

protein denaturation depresses enzyme activity.

Different enzymes have different optimum temperature characteristics. The enzymes of many common bacteria are most active between 30° and 50° C. The few peculiar bacteria that grow best at 60° to 75° C. (thermophiles) obviously possess enzymes and other proteins of very unusual properties.

pH.   The activity of each enzyme is greatest in a certain pH range and is less in the more acid and alkaline solutions (Fig. 12-13). The optima of many bacterial enzymes are between pH 6 and 8. Some yeast and mold enzymes are most active between pH 3 and 5. The influence of pH on enzyme action has been attributed to its effect on ionization of the enzyme and of the substrate.

Chemicals.   Heavy metals or their salts are notorious protein coagulants; many of them inactivate or "poison"

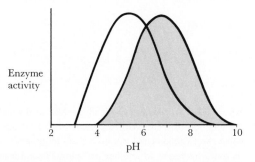

Figure 12-13.   Effect of pH on the activity of enzymes. Different enzymes have different optima.

enzymes. They combine with —SH groups rather than with the specific sites of enzyme activity; this is *noncompetitive inhibition.*

Other chemicals may also interfere with specific enzyme activity. A compound differing slightly from the normal substrate (for example, $CH_2Cl \cdot CHOH \cdot COOH$ instead of $CH_3 \cdot CHOH \cdot COOH$; Figure 12-11) might be adsorbed to the enzyme and prevent subsequent adsorption of the normal substrate. This would reduce the usual activity of the enzyme. Substances of this sort, which interfere with vital enzyme action, are called *antimetabolites;* inhibition at the enzyme site is known as *competitive inhibition.*

Concentration of Reagents. The concentration of an enzyme or of any required cofactors or coenzymes determines the amount of chemical reaction brought about, provided sufficient substrate is present. Likewise, the velocity of the reaction depends upon the presence of sufficient substrate to saturate the active sites on the enzyme.

Enzymes and Living Cells

Enzymes are not considered to be living, although they are vital components of all living cells. Enzyme inactivation may lead to the death of a cell containing the enzyme by depriving the cell of certain functions necessary to life. It will be shown in Chapter 14 that the same agents that inactivate enzymes also adversely affect the growth of bacteria and may even kill them.

Reversibility of Enzyme Action

Enzyme reactions, like most chemical reactions, are reversible under proper conditions. The long arrow in the following equation:

$$A + B \rightleftharpoons C + D$$

indicates that the forward reaction (i.e., from left to right) proceeds until most of A and B are used up in the formation of C and D. A point is reached eventually at which some uncombined A and B remain mixed with the products C and D. The addition of more C and D at this time reverses the reaction and yields some A and B. The equilibrium in this example is said to lie "to the right." It is apparent that the relative concentrations of the reactants (A and B) and the products (C and D) determine the direction in which the reaction is to proceed.

Many enzyme reactions in living cells *appear* to be irreversible, but apparent irreversibility is attributed to the removal of the products of reaction as fast as they form. The products may be used in subsequent synthetic reactions, which yield insoluble substances; they may be passed to another enzyme that catalyzes a further step in degradation; or they may be eliminated in a form (e.g., gaseous carbon dioxide) that escapes from the cell and even from the medium. Some reactions, however, are practically irreversible, because a large amount of energy is needed to reverse them.

Nomenclature, Classification, and Activities of Enzymes

Enzymes are usually named by adding *-ase* to the name (or the root) of the substrate or of the process catalyzed. A proteinase acts upon protein, a lipase upon lipid, a carbohydrase upon carbohydrate. Gelatinase hydrolyzes gelatin and maltase hydrolyzes maltose. Enzymes that split compounds by hydrolysis are known as hydrolases, those that cause direct oxidation are called oxidases, and those that remove hydrogen from the substrate are dehydrogenases.

Extracellular Enzymes. Exoenzymes or extracellular enzymes are secreted from a cell and catalyze reactions outside the cell (Table 12-8). They are usually hydrolases, and their function is the digestion of complex food materials.

Intracellular Enzymes. Enzymes whose activity is confined to the cell are endoenzymes or intracellular enzymes. They are classified according to the type of reaction or the process catalyzed.

Table 12-8. Typical Extracellular Enzymes

Name	Equation or Type of Reaction
Proteinases	Hydrolyze proteins to proteoses, peptones, peptides.
Gelatinase	Hydrolyzes gelatin and destroys its ability to solidify as a gel; produced by many bacteria.
Caseinase	Hydrolyzes casein of milk; produced by many bacteria.
Pepsin	Hydrolyzes proteins in the animal intestine.
Trypsin	Hydrolyzes proteins in the animal intestine.
Carbohydrases	Hydrolyze polysaccharides, disaccharides, etc.: $(C_6H_{10}O_5)_n + nH_2O \rightarrow nC_6H_{12}O_6$
Cellulase	Cellulose $\rightarrow \underset{\text{cellobiose}}{C_{12}H_{22}O_{11}}$
Amylase	Starch $\rightarrow \underset{\text{maltose}}{C_{12}H_{22}O_{11}}$
Maltase	$\underset{\text{maltose}}{C_{12}H_{22}O_{11}} + H_2O \rightarrow \underset{\text{glucose}}{2C_6H_{12}O_6}$
Lactase (β-galactosidase)	$\underset{\text{lactose}}{C_{12}H_{22}O_{11}} + H_2O \rightarrow \underset{\text{glucose}}{C_6H_{12}O_6} + \underset{\text{galactose}}{C_6H_{12}O_6}$
Sucrase (Invertase)	$\underset{\text{sucrose}}{C_{12}H_{22}O_{11}} + H_2O \rightarrow \underset{\text{glucose}}{C_6H_{12}O_6} + \underset{\text{fructose}}{C_6H_{12}O_6}$
Lipases	Hydrolyze fats to glycerin and fatty acids: $C_3H_5(O \cdot CO \cdot R)_3 + 3H_2O \rightarrow C_3H_5(OH)_3 + 3RCOOH$

Permeases. Penetration enzymes or *permeases* transport certain nutrients from the medium through the cell membrane and permit the accumulation of these substances within the cell in much greater concentration than that in which they exist outside the cell. Little is known about their mode of action.

Hydrolases. Intracellular hydrolases perform certain hydrolytic reactions within the cell. Acetyl phosphate and ATP, for example, may have their high-energy phosphates hydrolyzed to low-energy inorganic phosphates, with an accompanying loss of energy.

Group Transfer Enzymes. Enzymes that transfer phosphate radicals are essential in carbohydrate metabolism and also in the formation of high-energy phosphate bonds. Other radicals that may be added or removed by specific enzymes include the methyl, acetyl, amino, and carboxyl groups. These reactions are important in the interconversion of amino acids and other organic compounds and make possible the manufacture of protoplasm from whatever materials are at hand.

Oxidation-Reduction Enzymes. Oxidation-reduction enzymes catalyze the electron (and hydrogen) transfers by which energy is abstracted from or built into chemical bonds. Enzymes that remove hydrogen from a hydrogen donor are called *dehydrogenases.* They are usually further identified according to the substrate. The enzyme that dehydrogenates lactic acid, for example, is lactic dehydrogenase.

A dehydrogenase enzyme is usually specific for a particular substrate; that is, it will combine only with that substrate (lactic acid or succinic acid, for example). Coenzymes (NAD and NADP) are less specific and may function with several different dehydrogenases.

The type reaction for dehydrogenation is

$$AH_2 + B \longrightarrow A + BH_2$$

AH_2 represents the hydrogen donor and B represents the hydrogen acceptor. A few dehydrogenases utilize oxygen as the hydrogen acceptor and produce hydrogen peroxide. One of the hydrogens is removed from the substrate as a hydride ion (a hydrogen atom with its pair of electrons), and the other is removed as a hydrogen ion (proton). The hydride ion attaches to NAD, but the hydrogen ion remains in the medium:

$$AH_2 + NAD^+ \longrightarrow A + NADH + H^+$$

The reduced NAD can then pass electrons and hydrogen to a flavoprotein containing FMN or FAD:

$$NADH + H^+ + FAD \longrightarrow \\ NAD^+ + FADH_2$$

If the organism does not contain cytochromes, the reduced flavoprotein forms hydrogen peroxide by transferring the hydrogen to oxygen (Fig. 12-14). In most bacteria, the final carriers are iron-containing proteins known as *cytochromes*. Cytochromes are proteins that have an iron molecule in a ring structure called *heme* (as in *hemoglobin*). Heme, which is firmly bound to the protein, accepts electrons from reduced flavoproteins:

$$FADH_2 + 2Fe^{+++} \longrightarrow \\ FAD + 2H^+ + 2Fe^{++}$$

In most bacteria more than one cytochrome is involved (cyt c and cyt b). The reduced cytochrome transfers electrons via the enzyme cytochrome oxidase to oxygen:

$$4Fe^{++} + O_2 \longrightarrow 4Fe^{+++} + 2O^=$$

Finally, hydrogen ions from the medium react with activated oxygen to form water:

$$2H^+ + O^= \longrightarrow H_2O$$

The ultimate fate of the hydrogen depends upon the enzymes or carriers produced by the cell in question. Aer-obic bacteria, for example, usually produce cytochromes and can oxidize a substrate completely. Strict anaerobes, on the other hand, do not produce cytochromes and are therefore unable to transfer hydrogen to oxygen. Instead they utilize other final hydrogen acceptors and yield products that are only partially oxidized.

Two other related enzymes should be mentioned. *Catalase* splits hydrogen peroxide into water and gaseous oxygen:

$$2H_2O_2 \longrightarrow 2H_2O + O_2$$

This reaction provides a mechanism for the disposal of hydrogen peroxide, which might otherwise accumulate in a culture and kill the organisms that produce it. Anaerobic bacteria (which cannot grow in the presence of air) do not produce catalase. *Peroxidase* decomposes hydrogen peroxide to form water and active oxygen, which is then reduced to form a second molecule of water.

Specificity of Enzymes

A given enzyme is capable of adsorbing and acting upon only a given substrate or perhaps certain closely related substrates. Maltase, for example, hydrolyzes maltose but not sucrose or lactose. The fact that enzymes are so specific indicates that an organism that attacks many different substrates or causes a great variety of reactions must produce a correspondingly large number of enzymes. The total might well be in the hundreds.

Inductive and Constitutive Enzymes

Recent investigation confirms an older hypothesis that certain enzymes are produced by bacterial cells only when their specific substrates are present in the medium. These are known as *inductive enzymes*. Enzymes that are constantly present are called *constitutive enzymes*.

DIRECT OXIDATION

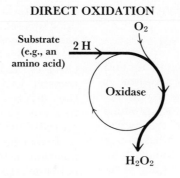

DIRECT CYTOCHROME PATHWAY

INDIRECT CYTOCHROME PATHWAY

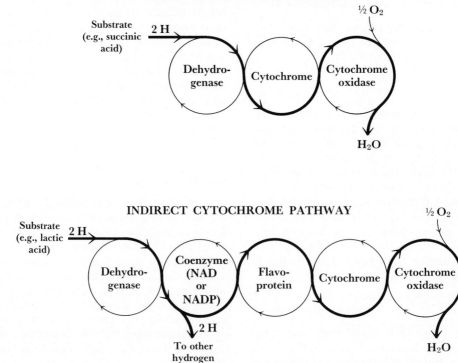

Figure 12-14. Mechanisms of respiration; the pathways to free oxygen (diagrammatic). Hydrogen follows the heavy lines.

An example of enzyme induction is provided by experiments with *Leuconostoc mesenteroides* (Table 12-9). This organism was grown in media containing either glucose, lactose, arabinose, or no sugar, and then transferred to test solutions containing one of the three sugars. Glucose was fermented in any

case, and the responsible enzymes were constitutive. Enzymes necessary for fermentation of lactose and arabinose were inductive: they were produced only by organisms cultivated in media containing the same sugar.

It has been suggested that trace amounts of inductive enzymes are pres-

Table 12-9. Inductive Enzyme Formation by *Leuconostoc mesenteroides*

After Growth in Medium Containing:	Leuconostoc Can Ferment:		
	Glucose	Lactose	Arabinose
Glucose	+	−	−
Lactose	+	+	−
Arabinose	+	−	+
No sugar	+	−	−

ent in all cells, but the formation of useful amounts depends upon a stimulus provided by an "inducer," which is often the substrate but may be a related substance. The ability of bacterial cells to produce inductive enzymes helps to solve the problem of where the cell keeps the hundreds of enzymes it was supposed to contain.

DISSIMILATION

Dissimilation is the intracellular breakdown of food materials; it yields compounds that can be incorporated into new protoplasm and also the energy that makes this possible.

Carbohydrate Dissimilation

Carbohydrate is the most generally and easily utilized source of energy. The dissimilation of glucose has been extensively studied, largely because it is so widely distributed and readily used by animals and by microorganisms.

Methods of Study. Glucose dissimilation by microorganisms is studied by cultivating an organism in a suitable broth containing the sugar. The nature and amounts of the various metabolic by-products are then determined by chemical analysis. They might include, for example, succinic, lactic, and acetic acids; ethyl alcohol; carbon dioxide; and hydrogen. This experiment provides only limited information—the final result of dissimilation—it does not tell how dissimilation occurred.

The intermediate steps are ascertained by trial and error. A mechanism to account for the various products is postulated and tested. It might be suggested, for example, that CO_2 and H_2 are formed by the decarboxylation of formic acid:

$$HCOOH \longrightarrow H_2\uparrow + CO_2\uparrow$$

The organism is therefore grown in a medium containing formic acid or a formate salt, and the production of these gases is presumptive evidence that this hypothesis is correct. If it is then proposed that formic acid is derived from pyruvic acid, a pyruvate medium is similarly tested.

A radioactive or other isotopic element can be employed as a tracer. Pyruvic acid containing C^{13} in the carboxyl group is used in the culture medium, and the reaction

$$CH_3 \cdot CO \cdot C^{13}OOH + H_2O \longrightarrow$$
pyruvic acid

$$CH_3 \cdot COOH + HC^{13}OOH$$
acetic acid   formic acid

not only shows that formic acid is produced from pyruvic acid, but proves that the carboxyl radical is its source.

Products of Carbohydrate Dissimilation. Microorganisms produce a variety of compounds in their dissimilation of carbohydrates: acids, alcohols, gases (see Table 12-10). Some organisms produce only one or two compounds (e.g., lactic acid); others yield a mixture of many. The products are determined by the nature of the organism, that is, the enzymes it possesses, and the environmental conditions. Respirative (i.e., aerobic) dissimilation by a facultative microorganism differs from fermentative (anaerobic) dissimilation by the same organism. Yeast, for example, produces carbon dioxide and water from glucose when growing in air, but yields carbon dioxide and ethyl alcohol in the absence of air.

Mechanism of Dissimilation. Most dissimilation processes are complex, requir-

Table 12-10. Partial List of Products of Microbial
Dissimilation of Carbohydrates

Acids	Alcohols, Etc.	Gases
$H \cdot COOH$ formic	C_2H_5OH ethyl	CO_2
$CH_3 \cdot COOH$ acetic	C_3H_7OH propyl	H_2
$C_2H_5 \cdot COOH$ propionic	$CH_3 \cdot CHOH \cdot CH_3$ isopropyl	
$C_3H_7 \cdot COOH$ butyric	C_4H_9OH butyl	
$CH_3 \cdot CHOH \cdot COOH$ lactic	$CH_3 \cdot CO \cdot CHOH \cdot CH_3$ acetylmethyl carbinol	
$COOH \cdot CH_2 \cdot CH_2 \cdot COOH$ succinic	$CH_3 \cdot CHOH \cdot CHOH \cdot CH_3$ 2,3-butylene glycol	

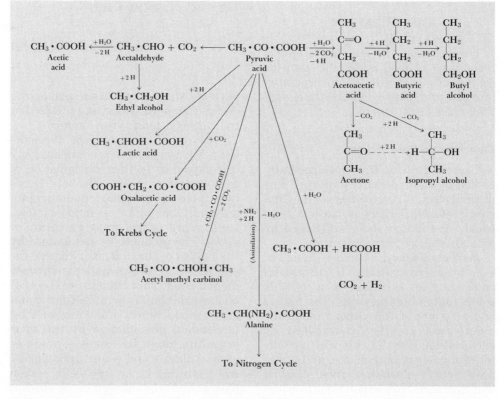

Figure 12-15. A few products of anaerobic dissimilation of pyruvic acid. Phosphate participates in some of these reactions but is not shown. Two molecules of pyruvic acid are required to make aceto-acetic acid.

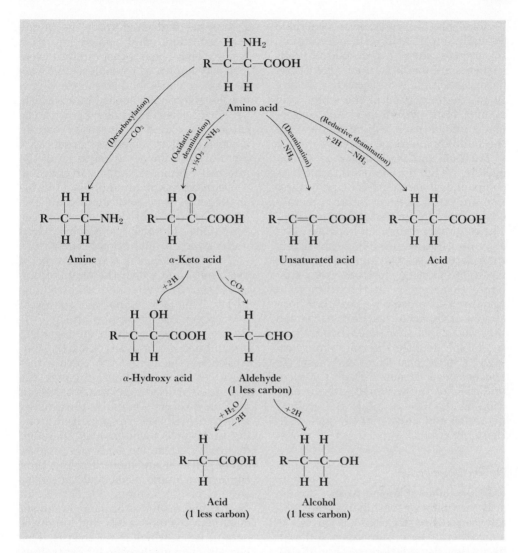

Figure 12-16. Dissimilation of amino acids. A variety of compounds may be formed, depending on the enzymes and conditions available.

ing many intermediate steps before the final products are formed. Each step is a *more or less* independent reaction, but successive steps follow one another so rapidly that the individual stages cannot ordinarily be detected. Once the chain of reactions is initiated, it usually goes to completion, just as a tennis ball bounces down an entire flight of stairs when given a slight push at the top.

Fermentation of Pyruvic Acid. Some of the products formed by microbial fermentation of pyruvic acid are shown in Figure 12-15. Many of the overall reactions indicated consist of several steps, and each step is catalyzed by a specific enzyme. It is obvious that the products of dissimilation by a given organism depend upon the enzymes it produces, and that a lack of a single enzyme may interrupt a whole series of reactions. Most products of fermentation are incompletely oxidized and hence contain available energy. Fermentation is therefore a poor method of securing energy.

Some of the products of anaerobic dissimilation are utilized in assimilation, the process whereby protoplasmic constituents are manufactured. One assimilatory reaction is indicated in Figure 12-15: the formation of the amino acid alanine from pyruvic acid and ammonia. Amino acids, it will be recalled, are the building blocks of proteins.

The Cell and Dissimilation of Carbohydrate. The numerous intermediate compounds in fermentation and respiration are rarely present within a metabolizing cell in appreciable quantities. The essential mechanism in oxidation is electron transfer, and it seems likely that nature uses the simplest possible means of passing electrons from substrate to acceptor. In the attempt to visualize this process we postulate a sequence of chemical reactions as though they occur one at a time. Intracellular conditions doubtless permit rapid passage of electrons from one atom to another in succession without the accumulation of the assumed intermediate compounds. The result is the gradual liberation and transfer of energy to synthetic reactions.

Protein Dissimilation

Dissimilation of Amino Acids. Amino acid dissimilation within the cell usually consists of decarboxylation or deamination or both, sometimes followed by further degradation (see Fig. 12-16). *Decarboxylation* yields amines, many of which are foul smelling compounds.

Putrescine is derived from the amino acid ornithine, and cadaverine from lysine. These and other amines were formerly known as ptomaines and were thought to cause food poisoning following the ingestion of spoiled meat or fish. True food poisoning is now known to be caused by toxins produced by certain bacteria; other digestive upsets are attributed to the actual invasion of the intestine by microorganisms in the food.

Deamination of an amino acid yields an organic acid and ammonia. The nature of the acid depends upon the conditions (aerobic, anaerobic, etc.) under which deamination occurs.

Transamination is a special type of deamination in which the amino group is transferred to an α-keto acid (see Fig. 12-17). This is an important source of new amino acids in protoplasm.

The manner in which an organism dissimilates amino acids is partly controlled by the pH of the culture medium. An acid medium promotes the formation of decarboxylases, whereas an alkaline medium stimulates the production of deaminases. An organism growing in an acid medium may therefore decarboxylate amino acids and produce amines, which are more alkaline than the parent amino acids, and thus raise the pH of the medium (Fig. 12-18). In an alkaline medium the same organism deaminates amino acids and produces organic acids, which lower the pH. This neat, built-in mechanism for controlling the reaction of the environment is the result of an evolutionary process of

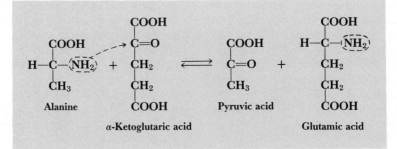

Figure 12-17. An example of transamination.

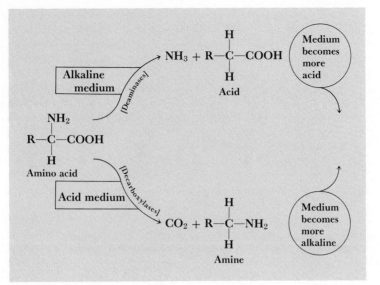

Figure 12-18. Effect of the reaction of the medium on the production of enzymes that dissimilate amino acids.

great survival value. For both deamination and transamination reactions, the coenzyme form of vitamin B_6 (pyridoxal phosphate) is required (Fig. 12-19).

ASSIMILATION

Assimilation is the constructive activity by which food materials are transformed into cell constituents. Proteins, carbohydrates, fats, and other substances are produced from the simpler compounds that result from dissimilation or diffuse directly from the culture medium.

Growth Factors. Vitamins, coenzymes, and other organic substances essential in trace amounts for energy transformations are synthesized by many organisms from simpler inorganic or organic materials. The syntheses can be represented as series of reactions. Four of the postulated steps in the formation of coenzyme I (NAD), for example, are shown in Figure 12-20. Many organisms, like *Escherichia coli*, perform all four steps and produce coenzyme I from the substrate *x*. *Proteus vulgaris* lacks the enzymes that convert *x* into nicotinic acid (step 1), but can perform steps 2, 3, and 4. Since it can produce coenzyme I if supplied with nicotinic acid, this substance is said to be a growth factor for *P. vulgaris*. Other more fastidious bacteria can perform steps 3 and 4 or 4 alone and hence must be supplied with nicotinamide or nicotinamide riboside, respectively. Some

Figure 12-19. Pyridoxal phosphate (vitamin B_6 phosphate), the coenzyme in transamination and deamination reactions.

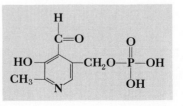

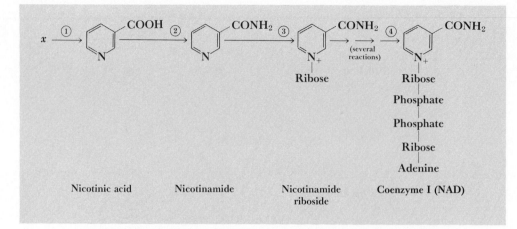

Figure 12-20. Postulated steps in the biosynthesis of coenzyme I (NAD).

organisms require not only growth factors but also one or more amino acids.

It will probably be no surprise to learn that bacteria with specialized nutrient requirements like the foregoing are often parasitic. Continued residence in a living host that supplies certain preformed substances seems to invoke some natural principle of laziness, and the parasite loses some of its synthetic ability. Not all fastidious organisms are parasitic, however. Specific growth factor requirements are also characteristic of saprophytes that have become adapted to natural environments like milk where certain growth factors are found.

Synthesis of Polysaccharides

Many microorganisms synthesize starch or glycogen or some other polysaccharide from glucose. Glucose phosphate forms first and then polymerizes, with elimination of the phosphate radicals. Starch (amylose) is a linear chain of glucose molecules; glycogen is a branched chain (Fig. 12-21).

Some polysaccharides are produced from disaccharides. A dextran can be formed from sucrose by union of the glucose residues; the fructose units are set free. Similarly, an organism that couples the fructose moieties and releases glucose produces a levan. Dex-

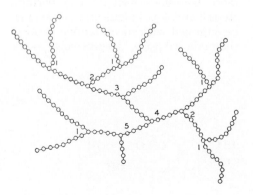

Figure 12-21. Branched chain structure of glycogen. Each circle represents a glucose molecule. Starch (amylose) is a linear chain.

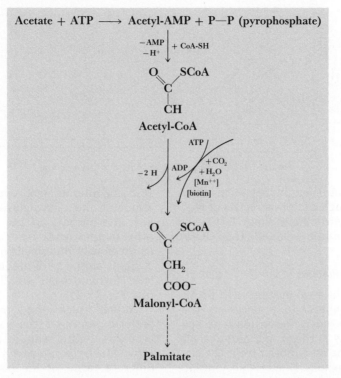

Acetate + ATP ⟶ Acetyl-AMP + P—P (pyrophosphate)

Acetyl-CoA

Malonyl-CoA

Palmitate

Figure 12-22. Steps in the formation of malonyl-CoA, preliminary to the synthesis of long chain fatty acids.

trans and levans are found in the capsules of certain bacterial species.

Synthesis of Fatty Acids

The substrate for building long chain fatty acids in bacteria is malonyl-CoA. To produce this compound from acetate, 3 ATP are required; the activation of acetate and a subsequent carboxylation form malonyl-CoA (Fig. 12-22).

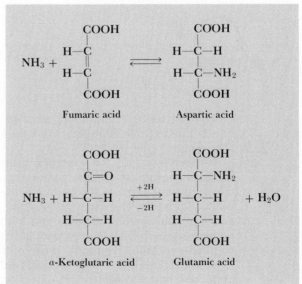

Fumaric acid   Aspartic acid

Figure 12-23. Pathways by which ammonia is converted to amino groups.

α-Ketoglutaric acid   Glutamic acid

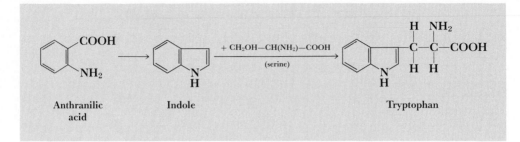

Figure 12-24.   Stepwise biosynthesis of tryptophan.

Malonyl-CoA then increases in chain length through a stepwise series of reactions to yield a long chain fatty acid such as palmitic acid ($C_{15}H_{31}COOH$).

Synthesis of Proteins

The synthesis of proteins will be discussed in Chapter 16. A necessary prerequisite to protein formation is an adequate supply of the proper amino acids. They may be assimilated from the surrounding medium. Bacteria accumulate and concentrate certain amino acids within their cells in a "metabolic pool."

Amino acids that are not taken into the cell intact must be synthesized. Ammonia appears to be the only inorganic form of nitrogen converted into amino groups; two pathways known to accomplish this are shown in Figure 12-23. Glutamic acid, produced from ammonia and α-keto-glutaric acid, is the key intermediate in the formation of other amino acids by transamination, as previously described (p. 218).

Some amino acids are formed in stepwise fashion from smaller molecules (see Fig. 12-24).

Animal, plant, and microbial cells perform many of the same chemical processes, both dissimilative and assimilative. It is of interest that so many different forms of life perform similar chemical reactions. Either the primitive organism from which all arose had developed a successful metabolic pattern, which persisted in the various evolutionary branches, or else these different branches ultimately arrived at the same pattern after separate trial and error processes.

BACTERIAL METABOLISM

SUMMARY

The net result of metabolic activity is the creation of two cells from one. It makes little difference what the species may be—the essentials are the same.

Escherichia coli, for example, grows readily in a simple synthetic medium containing glucose, ammonium chloride, and small amounts of a few mineral salts. It ferments glucose, forms pyruvic acid as an intermediate product, and then forms lactic, acetic, formic, and succinic acids; ethyl alcohol; carbon dioxide; and hydrogen. The result of this activity is the release of some energy, part of which is immediately transferred to coupled synthetic reactions, most of the rest being lost as heat. The pyruvic acid and other acids derived from it via the Krebs cycle react with ammonia, and a complete set of a score or so of amino acids is formed.

Meanwhile purines, pyrimidines, pentoses, and other compounds have been produced, and a precisely engineered group of nucleic acids has been assembled: DNA and RNA. These control all the enzyme activity of the cell.

As DNA replicates and the nuclear body divides, the cytoplasm also increases and something triggers the process of cell division. Cell wall substance is manufactured and surrounds the entire newly formed protoplasm.

Growth and division continue until the exhaustion of nutrients interrupts the release of energy or the supply of essential building materials, or until the accumulation of wastes interferes with one or more enzyme reactions. Growth and multiplication cease, and if the concentration of wastes is too great, some or all of the cells die.

E. coli performs the same fundamental activities whether it grows in a simple glucose–ammonia-salts medium or in the decomposing food matter within the human intestine. The most remarkable—but not surprising—feature of this process is that cells produced from glucose and ammonia are the same as those produced from the complex nutrients of the intestine, at least as far as can be determined by analytical methods now available.

STUDY QUESTIONS

1. How do microorganisms digest complex foods like cellulose, protein, and fat?
2. To what metabolic type do pathogenic bacteria belong?
3. Describe the path by which the energy of sunlight may finally appear in the protoplasm of a chemosynthetic heterotrophic bacterium.
4. What are *coupled reactions?* What role do they play in biologic processes?
5. Which of the following microbial reactions yields more energy? Explain.

$$C_6H_{12}O_6 + 6O_2 \longrightarrow 6CO_2 + 6H_2O$$
$$C_6H_{12}O_6 \longrightarrow 2CH_3 \cdot CHOH \cdot COOH$$

6. Differentiate (with examples) respiration, anaerobic respiration, fermentation. What is the common feature of these processes?
7. What role may antimetabolites play in the treatment of disease?
8. How is the apparent irreversibility of enzyme reactions in living organisms explained?
9. Describe how pyruvic acid plays a central role in carbohydrate, protein, and fat metabolism.
10. Discuss the comparative synthetic powers of autotrophic and heterotrophic organisms. Which probably appeared first in the evolution of living forms? Explain.
11. Would one expect the composition of a microorganism growing in a simple, chemically defined medium to differ from that of the same species growing within an animal body? Explain.

SUPPLEMENTARY READING

There are many books and parts of books on bacterial metabolism. Some familiarity with and liking for chemistry is a prerequisite to an understanding of much of the available literature. Chapters 10 to 14 in *The Microbial World* by Stanier et al. contain a good description of bacterial enzymes, the sources of energy, and the methods of securing energy. Porter has contributed long chapters on enzymes, nutrition, and metabolism, reviewing the literature to 1944. Thimann also presents an extensive treatment of carbohydrate metabolism, growth, and assimilation. Stephenson's *Bacterial Metabolism* is a classic, best suited for the more advanced student. Werkman and Wilson are editors of a volume containing chapters on special topics by authorities. The well written and interestingly illustrated book by Oginsky and Umbreit is also a little advanced for the beginner unless he is well grounded in chemistry. *The Bacteria: A Treatise on Structure and Function,* edited by Gunsalus and Stanier, is required reading for any serious microbiologist. Winogradsky's papers, mentioned on page 198, are found in Brock's *Milestones in Microbiology,* both in the original French and in an English translation. Present knowledge about the function of ferredoxin in photosynthesis is summarized by Arnon.

Arnon, D. I.: Ferredoxin and Photosynthesis. *Science, 149:*1460–1470, 1965.

Brock, T.: *Milestones in Microbiology.* Englewood Cliffs, N. J., Prentice-Hall, Inc., 1961.

Gunsalus, I. C., and Stanier, R. Y. (Eds.): *The Bacteria: A Treatise on Structure and Function,* Vols. II and III. New York, Academic Press, Inc., 1961, 1962.

Oginsky, E. L., and Umbreit, W. W.: *An Introduction to Bacterial Physiology,* 2d ed. San Francisco, W. H. Freeman & Company, 1959.

Porter, J. R.: *Bacterial Chemistry and Physiology.* New York, John Wiley & Sons, Inc., 1946.

Stanier, R. Y., Doudoroff, M., and Adelberg, E. A.: *The Microbial World,* 2d ed. Englewood Cliffs, N. J., Prentice-Hall, Inc., 1963.

Stephenson, M.: *Bacterial Metabolism,* 3d ed. New York, Longmans, Green & Co., Inc., 1949.

Thimann, K. V.: *The Life of Bacteria,* 2d ed. New York, The Macmillan Company, 1963.

Werkman, C. H., and Wilson, P. W., (Eds.): *Bacterial Physiology.* New York, Academic Press, Inc., 1951.

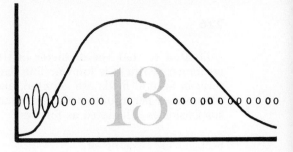

GROWTH AND DEATH
OF BACTERIA

METHODS OF STUDYING
GROWTH AND DEATH

Cell Growth

Growth of individual cells can be observed by microscopic methods. As described in Chapter 4 (pages 97 and 98), the chromatin body divides and the cell increases to several times its original size. Crosswalls then form, and the daughter cells become physiologically independent, often separating physically. The process of growth may be followed in unstained microcultures, but measurement of cell size is easier in stained preparations. However, drying and fixing shrink the cells in a smear, and the measurements obtained are only relative.

Population Changes

Bacterial growth is more frequently studied by counting the organisms in a culture at intervals than by tediously determining the average cell size. Casual inspection of a broth culture every few hours after inoculation reveals gradually increasing turbidity, which roughly parallels the increase in population. Turbidity estimations are more precise when made with a photoelectric turbidimeter. The bacterial mass can be determined by removing the cells from the culture (by centrifugation) and weighing them; for some purposes quantitative analysis of a characteristic chemical constituent such as nitrogen suffices. These methods indicate the total amount of bacterial growth but do not necessarily reveal the number of cells because of the variation in average cell size during the growth cycle.

Direct (Microscopic) Count of Bacteria. *Breed Method.* Microscopic examination of stained smears can also be used to estimate bacterial populations. A known volume of culture or suspension is smeared uniformly over a definite area of a slide; this is stained and examined with a microscope that has been calibrated so that the diameter of the oil immersion field is known. The bacteria in several fields are counted, and the number per milliliter of the original suspension is calculated as follows:

$$\frac{\text{bact./ml. of}}{\text{suspension}} = \frac{\text{avg. no. of}}{\text{bact./field}}$$

$$\times \frac{1 \text{ ml.}}{\text{vol. of susp.}} \times \frac{\text{area of smear}}{\text{area of field}}$$

In the Breed method of counting bacteria in milk, 0.01 ml. of the sample is smeared over a 1 sq. cm. area of a slide; it is then stained and the individual cells or clumps are counted. If the organisms in an entire oil immersion field, whose diameter is 160 μ, are enumerated, the equation becomes:

$$\frac{\text{bact./ml. of}}{\text{suspension}} = \frac{\text{avg. no. of}}{\text{bact./field}}$$

$$\times \frac{1}{0.01} \times \frac{100,000,000 \text{ sq. } \mu}{20,100 \text{ sq. } \mu}$$

$$= \text{avg. no. of bact./field} \times 497,500$$

In other words, every cell seen in the microscope represents approximately 500,000 per milliliter in the suspension. This method is fairly accurate with large populations; with small populations, however, the experimental error is great unless many fields are examined.

Counting Chamber Method. Various microscope slides are available with chambers designed to contain a cell suspension above an accurately ruled area etched into the glass. The Petroff-Hausser chamber is so constructed that the depth of the suspension is 0.02 mm., each ruled square being 0.05 mm. on a side. After the chamber is filled with suspension and covered with a special, flat coverglass, the average number of bacteria in the ruled squares is determined. The calculation of the cells per milliliter is made by the following equation:

$$\frac{\text{bact./ml. of}}{\text{suspension}} = \frac{\text{avg. no. of}}{\text{bact./square}} \times \frac{1 \text{ mm.}}{0.02 \text{ mm.}}$$

$$\times \frac{1 \text{ mm.}}{0.05 \times 0.05 \text{ mm.}} \times 1000 \text{ cu. mm.}$$

$$= \text{avg. no. of bact./square} \times 20,000,000$$

This method is particularly useful with suspensions containing large numbers of cells. It is similar to the method used in counting blood cells.

Cultural Counts of Bacteria. All the methods so far mentioned indicate the *total* population, including dead as well as living cells. This information is sometimes desired, but usually the living population is of principal interest. Living cells can be counted or estimated only by a method that depends upon a detectable, vital activity, such as cell multiplication, lactose fermentation, or cellulose digestion. Two culture procedures are in common use, the *dilution count* and the *plate count*. The basic assumption underlying both methods is that every viable (living) cell inoculated into fresh medium will multiply and produce easily detected evidence of growth: turbidity, acid or gas in broth, colonies on agar. This assumption is not always justified, particularly with very small numbers of bacteria, and constitutes a source of inaccuracy recognized by practicing bacteriologists. However, the results obtained by repeated examinations of a given specimen are reasonably reproducible, so that the methods have the virtue of consistency if not of strict accuracy.

Dilution Count. The dilution count provides an estimate of the number of bacteria in a population that are capable of multiplying in a liquid medium. Any medium may be used that will support the growth of the organisms of interest. To illustrate the method, assume a suspension containing 100 bacteria per milliliter. Serial dilutions (1 : 10, 1 : 100, 1 : 1000 . . .) are prepared by transferring 1 ml. into 9 ml. of sterile water and then mixing this dilution and transferring 1 ml. into another 9 ml. portion of sterile water, etc. (see Fig.

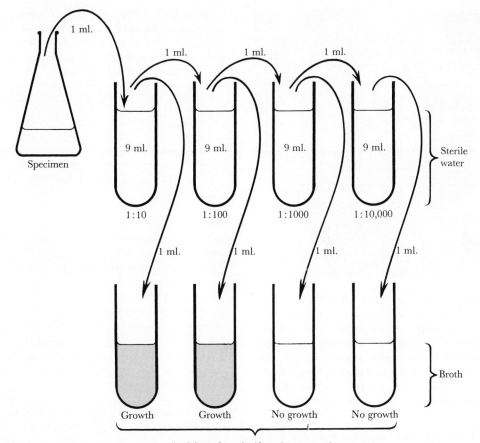

Figure 13-1. Procedure for dilution count of a suspension containing 100 bacteria per milliliter with anticipated results. Arrows indicate transfer of 1 ml. of specimen or dilution.

13-1). The respective dilutions theoretically contain 10, 1, 0.1 . . . bacteria per milliliter. One milliliter portions of each dilution are then inoculated into the desired broth medium and these cultures are incubated (Fig. 13-2).

The anticipated results in the example just described are also indicated in Figure 13-1. Growth should occur in tubes inoculated with the undiluted specimen and with the 1 : 10 and 1 : 100 dilutions. Growth is not expected in broth inoculated with the 1 : 1000 dilution; that is, in nine trials out of 10 there would be no organism in a 1 ml. portion. The same results might be obtained if the

specimen contained 500 or even 900 bacteria per milliliter, but there is obviously a greater probability that broth inoculated with the 1 : 1000 dilution will contain a viable organism and hence become turbid. It is usually *assumed,* however, that the highest dilution that yields growth in subculture contains one bacterium per milliliter; the minimum number of organisms in the specimen is therefore indicated by the reciprocal of this dilution.

The dilution count becomes more accurate if several tubes of broth are inoculated with 1 ml. aliquots of each dilution. Some aliquots of the critical

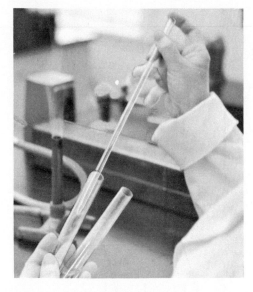

Figure 13-2. Transferring bacterial specimen by pipette. The culture tubes are held as usual. Plugs are also held as usual by the little and ring fingers of the other hand. This hand also manipulates the pipette, which was taken sterile from the long can in the background. Note that the index finger is used to control the flow of liquid in the pipette.

Table 13-1. Most Probable Number (MPN) of Bacteria per Milliliter of a Sample as Calculated from Observations of Broth Cultures Inoculated with 1 ml. of Three Decimal Dilutions*

No. of Positive Tubes from Each Dilution†			MPN of Bacteria per Ml.
10^0	10^{-1}	10^{-2}	
2	2	2	100
2	2	1	70
2	2	0	24
2	1	2	21
2	1	1	13
2	1	0	6.2
2	0	2	9.5
2	0	1	5.0
2	0	0	2.3
1	2	2	3.7
1	2	1	2.9
1	2	0	2.1
1	1	2	2.8
1	1	1	2.0
1	1	0	1.3
1	0	2	1.9
1	0	1	1.2
1	0	0	0.6
0	2	2	1.9
0	2	1	1.4
0	2	0	0.94
0	1	2	1.4
0	1	1	0.92
0	1	0	0.46
0	0	2	0.90
0	0	1	0.45
0	0	0	0

*Two tubes were inoculated with each dilution.

† Exponential notation is commonly used to designate decimal dilutions: 10^0 = undiluted; 10^{-1} = 1:10; 10^{-2} = 1:100.

dilution(s) then contain a viable organism and others do not. Tables have been calculated from which the most probable number of bacteria in the specimen can be read. One of these is Table 13-1, which shows the most probable number (MPN) of bacteria per milliliter of a specimen (culture, water or milk sample, etc.) as calculated from the observation of growth in duplicate broth cultures inoculated with 1 ml. aliquots of decimal dilutions of the sample. The figures representing positive results (i.e., growth) in the three successive dilutions may be termed the *significant number.* For example, if positive results are obtained from two tubes inoculated with an undiluted sample, one tube with a 1:10 dilution, and none with a 1:100 dilution, the significant number is 210. According to the table, this indicates that the sample most probably contains 6.2 bacteria per milliliter. The table can be used with

any set of successive decimal dilutions by multiplying the indicated *most probable number* (in Table 13-1) by the reciprocal of the dilution corresponding to the first figure of the significant number (in Table 13-2). In the examples in Table 13-2 the significant number is indicated in boldface (heavy) type:

Table 13-2. Examples of MPN in Successive Decimal Dilutions

Sample	Positive Dilutions						MPN per Ml.
	10^{-1}	10^{-2}	10^{-3}	10^{-4}	10^{-5}	10^{-6}	
A	2	1	0	0	0	0	62
B	2	2	2	0	0	0	2,400
C	2	2	2	1	1	0	13,000

This method of counting viable populations is not very accurate, but it affords a means of estimating certain physiologic groups of organisms (e.g., indole producers and lactose fermenters) for which other procedures are not available or are cumbersome. Its precision is increased by inoculating more tubes with each successive dilution, five or 10, for instance.

Plate Count. The plate count is based upon the assumption that each bacterium trapped in or on a nutrient agar medium will multiply and produce a visible colony (Fig. 13-3). The number of colonies should therefore be the same

Figure 13-4. Quebec colony counter. The magnifier and a darkfield type of illumination increase the accuracy of counting.

Figure 13-3. Pouring agar into a Petri dish. The mouth of the bottle or test tube of agar is flamed and inserted beneath the edge of the lid, which has been raised only enough to admit the agar container. The required medium is poured and the lid is carefully replaced.

as the number of viable bacteria inoculated into the agar. One milliliter of an undiluted specimen containing 100 bacteria per milliliter is expected to produce 100 colonies, a number that can be counted without difficulty.

A specimen containing 2,500,000 bacteria per milliliter would yield a plate far too crowded to count; moreover, metabolic products from the multiplying bacteria would inhibit the development of neighboring colonies. Such a specimen should be diluted, and 1 ml. of a 10^{-4} dilution (i.e., 1 : 10,000) should be plated. The number of colonies obtained (250 are expected in this case) has to be multiplied by 10^4, the reciprocal of the dilution, to find the number of bacteria per milliliter of the original specimen (Fig. 13-4).

Duplicate or triplicate plates are usually prepared from each of several dilutions in the anticipated critical range. Plates from the dilution that yields between 30 and 300 colonies can be counted easily and accurately. The average, multiplied by the reciprocal of the dilution, gives a result expressed as "bacteria per milliliter." Replicate plates show some discrepancies attributed to uneven distribution of bacteria, pipetting and counting errors, and other factors. The normal error in the plate count may be as great as 10 per cent.

The plate procedure provides a *minimum* count of viable bacteria. Some organisms normally occur in clusters that do not break up in the course of preparing dilutions, and hence each cluster produces a single colony. Moreover, individual bacteria may become trapped in the agar so close together that their colonies merge and are counted as one.

The dilution and plate count methods of estimating populations are widely used whenever a count of the number of living bacteria is desired. It should be emphasized that no cultural procedure can be relied upon to provide an accurate estimate of the total number of organisms in a physiologically heterogeneous population, because no one culture medium or set of incubation conditions will permit the growth of all kinds of bacteria. Nutritionally fastidious organisms require special ingredients in the medium; certain bacteria are inhibited by substances that favor others; and strict aerobes will not grow under anaerobic conditions nor anaerobes under aerobic conditions. Each group must be counted separately.

Turbidimetry. For some purposes, the number of bacteria can be determined with sufficient accuracy, and certainly with greatest ease, by estimating the degree of turbidity of the suspension. Optical nephelometers have been used for this purpose for many years; photoelectric turbidimeters provide greater accuracy, but any type of spectrophotometer can be used with equally great accuracy. There is an inverse relationship between the turbidity or optical density of a bacterial suspension and the amount of light that passes through it; the light transmitted can be measured accurately by a suitable photoelectric cell. Turbidimetry is most effective with suspensions of moderate density. It indicates the total amount of bacterial cells—dead as well as living. Results can be expressed in arbitrary units, or optical densities can be evaluated by standardization with a bacterial suspension of known cell content.

BACTERIAL POPULATION CURVES

Bacterial population curves are determined by inoculating a small number of organisms into a culture medium and counting the bacteria in aliquot samples at intervals thereafter (e.g., every hour). Counts made by microscopic examination represent the total number of cells, both living and dead, as shown in curve A of Figure 13-5. Dilution or plate counts indicate only the population of living cells, as shown in curve B. Logarithms are used to plot the numbers of organisms in order to present clearly the population changes when counts are low and yet show the maximum counts.

It will be noted that after a short latent period the population increases rapidly toward a maximum and then levels off.

Eventually the living population decreases toward zero (curve B). The graph (A) of total population shows a slow but gradually diminishing rise after the period of most rapid cell division, which indicates that limited multiplication continues even though most cells are dying. Ultimately multiplication ceases and the total count becomes stationary.

These curves are not peculiar to bacteria. Curve A is familiar to any mother who has plotted the weight of her child from the time of birth; a similar curve

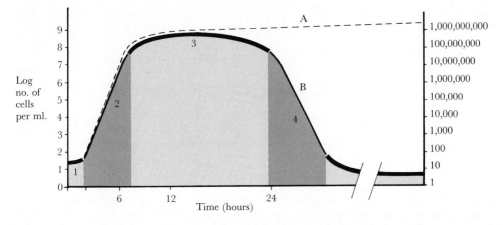

Figure 13-5. Idealized population curves obtained by counting the bacteria in a culture at intervals after inoculation. *Curve A*, Total (living plus dead) cells; *curve B*, living cells. *1*, Phase of cell enlargement; *2*, phase of logarithmic multiplication; *3*, maximum stationary level; *4*, phase of logarithmic death.

would depict the growth of many other forms of life. Curve B is characteristic of populations of any sort confined in a closed system and subject to starvation or to the harmful effect of toxic waste products, such as carbon dioxide, as the population increases. A similar curve depicts the rise and fall of ancient human populations in which geographic crowding, loss of economic productivity, disease, and war played their customary roles.

Curve B describes the normal viable microbial population changes in natural products, such as milk, cheese, sauerkraut, and silage, and in all kinds of decomposing animal and plant matter. Inasmuch as a "wild" or natural population usually consists of many species in intimate association with one another, the shape of the curve for each species is skewed one way or the other as the release of nutrients and other growth-promoting substances accelerates multiplication or as predation, antibiosis, and competition increase the death rate.

The term *population curve* better describes the over-all changes depicted than the older expression "growth curve." The curve is commonly divided into four principal sections or phases for further discussion.

Phase of Cell Enlargement

The first portion of the population curve in a bacterial culture is the phase of cell enlargement, sometimes known as the "lag phase." The latter name is misleading because it implies inactivity or dormancy, which is contrary to the true situation. It is true that the number of individual bacterial cells does not increase for a period of time that varies with the organism and the conditions, but protoplasm synthesis and cell growth begin almost immediately upon transfer to a fresh medium. As long ago as 1923, Henrici reported that the average size of bacterial cells increases markedly during the "lag phase," just before the period of active division (Fig. 13-6). Moreover, electron photomicrographs show that growth precedes cell division (page 96). The increase in size may amount to three or four times the initial cell volume, principally as a result of elongation.

Duration. The duration of the period of cell enlargement varies with conditions and with the species. A culture inoculated with cells that are already actively multiplying displays little lag in population increase and hence little if any unusual cell enlargement. The phase of enlargement is

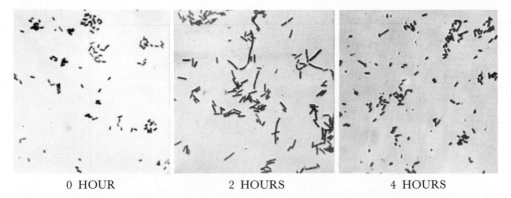

0 HOUR   2 HOURS   4 HOURS

Figure 13-6. Cell enlargement during the period preceding the phase of logarithmic multiplication. *Escherichia coli* on nutrient agar at 37° C., observed at the time of inoculation (0 hour) and two and four hours later.

prolonged, however, in a culture inoculated with "dormant" cells from an older culture. Bacteria that are capable of rapid multiplication under favorable conditions (e.g., *E. coli* or *P. vulgaris*) start to multiply within 30 minutes to two or three hours. Slowly growing organisms, such as *Mycobacterium tuberculosis,* do not start to divide until after a much longer interval.

Physiologic Activity. The "lag phase" was described as a period of intense physiologic activity before it was realized that protoplasmic growth begins almost at once. Measurements of oxygen utilization, carbon dioxide evolution, or deamination, when compared with the number of living cells, indicated great activity per cell. The same measurements compared with the total mass of protoplasm reveal that metabolic activity per unit of protoplasm is constant throughout this period.

The transition period between cell enlargement and active division is a critical interval. At this time the cells are unusually sensitive to unfavorable environmental conditions such as extremes of temperature (i.e., at either end of the growth range), high osmotic pressure, or disinfectant chemicals. Cells in the very early phase of enlargement or in the stationary periods of the population curve are more resistant.

The factors that prevent cell division during the phase of enlargement are unknown. It has been suggested that

traces of toxic minerals inhibit division or that division requires certain proteins or other nitrogenous substances that are synthesized only slowly. Whatever the cause, cell division begins slowly and then rapidly accelerates during a period that varies from only a few minutes to an hour. The culture then enters the phase of logarithmic multiplication.

Phase of Logarithmic Multiplication

Cell division occurs rapidly at a constant rate during this phase; that is, each successive division requires the same time as those preceding. A single cell of *E. coli,* for example, divides into two cells within 15 minutes. These cells divide and yield four cells in the next 15 minutes, and so forth. Each individual cell does not divide at exactly the same instant; some divide a little more rapidly, others a little more slowly, but the average division time is 15 minutes. A recent method of synchronizing bacterial cell divisions consists in alternately chilling and incubating cultures.

The population of a normal culture doubles in each consecutive time interval, so that the number of bacteria increases in an exponential or logarithmic manner. This is illustrated in Table 13-3, which shows the number of cells after each generation when observations are made starting with one cell, five cells, or any given number of cells (a).

Table 13-3. The Number of Cells in a Multiplying Bacterial Population as a Function of the Number Initially Present and the Generations Elapsed*

Generation	Number of Cells after Each Generation When Starting with:		
	1 Cell	5 Cells	a Cells
0	$1 = 2^0$	$5 = 5 \times 2^0$	$a = a \times 2^0$
1	$2 = 2^1$	$10 = 5 \times 2^1$	$2a = a \times 2^1$
2	$4 = 2^2$	$20 = 5 \times 2^2$	$4a = a \times 2^2$
3	$8 = 2^3$	$40 = 5 \times 2^3$	$8a = a \times 2^3$
4	$16 = 2^4$	$80 = 5 \times 2^4$	$16a = a \times 2^4$
5	$32 = 2^5$	$160 = 5 \times 2^5$	$32a = a \times 2^5$
n	2^n	5×2^n	$a \times 2^n$

*Numbers of cells expressed both arithmetically and exponentially.

Bacterial Generations. A *generation* is defined as a doubling of population. It is evident that the population after n generations is 2^n when the progeny of a single cell are enumerated. Five bacteria have 5×2^n progeny after n generations. The relationships are generalized in the expression $a \times 2^n$ for a case in which a bacteria undergo n cell divisions. It will be noted that the exponent is the same as the number of generations elapsed. The numeral 2 appears in the exponential expressions because each cell divides into two cells.

Generation Time. The rate of cell division can be expressed in various ways. It is most commonly stated as the generation time, the interval required for one generation. The confusing feature of this method of expression is that small figures indicate rapid multiplication and large figures indicate slow multiplication. An equation for calculating the generation time can be developed from the general expression worked out in the preceding paragraph as follows:

Let $a =$ number of bacteria at start of observation

$b =$ number of bacteria after n generations

$n =$ number of generations

$g =$ time (minutes) for each generation

$t =$ time (minutes) for n generations

Then $b = a \times 2^n$

$$\log b = \log a + n \log 2$$

$$n = \frac{\log b - \log a}{\log 2}$$

But $n = \dfrac{t}{g}$

So $\dfrac{t}{g} = \dfrac{\log b - \log a}{\log 2}$

And $g = \dfrac{t \log 2}{\log b - \log a}$

This relationship is used to calculate the average generation time from two bacterial counts during the phase of logarithmic multiplication. The multiplication rate of bacteria varies from one species to another; it also varies with the conditions of cultivation. Rapidly dividing bacteria like *E. coli* have a minimum generation time of 13 to 17 minutes. *M. tuberculosis,* on the other hand, divides no faster than once in 18 hours. It is not known with certainty why one species undergoes cell division at a different rate from another. The ease of penetration of nutrient materials into the cells may be a factor; concentrations of synthetic enzymes might also be significant.

Factors Affecting the Rate of Cell Division. The rate of cell division during the logarithmic phase parallels the rate of synthesis of protoplasm; in other words, it is correlated with the chemical activity of the organisms. Any factor that affects the numerous chemical processes concerned in synthesis can therefore be expected to influence the rate of cell division.

Classical chemistry teaches that the rates of chemical reactions increase as the temperature is elevated. Bacterial multiplication also increases as the temperature is raised, but within the limits imposed by thermal inactivation or denaturation of the cell constituents (enzymes and other proteins) responsible for synthesis. The upper limit for many mesophilic bacteria is 40° to 50° C.

The concentration of nutrients in the culture medium sometimes determines the rate of multiplication; it should be pointed out, however, that bacteria can grow in very dilute media. The nutrient broth used for routine cultivation of bacteria contains a great excess of nutrient materials. One milliliter of a 1 per cent peptone solution can support a population of 500,000,000 cells. These organisms weigh about 1 mg., of which 80 per cent is water. Only 2 per cent of the peptone therefore actually enters into the composition of the bacteria. The concentration of peptone can be varied within rather wide limits without affecting the rate of bacterial multiplication appreciably.

Growth and multiplication rates are increased by the addition of readily utilized sources of energy such as fermentable carbohydrates, growth factors normally present in minimal concentrations, and substances that an organism can synthesize slowly. The rate of multiplication is reduced by decreasing the concentration of nutrients, particularly an essential nutrient.

The duration of the logarithmic phase varies with conditions. It may be only 10 to 15 generations. The exhaustion of nutrients is ordinarily not a factor; the accumulation of toxic waste products, such as alcohols and acids, and the accompanying unfavorable pH appear to be more important. The rate of cell division gradually diminishes, and cells die in increasing numbers.

Continuous Logarithmic Multiplication of Bacteria. Bacteria transferred at intervals of a few hours to fresh medium remain in a state of logarithmic multiplication. A continuous flow apparatus called a *chemostat* has been devised to accomplish the same result, and by its use a culture can be maintained at a constant population and constant multiplication rate. The culture vessel is equipped with a nutrient inlet, air inlet, and overflow tube (Fig. 13-7). Each drop of fresh medium added displaces a drop of culture, so that the total population remains constant.

The medium used is adequate in all

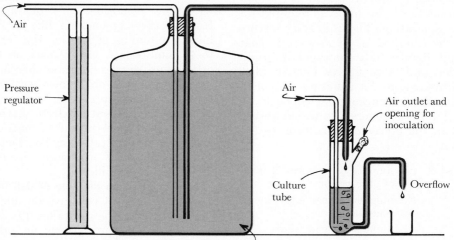

Figure 13-7.   Simplified form of a chemostat.

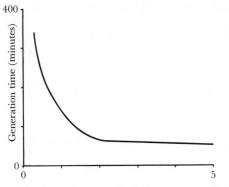

Figure 13-8. Effect of tryptophan concentration on the growth rate of a strain of *Escherichia coli* in a chemostat. (Replotted from data of A. Novick and L. Szilard: *In* E. J. Boell (Ed.): Dynamics of Growth Processes, Princeton, N. J., Princeton University Press, 1954.)

respects for the organism to be cultivated except that one essential nutrient (e.g., an amino acid) is provided in limited amounts. The rate of growth therefore depends on this ingredient and can be increased or decreased by regulating the flow of nutrient solution.

The chemostat is used in physiologic and genetic studies. The dependence of a mutant strain of *E. coli* on the amino acid tryptophan is shown in Figure 13-8; the generation time decreased sharply as the tryptophan level in the culture was increased to 1 μg. per liter and more gradually at greater concentrations.

Maximum Stationary Level

The maximum stationary level is a constant high population maintained by a balance between cell division and cell death; the net viable population does not change appreciably. Total (living plus dead) counts during this interval rise slowly and can be used to calculate the rate of death.

Two factors that limit bacterial growth have already been mentioned: nutrient supply and toxic wastes. At one time, in accordance with a hypothesis of Bail, it was believed that each individual organism required a certain amount of space. In dilute liquid media, the supply of nutrients or of any single essential nutrient may be limiting, whereas in normal, more concentrated media this is not the case. For any species growing under constant conditions, a more or less uniform maximum population per unit volume is usually attained. If the medium is made free of bacteria by centrifugation and then reinoculated, further growth occurs. Obviously, the medium still contains nutrients despite the fact that it has already supported maximal growth; moreover, the amount of wastes present is below the lethal level. This observation led Bail to propose that for each organism there is a maximum attainable population or *M concentration*. It is implied that each cell requires a certain *biologic space*, and as the available space becomes occupied, growth decreases and eventually stops.

This hypothesis did not really explain anything, but ultimately led to a suggestion regarding the nature of biologic space. It has long been known that, although bacteria ordinarily grow only slowly if at all in very dilute media, considerable growth takes place if the same media are placed in small containers or if glass beads, sand, or other solids are added. This phenomenon has been attributed to the adsorption of nutrients to inert surfaces and the development of local regions of increased concentration in which multiplication can occur. Evidently a certain minimal concentration of nutrient *per cell* must be available before sufficient nutrients can enter a cell to provide energy and building material for new cells. According to this concept, in a culture at the M concentration, the nutrient supply per cell may also be limiting. The removal of most of the bacteria increases the available nutrients per cell; consequently further multiplication can take place. It should be noted, however, that since the second crop is not as great as the first, other factors are also important. Among these is undoubtedly the nature and concentration of metabolic waste products.

It is readily demonstrated that the duration of the stationary level varies with the kind of waste products present, which, in turn, depends upon the composition of the culture medium. Fermentable carbohydrates, for example, are usually dissimilated to acids, which lower the pH and shorten the maximum stationary level; early death ensues. The incubation temperature also affects the height and duration of the maximum stationary level, particularly when very toxic wastes are formed. It will be shown later that chemical disinfection is promoted at elevated temperatures (page 264); the toxic substances that accumulate at high temperatures therefore quickly kill the bacteria that produced them, and the maximum population attained is lower.

The continued accumulation of wastes and the development of unfavorable conditions is followed by the complete cessation of multiplication. The culture then gradually enters the phase of logarithmic death.

Phase of Logarithmic Death

The death of cells in a culture often follows an exponential or logarithmic curve, half the surviving cells dying in each successive equal time interval. For example, a population decreases from 100,000,000 to 50,000,000 in the first hour, to 25,000,000 in the next hour, to 12,500,000 in the third hour, and so forth. Presumably the culture will be sterile when "less than one" survives. Actually, however, a few cells are likely to be unusually resistant and to survive much longer than anticipated: weeks or months.

Factors Affecting the Rate of Death. Some species are notorious for the rapidity with which they die in laboratory media; *Diplococcus pneumoniae* and *Neisseria gonorrheae,* the causes of lobar pneumonia and gonorrhea, respectively, die within a very few days. These organisms are particularly susceptible to autolysis, presumably the result of digestion by enzymes present in the bacterial cells.

The steepness and duration of the death curve depend in part upon the nature and concentration of toxic by-products elaborated during growth. A high concentration or unusually toxic substances produce a steep curve of logarithmic death.

The rate of death can be calculated by the same formula used to calculate the rate of logarithmic multiplication. The result in this case is a minus quantity and indicates the time required to diminish the population by 50 per cent. The same method can be used to compare the effectiveness of germicidal agents, a topic to be discussed in greater detail in the next two chapters.

GROWTH AND DEATH OF BACTERIA

13 SUMMARY

Microbial population studies are fundamentally similar to studies of other populations, animal or plant. They offer some experimental advantages; the short generation time permits many generations to elapse within a few hours or days, and an entire curve can be secured at the cost to the investigator of only one or two sleepless nights. Moreover, the whole population is confined within a single small piece of laboratory glassware, a test tube or flask. Elaborate equipment is not needed, and the conditions under which the population is studied can be varied at will.

Inoculation of fresh medium with bacteria that are not actively multiplying is followed by a short period of apparent lag during which nuclear division occurs and the cells enlarge rapidly but do not divide. Cell division then begins, and a constant logarithmic rate is soon established. After 10 to 15 generations the accumulation of toxic waste products retards cell division, and a stationary level of greater or lesser duration ensues, followed finally by the phase logarithmic death.

STUDY QUESTIONS

1. Sketch curves in which time is on the horizontal axis showing (a) the average size of the cells of a rod-shaped bacterium in a growing culture, (b) the number of viable cells, and (c) the total number of cells (living plus dead).
2. Describe the direct (microscopic) count procedure.
3. Describe the plate count procedure. On what assumption is it based?
4. Several consecutive decimal dilutions of a specimen are plated in triplicate, and the average colony counts are obtained as tabulated below. How many bacteria per milliliter should be reported? Explain.

	Colonies
Dilution	(Avg. No./Plate)
1:10	1350 (estimate)
1:100	170
1:1000	18
1:10,000	2

5. Discuss the factors that decrease the accuracy of methods of counting bacteria.
6. Why is the plating procedure said to give a minimum count of viable bacteria?
7. Describe the physical and physiologic changes that occur during the early development of a bacterial culture.
8. What is meant by *logarithmic* multiplication and *logarithmic* death?
9. What is the significance of the numeral 2 in the formula for calculating the generation time of cells in a culture?
10. How may bacteria be kept growing indefinitely at a constant rate?
11. Why do bacteria die in a normal culture instead of multiplying indefinitely?
12. The following viable bacterial counts were obtained in a broth culture at intervals after inoculation. Plot the population curve with time in hours on the X-axis and logarithms of bacteria per milliliter on the Y-axis. Calculate the generation time during the phase of logarithmic multiplication.

Time (Hrs.)	Bacteria/Milliliter
0	1,000
2	1,500
4	10,000
6	1,100,000
8	120,000,000
10	500,000,000
12	560,000,000
14	630,000,000
16	630,000,000
18	250,000,000
20	50,000,000
24	130,000
30	250
36	25

SUPPLEMENTARY READING

The classic early work on the growth of bacteria is found in Volume I of Buchanan and Fulmer's *Physiology and Biochemistry of Bacteria.* Most later authors used this as their point of departure. These include Porter, Lamanna and Mallette, Gunsalus, and Stanier, Doudoroff, and Adelberg, all of whom offer good discussions of the bacterial multiplication curve. Maaløe discusses the interesting problem of regulating bacterial cultures so that all cells divide simultaneously.

Buchanan, R. E., and Fulmer, E. I.: *Physiology and Biochemistry of Bacteria,* Vol. I. Baltimore, The Williams & Wilkins Co., 1928.

Gunsalus, I. C.: Growth of Bacteria. *In* Werkman, C. H., and Wilson, P. W. (Eds.): *Bacterial Physiology.* New York, Academic Press, Inc., 1951.

Lamanna, C., and Mallette, M. F.: *Basic Bacteriology,* 3d ed. Baltimore, The Williams & Wilkins Co., 1965.

Maaløe, O.: Synchronous Growth. *In* Gunsalus, I. C., and Stanier, R. Y. (Eds.): *The Bacteria: A Treatise on Structure and Function,* Vol. 4. New York, Academic Press, Inc., 1962.

Porter, J. R.: *Bacterial Chemistry and Physiology.* New York, John Wiley & Sons, Inc., 1946.

Stanier, R. Y., Doudoroff, M., and Adelberg, E. A.: *The Microbial World,* 2d ed. Englewood Cliffs, N. J., Prentice-Hall, Inc., 1963.

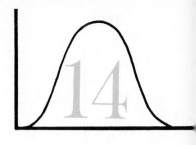

EFFECTS OF THE ENVIRONMENT ON BACTERIA

Bacteria are almost completely at the mercy of their environment. It is true, as previously noted (page 218), that some organisms possess limited means of regulating the pH of their surroundings and that motile organisms may be repelled by harmful substances or may possibly be attracted chemotactically to a source of food. Microorganisms in a compost heap, manure pile, or vinegar generator produce enough heat to raise the surrounding temperature several degrees. These, however, are unusual situations that depend upon the excellent insulating properties of the particular environments concerned.

Physical factors that affect microorganisms are discussed in this chapter. Sterilization and disinfection, particularly by chemicals, are discussed in Chapter 15.

TEMPERATURE

Growth Temperatures

The Cardinal Points. The temperature of the culture medium determines the rates of growth, multiplication, and death of microorganisms. Each organism can grow only within a *growth temperature range* characteristic of the species and sometimes of the particular culture. The lowest temperature at which growth occurs is the *minimum growth temperature;* this point is difficult to determine exactly, because there is no sudden increase in generation time as the temperature gradually drops. Generation times as great as 103 hours have been reported. The highest temperature at which growth can take place is the *maximum growth temperature.* The *optimum growth temperature,* commonly defined as the

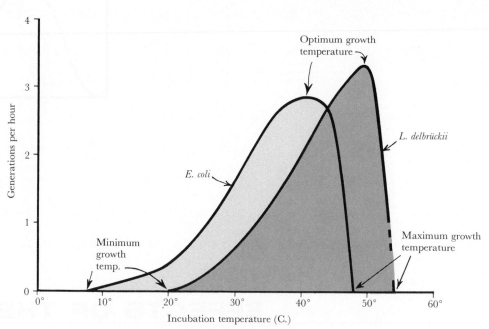

Figure 14-1. Effect of temperature on the rate of logarithmic multiplication of *Escherichia coli* and *Lactobacillus delbruckii*. Note in each case that the optimum growth temperature is much nearer to the maximum growth temperature than to the minimum growth temperature. (Plotted from data of J. L. Ingraham, J. Bact., 76:75–80, 1958; and A. Slator, J. Chem. Soc., 109:2T–10T, 1916.)

temperature at which most rapid multiplication occurs, is often only a few degrees lower than the maximum. Optimum and maximum growth temperatures can usually be ascertained with considerable accuracy from multiplication curves determined at short temperature intervals. The maximum, optimum, and minimum growth temperatures are known as the *cardinal points.*

The effect of temperature on the rate of growth of two bacterial species is illustrated in Figure 14-1. It is coincidental that each organism attained approximately the same maximum multiplication rate; the temperature at which this occurred was about 40° C. in the case of *E. coli* and 50° C. in the case of *L. delbrückii.* Maximum growth temperatures were only 5 to 10 degrees higher than the optimum growth temperatures, whereas minimum growth temperatures were approximately 30 degrees lower.

It is essential in determining the effects of temperature on microbial activity to specify exactly what is being studied, because the optimum temperature for growth is not always most favorable for other behavior. Certain by-products may be produced in greater yield or more rapidly at some other temperature. Moreover, the greatest total crop of cells is usually obtained at temperatures a few degrees less than the optimum growth temperature (Fig. 14-2), whereas the duration of the lag phase is greater. Temperature also affects the rates of respiration and fermentation, spore formation, pigment production, and other processes. These effects can be attributed in part to the differing temperature optima of various enzymes, in part to the greater toxicity of acids and other wastes at higher temperatures. Obviously one must be careful to measure the growth *rate,* if this is the accepted function, rather

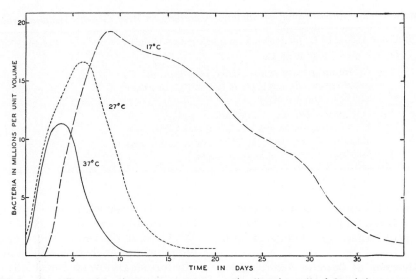

Figure 14-2. The effect of incubation temperature on the "total crop" of *Staphylococcus aureus* in broth cultures. (After Graham-Smith.)

than the *total yield* of cells or product after a single, arbitrarily selected interval of incubation.

Growth Temperatures and Habitats. The cardinal points of various bacterial species differ widely (Table 14-1). Such differences are a consequence of adaptation and natural selection. Highly parasitic organisms have become adapted to the temperatures of their natural hosts and through long association have lost the ability to grow at temperatures that depart widely from those of the hosts. These organisms therefore have a growth temperature range of only a few degrees; *Neisseria gonorrheae,* for example, grows only between 30° and 40° C. Many saprophytic bacteria, on the other hand, display a wide growth temperature range. In their natural habitats they are often exposed to extremes of temperature. *Bacillus subtilis* may grow within the range of 8° to 55° C.; it is found in soil and on plant materials, where it survives the freezing conditions of winter and the very warm

Table 14-1. Growth Temperatures and Habitats of Various Species of Bacteria

Species	Habitat	Growth Temperature (°C.)		
		Minimum	Optimum	Maximum
Pseudomonas gelatica	Sea water	0	20–25	30–32
Pseudomonas pisi	Garden peas	7	28	37
Bacillus subtilis	Soil, decomposing vegetable matter	8	28–40	50–55
Escherichia coli	Intestines of vertebrates	8	37	47
Clostridium tetani	Soil, feces	14	37	43
Neisseria gonorrheae	Human infection	30	37	40
Lactobacillus delbrückii	Fermenting vegetable and grain mash	20	50	55
Bacillus stearothermophilus	Soil, spoiled food products	33–37	50–65	70

Table 14-2. Classification of Bacteria According to Their Growth Temperatures

A. Grow well at 0° C. (generation time less than 48 hours)	1. Psychrophiles
AA. Do not grow well at 0° C.	
B. Optimum growth temperature less than 45° C. (most species do not grow below 10° C. or above 52° C.)	2. Mesophiles
BB. Optimum growth temperature greater than 45° C.; in general, grow at 55° C. (*obligate* thermophiles do not grow at 37° C. or less, whereas *facultative* thermophiles can do so.)	3. Thermophiles

conditions of summer. Other bacteria grow at subzero temperatures in cooling brines; still others are found in hot springs.

Classification of Bacteria According to Growth Temperature. The total temperature range within which bacteria may grow extends from a few degrees below 0° C. to approximately 80° C. Bacteria are sometimes classified roughly into three groups according to their temperature preferences (Table 14-2). These groups are not sharply defined; the distinctions are arbitrary, but the classification has some practical utility.

Psychrophiles

Some *psychrophilic* species multiply at temperatures as low as −5° C. in brines or sugar solutions that do not freeze solid. Organisms that grow well at 0° to 5° C. are frequently encountered as causes of spoilage in refrigerated foods. Their rate of multiplication at such temperatures is often slow, and spoilage is not apparent unless storage is greatly prolonged. Psychrophilic bacteria may grow at 30° C. or higher, and their optimum temperature is usually within 5 degrees of the maximum. The chief feature that distinguishes a psychrophile is its ability to grow at 0° C.

Mesophiles

Most of the commonly studied bacteria are *mesophilic,* and these fall into two reasonably well defined subdivi-

sions: (1) those whose optimum growth temperatures are from 20° to about 35° C., and (2) those whose optimum temperatures are between 35° and 45° C. The former group consists chiefly of saprophytes and plant parasites, whereas the latter are principally animal parasites or commensals (organisms that live in a host but do not harm it). Minimum and maximum growth temperatures vary correspondingly, but for the most part are within the range of 10° to 52° C.

Thermophiles

Thermophilic bacteria are interesting because they prefer temperatures intolerable to most forms of animal life. Water at 45° C. is hot to the touch—hotter than an ordinary bath; nevertheless, thermophilic bacteria grow best at temperatures above 45° C. Many will not grow below 40° C., and some will grow at 75° to 80° C. Vegetative cells of nonspore-forming mesophiles are usually killed within a few minutes at 60° C.; most other forms of life are also killed at this temperature.

In general, thermophilic bacteria are those that can grow at 55° C. *Obligate thermophiles* do not grow at 37° C., whereas *facultative thermophiles* can grow at both 37° C. and 55° C. It appears that facultative thermophiles carry on a mesophilic type of metabolism at temperatures below about 44° C. When they are warmed to 44° to 52° C. and allowed a few minutes to adapt, their metabolism shifts to the thermophilic type. Obligate thermophiles are incapable of adapting to the mesophilic type of metabolism.

Thermophiles obviously possess unusual proteins or an unusual physicochemical situation that permits, and even favors, physiologic activity at temperatures that denature the proteins of other organisms. The optimum temperature of various enzymes from thermophilic bacteria is known to be in the thermophilic range, and there is evidence that some enzymes are active at higher temperatures in the intact cell than after extraction from the cell.

Factors Affecting the Maximum Growth Temperature

A relationship between maximum growth temperatures of bacteria and the heat resistance of their enzymes is suggested by the data in Table 14-3. The maximum growth temperature of a strain of *Bacillus mycoides* is 40° C., and three respiratory enzymes of this organism are inactivated at 40° or 41° C. The same enzymes in species of higher maximum growth temperature withstand greater amounts of heat. The correlation between growth temperature and enzyme inactivation temperature is not perfect, so that some of these enzymes are evidently not vital to the growth of certain of the species. It has been shown that when an essential microbial enzyme is inactivated by heat, the organism can be made to grow at an otherwise unfavorably high temperature by adding the normal product of that enzyme to the culture medium.

Thermoduric Bacteria

Thermoduric bacteria are unusually resistant to heat. The term can be applied to endospore-forming species, but is more commonly restricted to nonspore-forming types. Thermoduric organisms are often found in pasteurized milk or other products that have been heated but not sterilized. They include *Microbacterium* species, various micrococci and streptococci, certain lactobacilli, and some gram-negative rod bacteria.

Mechanisms of Growth Control by Temperature

The effect of temperature on microbial growth is complicated; it can be expressed in its simplest terms as the resultant of two opposing activities. The rates of enzyme reactions, like those of all chemical reactions, vary directly with temperature. They are slow at low temperatures and accelerate as the temperature rises. Degradative processes, such as denaturation of proteins, including enzymes, are very slight at low temperatures and do not become marked until moderate temperatures are attained, but then they increase rapidly. The difference between beneficial enzyme activity and harmful denaturation is greatest at the optimum growth temperature, whereas at the maximum

Table 14-3. Relationships Between Maximum Growth Temperatures of Bacteria and Inactivation Temperatures of Their Enzymes

Species	Maximum Growth Temperatures (Means)	Inactivation Temperatures (Means)		
		Indophenol Oxidase	Catalase	Succinic Dehydrogenase
Bacillus mycoides (4 strains)	40° C.	41° C.	41° C.	40° C.
Bacillus cereus (21 strains)	45° C.	48° C.	46° C.	50° C.
Bacillus subtilis (10 strains)	54° C.	60° C.	56° C.	51° C.
Thermophiles (9 strains)	76° C.	65° C.	67° C.	59° C.

Table 14-4. Effect of Temperature upon the Thermal Death Times of Spores

Temperature	Clostridium botulinum (60,000,000,000 Spores Suspended in Buffer at pH 7)	A Thermophile (150,000 Spores per ml. of Corn Juice at pH 6.1)
	Minutes	
100° C.	360	1140
105° C.	120	
110° C.	36	180
115° C.	12	60
120° C.	5	17

growth temperature destructive activity is so rapid that it just balances constructive processes and growth ceases.

The Killing of Microorganisms at High Temperature

TDP vs. TDT. The lethal effect of high temperatures upon microorganisms was formerly indicated by a number called the *thermal death point* (TDP): the temperature at which an organism is killed in 10 minutes. Numerous factors affect the apparent thermal death point, and it is difficult to obtain reproducible figures. These factors include the number and previous history of the organisms and the nature and pH of the suspending medium.

More recently, *thermal death times* (TDT) have been determined. The thermal death time is the time required to kill a given number of cells or spores under stated conditions of temperature, taking into account the nature of the suspending medium and all other pertinent information.

Survivor curves (which resemble the death phase of a population curve) may be determined by the plate method. The results can be expressed as negative generation times, or the time required to kill a stated percentage (e.g., 99.9 per cent) of the population, or a death rate constant that indicates the rate of death by a positive figure.

Factors Affecting the Death of Microorganisms by Heat. *Temperature.* The striking effect of temperature on the

killing of bacteria is illustrated in Table 14-4. Six hours at the temperature of boiling water was required to kill spores of *Clostridium botulinum*. The sterilization time decreased markedly as the temperature was raised, so that only five minutes was required at 120° C. Not all strains of *Cl. botulinum* are as resistant as this. The thermophilic organism obviously possessed much higher heat resistance. It is presumably one of the most resistant encountered; yet even it was killed within 20 minutes at the highest temperature recorded. Hospital and laboratory sterilizers, commercial canning retorts, and home pressure cookers are often operated at 120° C., which is the temperature of steam at a pressure of approximately 15 pounds per square inch (Table 14-5).

Number of Organisms. Greater heat treatment is required to kill a large number of organisms than a small number (Table 14-6). Moreover, the cells or spores in a given suspension are of un-

Table 14-5. Relationship Between Steam Pressure and Temperature in the Autoclave

Gauge Pressure (lbs./sq. in.)	Temperature (°C.)
0	100.0
5	109.0
10	115.5
15	121.5
20	126.5

Table 14-6. Effect of the Number of Spores of *Clostridium botulinum* on the Thermal Death Time at 100° C.

Number of Spores	Thermal Death Time (Minutes)
72,000,000,000	240
1,640,000,000	125
32,000,000	110
650,000	85
16,400	50
328	40

equal resistance; a few highly resistant individuals may survive much longer than the majority. These few resistant cells are important in practical sterilization because they determine the total heat process required for preservation of canned goods, sterilization of surgical dressings, and preparation of culture media in the laboratory.

Species. The heat resistance of different bacterial species varies through a wide range. Any temperature above the maximum growth temperature is lethal to vegetative cells if applied for a sufficient time. *Treponema pallidum,* the cause of syphilis, is killed within one hour at 41.5° C. (Table 14-7). This species is unusually susceptible to heat. Most nonspore-forming bacteria are

Table 14-7. Thermal Death Times of Vegetative Cells and Spores of Bacteria

Organism	Temperature (°C.)	Time (Min.)
Treponema pallidum	41.5	60
Most nonsporeforming bacteria	60–65	10–15
Staphylococcus aureus	65	30
Lactobacillus thermophilus	71	30
Sporeformers, vegetative cells	60–65	10–15
Sporeformers, spores:		
Bacillus megaterium	100	16
Bacillus subtilis	100	180
Bacillus tostus	100	1200

killed within 10 to 15 minutes at 60° to 65° C., but a few thermoduric organisms require a higher temperature or longer time. Vegetative cells of spore-forming bacteria are killed as readily as nonspore-forming bacteria. Spores are much more resistant but differ widely according to the species.

Medium: Composition and Viscosity. The nature of the suspending medium affects the results of thermal death time studies as well as practical sterilization procedures. Proteins, fats, and other substances offer some protection to bacteria. A highly viscous medium retards the distribution of heat by convection and limits heat transfer to the slower process of conduction. These factors are illustrated in Table 14-8, which shows thermal-death-point (at 10 minutes of heating) determinations of *E. coli* suspended in cream, whole milk, skim milk, whey, and broth. Cream is the most viscous and contains a high percentage of fat; whole milk is next in viscosity and fat content. The remaining media contain little if any fat but decreasing amounts of protein.

pH. In general, the resistance of an organism to heat is greatest at a pH favorable for growth (often near neutrality), and death occurs more rapidly as the acidity or alkalinity of the medium is increased. The death time of *Cl. tetani* at 100° C. is 30 minutes at pH 7, but only 15 minutes at either pH 6 or 8. At 100° C. *Cl. botulinum* is killed in 50 minutes at pH 5.05 and in

Table 14-8. The Effect of the Medium upon the Thermal Death Point of *Escherichia coli**

Medium	Thermal Death Point (°C.)
Cream	73
Whole milk	69
Skim milk	65
Whey	63
Bouillon (broth)	61

*Heating time: 10 minutes.

15 minutes at pH 3.98. Most food spoilage bacteria grow best at approximately neutral reaction, and relatively little heating is necessary to sterilize acid foods (below pH 4.5). This explains why fruits are more easily preserved by canning than are meats, fish and nonacid vegetables such as corn or peas.

Mechanisms of Killing by Heat. The lethal action of heat is doubtless exerted in several ways, including denaturation of proteins and inactivation of essential enzymes. There are also indications that the osmotic barrier may be affected. Increased permeability would permit toxic substances to enter, or vital components to be lost; decreased permeability would retard the entrance of nutrients or excretion of toxic wastes.

Effects of Low Temperatures

Low temperature does not necessarily kill bacteria. Multiplication ceases below the minimum growth temperature, but the organisms may remain viable in the dormant condition, often for long periods. Growth and multiplication can resume when the temperature is again raised to the normal range.

The ability of bacteria to withstand freezing or subfreezing temperatures varies with the species. Endospores and certain cocci such as staphylococci are very hardy. Some gram-negative rod bacteria, e.g., *Pseudomonas pyocyaneus,* are killed more readily at subfreezing temperatures. The mechanism of death by freezing is not known but has been attributed to denaturation of cellular proteins.

The rapidity of death caused by temperatures below the growth range depends upon the temperature; oddly enough, bacteria often resist very low temperatures better than temperatures only slightly below the minimum for growth. One experiment, for example, showed that only 4 per cent of the cells of *E. coli* remained alive after 11 days at −1° to −2° C., whereas 25 per cent survived storage at −20° C. for 163

Table 14-9. Effect of Low Temperature on Survival of Staphylococci Dried on Garnets

Time of Storage	22° C.	5° C.	−190° C.*
	Survivors		
1 day	90,800	88,800	65,900
8 days	11,400	37,700	60,700
32 days	300	550	67,900

* Liquid air

days. Staphylococci can withstand the temperature of liquid air in practically unchanged numbers after the initial shock of freezing. The organisms in the experiment summarized in Table 14-9 were dried on garnets and then some were stored at room temperature, some in the refrigerator, and some at −190° C. Garnets were removed from the various storage conditions at intervals and the surviving bacteria were counted.

Preservation of Bacteria by Cold. The resistance of bacteria to low temperature provides a means of preserving many species for long periods without the necessity of frequent transfers. Hardy organisms frozen quickly on agar slants or, preferably, in dilute peptone or milk may be kept at −20° C. for a year or two without complete loss of viability. More delicate organisms like gonococci and meningococci, which ordinarily must be transplanted every two or three days, are preserved several days or weeks when properly frozen and stored. They survive even better if dried rapidly in a vacuum while frozen and kept at subfreezing temperatures.

Survival of Bacteria in Frozen Foods. The survival of bacteria at low temperatures is important in the food industry. Many years ago, several outbreaks of typhoid fever were reported that apparently were caused by bacteria in natural ice used several months after the ice was harvested. Laboratory tests later showed that typhoid bacteria can survive in ice as long as 22 weeks. Other intestinal pathogens possess similar survival power.

The tremendous expansion of the frozen food industry emphasizes the importance of bacterial resistance to low temperature. In one experiment, living typhoid bacteria were recovered from inoculated unsliced sweetened strawberries after storage at −18° C. for 14 months; the organisms died in berries stored for eight days at 5° C. or six hours at room temperature. Freezing is therefore not a means of destroying pathogens in food, and no food should be frozen that could not be eaten raw. Moreover, frozen food usually spoils more quickly after thawing than the original unfrozen food; freezing apparently damages the food tissues so that nutrient materials are released upon thawing to promote very active multiplication of surviving spoilage bacteria. Thawed frozen foods should therefore be used immediately or else discarded.

Toxin-producing bacteria, such as *Clostridium botulinum* and *Staphylococcus aureus,* may survive freezing, but if they did not multiply before freezing and if the food is used immediately it is safe. The harmful effects of these organisms are attributed to the toxins they produce while growing in food, not to the organisms themselves.

RADIATIONS

Investigators during the last quarter of the nineteenth century noted that sunlight is lethal to many bacteria, and the practice arose of cultivating microorganisms in the dark. Colored filters were used to test the effect of light of different colors; red, orange, and yellow did not harm bacteria, but blue-violet was markedly inhibitory. Later it was discovered that radiations outside the visible range were bactericidal; these were ultraviolet rays.

Germicidal Radiations

The electromagnetic spectrum is shown in Figure 14-3, which also indicates some of the radiations destructive to bacteria. Radiations of wavelengths greater than about 300 mμ possess little if any bactericidal power. These include visible light waves, infrared waves, and the much longer radio waves. Some of these radiations produce heat but are not germicidal per se.

Ultraviolet light at the wavelength 265 mμ is especially effective against the majority of bacteria and some molds and viruses (Fig. 14-4). Most work has been done with mercury vapor lamps that emit radiations of 253.7 mμ, well within the germicidal range. Many radiations shorter than ultraviolet are also germicidal, particularly the shorter

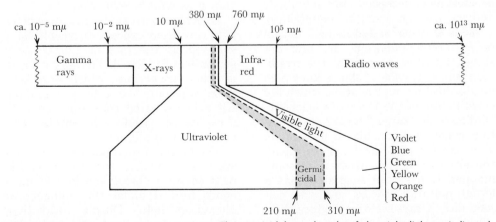

Figure 14-3. The electromagnetic spectrum. The germicidal wavelengths of ultraviolet light are indicated.

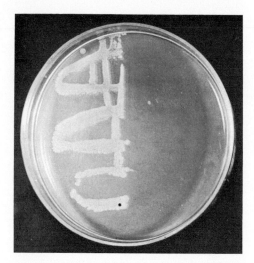

Figure 14-4. Killing of *Escherichia coli* by ultraviolet light. The bacteria were streaked uniformly on the agar in this dish. The left half was covered with black paper and the right half was exposed a few minutes to the light from a carbon arc. Only the protected bacteria on the left grew when the plate was then incubated.

x-rays and gamma rays. Some of these are even more efficient than ultraviolet radiations but are more difficult or dangerous to use.

Effects of Radiations

Radiations have two effects on microorganisms. The first is death, which appears to be logarithmic; that is, a constant percentage of the surviving cells is killed in each successive equal time interval. The other effect is the production of mutants in the surviving population. These genetically altered forms differ from the parent population, usually in one characteristic, such as resistance to bacteriophage, fermentative power, or the ability to synthesize a substance necessary for metabolic activity (i.e., an essential metabolite).

Mode of Action of Radiations. Lethal or mutagenic radiations are first absorbed by some portion of the irradiated cell. Ultraviolet light is known to be absorbed by nucleic acids, which are constituents of the DNA of nuclei. According to the "target" theory, the radiation makes a direct hit on a sensitive area like a nucleic acid molecule, and the absorbed energy alters it in some manner. It has been suggested that a lethal mutation occurs and the cell soon dies. X-rays seem to produce their effects by general bombardment, selective absorption by specific molecular structures playing little or no part. Instead, tracks or paths of ionization are produced, and OH^- or other ions cause lethal chemical reactions or genetic changes.

Killing by radiation depends upon the wavelength and the total radiation dosage, that is, the total amount of incident energy, but the dosage necessary to kill a given species varies with the wavelength. X-rays are more efficient than ultraviolet rays.

Photoreactivation. An interesting phenomenon recently discovered raises the question, When is a cell dead? Bacteria exposed to ultraviolet light "revive" when exposed to visible light of 365 to 510 $m\mu$ wavelength. This is known as *photoreactivation*.

E. coli cells treated with ultraviolet light and then exposed to visible light survived at the rate of 120,000 cells per million irradiated. The survival rate of other suspensions, which were kept dark, was only 4.5 cells per million. Ultraviolet-treated cells survived only if exposed to visible light within three hours after irradiation.

The mechanism of photoreactivation appears to involve the use of visible light energy to break specific chemical bonds formed under the influence of ultraviolet light. During irradiation, DNA strands are presumed to be distorted in such a manner that two thymine residues on the same or complementary strands join and form a dimer. This can be broken by visible light, by a change in temperature, or by a "photoreactivating enzyme."

The usual criterion of cell death is inability to multiply. According to this definition, nearly all the irradiated cells that were kept dark would have been considered dead. Most of the same cells, however, if exposed to visible light, would have proved to be capable of multiplication. This finding reemphasizes the fact that there is no sharp dividing line between life and death; in fact, the distinction is even more tenuous than previously believed.

Applications of Irradiation

Production of Mutants. Ultraviolet and x-irradiations cause mutations, and by the use of suitable techniques a desired mutant can be selected from the random population of induced mutants. This is a trial and error process; it is not yet possible to induce particular changes at will. Industrially important strains of microorganisms have been derived in this manner; for example, a culture of *Penicillium* that produces unusually large amounts of penicillin.

Sterilization. Ultraviolet irradiation is of some use for killing spoilage or disease bacteria. Practical sterilization is limited by the fact that glass, water, and organic matter absorb ultraviolet light and prevent its access to bacteria. It is therefore possible to sterilize only air and the surfaces of objects, such as surgical implements, glassware and chinaware, and the like. Ultraviolet lamps are used in some hospital operating rooms to reduce surgical infection and in classrooms to reduce respiratory disease. The lamps must be arranged and shielded so that human skin is not exposed for too long, lest serious damage be done. Ultraviolet irradiation has been used experimentally to inactivate viruses (e.g., influenza) for use in immunization.

The sterilization of food by gamma rays is currently under investigation. These rays penetrate deeply enough to be used with many products and sterilize very quickly (within a second).

PRESSURE

Bacteria seem to possess considerable resistance to mechanical or hydrostatic pressure. The findings of different investigators are not entirely consistent; some of the discrepancies are undoubtedly the result of differences in procedure. The statement can be found that nonspore-forming bacteria, such as *Serratia marcescens* and *Streptococcus lactis,* are killed within five minutes at 85,000 to 100,000 pounds pressure per square inch. Another report indicates that 88,000 pounds per square inch applied for 14 hours is necessary to kill nonspore-forming bacteria, and that twice that pressure is required to kill spores.

Zobell and co-workers found that spore-forming and nonspore-forming bacteria failed to grow in broth when subjected continuously to hydrostatic pressure of 2940 to 8820 pounds per square inch. Temperature was a factor; several species grew at 40° C. under 8820 pounds pressure but did not grow at 20° C. Marine bacteria seemed to possess somewhat greater ability to grow at high pressures than terrestrial bacteria. Morphologic changes also occurred under pressure; some species lost motility and some cells grew but failed to divide.

SONIC VIBRATIONS

The human ear detects sound waves with frequencies between 32 and 32,000 vibrations per second. Supersonic waves range from the higher audible sound, 9000 vibrations per second, to inaudible sound of 200,000 vibrations per second. Vibrations over 200,000 per second are classified as ultrasonic waves. High frequency sound waves generated by nickel bars or quartz crystals stimulated electrically have been used extensively for experimentation in biology. Most work has been done at about 9000 vibrations per second.

Effects of Sonic Vibrations

Supersonic vibrations drastically affect the cells of higher organisms, causing severe disturbance of the cellular contents and often eventual rupture of the cell walls and complete disintegration. Bacteria are much smaller and the effects of supersonic vibration cannot be observed as readily. Bacterial cultures, however, can be killed and lysed by high frequency sound. The sensitivity of different species to sonic energy varies greatly, as might be expected. *Neisseria gonorrheae* is easily sterilized, whereas most bacterial spores are unaffected.

Factors Affecting the Rate of Killing by Sonic Vibrations. The efficiency of sound waves depends more on their amplitude than on their frequency; that is, waves of relatively low frequency but of high intensity are more effective than high frequency waves of low intensity. The time required for sterilization is appreciable with intensities so far studied. For example, 99 per cent of a young (12 hour) culture of *E. coli* were killed in 20 minutes by high intensity waves at 8900 cycles per second. The cells of this culture died at a logarithmic rate. Older cultures contained a higher percentage of resistant cells. Logarithmic death of *Klebsiella pneumoniae* by ultrasonic waves is illustrated in Figure 14-5. Approximately 0.5 per cent of the initial population was still viable after 50 minutes.

According to the most favored hypothesis, death and lysis of bacteria by sonic vibrations are attributed to *cavitation*. It is presumed that the cell boundaries are bombarded by minute gas bubbles, which form in the suspending medium as a result of disturbance by the high frequency sound waves.

Microbiologic Applications of Sonic Vibrations

Sonic oscillators are used to study the composition of bacterial cells and to secure intracellular enzymes for biochemical investigation. Solutions of microbial constituents can be obtained for use as immunizing agents and for serologic analysis.

MOISTURE

Water is the vehicle by which holophytic organisms like bacteria, yeasts,

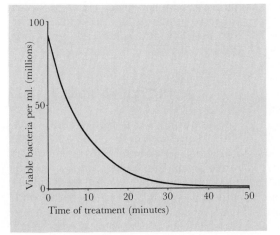

Figure 14-5. The killing of *Klebsiella pneumoniae* by ultrasonic waves (700,000 cycles per second). (Plotted from data of D. Hamre, J. Bact., *57:*279–295, 1949.)

and molds secure food and eliminate waste products. Most bacteria and yeasts prefer media of very high water content. Ordinary nutrient broth (0.3 per cent beef extract and 1.0 per cent peptone) contains 98.7 per cent water; some bacteria grow better when 0.5 per cent sodium chloride is added. Molds require much less water; many grow on substrates containing 50 to 60 per cent sugar, or even upon leather goods and book bindings during humid weather.

Osmotic Pressure

Osmosis is the diffusion of solvent molecules through a semipermeable membrane. The *osmotic pressure* of a solution is directly dependent on the concentration of dissolved substances in the solution. Two solutions of the same osmotic pressure are said to be *isotonic.* If two solutions of unequal osmotic pressure are compared, the one of higher pressure is *hypertonic,* the other *hypotonic.*

The osmotic pressure of the protoplasm of normal bacterial cells is greater than that of the usual culture media; that is, it contains a higher concentration of salts, amino acids, and other organic and inorganic compounds. This creates a tendency for water to enter the protoplast by osmosis through the semipermeable cytoplasmic membrane (Fig. 14-6). Under customary conditions of cultivation the cells maintain a state of *turgidity.*

Cells of animals and higher plants undergo drastic changes when placed in media of very low osmotic pressure such as distilled water. There is a tendency for excessive amounts of water to pass into the protoplasm, thus creating very high pressure. Cells without extremely strong walls undergo *plasmoptysis:* the cell walls burst and protoplasmic materials are extruded. Most bacteria do not suffer serious harm when suspended for a short time in distilled water, because their walls are very strong and rigid. However, bacteria that have become acclimated to very hypertonic solutions such as pickling brines may undergo plasmoptysis when transferred to very dilute media. Many species of marine bacteria fail to grow in fresh-water media.

Plasmolysis occurs when normal cells are placed in solutions of very high osmotic pressure. Water passes from the protoplasm into the surrounding medium, and the protoplasm shrinks to a small mass within each cell. Metabolic activity ceases, and the cells become

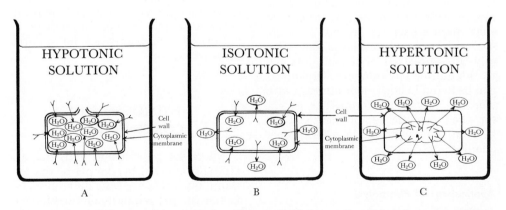

Figure 14-6.   A, Plasmoptysis (bursting) of a cell in a strongly hypotonic solution after water molecules have entered the cell; B, normal turgidity in an isotonic (or slightly hypotonic) solution; C, plasmolysis in a strongly hypertonic solution.

dormant and may even die. They may recover if they are returned soon enough to normal osmotic conditions. Gram-positive bacteria are more difficult to plasmolyze than gram-negative bacteria.

The morphology of cells grown in media of moderately high osmotic pressure may be atypical; long, filamentous, bloated, irregularly staining forms are frequently found.

Osmophilic and Halophilic Microorganisms

Microorganisms that have become adapted to high osmotic pressure are called *osmophiles*. Marine bacteria and other organisms that cannot grow in salt-free solutions are *halophiles*. Some halophilic bacteria can be readapted to normal media by successive transfers through media of lower and lower salt concentration. Less than 10 per cent of marine bacteria can grow in fresh water when first isolated, but about 75 per cent eventually can be adapted to solutions of low osmotic pressure.

Halophilic bacteria are interesting from the ecologic viewpoint, particularly those found in the sea and in other natural bodies of water of high salinity. The salt content of the major oceans is between 3.5 and 4.0 per cent, that of the Dead Sea is about 29 per cent. Some bacteria isolated from the Dead Sea have failed to grow in media containing less than 13 per cent salt. It is believed that marine bacteria are not separate species from terrestrial forms but actually are terrestrial organisms adapted to the marine environment. Organisms can be found in both environments with identical physiologic properties except for their osmotic requirements. They become indistinguishable after proper adaptation.

Applications of Plasmolysis

Plasmolysis is an important method of controlling bacterial growth. It has been used throughout recorded history to preserve foods. Experience has shown that 10 to 15 per cent sodium chloride or 50 to 70 per cent sugar are satisfactory preservative concentrations.

Desiccation. Desiccation is a practical means of applying osmotic relations to the control of microbial activity. Drying any material increases its osmotic pressure so that microorganisms cease to grow and some eventually die. As long as the product is kept dry, spoilage will not occur.

Many bacteria survive for long periods in the desiccated condition; endospores and gram-positive cocci are particularly resistant. Foods preserved by this method should therefore not be considered sterile. They may contain a large, dormant microbial population, which can begin to grow and cause spoilage almost immediately after reconstitution with water.

Preservation of Bacteria by Desiccation. Desiccation is used to preserve bacterial cultures. The organisms are first frozen quickly and then dried under high vacuum while still frozen. *Lyophilization* is one of the best known and most widely used processes. Bacterial suspensions in small ampules are frozen in a bath of alcohol and dry ice ($-76°$ C.) and evacuated under very high vacuum. The water evaporates from the ice and the ampules are then sealed in a flame. If freezing and drying are performed rapidly, even sensitive species are preserved in a viable condition without change in their physiologic or pathogenic characteristics for months or years.

HYDROGEN ION CONCENTRATION

Microbial growth and activities are strongly affected by the pH of the medium, but there are wide differences between the pH requirements of the various species. These differences reflect the normal habits and habitats of the organisms. Each species can grow only

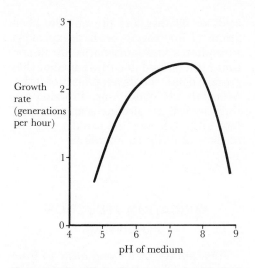

Figure 14-7. Effect of pH on growth of *Escherichia coli*. (Plotted from data of Gale and Epps, Biochem. J., 36:1942.)

within a certain pH range, and most rapid or luxuriant growth occurs in a narrow *optimum pH* zone (Fig. 14-7). Table 14-10 lists minimum, optimum, and maximum pH values for the growth of a few common microorganisms.

pH Ranges of Microorganisms

The intestinal bacteria tolerate greater acidity and alkalinity than most other animal parasites; their optimum pH is near or slightly below neutrality. These organisms gain access to the intestine only after withstanding the acid of the stomach, and in the intestine they encounter bile, which is highly alkaline. Their adaptation to acid or alkaline conditions is easily understood. The pH of blood

Table 14-10. Minimum, Optimum, and Maximum pH for the Growth of Various Bacteria and Fungi

Organism	Minimum pH	Optimum pH	Maximum pH
Animal parasites or commensals			
Intestinal			
Escherichia coli	4.3	6.0–8.0	9.5
Salmonella typhosa	4.0	6.8–7.2	9.6
Shigella dysenteriae	4.5	ca. 7.0	9.6
Blood or tissue parasites			
Diplococcus pneumoniae	7.0	7.8	8.3
Streptococcus pyogenes	4.5	7.8	9.2
Neisseria meningitidis	6.1	7.4	7.8
Brucella melitensis	6.3	6.6–8.2	8.4
Vibrio cholerae	5.6	7.0–7.4	9.6
Mycobacterium tuberculosis	5.0	6.8–7.7	8.4
Corynebacterium diphtheriae	6.0	7.3–7.5	8.3
Lactobacillus	3.8–4.4	5.4–6.4	7.2
Plant pathogens or commensals			
Erwinia caratovorum	4.6		9.3
Rhizobium leguminosarum	3.2–5.0		10.0–11.0
Bacterium radiobacter	4.5–5.0		11.5–12.0
Soil bacteria			
Bacillus subtilis	4.5	6.0–7.5	8.5
Nitrobacter	5.7	8.4–9.2	10.2
Nitrosomonas	7.6	8.5–8.8	9.4
Thiobacillus thiooxidans	1.0	2.0–5.0	9.8
Yeasts	2.5	4.0–5.8	8.0
Molds	1.5	3.8–6.0	7.0–11.0

and tissues, on the contrary, is much more constant. Normal blood has a reaction of about pH 7.3. Most blood or tissue parasites are favored by neutral or slightly alkaline media.

Many plant and soil bacteria prefer relatively alkaline conditions. Yeasts and molds tolerate a wide range of pH, but usually grow best in acid media. Acid foods, such as fruits, pickles, and other fermented products, are more susceptible to yeast or mold spoilage than to bacterial spoilage.

pH Changes in Cultures

The nature of microbial metabolic activities is such that the pH of a culture medium does not ordinarily remain constant after growth begins. Degradation of proteins and other nitrogenous compounds frequently yields ammonia or other alkaline by-products; carbohydrate fermentations often produce organic acids. The nature of the organism and of the substrate therefore determines whether the pH of a medium rises or falls as growth proceeds. The reaction may continue to change until the maximum or minimum pH for the organism is reached, whereupon the culture dies.

Reversion of reaction occurs when some species grow in certain media. *Aerobacter aerogenes* utilizes glucose vigorously and produces acid until the reaction falls to about pH 5.0. After the glucose is exhausted, the organism attacks its acid products and oxidizes them to carbon dioxide and water; the reaction therefore returns toward pH 7.0.

Buffers

Buffers are often added to culture media to retard pH change as acids or alkalies are formed. They combine with acids or alkalies and prevent the liberation of hydrogen or hydroxyl ions. Phosphates and carbonates are important buffers used in culture media; they greatly delay the development of lethal (suicidal) pH conditions. Proteins and their hydrolytic products are also buffers, although they are usually put into media primarily as nutrients.

OXIDATION-REDUCTION POTENTIAL

The ability of an organism to grow when transferred to a fresh culture medium depends in part upon the oxidation-reduction (O-R) potential of the medium. Oxidation-reduction potentials are controlled by the oxidizing and reducing agents present and can be determined by measurement with appropriate electrometric apparatus. Strongly oxidizing substances produce positive potentials (e.g., +200 mv.), and strongly reducing substances produce negative potentials. The potential of hydrogen at 1 atmosphere is about −400 mv.

The various bacteria differ with respect to the O-R potentials at which they can begin to grow. Aerobic organisms tolerate higher potentials than anaerobes, which usually require media with negative potentials. The aeration of culture media tends to produce positive potentials, but the initiation of growth of many bacteria (not only anaerobes) is favored by a somewhat lower potential. Consequently, the boiling of media to expel dissolved oxygen or the incorporation of a reducing substance is often helpful in starting the growth of small inocula. As soon as the bacteria begin to metabolize, the O-R potential falls, frequently to negative values.

14   EFFECTS OF THE ENVIRONMENT ON BACTERIA

SUMMARY

The growth and death of microorganisms are profoundly influenced by temperature, pH, and other characteristics of the environment. These factors affect the rates of biochemical reactions within a cell.

For each species there exists an optimum temperature at which the organism multiplies most rapidly, and maximum and minimum growth temperatures above and below which no growth occurs. Temperatures progressively higher than the maximum growth temperature are more and more rapidly lethal, but bacteria and many other microorganisms survive long periods at very low temperatures.

Each organism also exhibits a minimum, optimum, and maximum pH for growth. Ultraviolet and other radiations of certain wavelengths kill microorganisms. They may also be killed slowly by sonic vibrations.

Many microorganisms survive in solutions of low or high osmotic pressure, but growth is generally retarded in hypertonic media.

STUDY QUESTIONS

1. Compare the effects on microorganisms of temperatures below and above the growth range.
2. Is the optimum growth temperature the most favorable temperature for all microbial activity? Explain.
3. Discuss the relationship between growth temperatures of microorganisms and their habitats and parasitic nature.
4. Discuss the factors that affect the killing of microorganisms by heat.
5. Discuss the implications of the fact that the optimum growth temperature of thermophilic bacteria may be higher than the maximum growth temperature or even the thermal death point of other (mesophilic) bacteria.
6. What is the biologic significance of the observation that more time is required to sterilize a large population of bacteria by heat (or most other agents) than a small population?
7. Does the fact that *Treponema pallidum* is killed in one hour at 41.5° C. have any practical use? Explain.
8. How do radiations affect microorganisms? What are their modes of action?
9. Is it possible to define death (of a cell) accurately? Explain.
10. What is believed to be the mechanism of killing by sound?
11. What is pH? How is the pH of a solution determined? How can pH be controlled? What is the effect of pH on microorganisms?
12. Compare the effects of low and high osmotic pressure on bacteria, yeasts, and molds.

SUPPLEMENTARY READING

The early literature on the effects of the physical environment upon bacteria is thoroughly reviewed by Buchanan and Fulmer (to 1928) and Porter (to 1944). More recent work is discussed by Ingraham, Thimann, Salle, Lamanna and Mallette, and Mitchell. Oginsky and Umbreit offer a stimulating short chapter on this topic.

Buchanan, R. E., and Fulmer, E. I.: *Physiology and Biochemistry of Bacteria,* Vol. II. Baltimore, The Williams & Wilkins Co., 1930.

Ingraham, J. L.: *In* Gunsalus, I. C., and Stanier, R. Y. (Eds.): *The Bacteria: A Treatise on Structure and Function,* Vol. IV. New York, Academic Press, Inc., 1962.

Lamanna, C., and Mallette, M. F.: *Basic Bacteriology,* 3d ed. Baltimore, The Williams & Wilkins Co., 1965.

Mitchell, P.: Physical Factors Affecting Growth and Death. *In* Werkman, C. H., and Wilson, P. W. (Eds.): *Bacterial Physiology.* New York, Academic Press, Inc., 1951.

Oginsky, E. L., and Umbreit, W. W.: *An Introduction to Bacterial Physiology,* 2d ed. San Francisco, W. H. Freeman & Company, 1959.

Porter, J. R.: *Bacterial Chemistry and Physiology.* New York, John Wiley & Sons, Inc., 1946.

Salle, A. J.: *Fundamental Principles of Bacteriology,* 5th ed. New York, McGraw-Hill Book Co., Inc., 1960.

Thimann, K. V.: *The Life of Bacteria,* 2d ed. New York, The Macmillan Company, 1963.

INHIBITION AND KILLING OF MICROORGANISMS

NATURAL EQUILIBRIA

The vital activities of any organism or cell help to maintain a dynamic state or equilibrium condition. This is perhaps the most important feature differentiating a living organism from nonliving matter. The maintenance of intracellular equilibria is a function of the various enzymes. Each enzyme is under the control of a gene, and the genes are associated with the nuclear structure. Gene and enzyme activities are therefore affected by conditions within the cytoplasm: its composition, pH, oxidation-reduction potential, and other factors. Many essential enzymes are also associated with the cytoplasmic membrane, which must be intact in order for the enzyme activities to contribute to the cell's maintenance.

The disturbance of any cellular equilibrium by altering the factors controlling it may lead to death of the cell.

Reversible and Irreversible Injury

A distinction is often made between agents whose effects on equilibria are reversible and those whose effects are irreversible. Reversibly injurious agents produce *stasis* or inhibition without immediately lethal action. *Bacteriostatic* agents inhibit bacteria, *fungistatic* agents inhibit fungi, and so forth. Irreversibly injurious agents cause fairly prompt death; *bactericidal, fungicidal,* and *virucidal* agents kill bacteria, fungi, and viruses, respectively.

It should be emphasized that there is no sharp distinction between bacteriostatic and bactericidal action: the difference is quantitative rather than qualitative. This can be demonstrated by a simple experiment with various concentrations of phenol in nutrient broth. Three-tenths per cent phenol prevents the growth of *E. coli* but does not kill all the cells within a test period of several days; 1 per cent phenol broth similarly tested contains no viable bacteria after one hour. The lower concentration of phenol is bacteriostatic for *E. coli,* whereas the higher concentration is bactericidal. Eventually the bacteria will die in 0.3 per cent phenol broth, but in the meantime the survival of some cells can be shown by transferring a small portion to a medium lacking phenol, whereupon growth resumes.

Organisms exposed to a bactericidal concentration of a chemical survive only a short time; an endpoint of one hour is often arbitrarily selected. The distinction between bacteriostatic and bactericidal action ultimately becomes a matter of definition. Nevertheless, the terms bacteriostatic and bactericidal are useful with reference to various agents in the concentrations or under the conditions *in which they are normally employed.*

TYPES OF CELLULAR INJURY

Injury to Cell Membranes

Any agent that alters the permeability of the cell membranes either interferes with the intake of essential substances or the excretion of waste materials or else permits the entrance of toxic substances or the loss of essential cell components. Detergents, for example, break the osmotic barrier and allow leakage of metabolically active cellular components, such as nitrogen and phosphorus compounds. Some chemicals dissolve or remove the cell membranes and destroy the equilibria that maintain constant composition and osmotic pressure. Penicillin damages the amino acid transport mechanism of the cells of sensitive species; these organisms literally starve, because essential nutrients fail to pass the cell membranes.

Injury to the Nucleus and Genes

Certain agents have a particular affinity for nuclei or genes or they damage them specifically. Basic dyes such as crystal violet react strongly with the nucleic acids of nucleoproteins, presumably by salt formation. Dilute solutions are bacteriostatic; more concentrated solutions are bactericidal. Gram-positive bacteria are more sensitive than gram-negative bacteria, a difference probably associated with the more acid nature of the proteins of gram-positive cells. Heavy metals may react with the sulfhydryl (—SH) groups of nucleoproteins.

Any damage to genes is reflected by inhibition of the enzymes they control; if the enzyme is essential, growth will cease. Some enzymes are not essential if suitable alternate substrates are supplied or if another mechanism is available to form the required product.

Inhibition of Enzymes

Enzymes are proteins and as such are denatured by alcohols, phenols, heavy metals in high concentration, surface active substances, and other active agents. Denaturation is more or less irreversible. Low concentrations of heavy metals and mild oxidizing agents form inactive compounds by reversible reactions with —SH groups, which are essential for the activity of certain enzymes and coenzymes. Stronger oxidizing agents irreversibly oxidize —SH, phenol, indole, and amino radicals of enzymes or coenzymes.

Competitive Inhibition. Enzyme inhibition by competition or antagonism between either the substrate or the enzyme and the inhibitor substance is shown diagrammatically in Figure 15-1.

A.   Enzyme + Inhibitor 1 ⟶ Enzyme-Inhibitor 1

B.   Enzyme + Substrate ⇌ Enzyme-Substrate ⇌ Enzyme + Product(s)

C.   Inhibitor 2 + Substrate ⟶ Inhibitor 2-Substrate

Figure 15-1. Inhibition of enzyme action by chemical competition. The normal reaction is indicated at B; enzyme and substrate interact to form a product or products and the enzyme is released for further activity. At A, an inhibitor that is chemically related to the normal substrate reacts with the enzyme, thus blocking the enzyme from reacting with the usual substrate. At C, a different inhibitor reacts with the normal substrate and forms a compound that cannot react with the enzyme.

Competitive inhibition is illustrated by the behavior of sulfonamide drugs (Fig. 15-2). Para-aminobenzoic acid (PABA) is a constituent of folic acid. If the chemically related substance sulfanilamide is present, it may replace PABA and prevent the formation of folic acid. Folic acid is a coenzyme essential to the synthesis of amino acids, purines, and pyrimidines.

STERILIZATION AND DISINFECTION

Definitions

Sterilization is the destruction or removal of *all* forms of life, whether animal or plant; macroscopic, micro-scopic or submicroscopic; harmful or harmless. It can be accomplished by fire, by heat, by radiations, and by chemicals.

The word *disinfection* was originally used, about 1600, to express the idea of removing an agent capable of causing infection or disease. It is impossible to limit the term *disinfectant* to agents that combat infections, because many apparently harmless organisms produce disease under appropriate conditions. Moreover, pathogenic organisms such as *B. anthracis* and *Cl. tetani* are among the most resistant microorganisms, and any agent that kills them will also kill nearly all other species. Disinfectants are therefore essentially sterilizing agents.

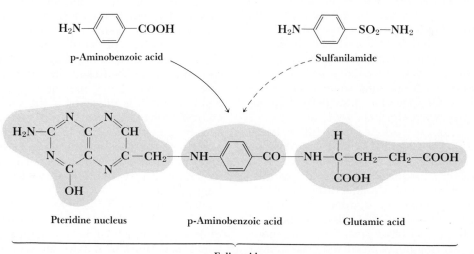

Figure 15-2. Competitive inhibition. Para-aminobenzoic acid is an essential part of folic acid. If sufficient sulfanilamide is present, it replaces p-aminobenzoic acid, and folic acid is not formed.

Germicides are chemicals that kill germs. Most bacteriologists dislike the colloquial reference to harmful microorganisms as germs, but accept the term germicide as practically synonymous with disinfectant.

The word *antiseptic* originally designated an agent used to prevent *sepsis* or putrefaction. Sepsis is caused by growing microorganisms; hence, an antiseptic may inhibit multiplication without necessarily killing. Antiseptics are therefore bacteriostatic or fungistatic. In the United States Federal Food, Drug and Cosmetic Act, it was stated that an antiseptic is essentially the same as a germicide except in the case of an inhibitory drug to be used in prolonged contact with the body (e.g., a wet dressing or ointment).

Sanitization is the process of making an object sanitary or safe to use; the term implies freedom from esthetically objectionable material as well as harmful microorganisms. Proper dishwashing practices constitute a form of sanitization.

Sterilization

Removal of Microorganisms. *Filtration* is a practical method of removing microorganisms from liquids, both in the laboratory and in industry. It is used in the laboratory and in drug manufacturing plants to sterilize solutions that deteriorate when heated. Certain culture medium ingredients, for example, decompose at a high temperature; antisera and some other solutions for injection lose desired properties when sterilized by heat.

There are various types of filters (page 178). The Chamberland filter devised by a co-worker of Pasteur in 1884 is a hollow, unglazed porcelain candle; Berkefeld and Mandler filters are hollow cylinders of diatomaceous earth; Seitz filters are flat disks or pads of asbestos; sintered glass filters are made by heating finely powdered glass almost to the point of fusion. One of the more recent filtering materials consists of thin sheets or disks of cellulose-ester.

The effectiveness of a bacterial filter depends upon the size of the pores, the electric charge on the filter material, and other factors. Obviously an organism 1 μ in diameter cannot pass through a filter with pores only 0.5 μ in diameter, but it is not necessarily true that an organism 0.5 μ in diameter will pass through a filter whose pores are twice as large. The irregularities of the pores as they twist through a thick filter may retain bacteria of much smaller diameter than the average pore. More important, however, is the electric charge on the filter. Most bacteria are negatively charged in solutions of neutral reaction. They are therefore retained more effectively by a filter possessing a positive charge, even though the pores of the filter are large, than by a filter with a negative charge. Most of the filters just mentioned carry a negative charge.

Natural processes of filtration purify water as it percolates slowly through the soil. Microorganisms adsorb to soil particles, and subterranean water at considerable depths is sterile or nearly so. Water and sewage purification plants often use filtration through sand and gravel as a method of removing bacteria.

Sedimentation is another natural process by which microorganisms are removed from bodies of water. The specific gravity of most bacteria is slightly greater than 1.0; they therefore settle slowly in the fresh water of lakes, reservoirs, and slowly moving streams. Sedimentation is hastened if the water contains soil or other particles of greater specific gravity to which the organisms adsorb. Natural sedimentation is a slow and uncertain method of purifying water, but it is reasonably effective over long periods.

Sedimentation is deliberately hastened in the laboratory by *centrifugation*. A centrifuge is a machine in which test tubes or bottles are whirled at high speed. The force on each particle within the container is several thousand times that of gravity, and bacteria can be thrown to the bottom of the container within a few minutes or hours. The supernatant liquid is rarely sterile, but its microbial population is tremendously reduced.

Sterilization by Heat. *Incineration* is the most effective method of sterilization but is obviously limited in application. It is employed daily in the laboratory when needles and loops are flamed; the bacteriologist's first move upon entering his laboratory is to light his Bunsen burner. Contaminated swabs, paper materials, inexpensive clothing, and the bodies of discarded animals are often disposed of by incineration.

Boiling is a satisfactory method of disinfection when it is known that spore-forming bacteria are not a problem. The safety of water suspected of containing intestinal pathogens is ensured by boiling for 15 or 20 minutes. Boiling can never be relied on for sterilization unless adequate time is allowed. This may be several hours, as indicated in the preceding chapter.

Intermittent sterilization (also called tyndallization after Tyndall, who devised the method) is used when temperatures above 100° C. cannot be employed. The material to be sterilized is heated in flowing steam or boiling water for one-half hour on each of three successive days to kill vegetative cells. The germination of surviving spores is fostered by incubation at 30° to 37° C. between periods of heating.

Intermittent sterilization was formerly employed in the preparation of culture media that appeared to be adversely affected by temperatures higher than 100° C. Later, it was found that many of the same media can be sterilized satisfactorily and without serious damage at higher temperatures for shorter periods if the process is carefully controlled. Intermittent sterilization of home canned foods was practiced before pressure cookers became available, but it was never considered very safe. Pressure cooking is the only recommended procedure today.

Steam under pressure is the most widely used sterilizing agent in the hospital, laboratory, and food cannery. Laboratory media are usually sterilized in an autoclave at 15 pounds per square inch steam pressure (Fig. 15-3). The temperature is approximately 121° C. (Table 14-5), and sterilization is accomplished within 15 minutes if the materials are in small containers (test tubes) and properly distributed so that the entire contents of the autoclave can reach the sterilizing temperature. Large containers, such as flasks of culture medium, require longer sterilization. Hospital autoclaves loaded with surgical dressings also require longer treatment. The actual exposure time at 121° C. required to kill the most resistant bacterial spore is no longer than five or 10 minutes; the additional period of treatment permits steam to penetrate all parts of the autoclave chamber and heat the contents of the containers to this temperature.

It is essential in operating an autoclave to be certain that the air has been completely exhausted. If steam at 15 lb. per square inch is introduced into an autoclave from which all air has been removed, a temperature of 250° F. (121° C.) can be attained (Fig. 15-4). When no air is removed, the final temperature reached is 212° F. (100° C.). Most autoclaves are so constructed that steam enters the chamber at the top and forces air out an exhaust port at the bottom. Only when pure steam issues uninterruptedly should the exhaust valve be closed to permit pressure to build up within the chamber. The 15 minute or longer period of sterilization is begun when a thermometer in the exhaust line indicates that the exhaust steam is at the sterilizing temperature (121° C).

Laboratory glassware, such as pipettes and Petri dishes, is usually sterilized dry in an oven. *Dry sterilization* requires a higher temperature for a longer time than moist sterilization: one to two hours at 160° to 180° C.

The presence or absence of moisture

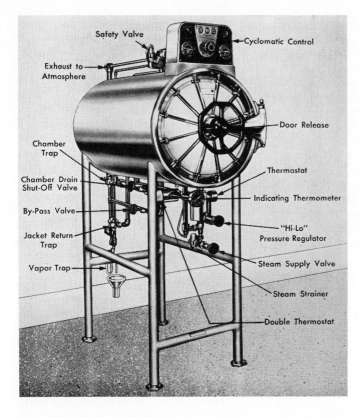

Figure 15-3. Autoclave with automatic controls used in bacteriologic laboratories. (Courtesy of American Sterilizer Company.)

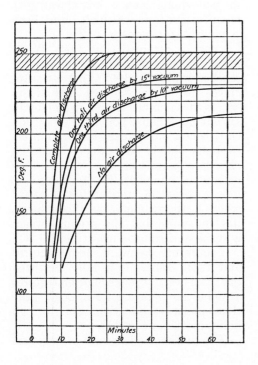

Figure 15-4. Temperatures of steam-air mixtures in an autoclave. Steam at 15 lb. per square inch was introduced into a chamber completely or partially evacuated or unevacuated, and the temperatures within the chamber were determined at intervals. (From W. B. Underwood: A Textbook of Sterilization. Erie, Pa., American Sterilizer Co., 1941.)

Table 15-1. Effect of Moisture on the Coagulation of Egg Albumin by Heat*

Water (Per Cent)	Coagulation Temperature (°C.)
50	56
25	74–80
18	80–90
6	145
0	160–170

*Heating time, 30 minutes.

is important in sterilization by heat. Water presumably assists the denaturation of proteins. The effect of water on heat coagulation of egg albumin was shown many years ago (Table 15-1). It is probably not entirely a coincidence that dry egg albumin coagulated at the same temperature as that recommended for dry sterilization, whereas dilute solutions coagulated at a temperature that kills nonspore-forming bacteria within a few minutes.

FACTORS AFFECTING DISINFECTION

Killing microorganisms by any means, physical or chemical, is influenced by various factors. These should be known and understood, not only by those whose vocation is directly concerned with microorganisms, but also by every individual.

Time

Time is one of the most important and most frequently overlooked factors in the control of microorganisms. Killing a microbial population is a gradual process, except in the case of incineration. The rate of death depends on the intensity or concentration of the killing agent as well as on various other factors which will be discussed.

The relationship between time and killing of spores of *B. anthracis* by phenol is shown in Figure 15-5. Curve *A* is an arithmetic plot of the surviving spores; the population decreased rapidly at first and more slowly thereafter.

Figure 15-5. Killing of spores of *Bacillus anthracis* by 5 per cent phenol at 33.3° C. A, Arithmetic plot; B, logarithmic plot of the same data. (Replotted from data of H. Chick, J. Hyg., 8:92–158, 1908.)

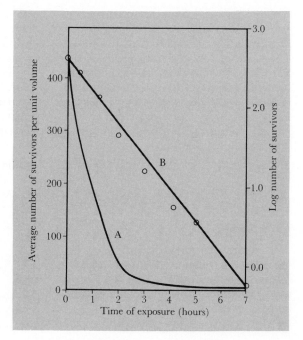

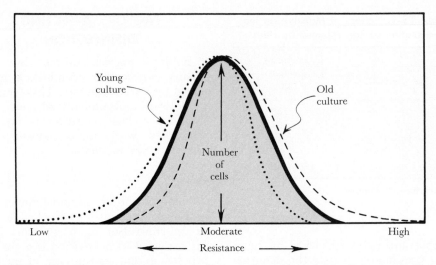

Figure 15-6. The resistance to disinfection of cells in a culture. Most of the cells in an average culture (*solid line*) are moderately resistant. Young cultures (*dotted line*) contain a greater proportion of susceptible cells; old cultures (*dashed line*) contain more resistant cells.

The same data plotted logarithmically lie close to the straight line *B*, which indicates that the rate of death was logarithmic; that is, half the surviving spores died in each successive equal time interval. The rate of death expressed as $-g$, calculated according to the equation on page 233, is 43 minutes.

Any microbial population consists of cells of varying grades of resistance. Most cells are intermediate in resistance, a few are of low resistance, and a few of high resistance (Fig. 15-6). The most susceptible cells die first; those of greater resistance die in successive intervals until eventually the most resistant are killed. Young, actively growing cells are unusually susceptible to disinfectant agents, whereas mature or dormant cells are very resistant (Table 15-2).

Temperature

Temperature markedly influences the efficiency of chemical disinfection. Killing is fundamentally a chemical process. The rates of chemical reactions increase with the temperature. It is to be expected, therefore, that disinfection will occur more quickly at high than at low temperatures. Table 15-3 shows that *S. aureus* is killed approximately five times as rapidly at 20° C. as at 10° C. by various concentrations of phenol. The factor 5, known as the *temperature coefficient* of disinfection (also called Q_{10}), indicates the effect of a 10 degree rise in temperature on the rate of killing. The Q_{10} of disinfection varies with the organism, the disinfectant, and other factors. It may be as low as 1.5 or as high as 50; average values are between 2 and 15.

If, as in the above instance, the temperature coefficient of disinfection is 5 between 20° and 30° C., the rate of destruction at 40° C. should be 25 times

Table 15-2. Susceptibility of Young and Older Cells of *Escherichia coli* to Disinfection by 0.01N NaOH at 30° C.*

Age of Culture (Hours)	Time to Kill 99.99% of the Cells (Minutes)
8	9.90
17	26.75

*From data of J. H. Watkins and C.-E. A. Winslow, J. Bact., 24:243–265, 1932.

Table 15-3. Effect of Temperature on Killing of *Staphylococcus aureus* by Phenol*

Phenol (Per Cent)	Disinfection Time at	
	10° C.	20° C.
	Minutes	
1.82	17.5	5
1.66	40	7.5
1.54	70	12.5
1.43	100	20
1.33	150	30

*From data of F. W. Tilley, J. Bact., 43:521, 1942.

as great as at 20° C., and at 50° C. it should be 125 times as great. The practical importance of this fact is obvious; whenever it is possible to employ high temperatures it is highly advisable to do so. This explains why dishwashing machines, which can operate at 80° C., are recommended or even required in eating establishments in preference to hand washing, which cannot be performed at temperatures much above 45° C.; the bactericidal efficiency of soap or detergents is enormously enhanced by the 35° temperature difference.

Concentration

The concentration of a disinfectant chemical profoundly influences the rate of killing of bacteria (Table 15-4).

Table 15-4. Effect of the Concentration of Phenol on the Killing Time of *Salmonella typhosa**

Phenol (Per Cent)	Killing Time (Minutes)
1.11	∞
1.17	50
1.25	30
1.33	15
1.43	10
1.54	5

*From data of F. W. Tilley, J. Bact., 38:499–510, 1939.

A moderate increase in concentration often multiplies the rate of killing by a large factor. Low concentrations exert no bactericidal action and still lower concentrations may actually stimulate microbial growth. This phenomenon is not peculiar to microbiology; small doses of poisonous substances are frequently used in medicine as stimulants (e.g., strychnine, epinephrine).

The concentration of a chemical to be employed for disinfection depends upon the chemical itself and upon the conditions in which it is to be used. The upper limit is usually dictated by the destructive or toxic action of the material and by economic considerations. Manufacturers' instructions are useful guides.

Nature of the Medium

The nature of the *medium* in or upon which the organisms are situated affects the efficiency of disinfection. Most disinfectants kill microorganisms by virtue of their ability to react with organic cell constituents. It is not surprising that extraneous organic matter also combines with the disinfectant and reduces its effective concentration.

pH

The pH influences the disinfection process by its effects on the organisms and on the disinfectant. Microorganisms are usually more resistant when suspended in media of a reaction satisfactory for growth, and killing by chemicals proceeds more rapidly as the pH departs from this value; pH also affects the degree of ionization of chemicals. Many disinfectants are more active in the undissociated state. Chlorine compounds decompose and liberate the effective constituent, chlorine, more rapidly in neutral or slightly acid solutions than in alkaline solutions. It is apparent that the optimum conditions must be determined for each specific application.

Nature of the Organisms

The nature of the organisms to be killed, of course, cannot be controlled, but this factor must be taken into account. Spores of bacteria are more difficult to kill than vegetative cells; bacteria possessing capsules are usually more difficult to destroy than non-capsulated cells; acidfast bacteria, although not spore-forming, resist many disinfectant agents. The previous history, age, and cultural conditions of the test organisms are important factors in their susceptibility to killing agents.

Contact

A final factor affecting chemical disinfection is the opportunity for effective contact between the disinfectant and the microorganisms. A dry chemical placed in contact with bacteria will obviously be ineffective. Moisture is essential for the disinfection process. Surface tension depressants such as soaps and synthetic detergents improve the contact between chemicals and microbial cells by concentrating the chemicals at the cell surfaces. An alcoholic solution of iodine (i.e., tincture of iodine) owes much of its usefulness to the alcohol that brings the chemical into effective contact with skin bacteria. Alcohol is an excellent wetting agent.

Chemical Disinfection

Evaluation of Disinfectant Chemicals. There are many methods of evaluating the disinfectant power of chemicals. No one method is satisfactory for all substances or for all conditions under which they may be used. Several methods will be described briefly.

Phenol Coefficient. One of the oldest procedures is the phenol coefficient method. This was originally intended to be used only for comparing compounds that act on bacteria in the same manner as phenol, that is, cresols and other derivatives or higher homologues of phenol. The procedure was later applied to chemicals that act in other ways, with the result that much useless or misleading information was secured and publicized. More recent awareness of this fact has led to the introduction of other methods of testing.

The phenol coefficient is a figure comparing the dilutions of phenol and of another chemical that possess equivalent killing power for a specified test organism, either *S. aureus* or *Salmonella typhosa*. Test tubes containing various dilutions of phenol and of the chemical of unknown potency, X, are inoculated with constant amounts of the test organism (Table 15-5). Five, 10, and 15 minutes later, subcultures are made from each solution in tubes of special nutrient broth, which are

Table 15-5. Phenol Coefficient Determination

Chemical	Dilution	Growth of *S. aureus* in Subculture after Exposure for		
		5 Min.	10 Min.	15 Min.
Phenol	1:80	−	−	−
	1:90	+	−	−
	1:100	+	+	−
X	1:400	−	−	−
	1:425	−	−	−
	1:450	+	−	−
	1:475	+	+	−
	1:500	+	+	+

Phenol coefficient of $X = \frac{1}{90} \div \frac{1}{450} = 5$

then incubated. Results like those in the table indicate that a dilution of 1:80 phenol is strong enough to kill *S. aureus* within five minutes; a dilution of 1:90 phenol does not kill in five minutes but does kill within 10 minutes; a dilution of 1:100 phenol kills the test organism within 15 minutes but not in 10. Similar results are obtained with chemical X in different dilutions. Those dilutions that kill the test organism within 10 minutes but not in five minutes are compared, and the phenol coefficient is the number obtained by division, as indicated.

The phenol coefficient indicates that chemical X can be diluted five times as much as phenol and still possess equivalent killing power for *S. aureus* under the conditions of the laboratory experiment. The results cannot necessarily be applied to any other organism; in fact, phenol coefficients with *Sal. typhosa* frequently differ from those with *S. aureus*. If chemical X has the same general chemical or biologic properties as phenol, the results are a little more significant than if the two chemicals are entirely different. A substance of different properties may be affected quite differently by extraneous organic matter, or by variations in pH, temperature, etc.

Agar Plate Tests. Agar plate methods are widely used to test the inhibitory power of chemicals, ointments, antibiotics, and other substances against various organisms. Appropriate nutrient agar inoculated heavily with the test organism is poured into Petri dishes and allowed to harden. Open-ended cylinders pressed into the agar are filled with the test chemical; filter paper disks saturated with the solution, or drops of ointment, are placed upon the agar. After the dishes are incubated, zones of inhibition of bacterial growth surround those substances that possess bactericidal or bacteriostatic action (Fig. 15-7). The diameter of the zones of inhibition depends upon the diffusibility of the chemicals and their antibacterial potency. This method does not necessarily measure killing effectiveness, because the chemical remains in constant contact with the test organism. However, it is useful for comparing the inhibitory powers of a variety of chemicals against any single organism or group of organisms; it is also convenient for testing the sensitivity of various bacterial species to any given inhibitory substance. The test is easily performed, and results are often available within a few hours.

Death Curves. The most laborious but for some purposes the best method of testing disinfectant chemicals is the death curve determination. Mixtures

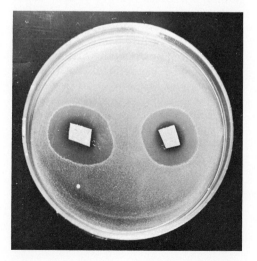

Figure 15-7. Inhibition of bacterial growth by a common household antiseptic. The agar in the dish was inoculated with bacteria. Pieces of paper were soaked in the antiseptic and laid on the agar. The chemical, diffusing out of the paper, prevented growth of bacteria in the immediate vicinity.

of the chemical solution and the test organism are prepared, and counts of the surviving viable bacteria are made at suitable intervals. The temperature, composition, and pH of the test solution, the number and previous history of the organism, and other factors can and must be controlled in order to secure consistent and significant results. The information obtained constitutes a complete study of the dynamics of disinfection by the chemical in question.

No laboratory test is as satisfactory as actual experience. The laboratory can, however, reduce the number of trials and errors that will be necessary in practice. The ultimate test of a surgical disinfectant is the occurrence or nonoccurrence of surgical infection; the test of a dairy disinfectant is the microbial quality of the milk.

Toxicity Tests. One other type of test applied to antiseptics or disinfectants used upon the human body should be mentioned. Any chemical used for personal hygiene must be nontoxic. Many antibacterial chemicals kill or damage human cells. The dividing line between toxicity for microbe and for man is often narrow.

Several methods are available to assay the toxicity of chemicals for human or other animal cells. Test cells or tissues include guinea pig leukocytes, the chorioallantoic membrane of the developing chick embryo, and tissue cultures of chick heart fragments. The toxicity of a germicide for animal cells is compared with its bactericidal power, and a figure known as the *toxicity index* is obtained. A chemical with a low toxicity index is less toxic to tissue than to bacteria, and is preferred for personal use if its germicidal activity is satisfactory.

Chemicals That Inhibit or Kill Bacteria. A few chemicals (Table 15-6) that are used to inhibit or kill bacteria will be discussed according to their principal mode of action (see page 258). Some will be mentioned more than once because their behavior is complex.

Chemicals That Injure Cell Membranes. *Soaps* are markedly surface active; that is, they tend to concentrate upon surfaces. These molecules orient themselves upon the surfaces of bacterial cells so that their hydrophobic fatty acid constituents adsorb to the relatively nonaqueous surface, and the cation is attracted to the surrounding aqueous medium. The mechanical strain thus established disrupts the cell membranes, and part of the protoplasm leaves the cells, or toxic materials enter. The extent of damage determines whether the effect is bacteriostatic or bactericidal.

The cleansing action of soaps is important because it reduces the number of organisms to be killed or removed by other means. The surgical scrub is an effective method of reducing "adventitious" skin bacteria: those that gain access from the environment.

Synthetic detergents, like soaps, contain both hydrophobic and hydrophilic radicals and are usually subdivided according to the nature of the hydrophilic group: anionic, cationic, or nonionic. Anionic and cationic detergents disrupt cell membranes and permit nitrogen and phosphorus compounds to leak out of the cells. Probably they combine with membrane lipids and proteins, and also denature proteins.

Strong solutions of *acids* and *alkalies* quickly digest any form of organic matter and destroy bacterial cell walls and membranes. The bactericidal action of mineral acids appears to depend upon the pH of their solutions rather than their normality. Solutions at pH 2 or less are bactericidal against nonspore-forming bacteria. Poorly ionized organic acids, such as acetic and benzoic, are bactericidal at higher pH values; their effectiveness is attributed either to specific action of the anion or to the undissociated molecule.

Alkalies owe their bactericidal properties to the hydroxyl ion concentration of their solutions. Sodium and potassium hydroxides are germicidal at pH 12 or higher. Ordinary household lye (NaOH) is the most practical disinfectant for barns, stables, and chicken houses. Quicklime in the form of *fresh* whitewash is also used to disinfect chicken houses. Trisodium phosphate combines cleansing action with alkalinity and is useful in cleaning dairy equipment and in dishwashing machines. Its effect is greatly enhanced at high temperatures.

Chemicals That Inhibit Enzyme Activity and/or Denature Proteins. Most bacteriostatic or bactericidal chemicals inhibit or kill microorganisms by reacting with proteins, which are distributed generally throughout the cells as structural and enzymic components. Some chemicals denature proteins, others oxidize radicals such as the sulfhydryl group (—SH), and still others form substitution or addition products.

Chemicals that *denature* proteins include alcohols, phenols, and heavy metals and their salts. Early reports of the disinfectant action of *ethyl alcohol* unduly emphasized a peculiar effect of concentration that has been handed down in textbooks and medical practice for many years without effective challenge. Some experiments, particularly with dried bacteria, indicated that the most effective disinfection occurred with solutions containing only 50 to 70 per cent alcohol in water; absolute or even 95 per cent alcohol had practically no killing effect. The belief therefore arose that reliance could not be placed upon the usual 95 per cent solution for practical disinfection. Later observations indicated that *moist* nonspore-forming bacteria of many species are killed within five minutes by ethyl alcohol in concentrations between 40 and 99 per cent.

Alcohol is one of the most widely used chemicals for the destruction of bacteria on the skin, for example, in surgical practice. Any concentration between 70 and 95 per cent destroys or removes approximately 90 per cent of the normal resident skin flora within two minutes.

Viruses are apparently not as readily inactivated or killed by alcohols as are bacteria. Outbreaks of serum hepatitis have been attributed to virus on hypodermic needles or lancets that had been cleansed or stored in alcohol between use on successive patients. Resterilized or disposable sterile needles and lancets are now recommended.

Phenols and phenolic compounds are highly bactericidal in proper concentration. Some phenols are poorly soluble in water but can be emulsified in dilute soap solutions to provide effective disinfectants. Lysol is such a preparation containing ortho-, meta-, and para-cresols. Phenol and Lysol are too irritating or caustic in germicidal concentrations to be used for personal disinfection, but they are often used as laboratory and household disinfectants.

Oxidizing agents, such as halogens, hydrogen peroxide, and ozone, are bacteriostatic or bactericidal and exert their inhibitory or lethal action by oxidizing chemical groups such as —SH, —NH$_2$, or the indole nucleus, which are essential for the activity of some enzymes or coenzymes. Halogens probably also damage cell membranes and form substitution or addition products with proteins.

Halogens and their derivatives were among the earliest chemicals used to control microbial activities. In 1854, before the role of microorganisms in putrefaction was known, chloride of lime was added to the sewage of London as a deodorant. The first large scale use of *chlorine* for water purification in the United States was in 1908 in Chicago. Chlorine is ordinarily used in the form of gas or as one of the hypochlorites, but in either case the reaction with water yields hypochlorous acid, HClO, some of which decomposes and liberates nascent oxygen. The disinfectant action is believed to be caused by the ClO$^-$ ion and by nascent oxygen.

Care must be taken in using chlorine compounds to ensure an adequate concentration for the desired purpose, because of the lability of chlorine and its great capacity for combining with extraneous material. The concentration of

Table 15-6. Properties and Uses of Representative Bacteriostatic or Bactericidal Chemicals

Group	Examples	Significant Properties	Mode of Action	Uses
		Chemicals that injure cell membranes		
Soaps		Na or K salts of long chain fatty acids; surface tension depressants; bactericidal action improved by high temperature; effective against pneumococci	Disrupt cell membranes and increase permeability	Cleansing, mechanical removal of microorganisms
Detergents		Hydrophobic hydrocarbon chain, sterol, etc., and a hydrophilic anion or cation; activity better at high temperature; inhibited by soaps	Disrupt cell membranes, probably by combining with lipids and proteins; N and P compounds leak out of cells	Cleansing and bactericidal action
	Sodium lauryl sulfate	Anion: carboxyl, sulfate, sulfonate, etc.; more active in acid solution		Selective culture media; kill grampositive bacteria
	Quaternary ammonium halides	Cation: substituted ammonium; more active in alkaline solution		Skin disinfection, dairy sanitation; kill gram-positive and gram-negative bacteria
Acids	Mineral acids: H_2SO_4	High concentration of H^+ ions	Destroy cell walls and membranes	Limited by corrosiveness mainly to laboratory use
	Organic acids: acetic, benzoic, boric, etc.	Poorly ionized	Anions or undissociated molecules combine with protoplasmic constituents	Preservation, mild antisepsis
Alkalies	Lye (NaOH), quicklime ($Ca(OH)_2$), Na_3PO_4	OH^- ions	Destroy cell walls and membranes	Disinfection of barns, chicken houses; dishwashing and dairy sanitation (Na_3PO_4)

Chemicals that inhibit enzyme activity and/or denature proteins

Alcohols	In order of increasing activity: methyl, ethyl, propyl, butyl, amyl		Bacteriostatic and bactericidal; denature and coagulate proteins	Skin disinfection (70-95% C_2H_5OH), used in tinctures to increase "wetting" power of other chemicals; kill vegetative cells, little effect on spores
Phenols	Phenol, cresols, lysol, hexyl-resorcinol, etc.	Surface tension depressants; activity improved by high temperature, acid	Bactericidal; denaturation and precipitation of proteins	Disinfection of laboratory equipment, instruments, bench tops, garbage pails, toilets
	Bis-phenols (hexachlorophene)		Bacteriostatic	Deodorants in soaps; inhibit gram-positive bacteria
Oxidizing	Halogens: Cl, Na or Ca hypochlorite	Inhibited by extraneous organic matter	Bactericidal; oxidize $-SH$, $-NH_2$, or indole nucleus of enzymes or coenzymes	Purification of water, dairy disinfection, restaurant sanitation
	Iodine			Skin disinfection, especially as tincture
	H_2O_2	Unstable; decomposes to H_2O and O_2	Bacteriostatic, mildly bactericidal	Antisepsis of cuts, minor wounds
Heavy metals	$HgCl_2$	Very toxic; combines with organic matter	Highly bacteriostatic; react with $-SH$ groups of enzymes or coenzymes; precipitate proteins	Laboratory disinfectant
	"Merthiolate," "Metaphen," phenyl-mercuric nitrate	Not greatly affected by organic matter; relatively nontoxic		Skin antisepsis, preservation of biologicals (sera, etc.)
	$AgNO_3$, silver proteinate (Argyrol)			Antisepsis of mucous membranes of throat and eyes (to prevent ophthalmia neonatorum)

Table 15-6.   Properties and Uses of Representative Bacteriostatic or Bactericidal Chemicals (*Continued*)

Group	Examples	Significant Properties	Mode of Action	Uses
Formaldehyde	HCHO	Reacts with —NH$_2$ and —OH groups; relatively unaffected by extraneous organic matter; effective against spores	Bactericidal in high concentration; reacts with enzymes, nucleic acids; coagulates proteins	Disinfection of contaminated laboratory and surgical instruments and equipment
Sulfonamides	Sulfanilamide, sulfadiazine, etc.	Chemically related to p-aminobenzoic acid	Bacteriostatic; compete with PABA in synthesis of folic acid	Chemotherapy of human and animal infections; inhibit pneumococci, meningococci, streptococci, *H. influenzae*
Antibiotics	Penicillin, streptomycin, chloramphenicol, tetracyclines, etc.		Bactericidal or bacteriostatic; interfere with one or more essential enzyme reactions	Chemotherapy of human and animal infections
		Chemicals that injure nuclei and genes		
Basic dyes	Crystal violet, brilliant green	React with acid radicals	Bacteriostatic; probably form salts with nucleic acids	Selective culture media, skin and oral antisepsis; inhibit gram-positive bacteria

chlorine necessary to kill nonspore-forming bacteria under favorable conditions is extremely small. Water that is free of organic matter is rendered safe for drinking within a few minutes by only 0.1 to 0.2 parts of available chlorine per million parts of water (p.p.m.).

Iodine is probably the most widely used skin disinfectant. It is strongly bactericidal against many kinds of microorganisms, including *M. tuberculosis* and bacterial spores, and the concentration required to kill does not vary greatly among different species. Moreover, iodine solutions are rapidly germicidal and relatively nontoxic. It should be cautioned that rapid germicidal action does not necessarily mean immediate germicidal action. Rubbing or swabbing an area of skin for two minutes or applying a wet solution for five minutes is usually recommended.

Chemicals that form *substitution* or *addition products* with proteins may interfere with cellular metabolism by reacting with enzymes. Heavy metals, such as mercury and silver, for example, combine with the essential —SH radicals of certain enzymes and coenzymes and produce compounds lacking the normal activity. Formaldehyde and the halogens may also react with $—NH_2$, —OH, and other radicals of proteins and nucleic acids.

Heavy metals and their salts are bactericidal only in relatively strong solutions, but they are almost unbelievably bacteriostatic in dilute solution. The mercuric ion reacts particularly with —SH radicals, and —S—Hg—S— linkages form. When low concentrations of mercury salts are used, the foregoing reaction is readily reversed by addition of H_2S or other compounds containing the —SH radical (e.g., thioglycollic acid, $CH_2(SH) \cdot COOH$). Organisms exposed to low concentrations of mercury salts appear to be dead when subcultured in a medium such as nutrient broth, which contains few sulfhydryl compounds; nevertheless they multiply readily when tested in thioglycollate broth. These solutions are bacteriostatic rather than bactericidal. Higher concentrations of mercury produce irreversible damage, perhaps by protein precipitation, and hence are bactericidal.

Silver and copper are bacteriostatic in extremely small concentration. A coin pressed lightly into the surface of nutrient agar inoculated heavily with *S. aureus* dissolves sufficiently to inhibit growth of the bacteria within a zone of several millimeters. The growth of *E. coli* is inhibited by one part of silver in 5 billion parts of broth, and the same species is apparently killed within a few hours by 10 to 100 parts of silver per billion parts of distilled water. This phenomenon is known as the *oligodynamic action of metals*. Bacteria, yeasts, and trypanosomes are killed by solutions calculated to contain only 100,000 to 10,000,000 silver ions per cell, a figure of the same order of magnitude as the estimated number of protein molecules in each cell. It can therefore be assumed that only one metallic ion per protein molecule suffices to kill the cell.

Formaldehyde inactivates most but not all enzymes. It reacts with $—NH_2$ and —OH radicals of enzymes, proteins, and nucleic acids, and is also a protein coagulant. It is bacteriostatic in low concentration and bactericidal in high concentration and is capable of killing spores of both aerobic and anaerobic bacteria. Formaldehyde disinfects contaminated surgical and laboratory implements after an exposure of several hours, despite the presence of considerable organic matter.

The inhibition of microbial growth by *chemical antagonism* or *competition* is one basis of the modern science of chemotherapy (treatment of disease by chemicals). It was first seriously proposed by Ehrlich in 1909. The sulfonamides provide one of the best examples of chemical competition.

Many bacteria require p-aminobenzoic acid as a metabolite. Some species can synthesize it, others secure it preformed, and still others must be supplied with a derivative such as folic acid (see Fig. 15-2).

The sulfonamides are related chemically to p-aminobenzoic acid, as already indicated (page 259). Bacterial species that require PABA either preformed or as a product of their own synthesis can be inhibited by sulfonamide drugs. The sulfonamide competes with PABA in the synthesis of folic acid. Thus its effectiveness depends upon its concentration in relation to that of PABA; sufficient sulfonamide completely prevents the formation of folic acid and inhibits growth. The production or addition of more PABA permits folic acid to be produced again, whereupon growth resumes. The sulfonamide drugs are therefore bacteriostatic rather than bactericidal. Their effectiveness in treating disease depends upon their ability to hold the infecting organisms in check until normal body defenses such as phagocytosis overcome them.

Sulfonamides are useful in the treatment of disease because animal cells do not utilize PABA as such and are therefore not inhibited by its analogues. Moreover, the p-aminobenzoic acid derivatives available within the animal body are not used by most bacterial species and cannot substitute for the growth factors with which sulfonamides compete.

Antibiotics useful in treating disease are products of microbial activity that specifically inhibit or kill other microorganisms in concentrations that can be tolerated by the host. Many metabolic products of microorganisms possess powerful antibacterial properties but are so toxic to animal or plant tissues that they are useless for chemotherapy. Relatively few of the thousands of antibiotics that have been tested are medically valuable.

Among the most widely used antibiotics are penicillin, streptomycin, chloramphenicol, and the tetracyclines. Penicillin and streptomycin are bactericidal; chloramphenicol and the tetracyclines are bacteriostatic in concentrations ordinarily employed.

Penicillin kills bacteria only under conditions that permit the growth of the organisms. Bacteria treated with penicillin frequently undergo swelling and elongation but fail to divide. Penicillin interferes with one of the last steps in cell wall synthesis, namely, polymerization of nucleotide intermediates or incorporation of mucopeptide into the wall. The usefulness of penicillin in treating disease depends upon the fact that the composition of animal cell walls is quite different from that of bacterial walls, and the identical synthetic stage is therefore missing. Susceptible cells exposed to penicillin in a solution containing 0.2M sucrose lose their cell walls and become protoplasts.

Streptomycin is believed to act, at least in part, by inhibiting the synthesis of normal cellular proteins. Its site of action appears to be the ribosome, where it interferes with the function of messenger RNA and can cause miscoding, so that abnormal and functionally inactive proteins are formed. This seriously damages the cell and may lead to its death.

Chloramphenicol and the tetracyclines inhibit protein synthesis. Oxytetracycline (Terramycin) and chlortetracycline (Aureomycin) seem to interfere with enzymes active in the Krebs cycle. All these antibiotics are inhibitory to a wide variety of bacteria, both gram-positive and gram-negative, and also to rickettsiae and some of the larger viruses. They are called *broad spectrum* antibiotics.

The nature of antibiotic activity and the specific uses of antibiotics in the treatment of disease are discussed in more detail in Chapter 22.

Chemicals That Injure Nuclei and Genes. A few chemicals with particular affinity for nucleic acids are bacteriostatic or bactericidal. Formaldehyde and other chemicals react with amino and hydroxyl radicals of nucleoproteins as well as other proteins. Basic dyes are known to stain nuclear material of higher forms intensely; they also stain bacteria deeply, presumably by combining with the nucleic acids. Crystal violet, brilliant green, and malachite green are powerfully bacteriostatic basic dyes, especially against gram-positive organisms; gram-negative bacteria are affected relatively little.

The hypothesis that basic dyes react with nucleic acids is supported by the observation that dye inhibition of bacteria is counteracted by adding nucleic acid or nucleotides. Inhibition can also be reversed by transferring bacteria from a medium containing dye to one lacking it, whereupon the organisms resume growth. The reversibility of inhibition by either method is evidence that the action of basic dyes is bacteriostatic rather than bactericidal.

Basic dyes are used in culture media to promote the selective growth of gram-negative bacteria. Drinking water is considered unsafe if it contains gram-negative rod bacteria of intestinal origin; these organisms are frequently mixed with gram-positive cocci and spore-formers, which confuse and prolong the analytical procedure. Brilliant green or crystal violet is added to culture media to inhibit the latter, while permitting growth of the gram-negative bacteria.

INHIBITION AND KILLING OF MICROORGANISMS

SUMMARY

Any factor that upsets normal cellular equilibria can inhibit cell growth or kill cells. Agents that injure cell membranes permit some of the cell contents to leak out or allow toxic substances to penetrate. Substances that react with the nucleus and genes may prevent essential enzyme activity (it seems well established that genetic control of cellular function is exerted at the enzymic level). Other chemicals or conditions retard or prevent microbial growth by reacting directly with enzymes or by competing with them.

Sterilization is accomplished by physical removal of microorganisms, by heat, or by suitable chemicals. The effectiveness of chemical disinfection is determined by such factors as time and temperature, the concentration of the chemical, the nature and pH of the medium, and the nature of the organisms. Different chemicals affect microorganisms in various ways, and no one disinfectant is suitable for all purposes. The choice is dictated by the nature of the material to be disinfected, the corrosiveness or toxicity of the available agents, economic considerations, and other factors.

STUDY QUESTIONS

1. Discuss the significance of the terms *bacteriostatic* and *bactericidal.*
2. Explain the antibacterial action of (a) detergents, (b) basic dyes, (c) heavy metal salts.

3. Describe four methods of sterilization and indicate situations in which they are applicable.
4. Is it possible to select any one chemical to be used as a universal, ideal disinfectant? Explain.
5. What is the significance of the phenol coefficient test?
6. Discuss the implications of the observation that bacteria apparently killed by heavy metal salts may grow when tested in a medium containing thioglycollic acid.
7. What is chemical antagonism? Describe an example.

SUPPLEMENTARY READING

Buchanan and Fulmer and Porter thoroughly cover the early work on the inhibition and killing of bacteria by various agents including chemicals. Disinfection is also discussed in one or more chapters of recent textbooks by Salle, Lamanna and Mallette, and Thimann. Davis and Feingold, Wyss, and Oginsky and Umbreit emphasize the mechanisms of disinfectant action.

Buchanan, R. E., and Fulmer, E. I.: *Physiology and Biochemistry of Bacteria,* Vol. II. Baltimore, The Williams & Wilkins Co., 1930.

Davis, B. D., and Feingold, D. S.: Antimicrobial Agents: Mechanism of Action and Use in Metabolic Studies. *In* Gunsalus, I. C., and Stanier, R. Y. (Eds.): *The Bacteria: A Treatise on Structure and Function,* Vol. IV. New York, Academic Press, Inc., 1962, pp. 343–397.

Lamanna, C., and Mallette, M. F.: *Basic Bacteriology,* 3d ed. Baltimore, The Williams & Wilkins Co., 1965.

Oginsky, E. L., and Umbreit, W. W.: *An Introduction to Bacterial Physiology,* 2d ed. San Francisco, W. H. Freeman & Company, 1959.

Porter, J. R.: *Bacterial Chemistry and Physiology.* New York, John Wiley & Sons, Inc., 1946.

Salle, A. J.: *Fundamental Principles of Bacteriology,* 5th ed. New York, McGraw-Hill Book Co., Inc., 1960.

Thimann, K. V.: *The Life of Bacteria,* 2d ed. New York, The Macmillan Company, 1963.

Wyss, O.: Chemical Factors Affecting Growth and Death. *In* Werkman, C. H., and Wilson, P. W. (Eds.): *Bacterial Physiology.* New York, Academic Press, Inc., 1951.

VARIATION AND
GENETICS OF BACTERIA

It has already been shown that bacteria possess most of the properties of other living organisms and function according to the same general principles. Each bacterial cell is a complete and independent individual in which all vital activities are performed; a pure culture therefore consists of a relatively homogeneous population of cells carrying on the same processes, whereas a multicellular organism contains a variety of cells performing somewhat different activities.

The fact that bacteria multiply more rapidly than higher forms presents a unique opportunity to study genetic phenomena on a greatly foreshortened time scale: 10 generations in the life of an animal or plant species may require years, whereas a few hours suffice in most bacterial species. Bacteria are therefore excellent subjects for the study of metabolic and genetic problems.

It is well established that bacterial chromatin bodies contain the genetic material of the cells. Preceding and during cell division, the chromatin bodies enlarge, undergo characteristic changes in shape, and divide (Fig. 16-1). The process is not identical with that observed in cells of higher plants and animals, but the net result is the same, i.e., replication of genetic units.

DNA is the principal reservoir of genetic information in bacteria as in other organisms. The nature of this substance has been mentioned earlier (see page 5). The DNA molecule consists of a double strand of nucleotides, which are held in a coiled configuration by chains of alternating sugar and phosphate molecules (Fig. 16-2). There are only four different nucleotides in DNA, and because of their structural affinities the bases in these nucleotides are always associated in pairs: adenine of one strand with thymine of the other, and guanine with cytosine.

The replication of DNA consists in the formation of a second double helix that is identical with the first. This is

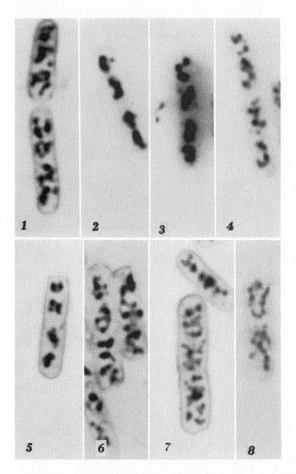

Figure 16-1. Cells of *Bacillus megaterium* in successive stages of chromosome division. Linear chromosomes condense (*1* and *2*), duplicate (*3*), separate (*4* and *5*), elongate (*6* and *7*), and form long, beaded threads (*8*). Three chromosomes are shown in the lower nucleus of the upper cell in (*1*). Magnification, 4450X. (Photographs and interpretations by E. D. DeLamater; from W. Braun: Bacterial Genetics. Philadelphia, W. B. Saunders Co., 1953.)

accomplished by unwinding the parent helix; at the same time new nucleotides assemble and join, by means of hydrogen bonds, with the corresponding nucleotides of each of the old strands: thymine with adenine and cytosine with guanine. The DNA molecule of a bacterium such as *Escherichia coli* contains approximately 10,000,000 nucleotide pairs. It is a circular molecule, about 1 mm. in length (see Fig. 4-23). Replication takes place as indicated in Figure 16-3. The process starts at one point, called the *replicator,* where the helix opens, thus providing single strands that act as templates for the DNA replicating enzyme. The replicator also serves as a swivel, allowing the two old strands to unwind as new DNA strands form and join the old DNA strands.

The bacterial DNA molecule comprises a series of polynucleotide regions that make up the functional units commonly called genes. One of the principal activities of these units is to direct the synthesis of proteins, both structural and enzymatic. The synthesis of a protein the size of hemoglobin (M.W. = 65,000) requires the information contained in approximately 2000 nucleotide pairs. The DNA in a bacterial cell therefore contains sufficient information for about 5000 different proteins.

The information in DNA is stored as a code in which the four nucleotide bases, adenine (A), guanine (G), thymine (T), and cytosine (C), represent "letters" of an alphabet, and each code word (*codon*) consists of three of these letters; e.g., –CAT–ATG–TTT–GTC–.

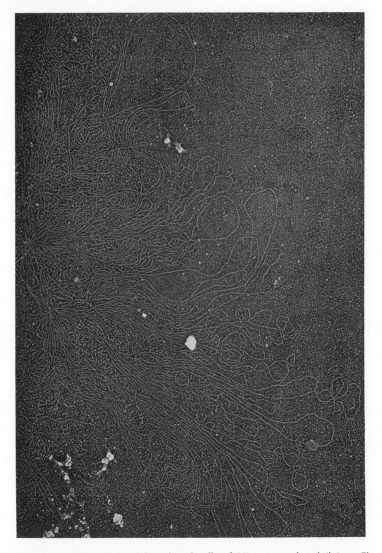

Figure 16-2. Shadowed DNA released from lysed cells of *Micrococcus lysodeikticus*. Electron photomicrograph at approximately 31,000X. (From Kleinschmidt et al., *Z. Naturforsch.*, *16b*:730, 1961.)

Each nucleotide triplet represents a specific amino acid used in the formation of a polypeptide chain. Twenty amino acids are found in proteins, and the four nucleotide bases provide 64 possible codons. As many as six codons correspond to a single amino acid. A sequence of nucleotide triplets that specifies the order of amino acids in a polypeptide is called a *cistron*. This is not necessarily equivalent to a gene, because some proteins are composed of more than one polypeptide chain; hemo-

globin, for example, contains two chains, one of 141 amino acid residues and the other of 146 residues.

A group of cistrons controlling the function and regulation of several different enzymes in a single biosynthetic pathway comprise an *operon*. The histidine operon, for example, contains seven cistrons, totaling about 13,000 nucleotides, which govern the formation of seven biosynthetic enzymes responsible for successive steps in the synthesis of this amino acid.

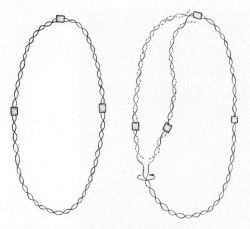

Figure 16-3. Replication of the bacterial chromosome. Replicators are indicated by squares, and newly synthesized DNA is shown as broken lines. Replication starts at the top replicator, which serves as a swivel so that the old strands can unwind, and proceeds counterclockwise. (From Adelberg et al., Bact. Rev., 29:163, 1965.)

The formation of a protein takes place in three principal steps (Fig. 16-4): (1) *transcription* of the coded information of DNA into correspondingly coded RNA, (2) *translation* of the RNA instructions into the indicated amino acid sequence, yielding a polypeptide, and (3) *assembly* and fold-

ing of the latter into protein configuration.

Several forms of RNA participate in protein synthesis. *Messenger RNA* (mRNA) receives the code from DNA. This is a single-stranded molecule complementary to a limited region of one of the two strands of circular DNA of the bacterial nucleoid. RNA differs from DNA in one particular of base composition: it possesses uracil instead of thymine, which is always found in DNA. Uracil is paired with adenine, as guanine is paired with cytosine. Since mRNA is formed in the nucleus in direct association with one strand of DNA, which must be present as a "primer," mRNA bears an exact structural relationship to DNA. It contains about 10,000 nucleotides, which represent sufficient information for several related proteins. Leaving the nucleus, mRNA associates with the ribosomes, where most of the actual work of polypeptide formation takes place.

Whereas the ribosomes of animal cells are attached to the folded membranes of the endoplasmic reticulum, in bacteria they exist as unattached cytoplasmic granules composed of about 60 per cent RNA and 40 per cent pro-

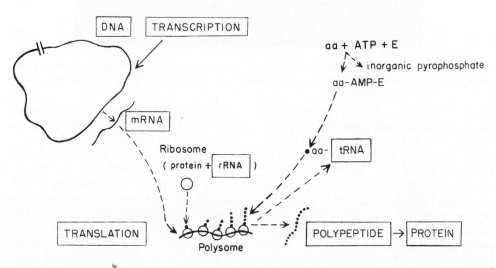

Figure 16-4. The principal steps in protein synthesis directed by DNA. (From W. Braun: Bacterial Genetics, 2d ed. Philadelphia, W. B. Saunders Co., 1965.)

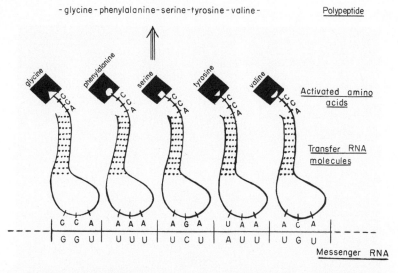

- glycine - phenylalanine - serine - tyrosine - valine -   Polypeptide

Figure 16-5. Diagrammatic representation of steps in the synthesis of a small portion of a polypeptide chain. Various amino acids (large black squares) are associated by an unknown but specific link with the terminal —CCA— trinucleotide of tRNA. tRNA is believed to double back like a hairpin, and at some region an exposed critical trinucleotide corresponding to the amino acid to which the molecule is joined is oriented by the appropriate complementary mRNA trinucleotide. (From Braun.)

tein. *Ribosomal RNA* (rRNA) is largely structural in function.

Transfer RNA (tRNA), or *soluble RNA,* serves as an amino acid carrier, bringing specific amino acids to the mRNA template associated with the ribosomes and holding them in the position specified by the coded instructions and properly oriented to be joined into a polypeptide structure (Fig. 16-5). Each tRNA molecule contains about 80 nucleotides and its molecular weight is about 25,000. These molecules seem to be double stranded in part, presumably by means of the hairpin-like folding back of their linear structure. Where complementary bases (A–U, G–C) oppose one another, hydrogen bonds form and confer stability upon the molecule. At some region there is an exposed specific trinucleotide sequence corresponding to the amino acid with which the tRNA can combine. This provides the point of attachment with the complementary code triplet of mRNA, so that the amino acids are aligned in proper order for the specified polypeptide. It is not known what structures or forces permit the specific fit

of amino acids to the various tRNA molecules.

The association between mRNA and ribosomes is loose. Ribosomes apparently move along an mRNA molecule, assembling amino acids in the proper order (Fig. 16-6). A string of ribosomes held together temporarily by mRNA

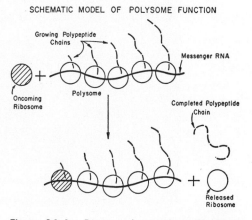

SCHEMATIC MODEL OF POLYSOME FUNCTION

Figure 16-6. Diagram showing how ribosomes, assembled along an mRNA molecule as a polysome, assist in forming a polypeptide chain. (From Rich et al., Cold Spring Harbor Symposium on Quantitative Biology, 28:269, 1963.)

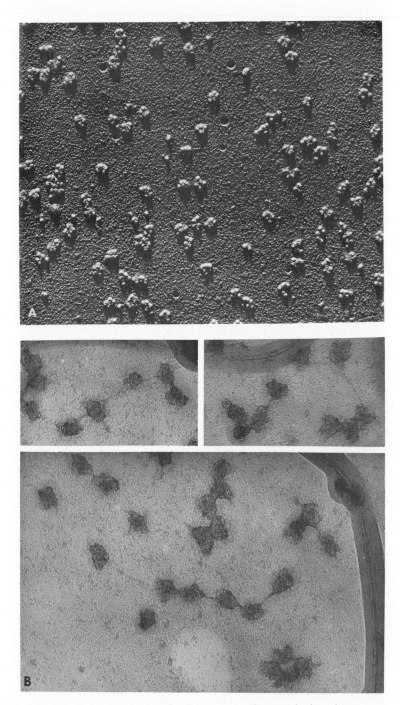

Figure 16-7. Electron photomicrographs of polysomes. *A*, Platinum-shadowed preparation of human cell culture (HeLa) polysomes. *B*, Reticulocyte polysomes stained with uranyl acetate, showing thin strands (10 to 15 Å in diameter), believed to be mRNA, between ribosomes. (From Rich et al., Cold Spring Harbor Symposium on Quantitative Biology, *28:*269, 1963.)

is called a *polysome* (Fig. 16-7). Ribosomes are nonspecific in the sense that they can serve as factories for the assembly of more than one type of polypeptide. The information supplied by mRNA is the important factor in specifying the nature of the polypeptide synthesized.

BACTERIAL VARIATIONS

The variability of bacteria has troubled investigators since the early days of organized bacteriology. Morphologic and other changes in supposedly pure cultures led to the doctrine of *pleomorphism,* which maintained that any organism might appear in a variety of shapes. *Monomorphism,* on the other hand, was the belief that organisms of different shape were actually different species and not merely variant forms of the same species.

The conflict of ideas between pleomorphists and monomorphists produced two different approaches to the classification of bacteria. One school lumped together all reasonably similar forms into a few categories. The other established separate names for organisms differing from one another by only a single minor characteristic. Eventually it was found that bacterial properties vary with the age and growth conditions of the culture, and that mutations occur as in other living organisms. These normal variations must be taken into account in identifying and classifying bacteria.

Bacteria undergo both temporary and permanent variations. *Temporary variations* are morphologic or physiologic changes accompanying the normal development of a culture or induced by a specific environmental factor such as high osmotic pressure. Reversion to the normal form occurs quickly, either in the natural course of aging or upon return to usual conditions. *Permanent variations* consist of mutations—sudden, usually unpredictable, random genetic changes—and occur with relative infrequency. Reversion to the normal form occurs very rarely, and then only as a consequence of back-mutation.

Temporary Variations

Morphologic Variations. The size and shape of bacteria vary continuously throughout the growth cycle (see page 74). This point is worth emphasizing because of the confusion students feel when attempting to identify their first "unknowns."

Old cultures of gram-negative rod bacteria such as *E. coli* consist almost entirely of cells so short that they appear coccoid. The same organism in a culture only a few hours old usually contains definite rods whose length is many times their diameter. In cases of doubt, therefore, it is often helpful to examine smears from young cultures; *true* cocci are rarely more than twice as long as they are broad at any stage of growth.

Another morphologic variation consists of irregular, bloated forms or bizarre shapes resembling the letters T, W, X, or Z. These odd shapes frequently occur in nature, whereas the same organisms appear as regular rods when growing upon suitable laboratory media. *Acetobacter* species in vinegar fermentation form long, bloated filaments. The root nodule bacteria, members of the genus *Rhizobium* (Fig. 16-8), produce irregular shapes like the last letters of the alphabet when growing on the roots of legume plants. Both types of organism are ordinarily gram-negative rods in smears from agar cultures.

Certain bacterial structures are produced only under particular conditions of cultivation. *B. anthracis* forms *capsules* only within the animal body. *Diplococcus pneumoniae* is heavily encapsulated in the body but also produces capsules in culture media containing blood or serum and carbohydrate. Capsulation of saprophytic *Leuconostoc* species is favored by culture media containing sucrose.

Morphologic changes accompany

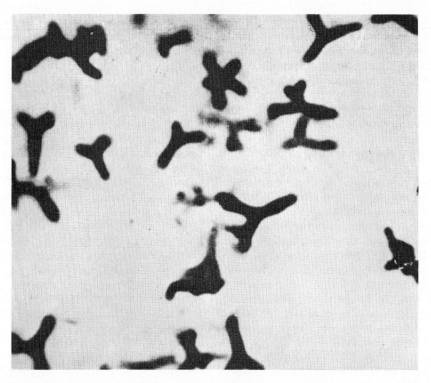

Figure 16-8. Bacteroids of rhizobia from the root of a legume plant. These oddly shaped cells are found only in the nodule; they grow on agar in the laboratory as ordinary short rod bacteria. Magnification, about 2000X. (From Sarles et al.: Microbiology. New York, Harper & Brothers, 1956.)

endospore formation, and sporangia of *Clostridium* and other species are characteristically swollen. Spores usually form late in the growth cycle, but the time of sporulation varies from one species or strain of bacillus to another. Moreover, certain cultural conditions must usually be met; for example, aerobic bacteria sporulate only in the presence of oxygen.

The *staining* of bacteria is also subject to variation. This is fundamentally a physiologic rather than a morphologic characteristic. The gram reaction in particular varies according to the stage of development and other conditions within a culture. Old cells of gram-positive species frequently decolorize more readily than young cells; the same is true of cells that have produced an acid reaction in a medium containing fermentable sugar.

Physiologic Variations. Nongenetic enzymatic adaptation is an example of physiologic variation. Many bacteria produce a particular enzyme only when the specific substrate of the enzyme or some other inducer is present in the medium.

The formation of the lactose-splitting enzyme β-galactosidase by *E. coli* is an inducible process. Cells of this organism do not produce β-galactosidase in a glucose medium; when transferred to a medium containing lactose they are unable to attack this sugar for a short time, but within 30 minutes sufficient β-galactosidase is produced to hydrolyze lactose vigorously. As soon as lactose disappears from the medium, the formation of the enzyme suddenly ceases. Lactose is the inducer and β-galactosidase is an *inducible enzyme*. Its formation presumably confers a competitive advantage on *E. coli,* because the monosaccharides of which lactose is composed can be utilized as sources of energy by the organism. It should be pointed out that there are variant strains of *E. coli* that do not produce this enzyme even in the presence of lactose and hence cannot ferment lactose. These are mutants, which appear following genetic variation.

Physiologic variation may occur in response to a change in the physical environment. *Lactobacillus arabinosus* can grow in a medium lacking the amino acids tyrosine and phenylalanine at 26° C., but it cannot grow in the same medium at 37° C. unless tyrosine and phenylalanine are added. The protoplasm of this organism always contains the two amino acids; therefore, they are synthesized by cultures incubated at 26° C. from other substances, but they are not synthesized at 37° C., presumably because an essential enzyme is inactive at the higher temperature.

Inducible enzyme formation and the temperature dependence of enzyme activity are both under ultimate genetic control, but their demonstration in cultures depends upon particular environmental conditions, and reversion to "normal" occurs when the inducing condition is withheld.

MICROBIAL MUTATIONS

The DNA macromolecules composed of individual genetic units are amazingly stable. Nevertheless they change to other equally stable configurations once in 10,000 to 10,000,000,000 gene generations. These gene changes are mutations and are caused by alteration in the base pairs at specific loci; for example, an adenine-thymine base pair may be altered to give a guanine-cytosine base pair. This produces a change in the genetic code, which will be expressed as a change in the polypeptide whose structure is determined by this gene.

The rate at which mutations occur is enhanced by x-rays, ultraviolet light, nitrogen mustard, or other agents.

Changes in the behavior of an organism are also caused by rearrangement of portions of a chromosome or translocation of portions between chromosomes. Individual genes are not affected by these processes, but their activities may be altered.

Most microbial mutations are *spontaneous;* those that take place at an increased rate in response to deliberately altered environmental conditions are called *induced mutations.* Both spontaneous and induced mutations are random; that is, it is impossible to predict which gene will be affected and hence what change in behavior will be observed.

In addition to mutations, there are types of genetic change over which it is possible to exert some control. Two of these are *transformation* and *transduction.*

Spontaneous Mutations

Colonial and Morphologic Mutations. A given bacterial species may produce more than one colonial form on agar media. The normal colony form (S) produced by many true bacteria is smooth, round, and glistening. Common mutant forms have rough (R) or mucoid (M) colonies. Rough colonies are dull, granular or wrinkled, often with irregular margins; mucoid colonies are shiny, round, transparent, and slimy in consistency. In addition, various minute colonies have been described: G and L colonies contain granules or other elements that pass through filters used to retain normal bacteria, and dwarf (D) colonies often contain irregular club-shaped organisms (diphtheroid forms).

The normal smooth colony contains single cells in no particular arrangement. As multiplication occurs the individual cells separate and freely slide past each other upon the agar. This assumption of a random arrangement is doubtless facilitated by slippery cell constituents (e.g., slime). Rough colonies contain multicellular units consisting of chains of four or more cells. If they also lack the surface slime layer they cannot easily slip past one another to produce the random arrangement. Microscopic examination of the edge of such a colony often reveals parallel chains or threads of bacterial cells. Mucoid colonies produce excessive slime materials or even capsules.

Frequency of Colonial Mutations. The frequency of colonial mutations varies widely from one species to another and even within species. Mutation rates from one per 100 to one per 10 billion cell divisions have been reported; the average is about one per 10 million. This figure means that, on the average, 10 million cells must be produced in a culture before one mutant cell will arise.

Detection of Colonial Mutants. Detection of one rough mutant in a population of 10 million cells is a difficult problem unless some culture change suppresses the smooth form or enhances multiplication of the rough form. This is actually the case with *Brucella abortus,* which undergoes the S ⟶ R mutation at the average one in 10 million rate. In an appropriate medium the amino acid d-alanine accumulates as a waste product and inhibits the smooth organisms but does not retard multiplication of the rough forms. The mutants therefore eventually predominate and are readily detected by plating.

Reverse Mutations. Reverse mutations from rough to smooth usually occur at a lower rate. In some cases an apparent reverse mutation yields a form having the same colony appearance as the parent but possessing some other genetic difference. Reversion of the R form of *B. abortus* produces a smooth colony that possesses much greater resistance to d-alanine than the original S form. The sequence of mutations is represented as S ⟶ R ⟶ S′. The S′ form will eventually predominate over both S and R.

Associated Characteristics. Colony form is associated with other characteristics of an organism. Smooth forms usually grow diffusely in liquid media, whereas rough forms tend to settle rapidly and produce a sediment. Smooth forms of pathogenic species are usually most virulent. A notable exception is *Bacillus anthracis,* but in this case the normal colony is rough, and avirulent mutant strains produce smooth colonies.

Resistance Mutations. Bacterial mutants can be obtained that are resistant to antibiotics or other chemicals, to bacteriophage, or to radiations. A normal population is exposed to the lethal agent for sufficient time to kill all sensitive cells. Subculture on appropriate medium then permits the growth of any surviving resistant cells. Mutation to the resistant form occurs at a very low rate (e.g., 1/1 billion), and large populations must be exposed to the inhibitory agent for a few resistant cells to appear. Repeated trials are often necessary.

Resistance to Antibiotics. Resistance to high concentrations of streptomycin can be obtained in a single step. Mutants resistant to penicillin and most other antibiotics appear in a series of steps. A culture is exposed to a low concentration of the drug, and progeny of those organisms that survive are then exposed to a higher concentration; surviving mutants are then isolated. This process is repeated until organisms resistant to high concentrations are obtained.

The isolation of mutants resistant to antibiotics or other chemicals is facilitated by the *gradient plate technique.* Nutrient agar is poured into a tilted Petri dish and allowed to solidify. A second layer of nutrient agar containing the chemical is then added and allowed to solidify while the plate is level (Fig. 16-9). The antibiotic diffuses downward in proportion to the relative thicknesses of the two layers and establishes a uniform concentration gradient across the plate. The upper layer is inoculated heavily with the organism whose resistant mutants are

(10 cm. diameter; 2 x 20 ml. agar)

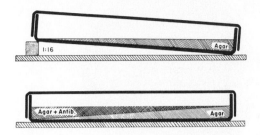

Figure 16-9. Preparation of a gradient plate. The lower layer consists of nutrient agar, which is poured into a slanted Petri dish. After the agar has hardened, the plate is placed in a horizontal position and nutrient agar containing antibiotic is added. Downward diffusion establishes a uniform concentration gradient of antibiotic across the plate, the highest concentration being at the left. (From W. Szybalski and V. Bryson, J. Bact., 64:489–499, 1952.)

desired. After incubation, dense growth is obtained at one side of the plate, in the region of tolerated low concentrations of the chemical. Higher concentrations toward the other side of the plate inhibit sensitive cells but permit colony formation by a few isolated resistant cells (Fig. 16-10).

Methods in which sensitive organisms are cultivated in contact with the inhibitory agent yield resistant mutants but do not demonstrate that the mutants arise spontaneously, even in the absence of the inhibitory agent. The Lederberg *replica plating technique* provides proof that such mutations do occur spontaneously. Plates of nutrient agar are inoculated on the surface with a normal or sensitive strain of the organism in question and incubated for a few hours or until colonies appear. Nutrient agar plates containing the inhibitory chemical are then inoculated from the first plate by means of sterilized velveteen wrapped tightly over the end of a wooden or metal cylinder slightly smaller than the Petri dish. The threads of cloth act as tiny inoculating needles, and when pressed against the agar upon which

colonies are present they pick up 10 to 30 per cent of the cells in each colony. They are then pressed against the agar containing the inhibitory chemical and inoculate it. Several plates can be inoculated in succession. The colonies that appear are located exactly as on the original plate, but only resistant organisms can multiply (Fig. 16-11). The corresponding colonies on the original plate are readily identified, and isolation from these original colonies provides organisms that have never been in contact with the inhibitory agents. They are found to be resistant to the chemical.

Mutants resistant to antibiotics appear *in vivo* with approximately the same frequency as they do *in vitro*. This fact has important consequences in the treatment of disease. The rate of mutation depends upon the antibiotic and the bacterial species, and in some cases is so high that therapy

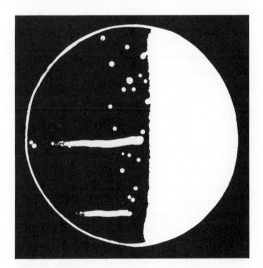

Figure 16-10. Growth of *Escherichia coli* on a gradient plate containing penicillin. A few resistant colonies are seen in the black area in the left half of the plate. Two such colonies were streaked out farther toward the left (toward the high concentration of penicillin); second step resistant colonies developed at the very left edge of the plate. (From W. Szybalski and V. Bryson, J. Bact., 64:489–499, 1952.)

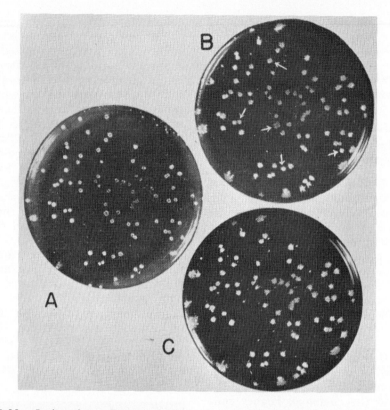

Figure 16-11. Replica plating. Portions of colonies from the initial plate, A, were imprinted on plates B and C by means of sterile velveteen wrapped tightly over a circular support of wood or cork. Plate B contained the same medium as A, but C contained a medium on which certain mutants could not grow. The mutants are indicated by arrows on B; corresponding locations on C are vacant. (From J. Lederberg and E. M. Lederberg, J. Bact., 63:399–406, 1952.)

with a single antibiotic is virtually useless. However, simultaneous administration of two antibiotics is often successful, and resistant mutants do not arise. The explanation of this observation is that resistance mutations occur independently, and therefore organisms resistant to one antibiotic are killed or inhibited by the second, and vice versa. If bacteria resistant to each antibiotic appear at the rate of one per 10 million, for example, cells resistant to both antibiotics can be expected to appear at a rate of only one per 100 trillion (that is, 1/10,000,000 × 1/10,000,000).

Bacteriophage Resistance. Bacterial mutants resistant to bacteriophage can often be secured by continued incubation of a lysed culture. Resistant mutants can also be obtained by the replica plate technique. The success of this method demonstrates that phage resistance is acquired by mutation, because the bacteria are not exposed to bacterial virus during the isolation procedure. This mutation occurs at the very low frequency of about 1/1,000,000,000.

The *fluctuation test,* devised by Luria and Delbrück, can also be used to demonstrate that resistance to bacteriophage or other agents arises spontaneously by mutation at a certain determinable frequency, rather than by somatic adaptation of a constant proportion of the cells in a culture. If the latter situation were true, the percentage of resistant organisms in a population or in a series of parallel subcultures would always be the same. According to the mutation hypothesis, however, there is a small but constant probability *per generation* that each bacterium will become resistant, but when mutation has occurred, *all* progeny of the mutant will be resistant. If mutation takes place early in the growth cycle of a culture, a large number of resistant cells will be present at a specified point in the history of the culture, whereas if mutation occurs late, few resistant cells will be present at the same point in the cycle of the culture. When several equal portions of a culture are used to seed subcultures, and the latter are examined after appropriate incubation, some subcultures are expected to contain many resistant organisms, others to contain fewer. The fact that a wide fluctuation in content of resistant bacteria actually occurs (Table 16-1) confirms the mutation hypothesis and supports the conclusion that the original resistant mutants arose prior to the exposure of the population to the phage or other inhibitory agent.

Table 16-1. Comparison of the Number of Phage-resistant Bacteria in Different Samples of the Same Culture with the Number in a Series of Parallel Cultures.*†

Number of Phage-resistant Bacteria	
10 Samples from the Same Culture	Samples from 10 Parallel Cultures
46	30
56	10
52	40
48	45
65	183
44	12
49	173
51	23
56	57
47	51

* Volume of samples = 0.05 ml.

† From data of S. E. Luria and M. S. Delbrück, Genetics, *28:*491, 1943.

Radiation Resistance. Resistance to ultraviolet irradiation can be acquired by mutation. Sensitivity to ultraviolet light is quantitative rather than qualitative within the proper range of wavelengths; therefore intermittent or fractional irradiation is used to select pure cultures of resistant mutants. Sensitive cells are easily killed; increasingly resistant mutants survive and multiply.

E. coli mutants that are resistant to ultraviolet light are also resistant to hydrogen peroxide, potassium tellurite, crystal violet, and various other substances. Some of these chemicals are oxidizing agents, and it is now believed that resistance to radiation is associated with resistance to oxidation (see page 248).

Biochemical Mutations. The basis of all mutations is biochemical, but the term *biochemical mutation* is employed in a specific sense to designate mutations in which a nutritional requirement is altered or some easily recognized enzymatic process is affected.

Auxotrophic Mutants. The "normal" or usually encountered form of an organism is designated the "wild-type" or *prototrophic* form. Auxotrophic mutants are derived from a wild-type organism and require one or more growth factors. Prototrophs of many species can grow in simple, chemically defined media without addition of other growth factors. The simple medium in which the wild-type organism grows is called a *minimal medium,* whereas a medium containing all the likely nutritional requirements is known as a *complete medium* (e.g., nutrient agar and yeast glucose agar).

The isolation of auxotrophic mutants is facilitated by irradiation of the prototrophic population with ultraviolet light or x-rays (see page 285). The irradiated culture is plated on complete medium, and a large number of colonies is subcultured on complete medium and also on minimal medium. Growth on the complete medium but not on minimal medium indicates that the isolate may be an auxotrophic mutant. Several hundred colonies must often be tested before an auxotroph is obtained. Replica plating greatly facilitates the foregoing process and eliminates most of the labor of sub-culturing.

Auxotrophic mutants are useful tools in the hands of the biochemist interested in tracing natural pathways of synthesis of organic compounds. Each gene controls the activity of a single enzyme, and therefore any mutation interrupts a single biochemical process or step. Tatum and Bonner in 1944 found two mutants of the mold *Neurospora crassa* that could not synthesize tryptophan, although the parent strain could. Both mutants grew if supplied with indole, and one grew on anthranilic acid. In either case the amino acid serine was necessary. The steps in biosynthesis of tryptophan therefore seemed to be those outlined in Figure 16-12.

Both mutants possessed enzyme (3) and could join indole and serine to form tryptophan, but only one mutant possesses enzyme (2) and produced indole from anthranilic acid. Neither was able to make anthranilic acid from its unknown precursor X.

Auxotrophic mutants can be employed to identify and determine the concentrations of growth factors, such as amino acids, vitamins, and nucleic acid derivatives. The nutritional re-

quirements of auxotrophic mutants are also being used as "markers" in the important new field of microbial genetics, just as hair and eye color are used in human genetics.

A historically and biologically interesting mutation appears in *S. typhosa*. This organism usually requires tryptophan when isolated from patients with typhoid fever, but some laboratory cultures will grow in media lacking this amino acid. It was originally believed that the organism gradually became "trained" by laboratory cultivation to synthesize its own tryptophan. Later, however, it was found that one cell in about 10 million mutates to a form able to grow without added tryptophan. This "tryptophan independent" mutant is not ordinarily detected in laboratory cultures, because the usual media contain sufficient tryptophan to permit luxuriant growth of the tryptophan-requiring parent. A medium containing enough tryptophan to support only 10 million to 100 million tryptophan-requiring cells eventually contains a considerable number of tryptophan independent mutants. If the medium contains even less tryptophan, visible growth appears only after prolonged lag, but most of this population consists of the mutant form.

The *S. typhosa* mutation is of interest biologically because it may represent the reverse of what happens during

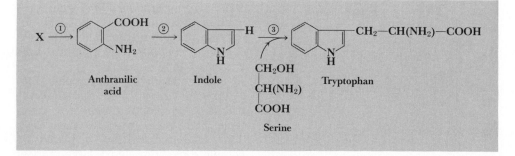

Figure 16-12. Steps in the biosynthesis of tryptophan. An auxotrophic mutant that cannot carry out step 1 (conversion of an unknown precursor to anthranilic acid) must be supplied with anthranilic acid, indole, or tryptophan if it is to grow. A mutant that cannot perform step 2 must be supplied with indole or tryptophan, etc.

acquisition of the parasitic mode of existence. A forebear of this species may have been a saprophyte that did not need an outside source of tryptophan. This organism was ingested by some animal or by man, established itself within the body, and mutated to a form that required tryptophan. The mutant was able to survive because an adequate supply of the amino acid was available in the host. Perhaps it multiplied a little more rapidly than the parent form, which was presumably completely eliminated and which disappeared except as the *back-mutation,* recognized in the laboratory, once more yields the form capable of synthesizing tryptophan.

Many species of parasitic bacteria can be cultivated only with great difficulty when first isolated, but ultimately they can grow upon much simpler media. When these organisms are studied in sufficient detail to reveal their specific nutrient requirements situations similar to that in *S. typhosa* will undoubtedly be found.

Fermentation Mutants. Fermentation mutants are forms that arise spontaneously in small numbers in populations consisting of cells with other fermentation properties, for example, the appearance of organisms that can ferment lactose or maltose in cultures that do not ordinarily possess these properties.

One of the best known fermentation mutants is derived from a variant of *E. coli* that fails to ferment lactose. This organism was at one time called *E. coli mutabile.* Young colonies of *E. coli mutabile* are white on E.M.B. agar (which contains lactose and other nutrients and an indicator system composed of eosin and methylene blue). Older colonies develop black secondary or daughter colonies known as *papillae* (Fig. 16-13). A black papilla may be subcultured and found to consist of stable, lactose-fermenting organisms. Replating the parent white colony continues to yield colonies that produce papillae. The lactose-fermenting mutants arise at the rate of approximately one per 100,000 cells.

The specific property affected in fermentation mutants is not known with certainty. It may be an enzyme necessary to attack the substrate in question, it may be permeability to the substrate or some other factor.

Fermentation mutants arise at a higher rate than nutritional or resistance mutants: between one in 100,000 and one in 10 million cells. The prolonged incubation period before the appearance of papillae is accounted for by the time required for mutants to arise and the additional period during which they multiply sufficiently to produce visible papillae.

Pigmentation Mutants. *Mutations affecting pigment production* are easy to observe, but the actual biochemical changes are unknown in most cases. The mutants are almost completely

Figure 16-13. Papillae of the lactose-fermenting mutant of *Escherichia coli mutabile* on colonies of the nonfermenting parent. (Parr.)

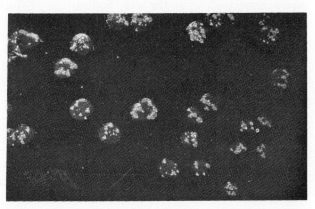

stable, and are distinguished by complete loss of color or production of intermediate tints. *Serratia marcescens,* for example, normally produces a dark, blood-red pigment, but some strains produce stable, white mutants; rose red and pink variants are also fairly common. *S. aureus* often loses its golden pigment after extended cultivation on laboratory media. Many other staphylococci or micrococci are notorious for the frequency with which white colonies appear in otherwise yellow populations.

Nonmutational variations in pigmentation are frequently encountered, particularly among cocci and gram-negative rod bacteria. These temporary variations are caused by changes in nutrients, temperature of incubation, oxygen supply, and pH. Aerobic or facultative organisms are often most intensely pigmented under aerobic conditions and at moderate or low temperatures.

Antigenic Mutations. The antigenic structure of bacteria is studied by techniques that will be described in Chapter 21. For the moment it will suffice to say that antigens are proteins or polysaccharides that stimulate the formation of modified blood proteins known as antibodies when injected into appropriate animals. Antibodies possess the ability to react detectably (e.g., by precipitation) with the corresponding antigenic substances. They are therefore *specific* reagents for the detection of antigens.

Bacterial cells contain many antigens, some associated with the cell bodies, some with the capsules, and others with the flagella. Their presence can be determined by proper tests with suitable antibody solutions (antisera).

Antigenic mutations occur with considerable frequency in bacteria and may involve any type of antigenic component. A motile organism that mutates to the nonmotile state and loses the power to produce flagella simultaneously loses its flagellar antigens. A mutation commonly encountered among *Salmonella* species results in the loss of some flagellar antigens and the acquisition of others. Mutations of this sort occur at a high rate: one mutant in about 10,000 cells is average, but rates as high as one in 250 cells have been reported.

Loss of cell body antigens by mutation is also a common occurrence. Freshly isolated *S. typhosa* usually possesses a component known as the Vi antigen, but this disappears after only a few transfers on laboratory media. The transformation from smooth to rough colonial forms is accompanied by the loss of other cell body antigens. These are all mutational events. Reverse mutations occasionally occur, but with much lower frequency.

Mutations Affecting Virulence. Since the earliest days of medical bacteriology it has been noted that the virulence or disease-producing power of pathogenic bacteria may vary, but the mutational origin of this variation has been demonstrated only recently. It must be understood that virulence depends on numerous factors, some affecting the pathogen itself, others affecting the host. Virulence can be measured only by determining the effect of the pathogen on a host, and a resistant host can withstand large doses of the pathogen without adverse effect. Some pathogens cause disease by means of the toxins they secrete; the ability to produce toxin can be lost by mutation. Pathogenicity of certain species depends upon capsulation, and this property also is subject to mutational loss.

Studies with *Brucella abortus, Pasteurella tularensis, S. typhosa,* and other bacteria have indicated a correlation between resistance to certain metabolic products and virulence, or between nutritional requirements and virulence. For example, mutants of *S. typhosa* that require purines, p-aminobenzoic acid, or aspartic acid are less virulent for mice than the parent organism. The mutants multiply more slowly in the host, apparently because of limited availability of the purines, PABA, and aspartic acid in mice; the injection or in some cases even the feeding of these metabolites increases the pathogenic effect of the mutants.

Much remains to be done before factors affecting virulence are completely understood, and nutritional and resistance studies like the foregoing may be very fruitful. Mutations affecting virulence occur, but the ability of the mutant to establish itself depends upon chemical conditions within the host. These chemical conditions are influenced by the diet and general physiologic state of the host and by changes caused by the pathogen itself. The interaction between host and parasite is complex.

Induced Mutations

Mutations resulting from exposure to *mutagenic agents* are known as induced mutations. Mutagenic agents increase mutation rates by a factor ranging from several hundred to as much as 100,000, but it is usually considered that they do not determine the type of mutation that occurs; they merely accelerate the rate of spontaneous mutation. The mutagenic agents that have been most widely used are x-rays, ultraviolet light, and nitrogen mustard. Other mutagens include peroxides, carcinogenic chemicals, and even some simple substances like manganese chloride.

Mutagenic agents are believed to damage or change a single genetic unit of DNA so that it possesses erroneous information. For example, if the wrong base (A instead of G, C, or T; G instead of A, C, or T; etc.) is incorporated at a given site in a polynucleotide chain, or if a nucleotide fails to replicate, all subsequent events at that site will be altered. Purines and pyrimidines occasionally undergo electron and proton rearrangements, which affect their ability to form hydrogen bonds, and hence they may attract different bases from the normal. The presence of base analogues may increase the frequency of such changes, as may a marked disturbance in the nature and concentration of nucleotide components. Excess replication of a given base may occur, as well as failure of replication, with the result that the information in the affected DNA region is altered or even "senseless."

There is some indication that oxidation plays a part; the presence of reducing substances in the culture medium decreases both the mutagenic and lethal effects of irradiation. Alkylating agents, nitrous acid, hydroxylamine, and other chemicals may add or change base radicals, thus producing different compounds that will react abnormally in the DNA strand.

All the progeny of a uninucleate cell that has undergone mutation display the mutated characteristic. Some bacterial cells are multinucleate, particularly during active growth phases, and only a portion of their progeny consist of mutated forms, because the probability that more than one nucleus in the parent cell will be affected by the mutagen is extremely small. Mutation in a multinucleate cell can lead to the appearance of "sectored" colonies (Fig. 16-14), which show particularly well when the affected characteristic is pigmentation, colony smoothness, or fermentation (of a sugar present in an indicator-agar medium). It should be pointed out that sectors of this sort may also arise when two or more individual cells are trapped upon the agar so closely together that their colonies merge; this is obviously not mutational sectoring.

Directed Genetic Changes

Genetic changes can sometimes be controlled specifically by the investigator. There are two principal methods of producing these changes: *transformation* and *transduction*. The techniques employed are dissimilar, but basically both consist of the transfer of DNA from one organism to another. They differ in the method by which transfer is accomplished.

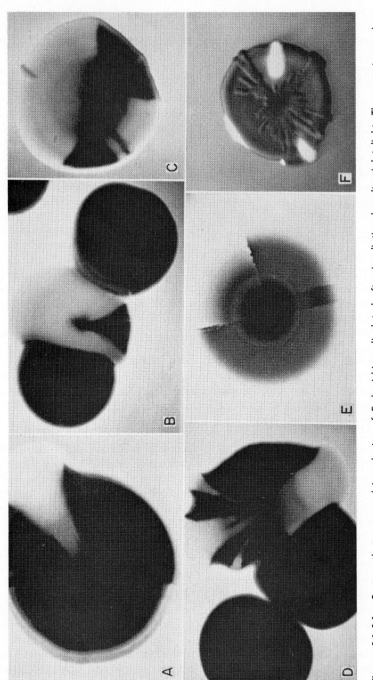

Figure 16-14. Sectors that appeared in colonies of *Escherichia coli* plated after irradiation by ultraviolet light. The parent organism ferments lactose and produces black colonies on the indicator-agar medium. Lactose negative mutant progeny produce white colonies or sectors. (Newcombe; from Braun: Bacterial Genetics, 2d ed. Philadelphia, W. B. Saunders Co., 1965.)

Transformations. The first transformation discovered was the conversion of one antigenic type of pneumococcus into another. There are nearly 100 pneumococcus types, which are distinguished by possession of different capsular polysaccharides. Antibodies against the polysaccharide of one type will not react with polysaccharides of other types.

Griffith in 1928 injected mice subcutaneously with noncapsulated, rough, type 2 pneumococci and capsulated type 3 pneumococci killed with heat. The animals that died were found to be infected with capsulated pneumococci of type 3. The type 3 organisms injected had been killed by heat; thus it was obvious that the rough, type 2 organisms had been transformed into type 3. The new type 3 culture maintained its type specificity through subsequent laboratory cultivation. Several other transformations of pneumococcal types were induced, and in each case the acquired property was that of the dead, capsulated organism injected.

Pneumococcus type transformations were later performed *in vitro* (Fig. 16-15). The substance in dead capsulated pneumococci that was responsible for transformation was eventually isolated and found to be deoxyribonucleic acid; its action was abolished by the depolymerizing enzyme, deoxyribonuclease, which specifically attacks DNA.

Transformation is not limited to pneumococcal polysaccharides. Other transformations include transfer of penicillin resistance, streptomycin resistance, and resistance to other drugs from one strain of pneumococcus to another by means of DNA derived from resistant strains, and transfer of various hydrolytic, oxidative, and synthetic enzymes from one strain of organisms to another.

Transformation has been demonstrated in most instances between strains of the same bacterial species,

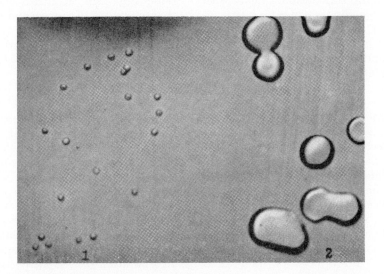

Figure 16-15. Colonies of *Diplococcus pneumoniae*. *Left,* A rough, noncapsulated, type 2 strain. *Right,* The same strain after cultivation with active, cell-free transforming principle (DNA) from a smooth, capsulated, type 3 strain. These large, mucoid colonies are identical with those usually produced by capsulated type 3 pneumococci. (From O. T. Avery, C. M. MacLeod, and M. McCarty, J. Exper. Med., 79:137–158, 1944.)

but it has also been effected between certain different, closely related species. Some strains of a species are more readily transformed than others, and transformation can often be more readily accomplished in a particular medium. These facts indicate that both genetic and environmental factors control the phenomenon. Cells of a transformable strain acquire a physiologic state suitable for transformation when placed within a favorable medium for a relatively brief period; such cells are said to be *competent*. The nature of competence is poorly understood. Inasmuch as the first steps in transformation involve adsorption and penetration of exogenous DNA, it is assumed that competent cells either possess specific, receptive surface components or develop "holes" or "naked" areas in the cell wall, or both. There is evidence that competent cells possess as many as 75 adsorption sites, and to be taken up, the DNA must be of a certain minimum molecular size (M.W. = 100,000).

After penetration, the next steps are association, or "pairing," and integration of the transforming DNA with the corresponding segment of the recipient's DNA; replication of the chromosome with the integrated new information; and formation of a transformed cell population. The genetic change is permanent; transformed cells and their progeny continue to produce DNA having the same properties as that which caused the transformation.

Transduction. Transduction is genetic transfer mediated by bacteriophage. Zinder and Lederberg reported in 1952 the transfer of several characters between strains of *Salmonella*.

Certain strains of bacteria normally contain bacteriophage in a sort of commensal relationship. The bacteriophage lyses only a few cells of its normal host and perhaps a few of some other strains. The bacteriophage is a *temperate* strain, which ordinarily does not replicate unrestrictedly, as does a virulent phage. Instead, its DNA attaches to that of the bacterial host and replicates at the same rate as the host DNA. Temperate phage, associated with bacterial DNA and known as *prophage*, spontaneously acquires the ability to replicate vegetatively in about one bacterium in every million, whereupon the host cell lyses. The bacterial strain infected with prophage is described as *lysogenic*. Replication of prophage can be induced in a higher percentage of lysogenic cells by exposure to ultraviolet light, nitrogen mustard, or other agents. Phage particles released by lysis, either spontaneous or induced, can infect other bacteria of an appropriate strain, on which they may attach to a suitable site on the chromosomal DNA. One view of the nature of attachment of prophage DNA to bacterial DNA and its subsequent separation is shown in Figure 16-16 (*A* and *B*).

Zinder and Lederberg found that when a lysogenic strain of *Salmonella* was cultivated with another *Salmonella*, which possessed certain different properties but was susceptible to the same bacteriophage, some cells of the lysogenic organism acquired one of the characteristics of the second organism. For example, a lysogenic mutant of *S. typhimurium* that required tryptophan was cultivated with another strain that required histidine but not tryptophan. A few prototrophic cells were recovered that required neither tryptophan nor histidine. This is the phenomenon of *transduction*. It is characterized by the ability of a few infecting phage particles to incorporate a small amount of the host DNA and subsequently transfer it to a susceptible cell. The mechanism by which this may occur is illustrated in Figure 16-16 (*C* and *D*). Faulty attachment of phage DNA to bacterial DNA results in the incorporation of a small portion of the latter into the phage and vice versa, so that upon subsequent infection and lysis of another bacterium, DNA from

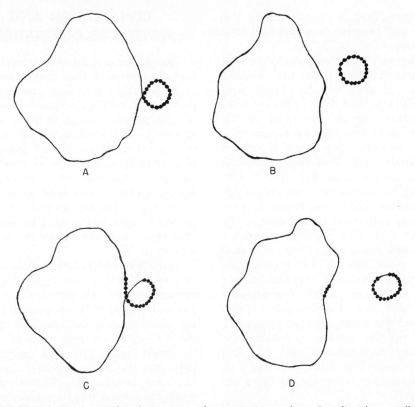

Figure 16-16. *A,* Large, circular chromosome of an organism such as *E. coli* with a small loop of prophage DNA attached. *B,* Separation of the phage DNA. *C,* Faulty attachment of phage DNA to bacterial chromosome, so that (*D*) separation leaves a bit of chromosome DNA incorporated in the phage DNA and vice versa. Subsequent infection of another bacterium with this aberrant phage introduces the piece of foreign bacterial DNA into the recipient's chromosome, producing a genetic change. (From Braun: Bacterial Genetics, 2d ed. Philadelphia, W. B. Saunders Co., 1965.)

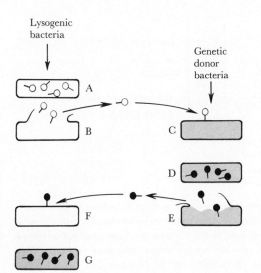

Figure 16-17. Transduction. Bacteriophage normally present in cells of a lysogenic strain of bacteria (*A*) lyses a few cells (*B*). If this organism is cultivated in mixture with a related but not identical strain of bacteria, phage infection of a cell of the second strain may occur (*C*), and the phage may acquire a small bit of the bacterial DNA (*D*), which it then carries to another cell of the lysogenic strain (*E* and *F*). Reinfection is followed by introduction of the new piece of DNA into the bacterial chromosome and expression of a characteristic derived from the donor strain (*G*).

the original host is transferred to the second and becomes incorporated into its genome (Fig. 16-17).

Zinder and Lederberg demonstrated that transduction does not require physical contact of the donor and recipient cells (and thereby differs from *conjugation,* to be described next); they accomplished this by means of a U-tube with the two arms separated by a fritted glass disk through which bacteria cannot pass (Fig. 16-18). The lysogenic auxotrophic mutant of *S. typhimurium* (22A) requiring trypto-phan was cultivated in one side of the U-tube, and the histidine-requiring auxotrophic mutant (2A) was cultivated in the other side. A few prototrophs that required neither tryptophan nor histidine were recovered from the first side. Phage from the lysogenic strain traversed the filter, infected strain 2A, picked up the genetic capability for producing tryptophan, lysed 2A, and then recrossed the filter, entering 22A and becoming incorporated into its genome.

Numerous traits have been trans-duced: ability to ferment various carbo-hydrates, resistance to antibiotics, and antigenic characteristics. Various well known types of *Salmonella* have been converted into other recognized types as well as into hitherto unknown types.

CONJUGATION AND GENETIC RECOMBINATION

The demonstration of bacterial trans-formation showed that genetic material could be transferred from one organism to another with subsequent alteration of the genetic characteristics of the recipient. This finding paved the way for an intensive search for indications of a natural sexual type of genetic ex-change in bacteria such as exists in higher forms. There was little or no microscopic evidence that sexual fusion occurred in bacteria, so it was presumed that this event was extremely rare if it existed at all.

Lederberg and Tatum in 1944 demon-strated that a sexual type of genetic recombination can occur in *E. coli*. Normal strains of this organism require no added growth factors. Two mutant strains were secured, one of which required biotin (B) and methionine (M), and the other required threonine (T) and leucine (L). Partial genetic formulae for the two organisms may be written as follows: $B^-M^-T^+L^+$ and $B^+M^+T^-L^-$. The symbols B^- and M^- mean that the strain is unable to syn-thesize biotin and methionine; T^+ and L^+ signify that the organisms can syn-thesize threonine and leucine.

About 100 million cells of each type

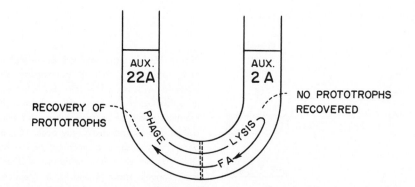

Figure 16-18. U-tube with fritted glass filter separating the two arms used in a transduction experi-ment to demonstrate that genetic material is filterable. A lysogenic, tryptophan-requiring auxotrophic mutant of *S. typhimurium* (22A) was grown in the left arm, and a histidine-requiring auxotrophic mutant (2A) was grown in the right arm. Prototrophs that required neither amino acid were recovered from the left arm. (From Braun: Bacterial Genetics, 2d ed. Philadelphia, W. B. Saunders Co., 1965.)

were mixed and incubated and then plated on a synthetic medium containing none of these four growth factors. Neither strain could grow alone on this medium, but several score colonies appeared when the mixed culture was plated. These were found to have the genetic composition $B^+M^+T^+L^+$; that is, they possessed the synthetic abilities of both parent strains.

The first demonstration of gene recombination in bacteria suggested that *E. coli* is capable of a sexual type of reproduction; it also showed that only about one cell in a million participates. The possibility of observing this phenomenon directly therefore appeared extremely remote.

Further experiments with other traits confirmed the probability of a sexual mode of reproduction. It was also demonstrated that bacterial genes are linked in a certain order and that recombination does not occur at random. This observation implied that the genes are arranged upon a chromosome as in higher organisms. It was found further that some cells of *E. coli* behave as genetic donors, others as genetic recipients, and finally that conjugation involving a few donor strains produces an unusually high frequency of genetic recombination.

Mechanism of Bacterial Conjugation

Each genetic donor or male cell possesses a "sex factor" or *conjugon* that distinguishes it from a recipient or female cell. The sex factors are composed of DNA and are probably circular, self-replicating structures like bacterial chromosomes, but only about $\frac{1}{100}$ as large (Fig. 16-19). They can replicate either autonomously or in association with (i.e., integrated into) the chromosomes. The sex factors have several functions, including that of providing the conditions necessary for establishing cell-to-cell contact, probably by directing the formation of a specific polysaccharide in the walls of male cells. During conjugation they

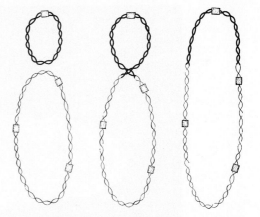

Figure 16-19. Diagrammatic representations of a bacterial chromosome (light lines) and a sex factor (heavy lines). Integration of the sex factor into the chromosome by breakage and reunion is indicated in the center and right sketches. (From Adelberg et al., *Bact. Rev., 29*:164, 1965.)

are usually transferred to the female cells. Independent genetic structures of this description that are additional to the normal chromosome content of the cells they inhabit are also called *episomes*.

Several sex factors are known. The first reported and most studied is the F (fertility) factor. Cells possessing it are called F^+, and those lacking it F^-. Others are the *resistance transfer factor* (RTF), which transfers resistance to certain antibacterial substances at the same time that it initiates conjugation, and the *colicine factor*, which is responsible for the production of certain polypeptide antibiotics.

In a mixture of F^+ and F^- cells, random collisions lead to the formation of specific mating pairs as F^- cells encounter the polysaccharide attachment sites of F^+ cells. Cellular connection, or conjugation, occurs and may (or may not) be followed by transfer of chromosomal material (Fig. 16-20).

Immediately before or simultaneously with this process, the chromosome of the F^+ cell replicates, and a strand of DNA remains in the linear (noncircular) state, in which form it can traverse the conjugation bridge and enter the

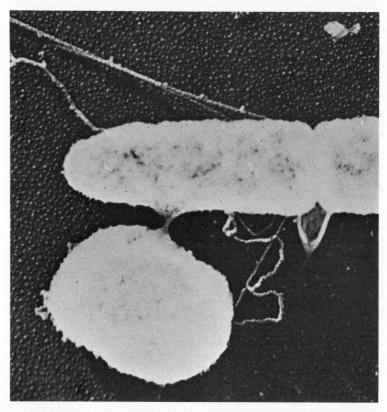

Figure 16-20. Conjugation of *E. coli*. The elongated cell in the process of dividing (*top*) is an Hfr strain of K-12, and the F⁻ recipient (plump cell) is strain C. The long, thin structures attached to K-12 are flagella. The conjugation bridge is clearly shown. (From Anderson et al., Ann. Inst. Pasteur, 93:450, 1957.)

F⁻ cell. DNA replication may provide the energy used in conjugation and transfer of genetic material. Usually only part of the male chromosome enters the female cell, because either the conjugation bridge or the polynucleotide chain breaks before transfer is complete. This can be detected by genetic analysis of the progeny. Under favorable conditions in certain strains of *E. coli,* transfer is completed in about 110 minutes.

The transferred genetic material integrates with that of the recipient, and replication and segregation take place. It should be noted that genetic transfer is not necessarily followed by recombination.

As stated earlier, certain bacterial strains participate in genetic recombination with unusual frequency. When

normal F⁺ cells mate with F⁻ cells, recombination occurs in about one cell in 100,000. Conjugation of strains designated *Hfr* (high frequency of recombination) with F⁻ cells is followed by recombination in approximately one of every 100 cells. The conjugation-promoting powers of Hfr and F⁺ cells are about the same, but genetic recombination is 1000 times more frequent with the former.

The progeny obtained in F⁺ × F⁻ matings are always F⁺ and, in fact, when F⁺ cells are grown with F⁻ cells, most or all of the latter become F⁺ within an hour, owing to the rapid replication and spread of the F factor. The progeny of Hfr × F⁻ matings are nearly all F⁻, only a few Hfr cells being produced.

These facts are explained by dif-

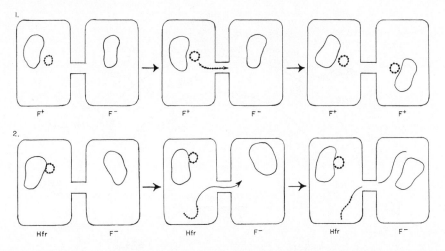

Figure 16-21. Diagram illustrating the location and transfer of F factor in (1) F⁺ × F⁻ matings and (2) Hfr × F⁻ matings. Chromosomal DNA is indicated by plain lines, F by dotted lines, and replicated structures in the process of transfer by lines with arrowheads. Both chromosomes and F factors are circular except when being transferred. In F⁺ cells, F is ordinarily autonomous, whereas in Hfr cells it is integrated with the chromosome and is transferred last (if at all) in conjugation. (From Braun: Bacterial Genetics, 2d ed., Philadelphia, W. B. Saunders Co., 1965.)

ferences in the location and behavior of F within F⁺ and Hfr cells (Fig. 16-21). The F factor is autonomous in F⁺ cells; that is, it is not normally associated with the chromosome and replicates independently of it. At conjugation it is often transferred alone, thus converting an F⁻ cell to F⁺. F may, however, become associated with the donor chromosome, and in such a circumstance genetic material is also transferred to the F⁻ cell, and a low frequency (e.g., 1 in 100,000) of recombination occurs. The association between F and chromosome material involves no particular site, so that any trait (marker) can be transferred.

In Hfr cells, F is regularly associated with specific chromosome sites, which differ from one Hfr strain to another. At conjugation, the circular chromosome breaks at the site where F is located, and the linear DNA strand transfers to the F⁻ cell with the F factor at the tail end. Since complete transfer rarely occurs, F does not ordinarily enter the recipient, which therefore remains F⁻; only in the occasional instance of complete transfer does the F⁻ cell become Hfr.

The fact that F is associated with different chromosome sites in different strains of bacteria can be shown by interrupted mating experiments. Conjugation can be terminated and DNA transfer stopped at any time by violently agitating the culture in a Waring Blendor to break the conjugation bridges. Genetic analysis of the recombinants then indicates what traits (markers) have transferred from the male cells to the female cells. The longer conjugation continues, the more traits are transferred. With a given Hfr strain, a certain marker always transfers first, followed by other markers in a particular order (e.g., A, B, C, D, E, . . .). When a different Hfr strain of the same species is used, another marker transfers first, and this is followed by markers in the same sequence (e.g., C, D, E, F, G, . . .). In some cases, markers transfer in the reverse sequence. These situations are illustrated in the circular genetic linkage map of E. coli, strain K-12 (Fig. 16-22). When Hfr substrain C is used in a conjugation experiment, marker *T6* is transferred first, followed by *ade, lac, pro,* etc., and finally *gal.* With substrain H, however,

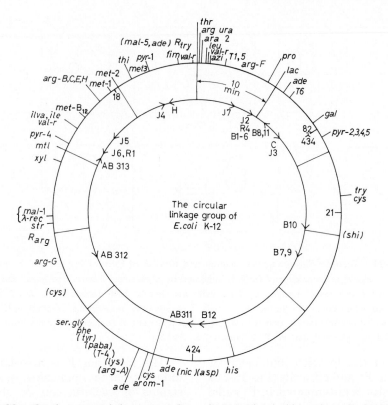

Figure 16-22. Circular genetic linkage map of E. coli K-12. The double circle is divided into 11 sections, each representing a 10 minute transfer interval as determined from interrupted mating experiments. Around the outer circle are located various genetic markers: e.g., gal = galactose fermentation; str = streptomycin resistance. Prophage loci are indicated inside the outer circle. The various Hfr substrains of E. coli K-12 are shown inside the inner circle at the arrowheads (J4, H, J7, etc.), which mark the leading end and direction of the transfer of markers. (From Hayes: The Genetics of Bacteria and Their Viruses. New York, John Wiley & Sons, Inc., 1964.)

transfer begins with *fim, R*$_{try}$*, val-r,* etc., and ends with *pyr-1.*

Genetic recombination has been studied most intensively in *E. coli.* The phenomenon is not restricted to this organism, but the extent of its occurrence in other organisms is not yet known.

16 VARIATION AND GENETICS OF BACTERIA

SUMMARY

Bacteria, by virtue of their rapid growth, and because they exhibit most of the genetic processes of higher organisms, are especially useful subjects for genetic research. In fact, the role of DNA and the various forms of RNA in the regulation of protein synthesis was worked out largely with microbial systems.

The variations that bacteria undergo are of interest to the systematist, to the manufacturer who uses microorganisms, to the physician, and to the geneticist.

Temporary morphologic or physiologic variations accompany the development of a culture. The organisms revert to normal with age or a change in cultural conditions.

Permanent variations or mutations resemble the genetic alterations that occur in higher organisms. Spontaneous mutations take place with an average frequency between 1 in 10,000 and 1 in 10 billion gene generations. The rate of induced mutations is increased by deliberate control of environmental conditions; for example, exposure of cells to x-rays. In both spontaneous and induced mutations the genes affected, and hence the mutations produced, are completely unpredictable.

Two types of directed genetic changes can be controlled to some degree. Transformations are produced by the transfer of DNA derived from one organism to another related organism. Transduction is a similar DNA transfer mediated by a bacterial virus. In each process, the transferred DNA may combine with that of the recipient by genetic recombination.

Genetic recombination also normally follows a sexual type of gene transfer. Conjugation of two cells permits passage of DNA from the male cell to the female, and the resulting recombinants possess characteristics derived from both. Sex factors such as the fertility factor (F), which are small, circular, self-replicating structures composed of DNA, play a vital role in the conjugation processes and, under certain circumstances, greatly increase the frequency of genetic recombination.

STUDY QUESTIONS

1. How can one determine whether a coccoid bacterium is actually a rod-shaped species or a coccus?
2. What is the basic difference between the mechanisms of permanent and temporary microbial variations?
3. Distinguish between spontaneous and induced mutations.
4. Would it appear preferable to treat patients with infectious disease by means of several small doses of an antibiotic such as penicillin or a single large dose? Explain.
5. What fundamental characteristic of mutation can be demonstrated by the replica plating technique?
6. What are mutagenic agents? What is their mode of action?
7. What is the common feature of genetic changes arising from transduction, transformation, and conjugation?
8. Why are microorganisms especially suitable subjects for genetic research?
9. Despite the fact that microbial mutations may occur with considerable frequency (e.g., five or 10 cells in a test tube culture containing a population of 10 billion), the characteristics of most species are remarkably constant. Explain.
10. Describe how the fluctuation test can be used to demonstrate that the presence of an antibiotic is not the factor that causes the appearance of antibiotic-resistant bacterial forms.
11. What is the *genetic code?*
12. What is the chemical basis of mutation?
13. What is meant by *transcription* and *translation* as applied to protein synthesis?

SUPPLEMENTARY READING

Lederberg in 1951 assembled 20 important papers published between 1936 and 1950 and reprinted them, with an introductory discussion, in a single very useful volume. Two years later Braun published the first edition of his valuable *Bacterial Genetics;* the second edition appeared in 1965. The textbooks by Stanier et al., Lamanna and Mallette, and Oginsky and Umbreit contain short but recent discussions that reveal how rapidly the field of microbial genetics is growing. The importance of microorganisms, including bacteria, yeasts, molds, and viruses, as tools in the study of genetics per se is obvious in the little volume, *An Outline of Chemical Genetics,* by Strauss. The fifth volume of the well known series, *The Bacteria: A Treatise on Structure and Function,* contains 10 excellent chapters by authorities in the various phases of genetics. Hayes's book starts with classic genetics as a basis for discussing the current molecular biologic approach. Finally, Adelberg and Pittard review the phenomena associated with chromosome transfer by bacterial conjugation.

Adelberg, E. A., and Pittard, J.: Chromosome Transfer in Bacterial Conjugation. *Bact. Rev., 29:*161–172, 1965.

Braun, W.: *Bacterial Genetics,* 2d ed., Philadelphia, W. B. Saunders Co., 1965.

Gunsalus, I. C., and Stanier, R. Y. (Eds.): *The Bacteria: A Treatise on Structure and Function,* Vol. V. New York, Academic Press, Inc., 1964.

Hayes, W.: *The Genetics of Bacteria and Their Viruses.* New York, John Wiley & Sons, Inc., 1964.

Lamanna, C., and Mallette, M. F.: *Basic Bacteriology,* 3d ed. Baltimore, The Williams & Wilkins Co., 1965.

Lederberg, J. (Ed.): *Microbial Genetics.* Madison, Wisc., University of Wisconsin Press, 1951.

Oginsky, E. L., and Umbreit, W. W.: *An Introduction to Bacterial Physiology,* 2d ed. San Francisco, W. H. Freeman & Company, 1959.

Stanier, R. Y., Doudoroff, M., and Adelberg, E. A.: *The Microbial World,* 2d ed. Englewood Cliffs, N. J., Prentice-Hall, Inc., 1963.

Strauss, B. S.: *An Outline of Chemical Genetics.* Philadelphia, W. B. Saunders Co., 1960.

III

APPLIED MICROBIOLOGY

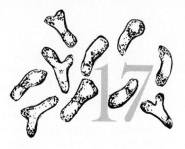

MICROORGANISMS
IN THEIR
NATURAL HABITATS

NATURAL HABITATS

The natural habitat of early microorganisms was undoubtedly aquatic. Some of the descendants of these organisms became adapted to terrestrial life; that is, they gradually acquired the ability to secure moisture and nutrients from comparatively dry soil particles.

Soil, Water, and Air

Soil and water are today the principal habitats of microorganisms. Most microorganisms in soil are found in a thin layer within a few feet of the surface. Microorganisms in bodies of water such as lakes or oceans are concentrated at the surface and at the very bottom, in the few inches just above the mud. Air is a reservoir of microorganisms, but little if any multiplication occurs here, as it does in soil and water. Airborne microorganisms are accidental wanderers blown from the soil or water; powerful updrafts sometimes carry them to heights of 20,000 feet or more.

Conditions for Survival and Growth of Microorganisms. Certain conditions must be met if an environment is to serve as a habitat or a reservoir for living organisms. Growth depends on adequate supplies of water and food materials, proper pH, suitable oxygen tension, moderate temperature, and other factors. Requirements for survival are not as rigid as those for growth. Some organisms can resist severe desiccation; nutrients may be in very short supply, and temperatures may vary more widely. It is obvious that some organisms will survive better than others; spore-forming bacteria and cocci are particularly well adapted for survival under adverse conditions.

The size and nature of the population in a given habitat depend on and are limited by these various factors. A body of water containing little organic matter can support only a limited microbial population, even though all other conditions are favorable. Another body of water with a higher concentration of organic matter can support a higher population, but there may be too little dissolved oxygen to permit growth of aerobic organisms. Soil often provides abundant food supplies but may be too dry to permit extensive microbial multiplication. Air lacks moisture and nutrients and is an extremely poor culture medium.

Ecology

The study of the effects of environment on the distribution and growth of organisms is known as *ecology*. It is fundamentally the application of physiology to populations. The student should have little difficulty in applying physiologic principles to situations encountered daily in which microorganisms play a part.

METHODS OF STUDYING ENVIRONMENTAL MICROORGANISMS

Direct Microscopic Examination

Direct microscopic examination indicates the morphologic types of organisms in a given location but provides no accurate information concerning their number.

A survey of soil microorganisms can be made by burying glass slides for an appropriate period, carefully removing them from the soil and staining (i.e., by the Cholodny method). Bacteria that stick to the slides are classified according to their general morphology; many fungi, algae, and protozoa can be identified completely.

Microscope slides immersed in lakes or oceans are used to collect bacteria and other microorganisms that attach to solid surfaces. Algae and protozoa are routinely identified by direct examination of a drop of water on a microscope slide, but frequently the specimen must be concentrated by filtration (e.g., through sand, paper, or fine cloth).

Airborne plant pollen and mold spores and other microorganisms are collected on slides coated with glycerin. This technique was used many years ago in airplanes to determine the types of bacteria at high altitudes.

Cultivation

Cultural methods are used to count and identify bacteria. The plate count is the most common procedure. The number and kinds of bacteria counted by this method depend on the composition of the culture medium and the incubation conditions. Autotrophic bacteria, for example, will not grow on media containing organic matter, nor will heterotrophic bacteria grow on completely inorganic media. Oxygen supply, temperature, pH, and other factors also affect the ability of bacteria to produce colonies. Numerous media have been devised for estimating bacterial populations in soil, water, and air, but no single medium or set of cultural conditions provides an accurate total bacterial count.

The foregoing limitation of plate counts can sometimes be used to advantage. Certain specific groups of bacteria can be counted in mixed natural populations by judicious selection of media and cultural conditions. For example, bacteria that attack urea are counted on a simple medium containing only this compound and appropriate minerals, and in which urea provides the sole source of carbon, nitrogen, and energy.

Certain types of bacteria cannot be counted satisfactorily on solid culture media, but an indication of their density in a mixed population can be obtained by the dilution count in suitable liquid media. This method is appropriate for estimating the number of organisms that ferment lactose, reduce nitrates, digest cellulose, produce hydrogen sulfide, and so forth. It is also used to determine the number of algae, protozoa, and certain other microorganisms in soil and water.

Chemical Analyses

The results of the physiologic activities of certain groups of organisms can sometimes be assayed by chemical analysis. The activity of nitrate-reducing bacteria in sewage, for example, is indicated by quantitative determination of nitrites and ammonia. Conversely, the action of soil bacteria that oxidize ammonia or nitrites is demonstrated by analyses for nitrite and nitrate. Chemical analyses do not reveal the actual number of bacteria but do indicate their total activity, which is often of more importance.

MICROORGANISMS IN SOIL, WATER, AND AIR

The Biosphere

Those regions of the Earth that support or contain life include the up-per few feet of soil, bodies of water, and the lower part of the atmosphere. Microorganisms from each habitat are found in both of the others, but their persistence is subject to the limitations on growth and survival previously mentioned. Certain organisms therefore predominate in the soil, others in water, and some in air.

Microorganisms of the Soil

The numbers and kinds of microorganisms in soil depend upon its fertility, acidity, moisture content, and other factors. There is no way to determine precisely how many microorganisms a gram of soil contains, and quoted figures are always estimates. Soil populations are often expressed as ranges. Table 17-1 indicates very roughly the relative abundance of various microorganisms per gram of surface soil. Microbial counts decrease markedly at greater depths.

Plate counts of soil bacteria and molds are much lower than microscopic counts. There are two major reasons for the great difference noted in Table 17-1: (1) the plating media permit growth of only a small segment of the mixed flora, and (2) many dead organisms are detectable with the microscope.

Table 17-1. Relative Abundance of Microorganisms in Surface Soil

Group	Method	Microorganisms Per Gram	
Bacteria	Microscopic count	1,000,000,000–	22,000,000,000
	Plate count	100,000–	100,000,000
Actinomycetes	Plate count	500,000–	14,000,000
Molds	Microscopic count (mycelium pieces)	3,000,000–	50,000,000
	Plate count (mycelium pieces and spores)	30,000–	1,000,000
Algae	Dilution count	10,000–	30,000
Protozoa	Dilution count		
Ciliates		50–	200
Flagellates		1,000–	10,000
Amebae		500–	2,000

Soil Bacteria. Bacteria are the most abundant microorganisms of the soil. Soil bacteria are of many types and physiologic activities: aerobic, facultative, and anaerobic; autotrophic and heterotrophic; carbohydrate- and protein-decomposing.

Of the 10 orders listed in *Bergey's Manual of Determinative Bacteriology,* the majority of soil bacteria are found in three: Pseudomonadales, Eubacteriales, and Actinomycetales. The principal member of the Pseudomonadales is the genus *Pseudomonas:* gram-negative, short, nonspore-forming rods, frequently producing green or blue fluorescent, water-soluble pigments. Eubacteriales includes the gram-negative, short, nonspore-forming, unpigmented rods of the genera, *Rhizobium* (associated with the roots of legumes), *Agrobacterium, Achromobacter;* the pigmented forms *Chromobacterium* (violet) and *Flavobacterium* (yellow to orange); cocci of the genera *Micrococcus* (irregular groups) and *Sarcina* (cubical packets); gram-positive, nonspore-forming rods of the genera *Corynebacterium* and *Arthrobacter;* and the gram-positive, spore-formers, *Bacillus* and *Clostridium.* Actinomycetales is represented by members of the genus *Streptomyces,* which produce filamentous, often hard and chalky colonies on media used to cultivate other bacteria and frequently give off an odor resembling that of decaying leaves (Fig. 17-1).

These organisms are particularly abundant in forest soil or other soil containing large amounts of organic matter, and are active in its decomposition.

Molds in Soil. There is no good method of determining the amount of mold in a specimen. Fragments of mycelium appear in microscopic preparations, and fragments and spores give rise to colonies upon agar media. The total mass of mycelium appears to make up an appreciable proportion of the soil microflora.

Molds actively decompose cellulose, plant and animal proteins, and other complex organic substances. The carbon and nitrogen of these substances therefore become available to other microbial life and eventually to plants.

Algae in Soil. Algae carry on photosynthesis at or near the soil surface and in so doing accumulate organic matter and energy. Their activity may temporarily decrease fertility because they need nitrogen and compete for this element with higher plants. However, the utilization of soluble nitrogen compounds may prevent the loss of these substances from the soil by leaching, and the nitrogen incorporated in algal protoplasm is gradually returned as dead algae decompose. The net result is beneficial.

Soil Protozoa. Protozoa are the most numerous animal forms in soil, and, by virtue of their relatively large size,

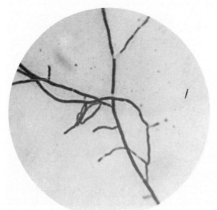

Figure 17-1. A branching, filamentous soil actinomycete (approx. 1000X).

they occupy a considerable percentage of its mass. Many protozoa, especially ciliates and amebae, ingest bacteria; some species feed solely on bacteria. Other species are saprophytic and utilize decaying organic matter. Destruction of soil protozoa is usually followed by a marked increase in bacterial population. It might be anticipated that the apparent battle between protozoa and bacteria is an important factor in soil fertility, but this does not seem to be the case. It has even been proposed that destruction of bacteria by protozoa permits more active and extensive multiplication and metabolism of the remaining bacteria, with the result that decomposition proceeds more rapidly. In general, protozoa appear to exert little direct effect on microbial processes within the soil.

Microorganisms in the Rhizosphere. The immediate vicinity of plant roots —*the rhizosphere*—is a region of great microbial activity and hence of large numbers of organisms. Bacteria appear to be most greatly stimulated in this area, and counts of a billion or more per gram are common. Gram-negative rods of the genera *Pseudomonas, Achromobacter,* and *Agrobacterium* are especially abundant, and there is also a marked increase in anaerobes, doubtless due to the utilization of soil oxygen and the formation of carbon dioxide by other organisms. Fungi and algae do not increase greatly, but small flagellate or ciliate protozoa are found in the water films on root hairs and plant epidermis.

The relationship between microorganisms and plants is often mutually beneficial. The roots excrete amino acids, simple sugars and nucleic acid derivatives, which are used as nutrients by bacteria. Some bacteria in turn produce plant stimulants known as auxins, such as indoleacetic acid. It has also been found that a flourishing rhizosphere microbial population provides a "buffer zone" in which many plant pathogens are suppressed, perhaps in part by antibiotics formed by the normal population.

Microorganisms of Water

Some microorganisms are indigenous to water; many gain access to it from the soil, air, or animals.

Rain Water. Rain water is practically free from microorganisms except during the early period of a storm, when it washes floating microorganisms from the air. Its flora is therefore that of the air, and usually includes soil organisms blown upward by the wind: bacteria and cysts or spores of protozoa, algae, and fungi. The number of these organisms during the first part of a storm is rarely more than a few score per milliliter.

Surface Water. Rain water that has collected in pools, brooks, and rivers is surface water. It contains many microorganisms derived from the soil. Bacterial counts may be as high as several hundred thousand per milliliter, depending on the extent of soil contamination. Rivers and streams are frequently contaminated by sewage, which greatly increases the number of bacteria. Algae, fungi, and a few protozoa are present in most surface waters.

Stored Water. Stored water is that in reservoirs, ponds, and lakes. Bacterial counts are usually no more than a few hundred per milliliter. The gradual settling of microorganisms tends to reduce the population in the main part of a large body of water. Many algae and protozoa are often present, particularly during warm seasons when the surface water temperature is high.

Ground Water. Ground water is subterranean water that has been filtered through successive layers of soil. It appears in springs and wells. Water from springs and deep wells is usually nearly sterile; bacterial counts range from zero to a score or so per milliliter. Chromogenic (pigment-producing) bacteria are prominent. Ground water is usually free from other microorganisms, which are larger and more effectively removed by filtration through the soil.

Kinds and Number of Microorganisms in Water. Bacteria found in water include organisms of the *Pseudomonas* *fluorescens* type and other chromogenic (violet, red, yellow) rods, coliform bacteria (organisms that resemble *Escherichia coli*), *Proteus* species, sporeformers, and cocci (white, yellow, pink). The significance of coliform bacteria is discussed in considerable detail on page 328.

The number of microorganisms in water depends on the initial contamination and the ability of the organisms to survive or to multiply. Multiplication is a function of food supply, oxygen, pH, temperature, and other factors. Food supply is determined by the surrounding terrain (e.g., gravel vs. rich, agricultural loam) and by waste materials introduced by man. Water containing organic matter supports a more luxuriant microbial population than pure water.

Microbial, Plant, and Animal Cycles. The interrelationships of microbial and higher organisms are illustrated diagrammatically in Figure 17-2. Algae flourish in bodies of water when the surface layers are warmed by the summer sun. They constitute the principal food for many fish, but in a hot season algae multiply faster than fish can eat them. The excess die and are decomposed by bacteria; this frequently causes the liberation of unpleasant odors. Bacteria in turn are succeeded by protozoa, and their death again provides food for bacteria.

Microorganisms of Air

Most microorganisms in the air are in a state of suspended animation. Many are soon killed by desiccation, starvation, ultraviolet irradiation, or other unfavorable conditions. Living airborne organisms are either unusually resistant or else have been in the air only a short time. Resistant forms may be capable of producing spores or cysts; some are spherical (spherical cells offer the least surface area and appear to

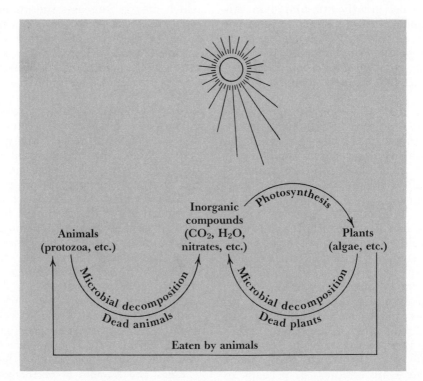

Figure 17-2. Plant, animal, and microbial cycles.

resist harmful agents better than cells of other shapes); and some resistant organisms possess pigments that protect against injurious radiations.

Sources of Airborne Microorganisms. Extramural (i.e., outdoor) microorganisms are derived from the soil and from bodies of water. Soil organisms on dust particles are carried into the atmosphere by the wind and rising currents of warm air; aquatic organisms enter the atmosphere in water droplets through the combined action of waves and wind.

Bacteria and fungi predominate in outdoor air. Terrestrial bacteria that survive in the air include gram-positive rods, spore-formers, and cocci. Marine bacteria found in air are principally gram-negative rods; fewer than half are spore-forming bacteria. Species of *Vibrio* or *Spirillum* have not been found, although they constitute 2 to 3 per cent of the bacterial flora of the oceans. Mold spores are always of terrestrial origin. Tremendous numbers are sometimes encountered as "clouds" or "storms," and they may travel thousands of miles from their point of origin. Spores or cysts of yeasts, algae, and protozoa are also present in the air. Some extramural microorganisms are important causes of plant disease (e.g., wheat rust).

Intramural microorganisms include not only the outdoor organisms characteristic of a geographic location but also those of man and the other inhabitants of the area. Man, for example, expels large numbers of microorganisms in saliva and mucus droplets when sneezing or—to a lesser extent—when coughing or even talking. Human pathogens are frequently found indoors, where ready access to susceptible hosts permits successful transfer despite their limited survival powers. Few if any human pathogens are transmitted long distances out-of-doors.

Number of Airborne Microorganisms. The number of microorganisms in the air is difficult to determine with accuracy. Simple comparisons are made by gravity plates: a nutrient medium in Petri dishes is exposed to the air for a definite period (e.g., 15 or 60 minutes), and the colonies that develop after incubation are counted.

Various devices are used to sample a definite volume of air: the air is drawn through moist sand or cotton or bubbled through sterile water; plate counts are then made of the entrapped organisms. Such methods rarely recover 100 per cent of the air flora. Cellulose acetate membrane filters have also been used for counting air bacteria. A known volume of air is drawn through the filter, and the filter is placed in a Petri dish on an absorbent pad moistened with a nutrient broth; visible colonies appear after short incubation.

BIOLOGIC INTERRELATIONSHIPS OF MICROORGANISMS

Microorganisms in their natural habitats are almost always associated with other kinds of microorganisms. The association is sometimes beneficial to both, sometimes beneficial to one and innocuous to the other, sometimes harmful to one kind. Associated growth of two organisms was earlier designated *symbiosis* (page 140).

The interrelationship between organisms in any environmental situation in which physiologic activity is possible is always dynamic. It is obvious by now that for each kind of microorganism there is a set of conditions that is essential for optimal growth, and any departure from these conditions adversely affects growth to a greater or lesser degree. It is equally apparent that microbial activity changes the environment: the atmospheric oxygen and carbon dioxide content increases or decreases; acids, alcohols, ammonia (NH_3), amino acids, sugars, and toxic peptides accumulate; the pH and oxidation-reduction potential rise or fall. These changes, together with climatic and other physical conditions, determine the population balance in any given ecologic niche. The situation in soil or sewage may become very complicated.

Mutualism

Mutualism is the ecologic relationship between two organisms, each of which benefits from the partnership. A favorite example is the association between *Rhizobium* species and legume plants: the plant provides nutrients and a source of energy, while the bacteria convert atmospheric nitrogen (N_2) into a combined form that becomes available to the plant. This is discussed in greater detail on page 320.

Commensalism

Commensalism is an association in which one species benefits while the second species is neither benefited nor harmed. Many microorganisms, such as the nitrogen-fixing bacterium, *Azotobacter,* cannot utilize cellulose directly as source of carbon or energy but multiply luxuriantly in soil containing fungi or bacterial species that digest cellulose. The extracellular hydrolytic reaction yields simple sugar molecules, some of which diffuse into the cells of organisms that cannot attack the complex carbohydrate. Both groups of organisms can multiply, and the cellulose-digesting forms are unharmed. This type of relationship is very common in soil.

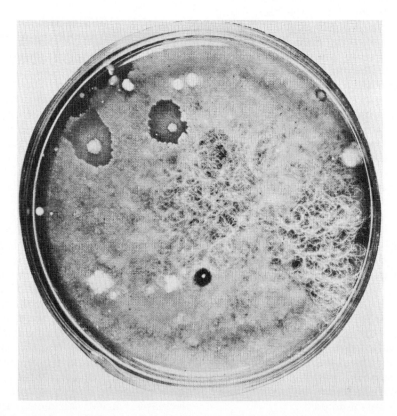

Figure 17-3.   Antibiosis. The agar in this Petri dish is covered with bacterial growth, principally of the *Bacillus mycoides* type. Several colonies of other kinds of bacteria have inhibited the spreading organism by producing antagonistic substances, which diffuse a considerable distance through the agar. (From Grant: Microbiology and Human Progress. New York, Rinehart & Co., Inc., 1953.)

Antibiosis

Many microorganisms are frankly harmful to other organisms. This phenomenon is generally called *antibiosis* (Fig. 17-3). Antibiotic action is caused by excretion of toxic waste products, such as acids and alcohols and the more complex chemicals designated as specific *antibiotics*. Waksman defines an antibiotic as a microbial product that inhibits or kills *certain* other microorganisms. This definition excludes acids and alcohols, which are nonspecifically inhibitory; it also excludes chemicals produced by higher plants. Antibiotic activity in the broad sense is general throughout natural habitats and undoubtedly helps to limit microbial populations.

Parasitism. Parasitism is a form of antagonistic activity that depends on the feeding habits rather than the toxic wastes of the antagonist. The parasite benefits at the expense of the host, whereas an organism producing antibiotic chemicals derives no direct benefit from so doing. Most microorganisms excrete substances that inhibit other microorganisms, and many produce chemicals that qualify as antibiotics. It should be noted that the majority of these are also toxic for human or animal cells.

Synergism

Synergism is a mutual relationship between microorganisms that is sometimes of interest to man but has little effect upon the organisms. Two organisms together may produce a reaction which neither can perform alone. Neither *Staphylococcus aureus* nor *Proteus vulgaris* alone can produce gas when growing in lactose broth, but a mixture of the two bacteria is able to do so. *S. aureus* hydrolyzes lactose extracellularly and *P. vulgaris* ferments the monosaccharides produced. Numerous other combinations of bacteria produce a similar result. Some diseases of man are said to be caused synergistically: Vincent's angina (trench mouth) is believed to be produced by a spirochete and a long, tapering fusiform organism, whereas neither the spirochete nor the fusiform rod alone produces disease.

BIOCHEMICAL ACTIVITIES OF MICROORGANISMS IN SOIL AND WATER

Transformation of Matter

Plants and animals differ principally with respect to their ability to utilize inorganic matter. Plants require only inorganic nutrients, whereas most animal food is in the organic form. It is possible for plant and animal life to coexist in a closed system to which nothing is added except the energy of light. Most students have at some time seen an aquarium so balanced that it could be completely sealed and still support animal and plant life. The Earth is essentially a system of this sort. Cyclic transformations of matter obviously must occur, both in the balanced aquarium and on Earth.

The Cycles of Life

The Earth may be considered a storehouse or reservoir of the chemical elements that make up living organisms. Fundamental to life is the process of photosynthesis, by which energy from the sun is converted into chemical bond energy as carbon dioxide is reduced. Stored in carbohydrates, this energy is released gradually during respiration, either by plants in the dark or by animals or microorganisms. The carbon is oxidized to carbon dioxide (CO_2) and again becomes available for photosynthetic reduction (see Fig. 17-2).

Free nitrogen makes up four-fifths of the atmosphere, but few plants can utilize it. Most plants require nitrogen in the nitrate form; a few secure it from some other inorganic compound. Sulfur is assimilated as sulfates. Both nitrates and sulfates are reduced by the plant. In this process, they are built into protoplasm, appearing as amino (—NH$_2$), sulfhydryl (—SH), and other radicals of organic compounds. They return to the inorganic state during decomposition of the plants or animals that eat them. Phosphates are not reduced but combine directly by esterification and produce organic phosphates; the phosphate radical is subsequently liberated intact during decomposition.

Microorganisms play vital roles in the transformation of carbon, nitrogen, and sulfur. The cycles of these elements in nature will therefore be discussed in some detail. In each it will be noted that there are two principal phases: (1) *immobilization* of elements by the formation of organic substances, and (2) *mineralization* or return of the elements to the inorganic form.

The Carbon Cycle

The main outlines of the carbon cycle are familiar: photosynthetic reduction of atmospheric CO$_2$ by plants, assimilation of plants by animals, and release of CO$_2$ by animal and plant respiration. If this were all there was to the cycle it would soon come to a halt, because some important plant constituents cannot be digested by animals, nor can animals return all their carbon to CO$_2$ by respiration.

Role of Microorganisms. Microorganisms play the essential role of scavengers, digesting the residues of plant and animal materials. Dissimilation and fermentation (see page 215) yield acids, alcohols, and other intermediate waste products; respiration oxidizes these to CO$_2$ (Fig. 17-4). Microbial transformations of carbon are carried out largely in the soil but also occur in water and in any other situation where organic matter decomposes. Under anaerobic conditions (e.g., some sewage disposal processes) methane (CH$_4$) is formed.

Energy Transformations. Plants and animals are placed at the top of the

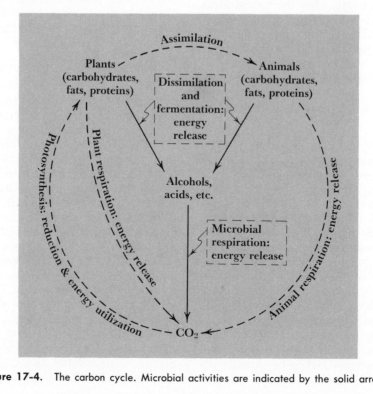

Figure 17-4. The carbon cycle. Microbial activities are indicated by the solid arrows.

carbon cycle in Figure 17-4 to indicate that they represent the highest form of organization of carbon compounds; CO_2, the simplest carbon compound, is at the bottom of the cycle. The carbon cycle is essentially a cycle of energy changes. Energy is acquired in the transformation from CO_2 to plant material. The dissimilation and respiration processes by which plant and animal substances are reconverted to CO_2 are energy-yielding reactions.

Microorganisms must not be considered external agents in this cycle or in any of the cycles; the cycles should actually be drawn to indicate incorporation of carbon and other elements within the microbial cells as protoplasmic constituents and their subsequent release by dissimilation and respiration. There are therefore cycles within cycles, but it is simplest to present the over-all picture, as in Figure 17-4.

The Nitrogen Cycle

The nitrogen cycle looks more complicated than the carbon cycle, but this is because it is easier to represent some of the intermediate stages in a diagram (Fig. 17-5).

The nitrates assimilated by plants are reduced, and most of the nitrogen in protoplasm is in the amino radicals of protein molecules. Plant proteins, when eaten by animals, are converted principally into animal proteins. Animal metabolism yields excretions containing nitrogenous compounds, such as urea or uric acid, from which the nitrogen is set free as ammonia by appropriate organisms. These excretions, however, account for only a small proportion of the nitrogen within the animal body.

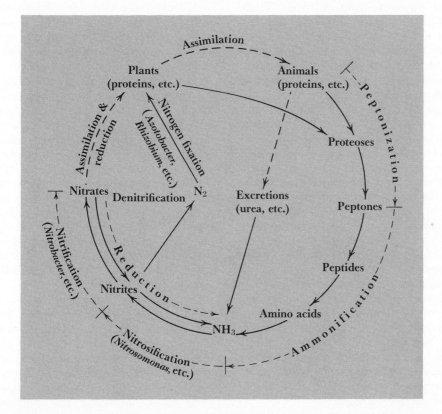

Figure 17-5. The nitrogen cycle. Microbial activities are indicated by the solid arrows.

Peptonization and Ammonification. The nitrogen of dead animal and plant tissues returns to the inorganic state by hydrolytic decomposition through the familiar stages—proteoses, peptones, peptides, amino acids—and deamination of amino acids, which releases ammonia. The early steps in hydrolysis are called *peptonization.* Many, but not all, microorganisms can attack native proteins. This hydrolysis is usually performed extracellularly, and other microorganisms may utilize the proteoses or peptones and cause *ammonification.* Ammonification converts the nitrogen of organic compounds to its most reduced form and is logically indicated at the bottom of the cycle.

Oxidation of Ammonia. It would seem appropriate for nature to have provided a mechanism whereby plants could assimilate ammonia directly but, as mentioned previously, most plants secure nitrogen from nitrates. There are, however, a few bacteria that can perform the necessary oxidations, but no one species oxidizes ammonia completely to nitrate. The first step, *nitrosification,* is the oxidation of ammonia to nitrous acid or nitrite. This is accomplished by species of *Nitrosomonas.* The second step is *nitrification,* the oxidation of nitrite to nitrate by *Nitrobacter* species. These and a few related species are apparently the only microorganisms that can convert ammonia into the form plants utilize. Destruction of either the *Nitrosomonas* or *Nitrobacter* type of organism quickly causes serious loss of soil fertility. Fortunately these bacteria are widely distributed.

Reduction. Nitrates that are not promptly assimilated by plants are likely to be lost, either by leaching or by reduction. It was mentioned on page 208 that many microorganisms utilize nitrate as a hydrogen acceptor in the course of anaerobic respiration. Reduction of nitrate yields nitrite, ammonia, or free nitrogen.

Nitrate reduction provides an important route of microbial assimilation of inorganic nitrogen. Ammonia formed intracellularly can react with organic acids derived from carbohydrate dissimilation to produce amino acids, from which cellular proteins may be built. *Denitrification* can be considered a special form of nitrate reduction or respiration in which the end product is gaseous N_2. This is given off to the atmosphere and constitutes a leak in the nitrogen cycle.

From the viewpoint of soil fertility, denitrification is definitely harmful, whereas nitrate respiration with the liberation of nitrite or ammonia may be harmful. Nitrite is toxic to some plants, and ammonia is not assimilated by many plants as readily as is nitrate. Microbial assimilation of nitrogen temporarily reduces fertility, but the nitrogen, in combined form, is still present in the soil and eventually becomes available for plant growth.

Nitrate reduction, including denitrification, is particularly apt to occur under anaerobic conditions, for example, in swampy or water-logged soil.

Nitrogen Fixation. The inability of higher plants and animals to utilize atmospheric nitrogen would be a catastrophe were it not for the fact that a few bacteria and blue-green algae can do so, because only a limited amount of nitrogen is converted into combined form by lightning and other natural means. Artificial methods of nitrogen fixation are expensive. The few organisms that perform biologic nitrogen fixation help to maintain a balanced condition in the soil and make up for loss of nitrogen by denitrification. Bacterial nitrogen fixation is classified as *nonsymbiotic* or *symbiotic.*

Mechanism. Biologic nitrogen fixation appears to consist essentially in the reduction of free nitrogen to ammonia. Glutamic acid may then be formed, and from it other amino acids are produced. Several mechanisms for producing ammonia have been proposed (Fig. 17-6), including the suggestion that nitrogen fixation is actually a form

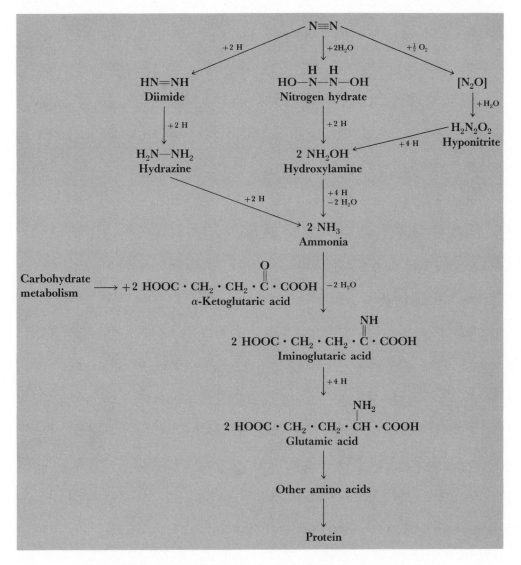

Figure 17-6. Three postulated mechanisms of biologic nitrogen fixation.

of respiration demonstrable under laboratory conditions by a large group of organisms. Whether the same situation applies in the soil has not been determined.

Nonsymbiotic Nitrogen Fixation. Nonsymbiotic nitrogen fixation is brought about by *Azotobacter* species, *Clostridium pasteurianum* and possibly other species of the same genus, and by a few other bacteria. These organisms grow independently in the soil; that is, they are not necessarily associated with other living organisms. They derive their energy and their carbon and other elements from the soil and secure nitrogen from the soil atmosphere in the absence of adequate combined nitrogen.

Azotobacter species are aerobic and grow and fix nitrogen in soils of nearly neutral reaction. *Cl. pasteurianum* fixes nitrogen anaerobically but can grow under somewhat more acid conditions. Nonsymbiotic nitrogen fixation adds as much as 40 pounds of nitrogen per year to an acre of soil; 5 to 10 pounds per acre per year is an average figure. The effectiveness of the nonsymbiotic bacteria varies with soil conditions; little fixation occurs if an adequate supply of combined nitrogen is already present.

Symbiotic Nitrogen Fixation: The Rhizobia. Symbiotic nitrogen fixation is brought about by species of *Rhizobium*. The rhizobia are called the *root nodule bacteria* because they "infect" the roots of legumes and produce nodules or tubercles containing millions of the bacterial cells (Fig. 17-7). Physiologic as well as physical communication between the nodules and the roots permits exchange of materials. The bacteria secure energy-yielding compounds, carbon compounds and other nutrients from the vascular system of the plant but take much of their nitrogen from the soil atmosphere. The bacterial nitrogen eventually becomes available to the root system of the plant. This mutually beneficial arrangement improves the growth of the plant,

especially on a soil that contains little combined nitrogen.

Legumes comprise one of the great groups of seed plants; they include such common plants as alfalfa, clover, peas, beans, and soybeans. Legumes contain more nitrogen than nonlegumes; alfalfa, for example, contains 300 to 350 pounds of protein per ton, whereas timothy contains only 115 to 150 pounds of protein per ton. Much of the nitrogen in alfalfa protein can be derived from the atmosphere through the action of root nodule bacteria. Legumes can therefore be grown in soil that would not support nonlegumes. Moreover, if the entire legume crop is plowed into the soil the nitrogen content of the soil increases markedly. Even if only the roots are left, fertility is not depleted as much as by comparable harvesting of a nonlegume.

The rhizobia produce bizarre, irregular forms known as *bacteroids* when growing in root nodules, but when transferred to appropriate culture media in the laboratory they appear as small, nonspore-forming rod bacteria (Fig. 17-8). Species are differentiated mainly according to the legumes they can infect. *Rhizobium meliloti*, for example, infects and produces nodules upon alfalfa, sweet clover, and bur clover. *R. leguminosarum* produces nodules upon the garden pea, field pea, sweet pea, vetch, broadbean, and lentil. The species of plants upon which the same species of *Rhizobium* fixes nitrogen are called *bacterial-plant groups* or *cross-inoculation groups*. There are more than a score of bacterial-plant groups.

Root nodule bacteria are reasonably well distributed in soil all over the Earth, but often not enough are present to ensure complete nodulation of all susceptible plants. The number of rhizobia decreases during periods of drought, unfavorable temperatures, and acidity, and as a result of the activity of bacteriophage and other antagonistic microorganisms. Moreover, effective nodulation occurs only when species

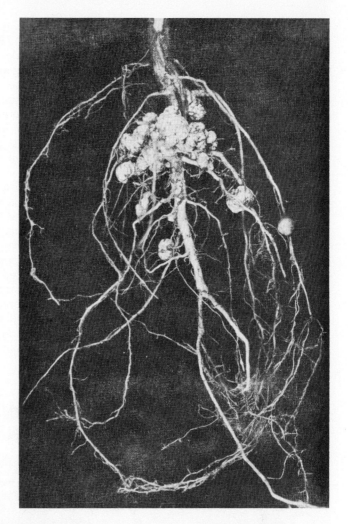

Figure 17-7. Nodules on the roots of a soybean plant. These are filled with *Rhizobium japonicum,* which fixes nitrogen from the soil atmosphere. (From Grant: Microbiology and Human Progress. New York, Rinehart & Co., Inc., 1953.)

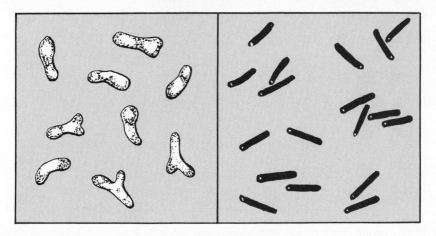

Figure 17-8. Bacteroids (*left*) and rod forms (*right*) of rhizobia. Bacteroids are found in smears from crushed nodules, rod forms in smears from agar slant cultures.

of *Rhizobium* of the proper bacterial-plant group are present, and these are not likely to be abundant in a soil upon which plants of another group have been raised for several years.

Inoculation of the seed is recommended to ensure an adequate number of bacteria for a given crop. A common practice is to mix the seed with the bacteria just before planting. After germination of the seed, the minute hairs covering the main root and its branches can be infected by rhizobia in the immediate vicinity, and the nodules that develop are the site of nitrogen fixation. Direct inoculation of the seed places the bacteria in the most advantageous position for infection.

Leguminous plants without nodules grow slowly in nitrogen-poor soils; their leaves turn yellow, and they may die of nitrogen starvation. Nodulated plants grow normally under the same condi-

tions and have a healthy green color (Fig. 17-9). Plants either with or without nodules grow normally in soils containing an abundance of nitrogenous foods. The beneficial effect of nodulation is particularly apparent in soils low in combined nitrogen. Not only is growth accelerated, particularly of the young plant, but the yield and protein content of the crop are also improved.

Symbiotic nitrogen fixation amounts to as much as 200 pounds per acre per year under favorable conditions; 50 to 100 pounds is an average figure. The importance of the root nodule bacteria can be appreciated more easily when it is realized that this amount of nitrogen is contained in 500 to 1000 pounds of commercial fertilizer containing 10 per cent nitrogen.

The beneficial effects of leguminous plants upon soil fertility have been

Figure 17-9. Growth of a legume in nitrogen-poor soil; *left*, without root nodule bacteria; *right*, with root nodule bacteria. (From Fred, Baldwin and McCoy: Root Nodule Bacteria and Leguminous Plants. Madison, University of Wisconsin Press, 1932.)

known for at least 2000 years. Vergil described crop rotation as practiced in ancient Rome; a nonlegume was grown one year, alfalfa was grown the next year, and the same field was allowed to remain uncultivated the third year. Similar procedures in use today not only help to maintain the nitrogen content of the soil but also improve its texture and moisture-holding capacity.

Nonrhizobial Symbiotic Nitrogen Fixation. A number of nonleguminous plants possess nodules containing nitrogen-fixing microorganisms on their roots. Among them are species of *Alnus,* the alder tree; *Myrica gale,* the bog myrtle; species of *Eleagnus;* and various other trees and shrubs in all parts of the world, from tropical to arctic regions. Nodules of these plants do not contain rhizobia, nor do rhizobia infect the plants and produce nodules. In fact, the organisms within the nodules have not been isolated. It has been suggested that they are obligately dependent upon the host plant and hence cannot be cultivated *in vitro.* That the nodules are essential for nitrogen fixation has been demonstrated by inoculating plants grown aseptically in nitrogen-poor soil with crushed nodules from infected plants: nodulation and normal growth then occurred. Cytologic studies indicate that the microorganisms responsible for nitrogen fixation are either actinomycetes or slime molds.

Nitrogen Transformation in Sewage. Most of the steps in the nitrogen cycle take place in water as well as in soil. Sewage contains plant and animal proteins, which decompose and form ammonia and other reduced nitrogenous compounds. Accumulation of these substances under anaerobic conditions creates unpleasant odors; moreover, some of the products are toxic and cannot be discharged into streams, lakes, or other bodies of water without danger to fish. In sewage treatment plants where sufficient aeration is provided, ammonia is oxidized to the inoffensive nitrate stage. The effective-ness of the treatment can be measured by quantitative determinations of nitrate.

The Sulfur Cycle

Sulfur is an essential component of proteins and hence is required by all organisms. It is found in three amino acids, cysteine, cystine, and methionine. Plants assimilate sulfates and reduce the sulfur to sulfhydryl (—SH) or disulfide (—S:S—). The sulfur cycle (Fig. 17-10) resembles the nitrogen cycle.

Dissimilation. Dissimilation of either plant or animal proteins through the usual series of intermediate breakdown products yields amino acids. The sulfur of the three amino acids mentioned above is completely reduced and removed as hydrogen sulfide. Many species of heterotrophic saprophytes bring about these dissimilation steps.

Oxidation of Sulfide and Sulfur. Sulfide oxidation by various facultative autotrophs produces globules of sulfur, which accumulate within the cells of some species, outside the cells of others. The photosynthetic sulfur bacteria, members of the Thiorhodaceae and Chlorobacteriaceae, contain pigments similar to chlorophyll. Hydrogen sulfide (H_2S) serves as hydrogen donor in the photosynthetic process, and elemental sulfur is released. The nonphotosynthetic sulfur bacteria of the families Achromatiaceae and Beggiatoaceae also oxidize H_2S to free sulfur.

Sulfur must be oxidized to sulfate before it can be utilized by plants. This process is brought about by various strictly autotrophic bacteria, particularly species of *Thiobacillus, T. thioparus* and *T. thiooxidans.* Certain strains produce so much sulfuric acid that the reaction of the medium falls to less than pH 1.0.

Sulfate Reduction. A reversal in the sulfur cycle may also occur, just as it does in the nitrogen cycle. Various familiar bacteria, including species of *Clostridium, Proteus, Desulfovibrio,*

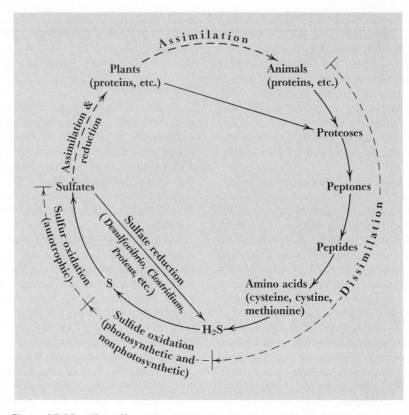

Figure 17-10. The sulfur cycle. Microbial activities are indicated by solid arrows.

and others, reduce sulfates to H_2S. Sulfate reduction is not as critical a matter as reduction of nitrate, because the supply of sulfate in soils is more nearly adequate.

Interrelationships of the Carbon, Nitrogen, and Sulfur Cycles

The student must not think of the carbon, nitrogen, and sulfur cycles as separate and independent series of processes. Rather, each is a simplified representation of a sequence of interrelated processes, and no cycle can operate in the absence of the others. In the carbon cycle attention is focused on the transformations of carbon, but nitrogen and sulfur transformations also occur at the same time. Similarly, transformations of sulfur and carbon accompany transformations of nitrogen, and so forth. Protein dissimilation

yields amino acids, and some of the same organisms set free ammonia (NH_3) and H_2S; moreover, part of the carbon of amino acids may be oxidized to CO_2. Soil conditions that favor oxidation of ammonia to nitrates also favor oxidation of H_2S to sulfates if appropriate bacteria are present, and conditions that favor nitrate reduction also favor sulfate reduction.

ROLES OF ENVIRONMENTAL MICROORGANISMS IN SANITATION

Microorganisms as Scavengers

Microbial decomposition of plant and animal remains prevents the accumulation of vast amounts of dead organic matter and permits the biologic transformations by which food supplies are continuously made available.

Microbial Antagonism. The antagonistic activity of various microorganisms in soil and water is directly related to human and animal health. Few human pathogens can be isolated from soil, even though it is undoubtedly often contaminated by these organisms. Polluted streams and other bodies of water gradually lose their pathogenic flora. Many soil microorganisms are capable of producing antagonistic or even antibiotic substances, and any specimen of soil is likely to contain organisms antagonistic to one another. Bacterial viruses that kill and lyse various bacteria, including pathogenic species, are frequently present in soil and water. These and other factors contribute to the brief survival of many kinds of pathogenic bacteria.

Sewage Disposal. Disposal of sewage in sparsely settled areas is usually no problem if a suitable stream or body of water is available into which it may be dumped. In contrast, industrialization and urbanization and the consequent crowding of millions of people into relatively small areas create serious problems of disposal of waste materials. The amount of domestic sewage is in the neighborhood of 100 gallons per person per day in most large cities of the United States.

Composition of Domestic Sewage. Domestic sewage consists of household wastes, often augmented by storm water, and is composed of 98.8 to 99.5 per cent water and 0.5 to 1.2 per cent solid matter, either large or small particles or colloidal or soluble substances. Colloidal and dissolved material are not removed by settling or by filtration. The solids of sewage contain carbohydrates, fats, proteins, and various salts. The reaction of sewage varies from pH 6.0 to pH 8.5. Little if any dissolved oxygen is present.

Domestic sewage contains between 500,000 and 20,000,000 microorganisms per milliliter. These are largely intestinal bacteria, but soil microorganisms are also abundant. Most of the microorganisms of sewage are nonpathogenic.

They include aerobic, facultative, and anaerobic types, both heterotrophic and autotrophic, and are principally mesophilic, but some psychrophiles and thermophiles are also present.

Industrial Wastes. Industrialization has created unusual problems of sewage disposal. Certain industries produce highly acid waste materials; others produce alkaline wastes; and some contribute troublesome chemicals, such as copper or silver salts, oils, or unusually large amounts of proteins, carbohydrates, or fats. A partial list of the types of industries will suggest the kinds of wastes that must be handled: meat packing, canning, brewing, dairy products manufacture, tanning of leather, manufacture of paper and textiles, oil refining, chemical manufacture.

Objectives of Sewage Treatment. The objectives of sewage treatment are (1) to remove or decompose organic matter capable of supporting microbial growth, and (2) to remove or destroy pathogenic microorganisms. Pathogens of many types gain access to sewage, but those likely to survive long enough to cause human infection are principally intestinal in origin: typhoid and paratyphoid, dysentery, and Asiatic cholera bacteria.

The percentage of organic matter in sewage seems so small as to be insignificant. However, it should be recalled that nutrient laboratory media containing less than one per cent organic matter support bacterial populations of a billion or more per milliliter. Sewage contains all the nutrients necessary to nourish many kinds of bacteria. Lack of oxygen means that the chemical activities of these bacteria are largely anaerobic; hence foul smelling compounds are produced. Part of the aim of sewage treatment is to eliminate these offensive odors.

Small amounts of sewage discharged into a stream or large body of water are diluted enough that aerobic conditions obtain. Soluble organic compounds are readily hydrolyzed and oxidized, and inoffensive products such as carbon dioxide, nitrates, and sulfates are formed. Complex compounds are hydrolyzed more slowly, but eventually the soluble products are also oxidized. Large amounts of sewage introduced into a body of water are not diluted sufficiently, and as a result conditions become highly anaerobic. Microbial respiration utilizes what little dissolved oxygen is present. Fish soon die, foul odors are produced, and the water is useless for drinking or for recreational purposes.

Sewage Purification Processes. Sewage is treated by chemical or biologic means to remove organic matter. Chemical treatment is more expensive but can be carried out in a smaller area. Suspended and colloidal matter is flocculated by the addition of alum or iron salts; the precipitate entrains and sediments much of the organic material. The supernatant liquid or *effluent* can then be discharged into a large body of water or onto porous soil, where microbial oxidation of the remaining dissolved organic matter can take place.

Biologic treatment of sewage is most widely used. Processes range from that of the household septic tank, which handles at most a few hundred gallons per day, to municipal plants, through which many million gallons pass each day (Fig. 17-11). Details of the purification procedures vary greatly, but a few steps are common to most processes.

1. Gross objects and large particles are removed from the sewage by *screening* and *sedimentation*. Slow passage of the liquid through a large tank or other chamber permits particles to settle; the accumulated solid matter is known as *sludge*. Some systems also provide facilities for removing the scum of grease.

2. The liquid from which settleable solids have been removed contains colloidal and soluble carbohydrates, proteins, and fats, which are subject to *microbial digestion*. The products of fermentation and putrefaction include ammonium salts of organic acids, alcohols, amines, amino acids, glycerin and other chemicals, and the gases H_2S, CH_4, CO_2, and H_2. Most of the gases are combustible and are used as a source of power in large sewage treatment plants.

3. *Oxidation* of the products of fermentation and putrefaction is promoted by aeration, either by bubbling air through the digested sewage in a tank, by spraying the fluid intermittently onto a bed of coarse stones (a *trickling*

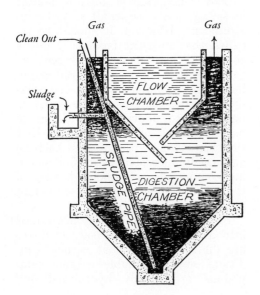

Figure 17-11. An Imhoff tank, in which partial purification of sewage is effected. The sewage passes slowly through the flow chamber (in a direction at a right angle to the page). Settleable solid matter falls through the bottom opening and collects in the digestion chamber, where anaerobic processes gradually convert part of it to soluble form and gases. The gases may be collected and burned for heat and power. The undigested "sludge" is removed periodically. (From D. B. Swingle and W. G. Walter: General Bacteriology, 2d ed. Princeton, N. J., D. Van Nostrand Company, Inc., 1947.)

Figure 17-12. A trickling filter. A large bed of stones over which partially treated sewage is sprayed by a rotating "sparger" (shown stopped in this picture). The stones are covered by a gelatinous film containing microorganisms, which oxidize soluble compounds as the sewage trickles slowly down to collecting drains at the bottom of the bed. (A, Courtesy of Dr. Gordon M. Fair, *in* Rosenau: Preventive Medicine and Hygiene, D. Appleton-Century Co.; B, courtesy of Communicable Disease Center, U. S. Public Health Service, Atlanta, Ga.)

filter; Fig. 17-12) over which it flows slowly in contact with air, or by distribution in drainage tiles through loose soil. The various organic compounds are oxidized by microorganisms, and the final products consist of CO_2 or carbonates, nitrates, and sulfates.

4. The *sludge* collected initially and also during subsequent stages is either removed periodically and dried for use as fertilizer, or it is allowed to digest, often as long as three months. The relatively indigestible residue or "stabilized" sludge that remains is dried and used as fertilizer.

5. The *effluent* liquid from the treatment plant contains no organic matter; it does contain dissolved oxygen and nitrates, sulfates, and phosphates. There are also as many as a few hundred thousand bacteria per milliliter. The treated sewage can be discharged directly into a large body of water without seriously affecting animal life, but the salts will stimulate growth of aquatic plants such as algae. Few pathogens remain alive, but to be safe chlorine is usually added at the rate of two to five parts per million parts of liquid.

Sanitary Quality of Drinking Water

Drinking water should be clear, cool, free from objectionable tastes and odors and from harmful chemicals and microorganisms. Of these desired qualities, freedom from harmful microorganisms is most difficult to achieve. It is not impossible, but it demands constant vigilance and repeated testing.

The problem is made more acute because sewage disposal is usually completed by discharging effluent liquid into bodies of water, and necessity often dictates that the same bodies of water be used as sources of drinking water by other communities. Many cities empty sewage into Lake Michigan, but Chicago has to take its water supply from the lake. Rivers receive sewage, and a short distance downstream are used as sources of drinking water. Although sedimentation removes most particulate material including bacteria from both standing water and running water, it cannot be relied on to free water from harmful microorganisms. Purification is therefore necessary and must be controlled by constant testing.

Bacteria That Indicate Pollution. The ideal method of testing water for microbiologic safety would be to search for pathogens transmitted by water. Unfortunately, this is impractical at present. Water containing only a very few pathogens in each liter may be sufficiently polluted to cause many cases of disease. If the discharges from a single person with typhoid fever find their way into a reservoir used for drinking water, scores or hundreds of cases of typhoid fever may follow. The pathogens are relatively few and far between, and large samples must be examined in order to detect a single disease-producing organism. Moreover, pathogenic species in water contaminated with sewage are vastly outnumbered by harmless, normal intestinal bacteria and are quickly outgrown in ordinary cultural methods of examination. The detection of pathogens in water or sewage, then, is virtually impossible; it has been accomplished only a few times.

Various groups of bacteria that normally occur in the intestine of man or animals have been used to indicate the pollution of drinking water by sewage: the so called fecal streptococci, certain spore-forming anaerobes, and the coliform bacteria. The coliform bacteria are the most widely accepted indicators of pollution, particularly in the United States.

The Coliform Bacteria. The coliform bacteria include *Escherichia coli* and certain other bacteria that resemble them morphologically and physiologically. These organisms frequently differ from one another in minor characteristics; at one time dozens of species were distinguished, but at present only six are recognized. Two are found with sufficient frequency to be mentioned: *E. coli* and *Aerobacter aerogenes.*

Coliform bacteria usually occur in the intestinal tract of man and animals. *E. coli* is rarely if ever found outside the intestines, except where pollution by human or animal excreta has occurred. *A. aerogenes* occurs on hay and grains and other vegetable matter, and from these sources it finds its way into milk and other dairy products and also into the digestive tract of man. It is therefore usually present in human feces, although often in fewer numbers than *E. coli.*

Coliform bacteria are short, gram-negative rods that ferment lactose, forming acid and gas. They are facultative anaerobes and multiply most rapidly between 30° and 37° C. They grow luxuriantly upon ordinary media such as nutrient broth and nutrient agar. *E. coli* can be distinguished from *A. aerogenes* by the appearance of its colonies on differential plating media. Colonies of *E. coli* on E.M.B. (eosin methylene blue) agar are 2 to 4 mm. in diameter, possess a large, dark or even black center, and have a green, metallic sheen when observed by reflected light. Colonies of *A. aerogenes* on the same medium are larger, very mucoid, and pinkish; they frequently have a small, brownish center.

Numerous other tests have been devised to distinguish the types of coliform bacteria. Four are so frequently used that their initials have been combined into the mnemonic *IMViC:* indole, methyl red (M.R.), Voges-Proskauer (V.P.), and citrate utilization. The indole test has already been described (page 112).

The M.R. and V.P. tests are performed on two to five day cultures in glucose-phosphate-peptone broth. A few drops of methyl red indicator added to some of the culture becomes red when the reaction is strongly acid; this result is called the positive test; a yellow color is the negative test.

The V.P. test is conducted by adding a small amount of 40 per cent KOH containing creatine to a portion of the glucose-phosphate-peptone culture, preferably with a catalyst such as alcoholic α-naphthol. The mixture is thoroughly shaken to aerate it and is then allowed to stand for 15 minutes. A positive test gives a pink color, which usually appears first at the top of the solution. This reaction is a test for acetylmethylcarbinol, which is oxidized to diacetyl under the conditions of test; diacetyl combines with the guanidine radical of creatine and produces a pink dye compound.

Utilization of citrate as a sole source of carbon is tested in a synthetic medium containing sodium citrate as the only carbon compound. Growth of the organism is the positive test. An acid-base indicator, which is sometimes added to the medium, assumes its alkaline color as the citrate radical is oxidized.

The IMViC reactions of a few coliform bacteria are listed in Table 17-2. The IMViC reaction of *E. coli*, + + − −, means that the organism produces indole and is M.R. positive and V.P. and citrate negative. There are 16 possible combinations of positive and negative tests of these four characteristics. Most of these combinations have been found, but the reactions of *E. coli* and *A. aerogenes* are by far the most frequently encountered. The remaining 14 types are usually designated "intermediates." All coliform bacteria are considered significant in water from the sanitary viewpoint, although some authors attempt to distinguish between the "fecal

Table 17-2. IMViC Reactions of Coliform Bacteria

Species	Indole	M.R.	V.P.	Citrate
Escherichia coli	+	+	−	−
Aerobacter aerogenes	−	−	+	+
"Intermediates"	−	+	−	+
	+	−	+	+
		etc.		

type" (*E. coli*) and the "nonfecal type" (*A. aerogenes*).

Sanitary Water Analysis. Detection of coliform bacteria in water samples is based on the ability of these organisms to produce gas from lactose. Aliquots (five portions of 10 ml. each) of the sample are inoculated into lactose fermentation tubes and incubated at 37° C. for 48 hours (Fig. 17-13). The tubes are observed after 24 and 48 hours, and the appearance of gas at either time constitutes a positive *presumptive test.*

Bacteria other than coliform organisms can produce gas in lactose; it is therefore necessary to isolate the lactose-fermenting species, and this is usually done by inoculating the surface of E.M.B. agar plates from one or more fermentation tubes containing gas. The appearance of typical coliform colonies is a positive *confirmed test.*

One or more colonies (typical, if present; otherwise any suspicious colonies) are then transferred to lactose fermentation tubes and nutrient agar slants and are incubated for 24 hours. If gas appears in the lactose tube and a Gram stain from the slant reveals gram-negative rods with no spores present, the result is designated a positive *completed test* for coliform bacteria.

Interpretation of the coliform test is arbitrary but is based upon experience. Each state or community in the United States may have its own requirements. The United States Public Health Service has established standards which are used as a guide by the various states or their subdivisions. The recommended standard requires essentially that acceptable water should contain, on the average, no more than one coliform organism per 100 ml. This means that when a single sample is examined none of the usual five 10 ml. portions should contain coliform bacteria. Experience has indicated that water conforming to this standard is almost certainly free from pathogenic bacteria.

Membrane Filter Coliform Count. A filtration technique for enumerating

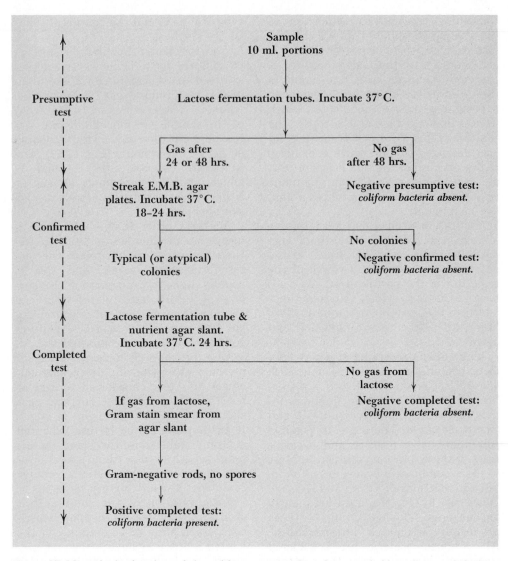

Figure 17-13. Abridged outline of the coliform tests used to detect probable pollution of drinking water with sewage. The three steps are called (1) the presumptive test, (2) the confirmed test, and (3) the completed test.

coliform bacteria in water, which was developed in Germany during World War II, has been accepted as an alternate standard procedure for determining the sanitary quality of water. A portion of the sample is passed through a cellulose acetate filter membrane of such porosity as to retain bacteria, while permitting the water to pass freely. The filter membrane is then placed aseptically in a Petri dish on an absorbent pad saturated with a differential nutrient solution such as M-Endo broth (buffered lactose-peptone-salts with bile salts and decolorized basic fuchsin) and incubated at 35° C. for 20 hours. The membrane is then examined under low-power microscopy, and purplish green colonies with a metallic sheen are counted. These are considered to be coliform bacteria (Fig. 17-14).

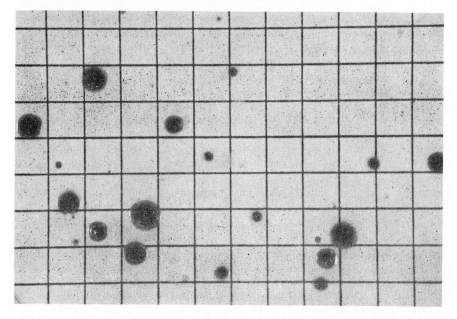

Figure 17-14. Magnified colonies of coliform bacteria on a filter membrane saturated with modified Endo medium. (From American Public Health Association: Standard Methods for the Examination of Water and Wastewater, 12th ed., 1965.)

The amount of sample to be filtered varies according to the nature of the specimen: 100 to 500 ml. of finished, municipal water may be examined, whereas 0.1 to 10 ml. of well water may yield 20 to 80 coliform colonies (the recommended density for most accurate counting). Greater precision is possible by the membrane filter technique than by the multiple lactose tube method of estimating coliforms, because larger volumes of samples can be examined, and results are secured more quickly. The method is limited, however, by the clogging of the filters with algae, colloidal and other materials, and by the inhibition of coliforms in specimens containing excessively high, noncoliform populations.

The Plate Count. A plate count of aerobic and facultatively anaerobic bacteria capable of growing on nutrient agar is often performed simultaneously with the coliform test, although the sanitary quality of a water supply is usually judged solely on the basis of the coliform content. Satisfactory water supplies usually contain no more than 100 bacteria per milliliter. A higher bacterial count indicates difficulty in the water purification process. Certain industrial concerns desire water that is almost free from bacteria, and the results of a plate count are of interest to them.

Purification of Water. *Protection of the Supply.* The first step in providing pure water, whether for a single household or for a large city, is to protect the source of supply against sewage pollution. Wells should be located at a considerable distance from septic tanks, barnyards, and other pollution; they should be carefully constructed to prevent seepage of surface water and should be capped with a concrete cover. Large watersheds from which water is collected into streams, ponds, or reservoirs should be carefully inspected; these are often fenced to exclude all sources of pollution.

Sedimentation. Purification by sedimentation as water flows slowly or stands in a reservoir is made more efficient by adding alum or iron salts; flocculent precipitates of the corresponding hydroxides entrain microorganisms and other suspended particles and settle rapidly. Sedimentation does not sterilize polluted water but markedly reduces its microbial population. It is often used as a first stage in purification.

Filtration. Filtration is an effective means of removing microorganisms and other suspended matter from water. Two types of sand filters are used in large scale filtration of water.

Slow sand filters are constructed of layers of fine sand, coarse sand, gravel, and rock. Water seeps through the filter slowly, and bacteria, algae, and protozoa are caught in the surface layers of fine sand. These microorganisms multiply and produce a gelatinous mass to which other microorganisms and suspended particles adsorb. The efficiency of the filter gradually decreases, and eventually the surface layer must be cleaned. Large filter beds are required because the rate of filtration is slow.

Rapid sand filters operate about 40 times as fast as slow sand filters. They also consist of layers of sand, gravel, and rock, but a coagulant such as alum or ferrous sulfate is added to the water before filtration. The water passes through a settling tank in which most of the precipitate settles out and the remainder is removed by the filter. Rapid sand filters soon become clogged and must be cleaned by forcing water backward through the bed of gravel and sand. These filters are usually operated in batteries so that some may be in operation while others are being cleaned.

Properly constructed and operated sand filters remove 90 to 99 per cent of the microorganisms and most of the suspended particles from water. Filtration does not sterilize water and cannot be relied upon to render it safe for human consumption; a final step is necessary.

Chlorination. Chlorination is the least expensive but most efficient means of rendering water safe for drinking.

The amount of chlorine gas added depends on the degree of pollution of the supply and its organic matter content. Water is usually treated to contain 0.1 to 0.2 part per million of residual chlorine. Residual chlorine is the available chlorine remaining 20 minutes after its addition to the water. During this 20 minutes some of the chlorine combines with organic substances and with bacteria; the more heavily polluted the water or the greater its organic matter content, the more chlorine must be applied to ensure a safe residual. Preliminary sedimentation and filtration are therefore helpful.

Chlorine kills most nonspore-forming gram-negative bacteria, such as the intestinal pathogens, but in the concentrations employed it does not kill spores or many gram-positive bacteria. Chlorinated water is therefore not always sterile, but it is usually safe for human consumption.

Small amounts of water can be made safe by boiling for 10 minutes. This practice is often recommended for household use during floods or other disasters that disrupt the normal water purification system.

Pathogenic Microorganisms in the Air

The presence of mold spores in extramural air has already been mentioned. Updrafts over heated land masses carry clouds of spores many thousand feet into the air. The spores then travel great distances before they settle back to Earth. It will be recalled that air masses over the United States travel from west to east at a rate of 500 to 700 miles per day. The rate of settling of droplets of water of the same general dimensions as those of mold spores indicates that several hundred to several thousand hours are required for spores to fall to the ground from an elevation of 10,000 feet (Table 17-3).

A storm of spores of the mold *Alternaria* covered the eastern third of the United States within a two day

Table 17-3. Approximate Rate of Fall of Water Droplets Through Air

Diameter of Droplet	Rate of Fall (Ft./Hr.)
1 μ	0.36
2 μ	1.44
5 μ	9
10 μ	36
50 μ	900
100 μ	3600

period in 1937. The spores originated in southern Minnesota and were carried aloft during the early hours of October 6. By the next day they were reported along a line from New York City to northern Texas and reached Florida and Georgia the following day (Fig. 17-15).

Outdoor Dissemination of Pathogens. There are two important aspects to the rapid and widespread distribution of spores. Some types of hay fever are caused by mold spores, and their gen-

eral dissemination in this manner produces suffering among thousands of people. Even more important is the fact that plant pathogens can be distributed by the same method. Certain wheat rusts, for example, are carried northward through the central plains states by southerly winds from Texas to southern Canada in the spring and are returned by northerly winds during the winter. The destructive potential of this method of distributing plant pathogens in biologic warfare need not be elaborated.

Indoor Distribution of Pathogens. Most human pathogens that gain access to indoor air do not survive long unless covered by saliva or droplets of mucus. Organisms protected in this manner may, however, remain alive for several hours. Moreover, the human population indoors is likely to be so dense that many respiratory pathogens can be present in the air of a room at any one moment. Droplet infection is the usual mode of transfer of respiratory

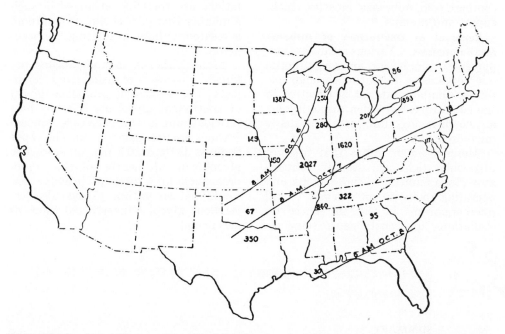

Figure 17-15. The mold spore "storm" of October 6 to 8, 1937. Numerals indicate the number of spores of *Alternaria* deposited on an area of 1.8 sq. cm. during the day of most intense activity. (From *Aerobiology*, Am. A. Adv. Sc., 1942.)

Figure 17-16.   Droplets of saliva and mucus discharged during a violent, unstifled sneeze. (Highspeed photograph by M. W. Jennison; A.S.M. LS-4.)

diseases (Fig. 17-16). The effectiveness of this means of distribution is attested by the frequency of epidemics of the common cold, influenza, measles, chickenpox, and mumps.

Removal or Destruction of Airborne Microorganisms.   Various means are employed to remove or destroy airborne microorganisms. Filtration through cotton or similar material is effective in the laboratory. Filtration through some air conditioning units removes many microorganisms.

Mercury vapor lamps that produce ultraviolet light are used in refrigerators, soda fountains, school rooms, and operating rooms in an attempt to kill microorganisms in the air. These installations apparently cause some re-duction in airborne agents of spoilage or disease. Prolonged exposure to ultraviolet light is harmful to man; installations are therefore arranged in such a manner that part of the air in a room is treated without irradiating the occupants.

Many airborne microorganisms are killed by aerosols of disinfectant chemicals. The vapors of propylene glycol or triethylene glycol are strongly bactericidal and in the necessary concentrations are nontoxic to man. The vapor from as little as 0.5 mg. of propylene glycol can kill nearly all the microorganisms in a liter of heavily contaminated air within 15 seconds. Triethylene glycol is nearly 100 times as germicidal.

 # MICROORGANISMS IN THEIR NATURAL HABITATS

SUMMARY

Soil and water are the principal natural habitats of microorganisms; moisture, nutrient, temperature, and other conditions control multiplication. Air is a reservoir in which certain kinds of microorganisms can survive, but it supports little if any growth.

Microbial activities in the soil are vital to life as we know it. Carbon, nitrogen, and sulfur compounds are made available for plant use and thus are provided indirectly for assimilation by animals. Microorganisms decompose the wastes and dead remains of plants and animals and are largely responsible for reconverting the products of dissimilation to oxidized forms that can again be utilized in plant nutrition. Some of the same processes are carried out in water and in sewage, and in the latter substrate are chiefly responsible for removing noxious or unpleasant components.

Considerable importance is attached to the sanitary quality of water and the search for coliform bacteria as indicators of sewage pollution. Physical, chemical, and biologic methods of purification that ensure the absence of these bacteria render water safe to drink.

Air is an important medium for the dispersal of microorganisms. The source of these organisms is soil, natural bodies of water, and man, animals, and plants. Certain moderately hardy organisms or spores may be carried long distances out-of-doors. Relatively nonhardy microorganisms are transmitted short distances indoors, but, since many of these are human pathogens, this means of dissemination is important in the spread of disease.

The interrelationships of microorganisms in soil and water include most forms of social behavior: mutualism, commensalism, antibiosis and parasitism, and synergism. Probably most microorganisms affect in some way the activity of other organisms in their vicinity through their utilization of nutrients, their metabolic products, physical crowding, and so forth.

STUDY QUESTIONS

1. What are the principal habitats of microorganisms? Why?
2. Why are cocci better adapted for survival under adverse conditions than most nonspore-forming rods?
3. Compare the advantages and disadvantages of direct microscopy and plate or dilution counts for determining the number of bacteria in soil, water, and other natural habitats.
4. What kinds of microorganisms are commonly present in soil? What are their interrelationships?
5. Discuss the types and sources of microorganisms in water. What kinds of associations exist between the various types?
6. Distinguish between mutualism, commensalism, antibiosis, and synergism. Give examples involving microorganisms.
7. Why are the *cyclic* transformations of carbon, nitrogen, sulfur, etc., important? What roles do microorganisms play in these cycles?
8. Explain why small amounts of sewage can be discharged into a stream without creating a nuisance, whereas large amounts cannot.
9. Describe the contributions of bacteria to the sewage purification process.
10. Discuss the significance of coliform bacteria in drinking water.
11. Of what importance are airborne microorganisms? How can they be partially controlled?

SUPPLEMENTARY READING

The book by Waksman is a monographic review of the early literature in soil microbiology. Alexander's book provides a good, up-to-date textbook introduction to the subject. Thimann has an interesting chapter on the number and kinds of microorganisms in the soil with a discussion of the physical and chemical properties of soil that influence its microbial population. This is followed by four chapters on various phases of the nitrogen cycle. The elementary textbook by Sarles et al., also contains good and readable chapters on the properties of soil, chemical and microbial changes, and nitrogen fixation.

The nature, treatment, and testing of water and sewage are discussed in two chapters of the Sarles textbook. An earlier but more thorough treatment of these matters is found in *Water Bacteriology* by Prescott, Winslow, and McCrady, a well known reference work. Gainey and Lord's *Microbiology of Water and Sewage* opens with introductory chapters on general microbiology and then deals in separate chapters with bacteria in water, pollution, purification of water, and sewage and its treatment. The American Public Health Association book is widely accepted as the standard reference for methods of testing water and sewage.

Aerobiology is a collection of papers presented at a symposium in 1942. About one-third of the volume deals with extramural organisms (upper air, marine, plant pathogenicity, etc.), and the remainder with the distribution, counting, and control of microorganisms indoors. The subject of airborne infection is further discussed in the interesting book by Rosebury.

Alexander, M.: *Introduction to Soil Microbiology*. New York, John Wiley & Sons, Inc., 1961.

American Association for the Advancement of Science: *Aerobiology* (Moulton, F. R. [Ed.]). Washington, American Association for the Advancement of Science, 1942.

American Public Health Association: *Standard Methods for the Examination of Water and Wastewater,* 11th ed. New York, American Public Health Association, 1960.

Gainey, P. L., and Lord, T. H.: *Microbiology of Water and Sewage*. New York, Prentice-Hall, Inc., 1952.

Prescott, S. C., Winslow, C.-E. A., and McCrady, M. H.: *Water Bacteriology,* 6th ed. New York, John Wiley & Sons, Inc., 1946.

Rosebury, T.: *Experimental Airborne Infection*. Baltimore, The Williams & Wilkins Co., 1947.

Sarles, W. B., Frazier, W. C., Wilson, J. B., and Knight, S. G.: *Microbiology, General and Applied,* 2d ed. New York, Harper & Brothers, 1956.

Thimann, K. V.: *The Life of Bacteria*. New York, The Macmillan Company, 1955.

Waksman, S. A.: *Principles of Soil Microbiology,* 2d ed. Baltimore, The Williams & Wilkins Co., 1932.

MICROBIOLOGY OF
FOODS AND
DAIRY PRODUCTS

Microorganisms produce both desirable and undesirable changes in foods. Many products would not be possible without microbial assistance: sauerkraut, ripe olives, cocoa, cheese. Acids produced by microorganisms help to preserve certain foods, such as pickles and fermented milks, from unpleasant microbial activity. The undesirable changes known as spoilage are all too familiar.

MICROBIAL SPOILAGE
OF FOODS

Spoilage is any change in the flavor, aroma, texture, or appearance of a food that renders it undesirable or unpalatable. The terms *undesirable* and *unpalatable* cannot be defined objectively; they depend on the customs and experiences of the individuals concerned.

In general, however, each population group has certain standards or norms of palatability, and a food that fails to meet these standards is considered spoiled.

Microbial spoilage of foods is an ecologic problem. Many foods are produced or manufactured under conditions that ensure contamination with a variety of microorganisms, but which of these organisms survive and multiply depends on the composition of the food and the conditions of storage. Those organisms that can grow bring about changes characteristic of their metabolic patterns and alter the flavor, aroma, texture, or appearance of the product in a certain way.

Human and animal foods may be classified according to their source as (1) plant products, (2) animal products, (3) manufactured products.

Initial Contamination of Foods

Plant Products. Plant products are subject to microbial contamination from the soil in which they are grown, from the air, from insects, and from human handlers. The internal tissues of fresh plant products are usually free from microorganisms. Plant surfaces are relatively impermeable, and microorganisms do not readily penetrate to underlying tissues, where they can multiply rapidly, unless the surfaces are bruised or the organisms are "inoculated" by insect bites.

Root crops such as potatoes, beets, and carrots are liberally coated with soil microorganisms when harvested, but these vegetables possess an exceptionally impenetrable skin. Low-growing leafy vegetables like lettuce, spinach, and cabbage are also likely to be heavily contaminated; these products have a softer surface and are easily invaded by microorganisms. Vegetables and fruits that grow some distance above the ground are contaminated by insects and by microorganisms in the air. The latter are principally soil organisms. Insects tend to feed upon the same type of plant and hence distribute organisms from one to another so that all have a uniform flora. Yeasts, for example, are almost universally present upon grapes as a result of insect inoculation.

Microorganisms found upon plant products include molds, yeasts, spore-forming and some nonspore-forming rods, and various cocci.

Animal Products. Animal products are subject to intrinsic as well as environmental and human contamination. The internal portions of a piece of meat are usually free from microorganisms if the animal has been properly slaughtered (i.e., killed quickly by a blow on the head or by cutting the jugular vein). The exposed surfaces are covered with bacteria derived from the animal's skin and intestines, the butchering equipment, and the air of the slaughter house. Fish fillets are even more likely to be covered by microorganisms, particularly when the fish are "cleaned" and cut on shipboard under poor handling conditions.

Microorganisms on meat include cocci, gram-negative rods such as *Achromobacter, Pseudomonas, Proteus,* and coliform species, anaerobic spore-forming bacteria, yeasts, and molds. Fish contain many of the same organisms, particularly nonspore-forming pigmented or nonpigmented rods.

Clean, fresh, uncracked eggs are usually free from microorganisms within the shell. Only about 8 per cent of fresh eggs contain microorganisms; the yolks frequently contain more bacteria than the whites. Dirty eggs are covered with microorganisms, which penetrate the shell under poor conditions of storage.

Milk. Cow's milk as secreted by the glands of a healthy udder is sterile, but it frequently becomes contaminated by the micrococci and streptococci normally present in the milk ducts and cistern of the udder. The number of these bacteria is usually no more than a few score to a few hundred per milliliter of milk.

The udders of diseased cattle may be infected with pathogenic species of *Staphylococcus* or *Streptococcus* or with the tuberculosis or brucellosis organisms; these bacteria are also discharged in the milk.

Organisms from inside the udder constitute only a small fraction of those found in freshly drawn milk. Bacterial counts in fresh milk vary from a few hundred to several thousand per milliliter, and under poor conditions may be half a million or more. The sources of these organisms depend somewhat on whether milking is done by hand or by machine. In hand milking into open pails there is opportunity for contamination from the air of the stable, the animal's coat, and the hands and clothing of the worker. Machine milking reduces the significance of these sources of microorganisms but increases the chance of contamination by unsanitary equipment, which may add thousands or millions of bacteria per milliliter to milk if it is not properly cleaned and sterilized.

No process is better than the humans that conduct it, and careless dairy workers may contribute considerable numbers of pathogenic or nonpathogenic bacteria at any stage in milk production and handling.

Kinds of Microorganisms in Milk. The bacteria ordinarily found in milk and other dairy products comprise four groups: (1) cocci, usually gram-positive, (2) gram-positive, nonspore-forming rods, (3) gram-positive, spore-forming rods, (4) gram-negative, nonspore-forming rods (Table 18-1).

The cocci of normal milk include various streptococci, notably *S. lactis,* which is almost always present in fresh milk. *Micrococcus* species are usually present, too. Both of these organisms may be derived from the healthy udder,

Table 18-1. Kinds and Sources of Microorganisms in Milk

| Organisms | Source | | | | | | Remarks |
	Hay, feed	Ma-nure	Equip-ment	Soil	Water	Udder	
Cocci							
Streptococcus	+	+	+			+	Early souring of milk, produces 0.8 to 1.0% lactic acid; used in butter and cheese starters.
Leuconostoc	+						Used in butter starters.
Micrococcus			+			+	May survive pasteurization.
Gram-positive non-sporeforming rods							
Lactobacillus	+	+					Produces 2 to 4% lactic acid; used in fermented milks and cheese.
Microbacterium		+	+				Resists pasteurization; survives 10 min. at 80° C.
Gram-positive sporeforming rods							
Bacillus	+	+		+			Survive pasteurization; late spoilage of dairy products.
Clostridium	+	+		+			
Gram-negative rods							
Coliforms	+	+		+			Usually in raw milk; not in properly handled pasteurized milk.
Pseudomonas	+	+	+	+	+		Low temperature spoilage.
Alcaligenes	+	+	+	+	+		Ropy milk, etc.
Achromobacter				+	+		Produces rancidity.
Flavobacterium				+	+		Produces rancidity.
Yeasts	+			+			Produce gassy fermentation.
Molds	+			+			Late utilization of acids.

and some are likely to withstand pasteurization. They may persist in utensils and other dairy equipment.

Lactobacilli are often found in milk and are important in the manufacture of fermented milks and many kinds of cheese. Their growth is favored by an acid medium, and for that reason they usually multiply better in milk that has already been partly soured by *S. lactis* or other organisms than in fresh milk.

Microbacterium lacticum is a thermoduric, nonspore-forming small rod that survives pasteurization and persists in milk equipment. It is frequently the cause of high bacterial counts in pasteurized milk.

Coliform bacteria are considered undesirable in milk and dairy products, because they indicate unsanitary conditions or practices. They are almost inevitably present in raw milk, because of their widespread occurrence in manure and on grains and other feeds, but they are easily killed by heat and should be absent from pasteurized milk. Their presence in pasteurized milk therefore indicates gross pollution of the raw milk, inadequate pasteurization, or recontamination after pasteurization.

Manufactured Products. The microbial flora of manufactured foods depends upon the nature of the food and the manufacturing process. Bakery products, for example, contain microorganisms derived from the various ingredients: flour, sugar, shortening, milk or milk powder, eggs or egg powder, and water. The equipment and the human handlers also contribute microorganisms. The baking process kills molds, yeasts, and nonspore-forming bacteria, but bacterial spores may survive. The outside of any product is subject to recontamination, and molds are particularly troublesome. Uncooked cream fillings or toppings are also likely to contain spoilage organisms.

Fermented foods, such as pickles, olives, and sauerkraut, contain microorganisms used in the manufacturing process. Undesirable organisms derived from the equipment, the air, and from man include molds, yeasts, and putrefactive bacteria.

Effects of Chemical Properties on Spoilage

The chemical properties of a food product influence the type of microorganism that can grow and hence determine the nature of the spoilage process (Table 18-2).

Composition. Proteins are subject to bacterial spoilage. Many species can attack them, especially spore-formers, gram-negative rods such as *Pseudomonas* and *Proteus,* and a few cocci. Mold spoilage is also common.

Carbohydrate foods are spoiled particularly by yeasts and molds. Bacterial species of the genera *Streptococcus, Leuconostoc,* and *Micrococcus* are saccharolytic, and many other bacteria can also attack carbohydrates.

Fats undergo hydrolytic decomposition and become rancid as malodorous

Table 18-2. The Influence of the Chemical Properties of a Food on the Type of Microbial Spoilage to Which It Is Subject

Composition			Acidity		Osmotic Pressure	
Protein	Carbohydrate	Fat	Acid (<pH 4.5)	Nonacid (>pH 4.5)	Low	High
PREDOMINANT SPOILAGE ORGANISMS						
Bacteria	Yeasts	Molds	Molds	Bacteria	Molds	Molds
Molds	Molds	A few bacteria	Yeasts		Yeasts	
					Bacteria	

fatty acids are set free. Relatively few microorganisms are capable of digesting fats: some molds and a few gram-negative rod bacteria and cocci.

Acidity. The reaction of nearly all foods is below pH 7, and some may be as acid as pH 2 to 3. Foods are classified as *acid* or *nonacid*. The reaction of acid foods is below pH 4.5, and this group includes most fruits (Table 18-3). Nearly all vegetables, fish, meats, and milk products are nonacid.

The pH of acid foods is sufficiently low to prevent most bacterial spoilage, but yeasts and molds grow luxuriantly. Nonacid foods are particularly subject to bacterial spoilage, but will also support growth of molds under proper conditions.

Moisture and Osmotic Pressure. Foods that contain less than 10 to 13 per cent water do not support growth of microorganisms. Molds require the least free water, and bacteria require most. Many molds and some yeasts can tolerate salt concentrations greater than 15 per cent, whereas bacteria are generally inhibited by 5 to 15 per cent salt. Sixty-five to 70 per cent sugar is required to inhibit molds; 50 per cent inhibits bacteria and most yeasts. Foods of high sugar or salt content are therefore most likely to be spoiled by molds; foods of low salt or sugar content may be spoiled by any kind of organism.

Table 18-3. Approximate pH of Some Canned Foods

Food	pH
Lemon juice	2.4
Cranberry juice	2.5
Rhubarb	3.1
Grapefruit	3.2
Apples	3.4
Cherries	3.4
Pineapple	3.5
Orange juice	3.7
Peaches	3.7
Apricots	3.8
Pears	4.3
Tomatoes	4.3
Carrots	5.1
Green beans	5.2
Pumpkin	5.3
Beets	5.4
Spinach	5.4
Asparagus	5.5
Broccoli	5.6
Tuna	5.8
Codfish	6.0
Peas	6.0
Lima beans	6.1
Duck	6.1
Mackerel	6.1
Chicken	6.2
Corn	6.3
Oysters	6.4
Clams	6.8
Crabmeat	6.8
Shrimp	7.0

Effects of Storage Conditions on Spoilage

Oxygen. The presence or absence of oxygen determines the types of organisms that can multiply and the kind of spoilage produced (Table 18-4). Molds and aerobic bacteria (species of *Bacillus* and *Pseudomonas*) grow only where there is plenty of air and cause chiefly surface spoilage; yeasts and facultative bacteria can grow in closed containers as well as when exposed to the air. Spoilage by the genus *Clostridium* is strictly anaerobic.

Temperature. Refrigerated foods are subject to spoilage by molds and by some yeasts and bacteria, including several species of gram-negative rods and a few micrococci. Low temperature retards spoilage, but even subfreezing temperatures do not prevent multiplication of all microorganisms until about $-7°$ C. is reached. Foods stored at $-18°$ C., the temperature of a home freezer, remain free from microbial growth, and a slow decrease in population may even occur.

Products stored in warm warehouses, ship holds, or other warm locations may be spoiled by thermophilic bacteria, most of which are spore-forming and hence resist heat sterilization in canning processes.

Table 18-4. The Influence of Storage Conditions on the Type of Microbial Spoilage to Which a Food Is Subject

Air		Temperature		
Present	Absent	Low (<10° C.)	Moderate	High (>40° C.)
PREDOMINANT SPOILAGE ORGANISMS				
Molds	Bacteria	Molds	Molds	A few bacteria
Yeasts	Yeasts	A few yeasts and bacteria	Yeasts	
Bacteria			Bacteria	

Spoilage of Plant Products

Spoilage of plant products is determined principally by their acidity and chemical composition, because all are subject to similar initial microbial contamination.

Fruits. Fruits, including tomatoes, are highly acid, and about 90 per cent of their organic matter is carbohydrate, chiefly sugar (Table 18-5). Spoilage is therefore limited to molds and yeasts. Fruits usually become moldy after a few days at room temperature or even in the refrigerator, and crushed fruits or fruit juices not only become moldy but may develop gas and an alcoholic flavor as a result of yeast activity.

Vegetables. Most of the common vegetables contain less carbohydrate and more protein than do fruits. A high percentage of the carbohydrate of vegetables like corn and potatoes is starch, which can be digested by relatively few microorganisms. Protein may amount to as much as 40 per cent of the organic matter. Lack of acidity permits spoilage of vegetables by bacteria; yeast spoilage is relatively uncommon.

Aerobic bacteria and molds produce *decay* under conditions of sufficient aeration and humidity or free moisture; this type of spoilage is not accompanied by unpleasant odors. Anaerobic bacteria attack starch and proteins in the absence of air and produce the foul odors of *putrefaction*. Spoilage of home canned beans or corn illustrates the changes produced.

Spoilage of Animal Products

Animal products such as meat, fowl, fish, and eggs contain almost no carbohydrate. Proteins constitute 35 to 95 per cent of the organic matter; the remainder is fat. These products are therefore subject to spoilage by proteolytic bacteria and by molds. The nature and extent of spoilage depend on various environmental factors.

Meat. Spoilage is slow in meat that is properly refrigerated or stored under such conditions that the surfaces become dry, because the initial microbial contamination is confined to the surface; interior tissues are normally sterile. Microorganisms that penetrate slowly or that enter cut surfaces eventually produce anaerobic putrefaction. Putrefactive decomposition occurs rap-

Table 18-5. Approximate Composition of Various Types of Foods

Type of Food	Per Cent of Organic Matter		
	Protein	Carbohydrate	Fat
Fruits	2–8	85–97	0–3
Vegetables	15–30	50–85	0–5
Fish	70–95	0	5–30
Poultry	50–70	0	30–50
Eggs	51	3	46
Meats	35–50	0	50–65
Milk	30	40	30

idly in ground meat and flaked fish because the surface organisms are thoroughly distributed throughout the mass of food. Bacterial counts reach hundreds of millions per gram within a few days, even in the refrigerator, and obvious spoilage quickly results.

Storage at a temperature just above freezing greatly retards spoilage. Fresh beef and mutton are often "aged" for several weeks at low temperatures to permit autolysis, which improves their texture and flavor. The layer of fat covering these meats retards drying and protects the underlying muscle from microbial attack.

Fish. Microorganisms on the surface of fish fillets multiply rapidly, particularly if icing or refrigeration is delayed. Bacterial counts in fish stored for four days at 10° to 20° C. may be in the hundreds of millions per gram. The fish become slimy, and proteolysis occurs.

Shellfish such as oysters and clams present a peculiar problem, because they are frequently eaten raw or barely warmed, as in stews or chowders. These fish are taken from the mud at the bottom of shallow bays, and the shells are heavily loaded with bacteria. The bacterial content of the animal itself depends on that of the surrounding water, which is constantly taken into the animal, passed over its gills, and discharged. Shellfish that have been "fattened" in water containing sewage have a high bacterial count, including many sewage bacteria. Numerous outbreaks of typhoid fever have been traced to oysters from such sources. The bacterial content of oysters is decreased by removing them to clean water for a time, whereupon many bacteria are removed from the gills during normal passage of water through the animal's body. Shucked shellfish are likely to contain large numbers of bacteria and require prompt refrigeration to avoid putrefactive decomposition.

Milk. Milk presents a special problem because the temperature of freshly drawn milk is favorable for rapid multiplication of many bacterial species with

which it is normally contaminated. Unless it is immediately cooled, the initial population of several thousand to a few hundred thousand bacteria per milliliter increases 20 times or more within two or three hours. Prompt refrigeration prevents bacterial multiplication for a day or two and inhibits it for several days thereafter (Fig. 18-1).

Normal Fermentation of Raw Milk. Raw milk stored at a moderate temperature supports a sequence of microorganisms (Fig. 18-2). *S. lactis* and related bacteria multiply promptly and rapidly and produce sufficient lactic acid to decrease the reaction to about pH 4.5, causing curdling. Lactobacilli start to multiply below pH 6 and continue the fermentation, producing 2 to 4 per cent lactic acid and bringing the reaction to pH 3.0 to 3.5. Few microorganisms can grow in a medium of this acidity. Under aerobic conditions, however, molds and film-forming yeasts can utilize the acid as a source of energy by oxidizing it to carbon dioxide and water. The reaction

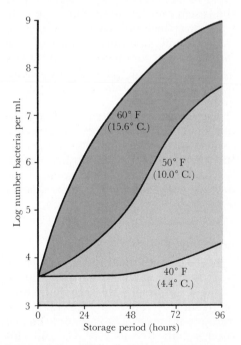

Figure 18-1. Effect of storage temperature on bacterial multiplication in raw milk. (Data of Ayers et al.: U.S.D.A. Bull. 642, 1918.)

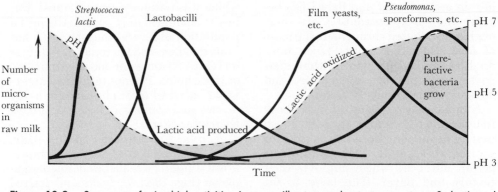

Figure 18-2. Sequence of microbial activities in raw milk at a moderate temperature. *S. lactis* and lactobacilli multiply rapidly, ferment lactose, and produce sufficient lactic acid to bring the reaction to pH 3.5 or lower. Film yeasts, molds, etc., then oxidize the acid, and the pH rises, which permits putrefactive bacteria to grow.

therefore once more becomes nearly neutral. Most of the lactose has been utilized by this time, and further growth of lactic acid–producing bacteria does not occur. *Pseudomonas,* spore-formers, and other proteolytic and lipolytic bacteria, which were held in check by the rapid lactic fermentation, finally digest the casein and fat and reduce the milk to a dirty-looking, watery, putrid or rancid liquid. The initial stages of acid formation are completed in only a few days; oxidation of the acid and decomposition of the protein and fat may require several weeks.

This sequence of microbial changes is fairly common and occurs with modifications in food fermentations, such as the manufacture of sauerkraut, and in the manufacture of cheese; some of the more highly ripened cheeses display obvious evidence of putrefaction.

Spoilage of Manufactured Products

Baked Goods. Baking does not necessarily kill all bacterial spores within a loaf of bread despite the fact that a high temperature (190° C.) is used for 40 minutes or longer. The center of the loaf reaches only 97° to 100° C., and this temperature is maintained for about nine minutes in properly baked bread. Surviving spores of *Bacillus mesentericus*

and other species germinate if the bread is not cooled quickly or is stored at too high a temperature; these organisms produce a stringy decomposition known as *ropy bread*. Ropiness is prevented by acidifying the bread dough before baking to a reaction of about pH 5 with vinegar or lemon juice or with acetic, tartaric, lactic, or citric acid. Acidity inhibits the growth of spore-forming bacteria.

Mold spoilage is another problem in bakeries. Molds do not survive baking, but bread may easily be contaminated after it leaves the oven, particularly during slicing. Extreme care is therefore necessary to prevent mold contamination before wrapping. Some bakers add sodium or calcium propionate to the bread dough to prevent mold growth on the loaf (propionates also prevent ropiness).

Cream or custard products such as cream puffs and eclairs are notorious, particularly during warm weather. The filling is an excellent culture medium and supports rapid multiplication of many kinds of bacteria, some of which are pathogenic. Many bakeries refuse to manufacture such products during the warm summer months.

Fermented Foods. Acid foods manufactured by fermentation or by the addition of vinegar (sauerkraut, pickles, olives, etc.) do not ordinarily support the growth of bacteria because their pH is too low. Molds and film-forming yeasts ("false yeasts") grow luxuriantly on such products, however, particularly when they are exposed to air in an opened jar or at the top of a fermentation or storage tank. As in the normal fermentation of milk, these organisms oxidize the acid and reduce the acidity to such an extent that putrefactive spore-forming and nonspore-forming bacteria can multiply. This type of spoilage is easily prevented by keeping the acid food in a tightly closed container so that molds, yeasts, or air cannot enter.

FOOD PRESERVATION

Food preservation practices range from the ancient use of drying to the ultramodern experimental application of gamma rays. There are five general methods: (1) control of moisture, (2) use of chemical preservatives, (3) storage at low temperature, (4) use of high temperatures, (5) treatment with radiation. Each method is suited to the preservation of certain products.

Asepsis is important in the successful application of any preservation procedure. This means that contamination of the food product must be reduced or prevented at all times, from its production, slaughter, or manufacture, through all the various processing and handling steps, to its distribution, sale, and final storage in home or restaurant.

Control of Moisture

Drying. The ancient practice of sun drying consisted in exposing fruits, vegetables, and small pieces of meat to the warm sun until they could no longer support bacterial, yeast, or even mold growth. The method is still used in favorable climates.

Commercial drying is usually carried out under controlled conditions of temperature, relative humidity, and air flow; the process is called *dehydration* or *desiccation*. Milk can be dried by being sprayed as a fine mist into a stream of warm air, which evaporates most of the water, or it may be sprayed upon hot rollers, from which the powder is scraped. Other products are heated at moderate temperatures, with or without forced air circulation.

Desiccation cannot be relied upon to sterilize a product, although some organisms are killed. Spores of bacteria, yeasts, and molds survive long periods in the dry state. However, products containing less than 10 per cent of free water generally keep indefinitely without spoilage, provided they are stored under dry conditions.

Addition of Salt or Sugar. Available moisture is reduced by the addition of solutes, such as salt and sugar. Salt is widely used to preserve fish and meat. In pickling, and in the manufacture of various fermented products, low concentrations of salt prevent the growth of spoilage organisms but permit the multiplication of desired fermentative types; this will be discussed later (see page 352).

Preservation of jellies, jams, maple syrup, and honey is attributed to their high sugar content (65 to 80 per cent), but poorly sealed or opened containers frequently allow the slow growth of molds. Osmophilic ("high osmotic pressure loving") yeasts occasionally grow in honey and produce sufficient carbon dioxide to burst the jar.

Preservatives

Various chemicals, including formaldehyde, boric acid, benzoic acid, and sulfur dioxide, have been used in the past to prevent spoilage of certain food products, including milk. Most of these chemicals are harmful, and their use is now prohibited or limited and strictly regulated (e.g., sodium benzoate).

Some fish and meats are preserved by smoking, often combined with salting. The smoke from sawdust or corncobs contains formaldehyde and pyroligneous acid (a mixture of creosote compounds), both of which inhibit bacteria;

a small amount of these materials diffuses into the product. The smoking process also dries the surface of the meat or fish, and this helps to prevent microbial growth.

Organic acids are common preservatives that are particularly effective against putrefaction. They may be added directly (as is vinegar) or developed by fermentation of sugars in the food itself.

Approval has been given by the U. S. Food and Drug Administration for the use of certain antibiotics in the preservation of poultry. A condition of the granting of approval is that the antibiotic must be present in sufficiently low concentration to be destroyed by subsequent cooking. This is important because some individuals are or become sensitive (i.e., allergic) to certain antibiotics; moreover, continued use of an antibiotic may alter the microbial flora of the body and permit the establishment of antibiotic-resistant mutant bacteria. If the same resistant organisms subsequently cause an infection, it is impossible to treat the disease with the antibiotic in question. The deliberate or accidental introduction of antibiotics or other antibacterial chemicals into milk is considered adulteration and is forbidden by the federal government.

Low Temperature

Ordinary Refrigeration. Low temperature retards food spoilage. The ordinary household refrigerator operating at 40° to 45° F. (4° to 7° C.) keeps most foods in a palatable condition for a few days. Temperatures only slightly above freezing are used for commercial storage of meats, fish, eggs, milk and other dairy products, and some vegetables and fruits that must be held several days or weeks before marketing.

Freezing and Cold Storage. Many foods can be kept several months in the frozen state. Quick freezing is preferred to slow freezing. Quick freezing implies a freezing time of 30 minutes or less and is accomplished in various ways,

one of which consists of blowing cold air at 0° to −30° F. (−18° to −34° C.) across the materials being frozen. Ordinary or slow freezing requires three to 72 hours, and the temperature varies downward from 5° F. (−15° C.). Slow freezing is believed to produce large crystals of ice, which rupture cell walls and cause extensive "drip" or loss of fluid upon thawing, whereas quick freezing produces smaller ice crystals and less damage to the food tissues. Quick freezing reduces the loss of vitamins and stops tissue autolysis promptly. Frozen foods may be stored between 0° and 30° F. (−18° and −1° C.) with little further change.

Foods to be frozen should be prepared as carefully as if they were to be eaten directly. They should be sorted, trimmed, and washed, and in some cases "blanched" or scalded. Washing and blanching remove or destroy as many as 99 per cent of the microorganisms. Blanching consists in immersing the food in boiling water or exposing it to live steam for a very few minutes. The food is then immediately packaged and frozen as rapidly as possible. The interval between harvesting and freezing in many commercial operations is no more than two or three hours.

It should be emphasized that freezing does not improve the quality of any product. Only foods of high quality (that is, foods that would be acceptable if not frozen) should be preserved by this method. It is true that there may be some reduction in microbial count when the food is frozen and a slow reduction in count thereafter, but representatives of most species are likely to survive for months or years. This includes pathogenic as well as nonpathogenic types. All microbial activity ceases below −10° C., so that foods stored below this temperature remain free from spoilage indefinitely.

Quick freezing reduces but does not entirely prevent tissue damage. Frozen food is therefore highly susceptible to microbial invasion after thawing and should be used immediately, because the surviving bacteria begin to multiply as soon as they are warmed to their normal growth-temperature range. It is dangerous to refreeze frozen food that has thawed, because spoilage may have occurred during the interval of thawing.

High Temperature

High temperatures kill microorganisms, the rate of death varying with the species of organism, presence of spores, nature of the suspending medium (pH, consistency, etc.), temperature, and other factors. Heat treatments useful for preserving foods are subject to an upper limit determined by the characteristics of the food. Many foods acquire an overcooked taste or become soft and mushy when heated at too high a temperature or for too long an interval. The food processor must therefore select a heat process (temperature and time) that will yield a product that is safe from the health standpoint and capable of being stored without spoiling, and yet retains its taste, texture, and nutritional properties insofar as is possible. Whether a product must be bacteriologically sterile depends upon the possibilities for growth of microorganisms during storage periods. For example, thermophilic bacteria do not necessarily have to be killed in a product that will be stored at a temperature below the growth range of these organisms; many bacteria cannot multiply in acid foods and hence do not necessarily have to be killed.

Pasteurization. Heat treatment that kills some but not all microorganisms, usually at temperatures below 100° C., is known as *pasteurization*. It is usually employed in products whose quality would be adversely affected by higher temperatures and is often used in conjunction with other methods of preservation, such as drying, refrigeration, or cold storage.

Pasteurization was devised by Pasteur to prevent spoilage of wine and beer. It was later applied to the destruction of disease-producing bacteria in milk. It is used widely in the dairy industry, both in manufacturing processes in which certain specific microorganisms and none others are desired, and in the preservation of products such as processed cheese. Dried fruits, syrups, honey, apple juice, and other juices are also pasteurized. Spoilage of maple syrup by sugar-tolerant yeasts is prevented by heating the syrup to 93° C. at the time it is filled into cans and sealed. Similar spoilage of honey is prevented by heating at 71° C.

Pasteurization of Milk. Pasteurization of milk is usually performed in special processing plants rather than on the dairy farm, because the equipment is expensive. Pasteurization has two important purposes: (1) to destroy all harmful microorganisms and (2) to improve the keeping quality of milk.

There are two procedures employed in pasteurizing milk: the low temperature–long time or "holding" method and the high temperature–short time or "flash" process. The holding method consists in heating the milk in covered tanks, where it is agitated constantly at not less than 143° F. (61.7° C.) for at least 30 minutes; it is then immediately cooled to approximately 40° F. (4.4° C.). Flash pasteurization is carried out at 161° F. (71.7° C.) for at least 15 seconds. The milk flows continuously through a heated pipeline for the necessary time and then passes to cooling coils, where its temperature is brought down to 40° F. Either method of pasteurization, if properly performed, yields a safe product of good keeping quality.

Commercial pasteurization of milk began about 1890, and its acceptance was accelerated by knowledge that several diseases may be transmitted by raw milk. Investigators attempting to ascertain the best processing conditions for pasteurization soon found that *Mycobacterium tuberculosis* is the most resistant pathogen likely to be present in milk; subsequent studies were devoted principally to determining times and temperatures necessary to kill this organism in milk, cream, and other dairy products. A sample of the results is presented in Figure 18-3.

Economic factors dictated the upper limits placed on the heat treatment of milk. Excessive heating produces a "cooked" taste, which many consumers find undesirable. Heat also changes the "cream line," the height of the cream layer at the top of a bottle, by altering the physical condition of the butterfat so that the fat globules coalesce into a smaller volume. The vitamin content and other properties of milk change when heated. The cream line, however, is the factor that finally limited the time and temperature of pasteurization.

Pasteurization does not sterilize milk. It may reduce the bacterial count from a few hundred thousand to a few thousand per milliliter, but the surviving bacteria must be kept from multiplying by constant refrigeration. Pasteurized milk usually keeps better when refrigerated than raw milk of a comparable bacterial content, because pasteurization kills those bacteria that grow most readily at low temperatures. The sur-

viving bacteria are relatively thermoduric and often possess higher growth temperatures.

Canning. Preservation by canning has been practiced for about 150 years. Early in the nineteenth century the French government offered a prize of 12,000 francs for a method of preserving food for use by the army. The prize was won in 1809 by a Paris confectioner, Nicholas Appert. His book on canning was published the following year, and the English translation, which appeared in 1811, bears the imposing title, *The Art of Preserving All Kinds of Animal and Vegetable Substances for Several Years.* Appert used wide-mouthed glass bottles, which were filled, corked, and heated in boiling water.

Tin-coated steel containers were introduced by Durand in England in 1810. Canning was apparently started in the United States in 1819 by Underwood in Boston, and by the next year Kensett in New York was engaged in the commercial production of canned foods. The Civil War caused a great expansion of the canning industry, as did the

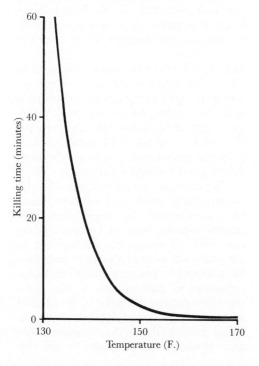

Figure 18-3. Time required to kill *Mycobacterium tuberculosis* in milk at various temperatures. (Data of Park, Am. Rev. Tuberc., 15:399, 1927.)

Spanish American War and the first World War.

It was recognized early that boiling water does not provide sufficient heat for sterilization of some kinds of food and that temperatures above 100° C. are necessary. In 1861, canneries increased the processing temperature by adding calcium chloride to water baths, and by 1874 steam pressure cookers or "retorts" were introduced. Methods of calculating heat processes from bacteriologic and physical data were perfected between 1923 and 1928, and since then the canning industry has been on a firm scientific basis.

The basic steps in canning are the same, whether at home or on a commercial scale (Fig. 18-4). The food should be fresh and of high quality. It is washed to remove gross dirt and as many microorganisms as possible; this reduces the burden on subsequent heat treatment. The second step is blanching or scalding in hot water or steam. The food is then filled into cans or jars while still hot. Commercial canners follow this step by exhausting or preheating the filled containers in a hot water or steam chest. Exhausting expands the food, drives off air or gas bubbles, and provides an atmosphere of steam in the "head space" at the top of the can. The can is then immediately sealed.

Heat processing follows at once so that the contents of the cans do not have an opportunity to cool. The treatment employed depends on the nature of the food and the size of the container. Acid foods require very little heat processing and are usually immersed in boiling water for only a few minutes (Table 18-6). Nonacid vegetables are processed in retorts heated by steam under pressure at 240° to 250° F. (116° to 121° C.) for periods as long as one or two hours. Meats, fish, and poultry are usually processed for one and one-half to two hours at 250° F. Viscous or solid foods, like pumpkin, into which heat penetrates only by conduction, require more thorough processing than fluid materials of comparable composition through which heat travels by convection. Large cans must be heated longer than small containers.

The processed cans are promptly cooled, either in the air or in cold water. Rapid cooling prevents overcooking and undesirable changes in texture and flavor. It also prevents germination and multiplication of the spores of highly resistant thermophiles, which might survive an inadequate heat treatment.

Canned foods are not always bacteriologically sterile but are considered "commercially sterile" if they contain no organisms capable of multiplication under usual conditions of storage. Bacteriologic sterility is preferred if it can be achieved without sacrifice of the physical or chemical quality of the food material. Home canned products undoubtedly are often only commercially sterile.

The only highly resistant food poisoning organism of concern in canning is *Clostridium botulinum.* Spores may survive 10 minutes or longer at 240° F., but even the most resistant spores are killed in 15 minutes by steam at 250° F. A hot water bath process cannot be relied on to destroy this organism in nonacid foods, because boiling for six hours may be necessary.

Home use of the pressure cooker in canning has done much to reduce the incidence of disease as well as to enhance the keeping qualities of home canned foods. Careless use of the pressure canner, however, may create a false sense of security, and strict attention must be paid to the manufacturer's directions. It is particularly important to be sure that no air remains in the canner during the processing interval. A mixture of steam and air has a lower temperature than steam alone at the same pressure (see Fig. 15-4). The pressure cooker should therefore be heated with the air vent wide open until *pure steam* issues for at least four minutes. Pressure may then be allowed to build up to the desired point. The best type of canner has a thermometer as well

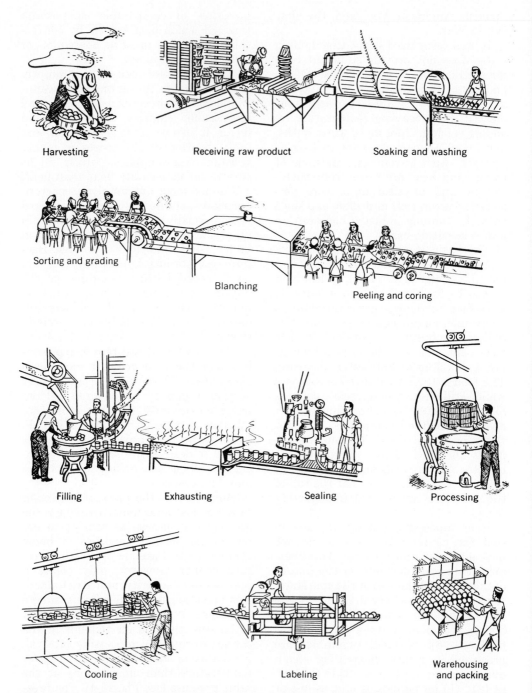

Harvesting

Receiving raw product

Soaking and washing

Sorting and grading

Blanching

Peeling and coring

Filling

Exhausting

Sealing

Processing

Cooling

Labeling

Warehousing and packing

Figure 18-4. Commercial canning; a food passes through many steps between harvesting and final storage or shipment. (From Pelczar and Reid: Microbiology. New York, McGraw-Hill Book Co., Inc., 1958.)

Table 18-6. Heat Processes Recommended for Home Canning

Acid Foods (Pint or Quart Glass Jars, Packed Hot, Processed in Waterbath)

Food	Time at 212° F.
Applesauce	5 min.
Raspberries	5 min.
Cherries	5 min.
Peaches	15 min.
Rhubarb	5 min.
Tomatoes	5 min.

Nonacid Foods (Pint Glass Jars Processed in Pressure Cooker)

Food	Time at 240° F. (10 Lbs. Pressure)	Time at 250° F. (15 Lbs. Pressure)
Lima beans	50 min.	
Snap beans	30 min.	
Corn, whole kernel	60 min.	
cream style		75 min.
Greens		60 min.
Peas	45 min.	
Pumpkin		60 min.
Beef		85 min.
Chicken, boned		85 min.
Hamburger		90 min.
Lamb or mutton		85 min.

as a pressure gauge; the processing time should be determined by the thermometer.

Irradiation

The ancient method of preserving certain foods by drying in the sun owed part of its success to ultraviolet irradiation. Commercial attempts to utilize ultraviolet light have met with limited success. It will be recalled that this form of radiation is readily absorbed by particulate matter of all kinds and even by glass; therefore, only the surfaces of foods could be expected to be sterilized by this method.

Other radiations are being studied as sterilizing agents for foods. Gamma rays have been used successfully for the experimental preservation of hamburger patties in paper or plastic bags; the sterilized product could be stored at room temperature. Irradiation appears to offer advantages for preserving certain kinds of food, but at present it is expensive. The food industry is so highly competitive that continued research can be anticipated.

MANUFACTURED FOODS

Numerous foods are prepared by fermentation processes in which one or more kinds of microorganism are responsible for the characteristic flavor or texture and sometimes for the keeping quality of the product. Fermented milks, alcoholic beverages, and other fermented foods have been used for thousands of years. Rule-of-thumb methods were handed down from one generation to the next, but why they worked—or on occasion failed to work—was not known. Only within the past hundred years have food fermentations been studied scientifically and the roles of the various microorganisms determined.

The manufacture of fermented vegetable products is a large industry, but it is also carried out on a small scale in homes in every country. Cabbages, cucumbers, lettuce, beets, turnips, and other vegetables can be used to make fermented products that are palatable and that possess greater freedom from spoilage than the natural vegetables. Most of the processes depend on the normal microflora of the vegetable to cause fermentation. They attack the natural sugars and yield organic acids, principally lactic, which serve as the preserving agents. The lactic fermentation of glucose by various species of bacteria is represented by the following equation:

$$C_6H_{12}O_6 \longrightarrow 2CH_3 \cdot CHOH \cdot COOH$$
$$\text{Glucose} \qquad\qquad\qquad \text{Lactic acid}$$

This equation omits the numerous intermediate steps between glucose and lactic acid, but it indicates that the fermentation is an anaerobic intramolecular oxidation-reduction process. The homofermentative lactic bacteria that bring about this fermentation include certain cocci and lactobacilli. The heterofermentative lactic bacteria (*Leuconostoc* and some species of *Lactobacillus*) produce formic and acetic acids, ethyl alcohol, carbon dioxide, and other products, in addition to lactic acid. Both types of lactic bacteria participate in vegetable fermentations.

The original source of lactic bacteria is the soil, and these organisms are therefore universally present upon vegetable products, along with all other types of soil organisms. The initial problem is to limit microbial growth to the desired lactic bacteria. This is accomplished in part by the creation of anaerobic conditions and in part by the use of salt. Salt serves at least two functions: it helps to draw juices and sugars

from the vegetable material and it increases the osmotic pressure of these juices to such an extent that most soil organisms cannot multiply. The sugars are fermented by the lactic bacteria.

Sauerkraut

Sauerkraut is fermented cabbage. The shredded cabbage is packed with about 2.5 per cent salt in containers, which may vary in size from a quart jar to a large tank. Weights are applied and the combined action of salt and pressure withdraws juice from the vegetable. Oxygen is soon exhausted, and a succession of bacteria ferment the plant sugar, producing lactic acid and small amounts of acetic acid, alcohol, and other products.

Leuconostoc mesenteroides and other cocci initiate fermentation and produce 0.7 to 1.0 per cent lactic acid. Lactobacilli then multiply and continue the fermentation, increasing the acidity to as much as 2.4 per cent lactic acid. The final reaction is approximately pH 3.5. Fermentation requires two to three weeks at 70° to 85° F. (21° to 29° C.).

Salt and anaerobic conditions prevent the growth of molds and aerobic bacteria throughout the fermenting mass, and the acidity that quickly develops inhibits most bacteria. Some halophilic yeasts are a cause of abnormal fermentation, and molds and film-forming yeasts can grow at the top of a fermentation tank; however, they spoil only the upper layers. These organisms oxidize the acids produced in the normal fermentation, and the decreased acidity then permits the growth of putrefactive bacteria.

Pickles

Cucumber pickles have been made in the home for many years, but the commercial manufacture of pickles is a large industry. Homemade pickles are preserved by a combination of salt and vinegar. It is more economical for commercial manufacturers to allow cucumbers to undergo lactic fermentation and produce the acidity necessary for preservation.

Fresh cucumbers packed in tanks, whose capacity may be as great as 15,000 bushels, are covered with brine containing 10 to 20 per cent salt, which limits growth of microorganisms to *Lactobacillus plantarum* and other lactic bacteria. Fermentation proceeds under favorable conditions for six to eight weeks, during which time the centers of the cucumbers change from an opaque white to a transparent green, and as much as 1 per cent lactic acid is produced.

Fermented cucumbers in brine are known as "salt stock" and can be kept for years without spoilage as long as the salt content is at least 10 per cent. Salt stock can be used to prepare sweet, sour, mixed, and other types of pickles according to the market demand.

Pickles are subject to loss of acidity by film-forming yeasts and subsequent spoilage by proteolytic bacteria.

Dairy Products

Manufactured dairy products include fermented milk, butter, and cheese. Those mentioned are produced with the aid of a lactic type of fermentation in which bacteria of the *S. lactis* group and the genus *Lactobacillus* participate.

The origin of these products is lost in antiquity, doubtless because lactic fermentation has long occurred naturally in milk. Later it was found that the acid flavor was produced more rapidly and consistently if a small amount of previously fermented product was added to fresh milk and the mixture kept at a suitable temperature. This was the origin of "starters."

A *starter* is a pure or mixed culture of microorganisms that is added to a substrate to initiate a desired fermentation. Starters are widely used in the dairy industry to produce characteristic changes in the manufacture of butter, cultured milks, and cheese. Many of the same products could be manufactured without the use of starters, but the processes would be waste-

ful because the proper mixture of microorganisms is not always present in a given batch of milk.

Butter starters are used in the manufacture of several products: they ripen cream to be used in making butter, they are used to manufacture cultured sour cream and buttermilk, and they improve the flavor and texture of cottage and cream cheese. Butter starters contain two types of bacteria: (1) vigorous lactic acid–producing species such as *S. lactis* and *S. cremoris* and (2) bacteria that produce flavor and aroma compounds— *Leuconostoc citrovorum* or *L. dextranicum*. These two types of bacteria will grow indefinitely together if handled properly. The flavor and aroma of sour cream butter are attributed to diacetyl, which is produced by the *Leuconostoc* species from citrates normally present in small amounts in milk.

Cheese starters vary according to the cheese to be manufactured. Cheddar cheese, for example, may be manufactured by use of a single strain culture of *S. lactis* or *S. cremoris. Lactobacillus, Propionibacterium* or other bacterial species, or yeasts or molds assist in developing the flavor, aroma, and texture characteristic of other cheeses.

Fermented Milks. Fermented milks are prepared by cultivating lactic bacteria in milk. The lactic acid thickens or curdles the milk and produces the desired sour flavor. The nature of the product depends on the source of the milk (cows, goats, sheep, mares, buffaloes, etc.), the temperature to which it is heated before inoculation, the kinds of microorganisms in the starter, and the incubation temperature. Fermented milk products include cultured buttermilk, Bulgarian buttermilk, and acidophilus milk, all of which are used in the United States; yoghurt, also popular in this country but originally derived from the eastern Mediterranean area; the Armenian mazun, Egyptian leben, and Indian dadhi; kefir of the Balkan countries and koumiss of southern Russia.

Yoghurt can be made from the milk of cows, goats, sheep, or buffalo. Originally the milk was concentrated by boiling, inoculated with part of a previous batch of yoghurt, and kept at 38° to 46° C. until a thick curd developed, usually within 10 to 12 hours. The acidity attained was greater than 1 per cent —sometimes as great as 3 per cent. The high incubation temperature limited fermentation to *Streptococcus thermophilus* and *Lactobacillus bulgaricus,* the latter producing the strong final acidity.

Yoghurt is made commercially in the United States from milk concentrated under vacuum or by adding milk powder or condensed milk. The concentrated milk is heated at 80° to 90° C. to kill nonspore-forming bacteria and is then inoculated with a starter containing equal numbers of *S. thermophilus* and *L. bulgaricus.* After thorough mixing it is dispensed into the final retail jars or cartons, incubated at 45° C. for two and one-half to three and one-half hours, and then refrigerated. The acidity attained is about 0.9 per cent as lactic acid. The product has a heavy, smooth, custard-like consistency, and a mildly sour, nutty flavor. It can be kept one to two weeks under refrigeration. *S. thermophilus* initiates acid production and, at the end of the first hour of fermentation, outnumbers *L. bulgaricus,* which then grows rapidly and produces lactic acid and volatile products responsible for the characteristic flavor and aroma.

Butter. Butter contains approximately 80 per cent fat, small percentages of lactose and protein, and often 2.0 per cent salt. The remainder is water in the form of minute droplets dispersed throughout the butterfat. The salt is dissolved in this water.

Butter is made from either sweet or sour cream by churning, which separates the fat from most of the rest of the cream. The cream is usually pasteurized to destroy pathogenic bacteria and reduce the number of spoilage microorganisms. Butter culture is added if a more highly flavored and aromatic product is desired. After churning, the buttermilk is removed, and the butter is washed and finally "worked" to distribute the water droplets and salt, if added, uniformly.

Cheese. Cheese is the product made by separating the casein of milk from the liquid or whey. The butterfat often accompanies the casein, but most of the lactose and other soluble milk constituents remain in the whey. Approximately 400 kinds of cheese are known, and most of these can be prepared from any given batch of milk by properly regulating the conditions of manufacture.

Classification of Cheeses. Cheeses are classified according to their consistency and the use and nature of microbial ripening agents. The following outline lists the principal groups with examples of each:

A. *Unripened cheeses*
  1. Low fat (cottage cheese)
  2. High fat (cream cheese)
B. *Ripened cheeses*
  1. Hard cheeses (internal ripening)
    a. Ripened by bacteria (Cheddar cheese, Swiss cheese)
    b. Ripened by mold (Roquefort and other blue cheeses)
  2. Soft cheeses (ripening proceeds from outside)
    a. Ripened by bacteria (Limburger cheese)
    b. Ripened by bacteria and molds (Camembert cheese)

Principal Steps in Cheese Manufacture. A brief summary of the process of cheese making follows.

1. The milk is inoculated with a starter culture and warmed to a temperature favorable for acid production.

2. When a certain acidity has been reached, rennet extract is added. At the proper pH and temperature, curdling takes place within one-half to one hour.

3. The curd is cut into small cubes and the whey is drained off. Heat may be applied to hasten separation of the curd particles from the whey.

4. The curd is put into frames; it is then either pressed or allowed to stand to continue the removal of whey. The frames are removed as soon as the curd has set sufficiently to maintain its shape.

5. Salt is applied, either to the curd

before it is placed in the frames or to the outside of the pressed cheese.

Cottage cheese is highly perishable. It contains insufficient acid or salt to prevent microbial spoilage and must be constantly refrigerated. It is subject to spoilage by all kinds of microorganisms, including molds, yeasts, and slime-producing bacteria.

The flavor of raw cheese curd is very bland, and it is rubbery in consistency. During ripening, cheese develops a distinctive flavor and aroma, and its texture changes; a hard cheese becomes crumbly, and a soft cheese may become smooth and semiliquid. Chemical changes that accompany ripening include a marked increase in soluble nitrogen compounds, such as amino acids and ammonia. The fatty acid content of some cheeses also increases as butterfat is hydrolyzed. The flavor and aroma of well-ripened cheese are attributed to these various compounds.

Lactic acid formation is important in the early stages of cheese manufacture and curing. Acidity hastens curdling; suppresses the growth of undesirable gas-forming and putrefactive bacteria; activates the proteolytic enzyme pepsin, which is usually present in rennet extract; and helps the curd to fuse together and expel whey. Acidity therefore assists in the formation of the curd and in the texture and flavor changes of the young cheese.

Ripened cheeses are subdivided into hard varieties and soft varieties. Hard cheeses such as Cheddar, Swiss, and Roquefort contain no more than 39 per cent moisture. They are ripened by microorganisms growing throughout the cheese; bacteria are the principal ripening agents, but Roquefort and the other blue cheeses are ripened by molds. Ripening usually requires several months. Steps in the manufacture of Cheddar cheese are illustrated in Figure 18-5.

Soft cheeses contain more than 39 per cent water. They are ripened by molds, yeasts, and bacteria growing on the surface; these organisms produce hydrolytic enzymes, which diffuse inward, digesting the protein of the curd. Ripening is complete as soon as the enzymes reach the center of the cheese, which usually requires four to eight weeks. Cheeses of this kind are small because the greater water content of the curd prevents larger cheeses from holding their form and because the prolonged ripening period would result in over-ripening of the outer portions.

FOODBORNE DISEASES

Microbial diseases spread by food are either food infections or food intoxications. A food infection is an illness caused by invasion of the host by pathogenic microorganisms from food; food intoxication is produced by a poison or *toxin* present in food when it is consumed.

Food Infection

Food infections are of two types: (1) those in which the pathogen does not ordinarily multiply in the food but is merely transmitted by it—typhoid and paratyphoid fevers, dysentery, brucellosis, cholera, tuberculosis, and diphtheria are included; (2) those in which the pathogen multiplies in the food, usually to very high numbers, before ingestion—gastroenteritis caused by many species of *Salmonella* is the principal example.

Typhoid Fever. Food infection of the first type is illustrated by typhoid fever. *Salmonella typhosa,* the causative organism, enters foods on the hands of carriers or ambulatory patients. A *carrier* is an individual who does not have an active infection, but who harbors and excretes the organism. Excreted bacteria frequently contaminate the hands of both patients and carriers.

S. typhosa survives well in nonacid foods, and only small numbers are needed to initiate infection in susceptible individuals. Major epidemics of typhoid fever in the past were usually transmitted by water or milk, but emphasis on sanitation in the past 50

Figure 18-5a. The first step in making Cheddar cheese. The milk in the vat has just curdled and is ready to cut. ←

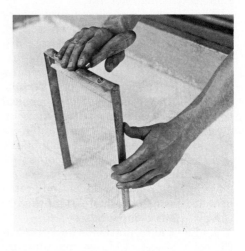

Figure 18-5b. The soft curd is cut into small cubes with "knives" such as this. ⟶

Figure 18-5c. The draining curd is cut into "mats." ←

Figure 18-5d. The "mats" are turned frequently to promote expulsion of whey, and the curd gradually fuses together until its consistency resembles that of chicken breast meat. ⟶

Figure 18-5f. The salted curd is packed in frames and pressed overnight. Part of the press is shown in the upper right corner. $\longrightarrow$

Figure 18-5e. The matted curd is milled and salted. $\longleftarrow$

$\longleftarrow$
Figure 18-5g. The pressed cheeses are removed from the frames and cured in a cool room for several weeks or months. The tall cheeses are a variety of Cheddar called longhorn. The flat cheeses with rounded edges at the right are Swiss.

years has reduced the importance of these modes of transmission in most civilized countries. The smaller outbreaks of this disease that are now observed are attributed largely to carriers and foodborne infection.

The majority of cases of paratyphoid fever and dysentery are also probably the result of food contamination by carriers. In this country the control of food infection transmitted by carriers is based principally on bacteriologic examination of food handlers.

Intestinal diseases are also disseminated by means of vegetables such as lettuce, watercress, radishes, and cabbages in countries where human excrement is used as fertilizer.

Gastroenteritis. The gastroenteritis type of food infection is caused by several dozen species of *Salmonella* and occasionally by certain *Streptococcus* or *Shigella* species.

The incubation period following ingestion of food in which gastroenteritis *Salmonella* species have multiplied is short—usually eight to 24 hours—because the infecting dose of bacteria is often several billion cells. The incubation period in the paratyphoid fevers is one to 10 days; that in typhoid fever is 10 to 14 days.

Symptoms of gastroenteritis include severe headache, nausea, vomiting, diarrhea, and abdominal pain. Fever may be as high as 102° F. Symptoms gradually abate, and recovery occurs within one week. Mortality is less than 1 per cent. Infants and old persons are more susceptible, and most of the deaths occur in these age groups.

Many species of *Salmonella* have been isolated from foodborne gastroenteritis; *S. typhimurium* and *S. enteritidis* head the list. Foods by which these organisms are transmitted include meats and fish, milk, and eggs or egg products (e.g., spray-dried egg powder). Partially cooked meat products such as sausage are frequently responsible. Vegetables, cereals, and fruits are rarely involved.

Foods are infected by two principal methods. Some *Salmonella* species are natural pathogens of domestic and other animals, and their meat or products may contain the organism. Eggs from infected chickens may be contaminated and the bacteria may be present in the yolk. Between 2 and 10 per cent of hogs and cattle have been reported infected with *Salmonella*.

Foods also become infected with *Salmonella* during preparation for eating. Not only do human carriers inoculate foods with these organisms, but infected rats and mice that inhabit storage warehouses and kitchens also contaminate foods.

Salmonella species are nonspore-forming rod bacteria; they are killed within a few minutes at 60° to 65° C. and therefore should not survive in properly cooked foods. However, infected raw eggs used in uncooked salad dressings, custards, or fillings contain an adequate inoculum, especially if the food is stored for several hours without proper refrigeration.

Food Intoxication

The exotoxins manufactured by certain strains of *Staphylococcus aureus* or by *Clostridium botulinum* are of particular concern in food intoxications.

Staphylococcal Food Intoxication. The average incubation period after the ingestion of food containing staphylococcal enterotoxin is about two hours. Symptoms include headache, nausea, violent vomiting, and severe prostration. Fever may be absent. Recovery is rapid and usually occurs within 24 hours. Fatalities are rare.

Staphylococci are widespread upon the skin and mucous membranes of the human body, both in healthy individuals and in those with upper respiratory disease, boils, and other infections; some of these organisms are capable of producing the enterotoxin. Food may thus be inoculated with these bacteria, and when the food is stored for a few hours without proper refrigeration there is ample opportunity for the production of a considerable quantity of toxin.

The foods most commonly involved include salads, bakery products containing cream or custard fillings, and creamed potatoes; canned or potted meat or fish, meat pies, pressed beef, ham, and tongue have also been implicated. Staphylococcal enterotoxin is unusual because it is thermostable; that is, it withstands boiling for 30 minutes or longer, and therefore is not destroyed by cooking.

Botulism. Botulism is caused by ingestion of the exotoxin of *Cl. botulinum,* one of the most powerful poisons known. The toxin is produced in food before it is consumed and is absorbed by the mucous membranes of the stomach and the upper intestine. Animal experiments indicate that a fatal dose for an adult man may be as small as 0.01 mg. or even less, an amount that might be contained within a single infected bean.

The incubation period is usually less than 24 hours. Symptoms include vomiting, constipation, double vision, thirst, paralysis of the pharynx, and secretion of thick, viscid saliva. Consciousness remains unaffected until the patient is near death; the temperature is usually subnormal. Death may occur within 24 hours after onset or may be delayed for a week. Complete recovery may require as long as six or eight months. Sixty to 70 per cent of cases are fatal.

Nearly all outbreaks of botulism are attributed to foods that have been smoked, pickled, or canned, allowed to stand for a time, and then eaten without cooking or with insufficient cooking. Most outbreaks in this country are attributed to canned vegetables, such as olives, corn, string beans, spinach, and peas. Outbreaks in Europe are usually associated with sausages, ham, preserved meats, fowl, or fish. Frequently the foods have been obviously spoiled, but this is not always true.

The danger in home canning lies in the fact that *Cl. botulinum* is fairly widely distributed in garden soil and its spores are frequently very resistant to heat. Boiling for several hours is necessary to ensure their destruction, and even prolonged heating under steam pressure is necessary to kill them in nonacid foods.

Fortunately the toxin of *Cl. botulinum* is destroyed in a few minutes at 65° C. and very quickly at the boiling temperature. Home canned food should always be heated at the boiling point for several minutes before use.

Milkborne Disease

The sources of pathogenic microorganisms in milk are either infected cows or human handlers.

Cattle Pathogens Transmitted by Milk. Pathogens of cattle transmitted to man by means of milk include the organisms that cause tuberculosis, brucellosis, septic sore throat, scarlet fever, and Q fever. Pasteurization markedly reduces this source of human infection, but persons who continue to use raw milk run the risk of acquiring these diseases.

Tuberculosis of cattle is particularly likely to be transmitted to infants and children, who consume greater amounts of milk than adults.

Brucellosis (i.e., undulant fever), is caused by three species of *Brucella,* one of which produces contagious abortion of cattle and is discharged in the milk of infected animals. The human disease is characterized by fever, lassitude, and general debilitation; it persists for many months.

Mastitis and other udder infections are caused by hemolytic streptococci or by *Staphylococcus aureus.* Hemolytic streptococci are versatile pathogens capable of producing a variety of disease conditions. The strains that cause udder infections in cattle may produce septic sore throat or even scarlet fever in man. The growth of *S. aureus* in milk may be accompanied by the production of the thermostable enterotoxin previously mentioned (page 358).

A rickettsial pathogen, *Coxiella burnetti,* the cause of Q fever in cattle, sheep, and goats, is transmitted to man by means of milk. Symptoms in man include fever and an acute but localized lung inflammation; mortality is low.

Human Pathogens Transmitted by Milk. Pathogens derived from man are transmitted by milk as a result of carelessness or ignorance. Persons with active cases of disease or carriers may unintentionally inoculate milk or dairy equipment with human pathogens, including the typhoid, paratyphoid, and dysentery bacteria; hemolytic streptococci; and diphtheria bacteria. In many localities a typhoid carrier is not permitted to engage in dairying operations as long as his carrier state persists. Persons with any kind of intestinal or respiratory infection must be extremely careful to avoid distributing their pathogens to milk or milk utensils and should not rely upon pasteurization to keep milk safe.

MAINTENANCE OF MILK QUALITY

High quality milk has a low bacterial count and contains no pathogenic bacteria; it is of good flavor and adequate keeping quality, normal in composition, and free from extraneous matter and toxic substances. The sanitary quality of milk is appropriately judged by its bacterial population. Federal regulations proposed by the United States Public Health Service apply to milk used in interstate commerce. The U.S.P.H.S. ordinance and code is recommended for adoption by states or smaller governmental agencies; many of these have adopted even more strict requirements than those recommended.

Grades of Milk

Several grades or classes of milk are distinguished on the basis of the number of bacteria they contain (Table 18-7). Many states or municipalities now permit the sale of only pasteurized milk. Grade A pasteurized milk must be prepared from raw milk that contains no more than 200,000 bacteria per milliliter; after pasteurization it must contain no more than 30,000 bacteria per milliliter, and the coliform count must not exceed 10 per milliliter. Certified milk is produced under conditions rigorously controlled by the American Association of Medical Milk Commissions, Inc.

Methods of Testing Milk

Standard Plate Count. The plate count is the official method of counting bacteria in pasteurized milk and is often used in examining raw milk. Dilutions

are prepared and plates poured with either yeast extract-tryptone-dextrose agar (Difco Laboratories) or milk-protein-hydrolysate-glucose agar (Baltimore Biological Laboratories). The plates are incubated at 32° C. or 35° C. and counted after 48 hours. Plates containing between 30 and 300 colonies are counted if available, and the results are multiplied by the proper dilution factor and expressed as "standard plate count per milliliter (or gram)." The expression *standard plate count* is used in preference to *bacteria* because milk contains chains or clumps of bacteria that yield single colonies.

Direct Microscopic Count. The number of bacteria in milk can be determined by direct microscopic examination. A special capillary pipette (Breed) or special loop is used to measure 0.01 ml. of milk, which is spread uniformly over an area of 1 sq. cm. on a *clean* microscope slide. After drying, the film is defatted by a solvent, such as xylene, and stained with methylene blue or another appropriate dye. The stained film is then examined under the oil immersion objective of the microscope. The area of the microscope field must first be standardized by measurement with a stage micrometer and a *microscope factor* is calculated, by means of which the number of bacteria seen per field can be translated into the number of bacteria per milliliter of the milk sample. A microscope whose oil immersion field has a diameter of 160 μ has a microscope factor of about 500,000; this means that

Table 18-7. Bacterial Standards for Raw and Pasteurized Milk Recommended by the U. S. Public Health Service Milk Ordinance

Grade	Raw Milk for Pasteurization; Standard Plate Count Not to Exceed	Pasteurized Milk	
		Standard Plate Count Not to Exceed	Coliform Bacteria Not to Exceed
	PER MILLILITER		
A	200,000	30,000	10
B	1,000,000	50,000	10
C	No limit	No limit	No limit
Certified	10,000	500	1

each bacterium seen with the microscope represents 500,000 bacteria in the milk sample. Bacterial clumps are usually counted rather than individual cells, because the results are more nearly like those of the standard plate count.

The direct microscopic count has many advantages. It is more rapid than the standard plate count; results are obtained in a few minutes by a skilled operator, and the stained slide can be filed and kept for a permanent record. It is less expensive, requiring a smaller outlay for equipment, media and time. Moreover, the morphology of the organisms indicates improper practices or conditions, which should promptly be corrected. Large numbers of micrococci are often found when utensils are inadequately cleaned; improperly cooled milk usually contains many cocci in pairs or short chains; and the long-chained streptococci that may cause mastitis are easily recognized.

The microscopic count cannot be used satisfactorily with milk of low bacterial content, because many fields must be examined before a single bacterium is encountered. Moreover, recently heated milk contains bacteria still capable of retaining stains and hence appears to possess a higher bacterial count than is actually the case. The microscopic count is valuable principally as a method of rough grading, and is often used by dairies to classify incoming raw milk before pasteurization.

Dye Reduction Tests. The ability of bacteria to transfer hydrogen to dyes is utilized in the dye reduction test for grading raw milk. The amount of hydrogen transferred depends on the species and number of bacteria, the temperature, and other factors. The conditions for the test are kept constant, and the assumption is made that the microbial flora of raw milk samples is generally similar. The number of organisms is therefore the unknown factor, and the greater the number of bacteria, the shorter is the time required to reduce the dye. The dyes used are those that decolorize (e.g., methylene blue) or change color characteristically (e.g., resazurin)

as hydrogen is accepted. The time required for a given color change is noted.

The methylene blue reduction test is performed by mixing 10 ml. of milk with sufficient methylene blue solution to produce a final dye concentration of one part in 300,000 parts of milk. Test tubes containing the mixture are placed in a waterbath at 37° C. and observed periodically. The reduction endpoint is 80 per cent decolorization of the methylene blue; that is, the upper 20 per cent of the milk may retain the blue color. A milk sample that produces this endpoint within one-half hour contains many bacteria, probably millions per milliliter. Grade A raw milk to be pasteurized should not reduce methylene blue in less than five hours.

Resazurin undergoes a series of color changes during reduction from its slate-blue oxidized form through blue, purple, lavender, and pink; finally it becomes colorless. Reduction tests require only one hour of incubation, and the color developed is compared with standard colors.

Dye reduction tests are used to grade raw milk to be pasteurized or evaporated. The tests can be performed by unskilled help following simple directions, and results are obtained within a few hours. Abnormal milks are often detected quickly enough to be diverted to other uses. The tests are not appropriate for final examination of pasteurized milk.

Phosphatase Test. The phosphatase test is used to check the adequacy of pasteurization and to detect any admixture of raw milk with pasteurized milk. The enzyme phosphatase is secreted by the mammary gland of the cow and is always present in raw milk. Its normal action is hydrolysis of phosphoric acid esters.

Phosphatase is only slightly more resistant to heat than *M. tuberculosis* throughout the entire range of pasteurization conditions, both by the holding method and the flash method. Pasteurization practices can therefore be controlled by testing milk for its phosphatase content. Sensitive tests detect slight irregularities in the temperature or duration of heating or the addition of as little as 1 ml. of raw milk to 1000 ml. pasteurized milk.

The phosphatase test is performed by mixing milk and a buffer substrate containing disodium phenyl phosphate and incubating at 37° to 45° C. for a short time. Phosphatase hydrolyzes disodium phenyl phosphate, and the resulting phenol is detected by adding BQC indicator (2,6-dibromoquinone chloroimide), which produces a blue compound, indophenol.

Thermoduric Bacteria. Thermoduric bacteria as defined by dairy bacteriologists are those that survive pasteurization. Their significance for the milk processor derives from the fact that they do survive pasteurization and contribute to the bacterial count of pasteurized milk. They are not necessarily harmful, and they produce acid or digest proteins only slowly. Thermoduric bacteria are found in milk as the result of poor sanitation and carelessness. They are derived from dirty utensils, unclean cows, dirty milking barns, and also from unsanitary dairy plants.

The presence of thermoduric bacteria in milk is detected by laboratory pasteurization of samples of the raw milk. A 10 ml. specimen in a screw-capped vial is heated for 30 minutes at 61.7° C. and then plated. A standard of 5000 to 10,000 thermoduric bacteria per milliliter is often set; this limit can easily be met by proper attention to sanitary conditions.

Inspection

Inspection of milk-producing farms and processing plants is a necessary part of any program for maintaining the sanitary quality of milk. The U. S. Public Health Service Milk Ordinance contains numerous recommendations regarding conditions on farms and in milk plants: recommendations concerning removal of manure from barns, general sanitation, cooling of milk, and so forth. Farms and milk plants from which grade A milk is secured must be inspected at least once every six months. Both the raw milk from each farm and the finished product must be tested at least four times every six months.

Tests of Cattle and Personnel

Detection of Infected Cattle. Tuberculosis, brucellosis, and mastitis in cattle are detectable by examination of the animals or by appropriate tests of their milk.

Tuberculosis. Past or present tuberculosis is detected by the tuberculin test.

Brucellosis. Laboratory diagnosis of brucellosis (contagious abortion) in cattle consists in demonstrating the presence of *Brucella* antibodies in the blood or milk of infected animals. Brucellosis in cattle is controlled by eliminating infected animals from herds.

Mastitis. Mastitis is more serious to the milk producer than to the consumer because milk production decreases. The presence of excessive leukocytes in milk and an alkaline reaction indicate probable mastitis; the causative organism is determined by microscopic examination and by isolation and identification.

Examination of Human Handlers. Human diseases spread by milk fall into two classes: intestinal and respiratory. Detection of undiagnosed or ambulatory cases and of carriers among the hundreds of thousands of farm and dairy personnel is an almost impossible task.

Carriers of intestinal infection can be detected by the isolation of pathogens from stool samples or rectal swabs; special enrichment media that suppress normal coliform bacteria are used, but even so, repeated examinations are necessary. Respiratory pathogens are detected in cultures from sputum samples and throat and nasal swabs. Blood agar and other enriched media are required to cultivate these organisms, many of which are nutritionally fastidious.

Employees of dairy plants from which the final pasteurized dairy product goes to the consumer should be examined periodically for intestinal and perhaps even respiratory pathogens. Regardless of whether this can be done, employee education will assist materially in controlling the spread of milkborne infection. Most individuals would be startled to know how much of the time their hands are contaminated by bacteria from their own oral, respiratory, and intestinal excretions.

MICROBIOLOGY OF FOODS AND DAIRY PRODUCTS

SUMMARY

The microbial spoilage of foods exemplifies the application of ecologic principles, because the flora and hence the type of alteration produced depend on the source of the food, its chemical nature, and the environmental conditions under which it is stored. The basic information is summed up as follows: (1) molds and yeasts are favored by acidity; (2) yeasts grow particularly well in sugar media; (3) molds tolerate materials of high osmotic pressure; (4) molds, yeasts, and bacteria can grow at low to moderate temperatures, but only certain bacteria can grow at moderate to high temperatures; (5) molds and a few bacteria are strongly aerobic, whereas yeasts and many bacteria can grow under anaerobic conditions.

Preservation is accomplished by (1) control of moisture, (2) chemicals, (3) storage at low temperature, (4) destruction of microorganisms at high temperature, (5) irradiation. Some manufactured foods are preserved by chemicals (e.g., acids) produced in them by microorganisms.

Milk preservation poses a special problem because it is such an excellent culture medium and is so difficult to produce aseptically. The microorganisms in milk multiply rapidly unless prevented by prompt refrigeration. Pasteurization kills pathogenic bacteria and reduces the number of other organisms to a few hundred or thousand per milliliter.

The safety and "keeping" quality of milk are best judged by testing; the bacterial count and the phosphatase test are especially important. The testing program, coupled with continuous inspection, helps to maintain satisfactory quality.

There are two principal types of foodborne microbial disease. Food infections are caused by actual invasion of the host tissues by microorganisms in the food. Food intoxications are produced by bacterial toxins formed in the product before it is consumed. These diseases can be prevented by careful attention to sanitation in preparation, handling, and storage and by proper cooking.

STUDY QUESTIONS

1. What is a "spoiled" food?
2. Discuss microbial spoilage of food as an aspect of ecology.
3. Describe the normal sources of microorganisms on meat, fish, vegetables and in dairy and bakery products.
4. Although sterilization of cans or jars of food might be desirable, it is not always necessary. Explain.
5. What fault in the preservation operations is indicated by each of the following instances of spoilage? Explain.
   a. Mold growth at the top of a jar of home-canned tomatoes.

  b. Canned corn that has a putrid odor when the container is opened.

  c. Frozen hamburger that smells foul when thawed.

6. Why is it important to exhaust all air from the pressure cooker when processing jars of food?

7. What is the preservative agent in sauerkraut? What is its source? What happens if molds and film yeasts grow on it? How can growth of these organisms be prevented?

8. What are thermoduric bacteria? What is their significance in raw milk? in pasteurized milk?

9. What is the purpose of pasteurization of milk? How is the process determined? How can milk be tested to determine whether it has been adequately pasteurized?

10. What is the significance of coliform bacteria in raw milk? in pasteurized milk?

11. What are starter cultures? What is their purpose?

12. What changes do microorganisms bring about in the manufacture of cheese?

SUPPLEMENTARY READING

The monographic treatise by Tanner contains a wealth of detail on microbial contamination and populations in foods, together with methods for examining all kinds of food products. Frazier's textbook, *Food Microbiology,* begins with a section on important food microorganisms, and then discusses preservation and spoilage, foods produced by microorganisms, foodborne disease, sanitation, and control. This book contains much useful information in easily read form. *Microbiological Quality of Foods* is a provocative volume containing over two dozen papers presented at a conference in 1962. One of the best known books in the field of dairy microbiology in this country is that by Hammer and Babel. Milk tests are described, as are the growth of bacteria in milk and the changes produced, milk plant processes and operations, and pathogens that may be present in milk. A series of chapters treats of the microbiology of various products including ice cream, fermented milks, butter, and cheeses. *Dairy Microbiology* by Foster et al. is somewhat similar in plan. Introductory chapters apply the principles of microbiology to the dairy industry, and then individual products are discussed in considerable detail—chemistry and microbiology of manufacture, defects, preservation, and testing. Elliker's *Practical Dairy Bacteriology* is intended for use as a teaching text for students who may not have had previous work in microbiology. The subject is introduced and then applied in practical discussions of procedures used in the handling and manufacture of milk and other dairy products. *Standard Methods for the Examination of Dairy Products* is a necessity in any dairy bacteriology laboratory, and the *Milk Ordinance and Code* contains the recommended standards of quality.

American Public Health Association: *Standard Methods for the Examination of Dairy Products,* 11th ed. New York, American Public Health Association, 1960.

Elliker, P. R.: *Practical Dairy Bacteriology.* New York, McGraw-Hill Book Co., Inc., 1949.

Foster, E. M., Nelson, F. E., Speck, M. L., Doetsch, R. N., and Olson, J. C.: *Dairy Microbiology.* Englewood Cliffs, N. J., Prentice-Hall, Inc., 1957.

Frazier, W. C.: *Food Microbiology.* New York, McGraw-Hill Book Co., Inc., 1958.

Hammer, B. W., and Babel, F. J.: *Dairy Bacteriology,* 4th ed. New York, John Wiley & Sons, Inc., 1957.

Slanetz, L. W., Chichester, C. O., Gaufin, A. R., and Ordal, Z. J. (Eds.): *Microbiological Quality of Foods.* New York, Academic Press, Inc., 1963.

Tanner, F. W.: *The Microbiology of Foods,* 2d ed. Champaign, Ill., Garrard Press, 1944.

United States Public Health Service: *Milk Ordinance and Code.* Public Health Bulletin 220, 1953.

INDUSTRIAL MICROBIOLOGY

The microbiologist plays a constant and important role in any microbial manufacturing process. He selects the microorganism to be used, devises the most favorable culture medium, and chooses proper cultural conditions (aeration, agitation, pH, temperature). He tries out the process in test tubes and flasks in the laboratory and then in the pilot plant. Methods that are satisfactory in the laboratory do not always give the best results on a larger scale, and readjustments may be required for commercial application. Constant control is necessary throughout the manufacturing process to ensure economy of materials and time and uniformly high quality of the product.

Industrial applications of microbiology include mass cultivation of microorganisms, manufacture of various chemicals, and textile manufacture.

MASS CULTIVATION OF MICROORGANISMS

Outside the laboratory, microorganisms are cultivated on a large scale principally for use in other industries. Bakers' yeast is used as a leavening agent by commercial bakers as well as in the home. Farmers inoculate legume seed with rhizobia, the root nodule bacteria, to ensure well nodulated plants. Butter and cheese starter cultures are necessary in dairy manufacture. In addition, yeasts and molds have been used as food or feed at one time or another, and mass cultures of pathogenic bacteria are required for the preparation of immunizing materials for the protection of man and domestic animals.

Bakers' Yeast

Bakers' yeast is a strain of *Saccharomyces cerevisiae* carefully selected for its capacity to produce abundant gas quickly, its viability during ordinary storage, and its ability to produce a desirable flavor.

A pure culture of the chosen yeast must first be grown in the laboratory and gradually "built up" to larger and larger volume by transfer from test tube to small flask to large flask, and so forth, until eventually sufficient yeast is obtained to inoculate the main tank or fermenter. Great care is taken to avoid contamination at any stage of development of the culture.

The medium contains 0.5 to 1.5 per cent sugar, nitrogen in the form of peptones, peptides, amino acids, or ammonia, and mineral salts. The sugar is derived from molasses or from grains that have been cooked and treated with amylases to digest the starch. The reaction is adjusted to pH 4.4 to 4.6 by addition of sulfuric acid or by preliminary fermentation with *Lactobacillus delbrückii*. Acidity favors growth of the yeast and discourages most bacteria that might cause spoilage. The pH of the medium is controlled during yeast multiplication by addition of ammonia or sulfuric acid as required.

The optimum temperature is 25° to 26° C.; the temperature frequently rises during fermentation, and cooling coils keep it from exceeding 30° C. Vigorous aeration provides the oxygen required for rapid growth. It will be recalled that a disaccharide such as sucrose or maltose is first hydrolyzed by yeast and then oxidized under aerobic conditions:

$$C_{12}H_{22}O_{11} + H_2O \longrightarrow 2C_6H_{12}O_6$$

$$2C_6H_{12}O_6 + 12O_2 \longrightarrow 12CO_2 + 12H_2O$$

This reaction yields the maximum available energy, a large part of which is utilized for synthesis of microbial protoplasm. The yeast cells multiply rapidly and exhaust the sugar supply within 10 or 11 hours.

The yeast is removed from the fermented medium by centrifugation, washed, and mixed with starch or corn meal before being pressed into cake form. The starch or corn meal helps to maintain the shape of the yeast cake. Yeast cakes must be kept cool to preserve the cells and to retard spoilage by other microorganisms. Today, an increasing amount of yeast is dried to about 10 per cent moisture; dried yeast remains viable for several months without spoilage.

Yeast for animal feed can be manufactured from waste materials such as wood shavings and sawdust, straw, corn cobs, and other agricultural waste. The carbohydrates in these materials must first be converted into fermentable form, usually maltose or glucose, either by enzymic digestion or by acid hydrolysis.

Microorganisms for Medical Use

The theory and principles of artificial immunization of man and animals will be discussed in Chapter 21. The immunizing agents, which are known as *vaccines,* are heavy suspensions of attenuated (i.e., weakened) or killed microorganisms. Microbial strains are carefully selected to possess the greatest possible immunizing power.

Vaccines are manufactured under strictly controlled conditions. Bacterial vaccines are prepared from cultures grown on agar or broth media. Cells on agar are suspended in saline (0.85 per cent sodium chloride); cells in broth are removed by centrifugation. The bacteria are washed by centrifugation with saline to eliminate extraneous material from the culture medium; they are finally suspended in saline at a standard concentration or density (e.g., one billion cells per milliliter).

Rickettsiae and viruses must be cultivated in living tissue: an animal body, chick embryo, or tissue culture. Vaccines prepared from these materials contain substances derived from the animal or tissue, which contribute nothing useful and may occasionally cause allergic or other undesirable side reactions. It is possible in some cases to reduce these effects by harvesting only portions of the infected tissue (e.g., certain organs of an inoculated animal, allantoic fluid from a chick embryo).

Many vaccines are killed or inactivated by heat (55° to 60° C. for 30 to 60 minutes), ultraviolet irradiation, or chemicals (formaldehyde, phenol, etc.). Other vaccines consist of organisms attenuated so that they are unable to produce disease. Pasteur attenuated *Bacillus anthracis* by cultivating it at

42° to 43° C. He also attenuated the virus of hydrophobia by drying infected rabbit spinal cords for several days. Other viruses may be attenuated by cultivation in unnatural hosts; for example, the yellow fever virus lost its normal pathogenicity for man when grown in mice.

The final product is tested for its content of the proper immunizing material, its immunizing potency, its freedom from contamination, and, in the case of a killed vaccine, its sterility. It is dispensed in bottles or vials and stored at low temperature until used. Chemical preservatives are added when possible to prevent growth of contaminants; otherwise, low temperature is relied on for preservation as well as maintenance of immunizing potency.

MANUFACTURE OF MICROBIAL PRODUCTS

In addition to their use in the manufacture of dairy products and other fermented foods, microorganisms are utilized in the manufacture of numerous chemicals that are useful domestically or industrially or for the purpose of controlling disease: ethyl alcohol, acetic acid, solvents such as acetone and butyl alcohol, organic acids resulting from mold fermentations, antibiotics, enzymes, toxins, and toxoids.

Alcoholic Fermentation

The equation that describes the net result of the alcoholic fermentation by yeast:

$$C_6H_{12}O_6 \longrightarrow 2C_2H_5OH + 2CO_2$$

indicates that a sugar is the substrate and that the process is anaerobic. Ethyl alcohol and carbon dioxide accumulate in amounts as high as 90 per cent of the theoretical yield. Small amounts of other products usually are formed also.

The common yeasts can ferment the monosaccharides glucose and fructose and the disaccharides sucrose and maltose. Fruit juices, molasses, and other syrups can therefore be fermented with little preliminary treatment because they contain glucose, fructose, or sucrose. The polysaccharides starch and cellulose cannot be fermented directly by yeasts; they require preliminary hydrolysis by enzymes or acid to the disaccharide or monosaccharide stage.

Details of the process of alcoholic fermentation vary according to the desired product: beer, wine, distilled liquors, or industrial alcohol. Beer is manufactured from grains (i.e., a starchy source of carbohydrate), wines are made from fruit juices (i.e., sugar solutions), and distilled liquors and industrial alcohol may be made from either type of raw material.

Brewing. There are five major steps in the manufacture of beer or ale from grain: malting, mashing, fermenting, maturing, and finishing. Malting and mashing are concerned with the conversion of starch into fermentable form as maltose or glucose; fermentation is the actual production of alcohol and carbon dioxide; maturing is the aging process that improves the flavor of the beverage; finishing includes bottling and other steps necessary to market the product.

Malting. Malt is the chief raw material in the manufacture of beer and ale. It is germinated barley that has been dried and ground, and contains starch, proteins, and high concentrations of amylases and proteinases. Amylase converts the starch of barley and other grains such as wheat, corn, and rye into fermentable sugar. Most American beer is made from a mixture of grains in which barley malt represents 65 to 80 per cent of the raw material.

Barley grain is first *steeped* or soaked in water and then placed in a revolving drum to *germinate* at 15° to 21° C. for five to seven days. Germination is halted by drying when the sprout is about three-quarters of the length of the kernel, at which time the enzyme content is maximal. The dried malt can be stored without microbial spoilage, and the enzymes remain stable for a considerable period.

Barley malt is commonly used in Europe and America for converting starch into sugar for brewing. Mold amylase derived from *Aspergillus oryzae* is used for the same purpose in some countries; it is also used to produce sugars from grain and potatoes for manufacturing industrial alcohol.

Mashing. Mashing is the process by which the starch and proteins of malt and other grains are digested to produce *wort.* Wort contains dextrins, maltose and other sugars, protein breakdown products, minerals, and various growth factors.

Ground malt, with or without other cooked grain, is mixed with water at 65° to 75° C. and pH 5.0 to 5.8. After partial hydrolysis of the starch and protein, the solution is filtered, and hops are added if it is to be used for making beer or ale. Hops are the flowers of *Humulus lupulus* or *H. americana;* they contribute a characteristic flavor and mild antiseptic properties, which discourage the growth of certain spoilage bacteria.

Fermentation. Wort is inoculated heavily with a selected strain of *S. cerevisiae.* Yeasts used in brewing are classified as "top yeasts" or "bottom yeasts." Top yeasts float to the surface of a fermenting mixture; they are usually employed in making ale. Bottom yeasts settle in a fermentation tank; they are used in making beer. The beer fermentation continues for eight to 10 days at 6° to 12° C., whereas ale fermentation is complete in five to seven days at 14° to 23° C. The alcoholic content of beer is rarely more than six per cent; that of ale is often somewhat greater.

Maturing. Fresh beer or ale has a harsh flavor and other undesirable characteristics that are removed by maturing or aging. The fermented wort is refrigerated at approximately 0° C. for two weeks to several months. Unstable proteins, yeasts, resins, and other substances precipitate, the harshness disappears as esters are produced and the beer becomes mellow. Some of the harshness is attributed to fusel oils, actually higher alcohols, which are oxidized or esterified during aging.

Finishing. Finishing consists of carbonation, cooling, filtering, and "racking" or dispensing into barrels, bottles, or cans. Bottled or canned beer is usually pasteurized at 60° to 61° C. for 20 minutes to kill yeasts and any undesirable microorganisms that may be present.

Wine Manufacture. Wine is, by definition, the product made by the "normal alcoholic fermentation of the juice of sound, ripe grapes and the usual cellar treatment." Beverages produced by the alcoholic fermentation of other fruits and berries are also often called wines; for example, orange wine, peach wine, blackberry wine.

Preparation of the "Must." Each wine is best made from a particular type or variety of grape. In making red wines the grapes are crushed and stemmed, but the skins and seeds are left in the "must" or nutrient sugar solution of expressed juices. White wines are made from white grapes or from the juice of grapes from which the skins have been removed.

The pressed juice of grapes will undergo spontaneous alcoholic fermentation caused by yeasts normally present on grapes, and in fact the characteristic qualities of famous wines are attributed in part to strains of yeast found in certain localities. However, undesirable molds, wild yeasts, and bacteria are also likely to be present, and many wine makers now destroy these by adding sulfur dioxide to the must.

Fermentation. A starter of a selected strain of *Saccharomyces ellipsoideus* is added to the must; aeration promotes rapid early growth, but conditions are soon permitted to become anaerobic for the alcoholic fermentation. After three to five days at 21° to 32° C., the wine is drawn off from the pomace (skins, seeds, etc.), and further fermentation takes place for seven to 11 days.

The yield of alcohol varies from 7 to 14 per cent according to the strain of yeast, the temperature of fermentation, and other factors.

Aging and Finishing. Fermentation is followed by *racking;* that is, the wine is drawn off from the sediment. It is then aged in wooden tanks for two to more than five years, during which time the wine gradually clears and develops bouquet and flavor as volatile esters are produced. Final *clarification* is accomplished by adding casein, gelatin, or Spanish clay and then filtering. The bottled wine may be pasteurized at 60° C. for 30 minutes.

Types of Wines. *Dry wines* are those in which "the fermentation of the sugars is practically complete." They contain too little sugar to be detected by the sense of taste. In *sweet wines,* "the alcoholic fermentation has been arrested," and the sugar content is great enough to be detected by taste. *Fortified wines* contain added alcohol in the form of brandy (i.e., the product resulting from distillation of wine). Fortified wines usually contain not less than 17 per cent alcohol, whereas the alcohol content of natural wines is less than 14 per cent. *Sparkling wines* contain carbon dioxide; the final stages of fermentation take place within the bottle.

Distilled Liquors. The characteristic flavor and aroma of a distilled liquor depend on the nature of the solution distilled. Whiskey is distilled fermented grain mash; it contains 40 to 55 per cent ethyl alcohol. Bourbon is whiskey prepared from a mash in which corn is the predominant grain; rye whiskey is manufactured from a mash in which rye grain predominates. Brandy usually contains 40 to 50 per cent alcohol and is prepared by distillation of fermented fruit juice, that is, wine. Rum is produced by distillation of fermented molasses or other sugar cane by-products and contains not less than 40 per cent alcohol. Gin is usually produced by extracting juniper berries with alcohol and distilling off the alcohol; it contains volatile extractives from the berries.

Cordials and liqueurs are sweetened alcoholic distillates from fruits, flowers, leaves, etc.

Acetic Acid Production

The equation for the production of acetic acid (vinegar):

$$C_2H_5OH + O_2 \longrightarrow CH_3COOH + H_2O$$

indicates that a source of ethyl alcohol is necessary and that the process is aerobic. The alcohol is usually derived from an alcoholic fermentation without distillation.

Vinegar is a solution containing at least 4 per cent acetic acid and small amounts of alcohol, glycerin, esters, sugars, and salts. Most vinegar is made from wine, apple cider, or fermented malt.

Acetobacter. The microorganisms that produce acetic acid from ethyl alcohol are species of *Acetobacter, A. aceti, A. orleanense, A. schützenbachii,* and others. They are widely distributed in the soil and hence in the air, and are almost universally present on grapes, apples, and other fruits; the juices therefore usually undergo acetic fermentation following spontaneous alcoholic fermentation unless precautions are taken to prevent it.

Home Method. Vinegar is commonly made at home from cider, grape juice, or miscellaneous pooled fruit juices in a barrel provided with two openings. Yeast naturally present or deliberately added ferments the sugar, and during this period the openings are closed except for a trap to release gas pressure. Cessation of gas evolution is a sign that the alcoholic fermentation has ceased. The barrel should be laid on its side and the openings unstoppered to permit air circulation. Several weeks or months are required for spontaneous vinegar fermentation, and periodic sampling is necessary to ascertain when the product is of suitable strength.

More satisfactory results may be secured if the yeast is allowed to settle after the alcoholic fermentation. The solution is carefully drawn off and transferred to a vinegar barrel and inoculated and acidified by adding 10 to 25 per cent of pure vinegar. When fermentation is complete the vinegar should be bottled and stoppered tightly to prevent continued growth of *Acetobacter,* because these organisms can oxidize acetic acid after the alcohol concentration drops below 1 or 2 per cent, thus reducing the strength of the vinegar. Aging for a year or more greatly improves the flavor and aroma of the product. The vinegar may finally be pasteurized.

During acetic fermentation the bacteria grow as a slimy zoogleal mat or membrane over the surface of the solution, where they have access to both ethyl alcohol and oxygen. If the mat is disturbed and sinks to the bottom

("mother of vinegar"), acetification stops until another mat forms.

Orleans Method. The French or Orleans process of manufacturing vinegar employs casks of about 200 liters (50 gallons) capacity. These are one-third filled with good vinegar, and 10 to 15 liters of wine are added at weekly intervals. After five weeks, 10 to 15 liters of vinegar are drawn off each week and the same amount of wine is added. Several holes are drilled in the barrel for air circulation, and often a grating or lattice of wood is provided to support the film of *Acetobacter.* This process is more or less continuous but requires constant attention and maintenance.

Generator Method. Vinegar or commercial acetic acid is made by the German or generator method in a tank

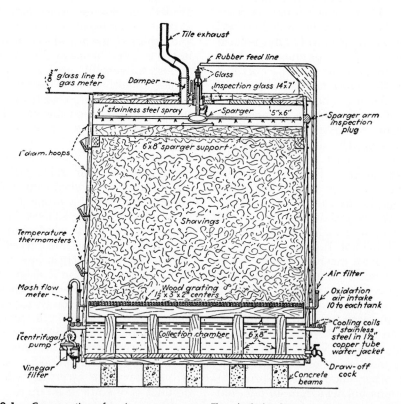

Figure 19-1. Cross section of a vinegar generator. The alcohol solution is sprayed over the shavings by the rotating sparger of stainless steel. It trickles slowly down and accumulates in the collection chamber at the bottom, from which it may be recirculated or flow to another generator. (From Frobisher: Fundamentals of Microbiology, 7th ed., Philadelphia, W. B. Saunders Co., 1962.)

that may be as large as 15 feet in diameter and 20 feet high (Fig. 19-1). A perforated false bottom supports beechwood shavings, and a perforated false top provides an opportunity for air to pass upward through the shavings.

The shavings are thoroughly soaked in good vinegar to inoculate them with *Acetobacter* organisms. An alcohol solution distributed over the false top trickles slowly over the shavings. The bacterial oxidation of alcohol to acetic acid on the shavings evolves heat, and the generator behaves like a chimney, drawing air in at the bottom. Cooling coils are sometimes necessary to keep the temperature within the favorable range of 25° to 30° C.

Several passages through a generator are required to produce vinegar of legal (4 per cent) strength. This is accomplished by recirculation or by use of several generators in series. Eight to 10 days are required for complete acetification in a recirculating generator. The yield under favorable conditions is 50 to 55 gm. of acetic acid for every 100 gm. of sugar. This is about 80 per cent of the theoretical yield.

Industrial Solvents

Acetone–Butyl Alcohol Fermentation. The acetone–butyl alcohol fermentation is one of several important microbiologic processes employed in the manufacture of useful solvents. In addition to butyl alcohol and acetone, ethyl alcohol, carbon dioxide, hydrogen, and small amounts of acetic and butyric acids are produced. Acetone is used in making explosives, cellulose acetate, and adhesives and is a common chemical solvent. Butyl alcohol is used in lacquers.

The principal raw materials used in the United States are molasses and corn. Sterile diluted molasses or cooked corn mash in 50,000 gallon fermentation tanks is inoculated with *Clostridium acetobutylicum* (Fig. 19-2). Fermentation under anaerobic conditions is complete after 48 to 72 hours at 37° C. (Fig. 19-3). The carbon dioxide and hydrogen gases that evolve during the fermentation account for approximately 60 per cent of the fermentable carbohydrate; they are recovered for industrial use. The neutral solvents, butyl alcohol, acetone,

Figure 19-2. The lower portion of 50,000 gallon fermentation tanks. (Courtesy of Commercial Solvents Corp.)

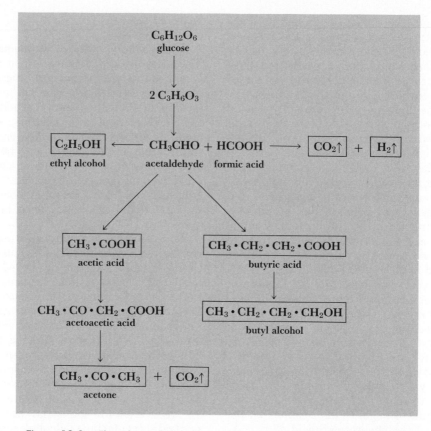

Figure 19-3.   Flow sheet of the acetone–butyl alcohol fermentation (abridged).

and ethyl alcohol, are recovered by fractional distillation.

Mold Fermentations

Molds manufacture numerous organic acids by partial oxidation of glucose or other substrate: gluconic, oxalic, citric, etc. Gluconic acid is produced by certain strains of *Aspergillus niger;* calcium gluconate is sometimes prescribed as a source of calcium for children and pregnant women. Gallic acid, produced by *A. niger* from tannin or tannic acid, is used in manufacturing inks and dyes.

Citric Acid Manufacture.   More than 10,000 tons of citric acid are produced each year in the United States. It is used in soft drinks and other foods and in medicinal preparations.

Many molds are able to produce citric acid; strains of *A. niger* are most

satisfactory commercially. The medium contains 14 to 20 per cent glucose or sucrose, ammonium nitrate as the source of nitrogen, and other salts; the pH is adjusted to 1.6 to 2.2 Fermentation in shallow pans at 25° to 30° C. requires seven to 10 days. A shallow pan provides a large mat of mold, which is necessary for converting sugar into citric acid. An aerated submerged tank process is also used; fermentation is more rapid by this method. The citric acid is precipitated as calcium citrate and recovered by treating with sulfuric acid.

Antibiotics

The manufacture of antibiotics is an industry that did not exist in 1941, but whose products sold for more than $300,000,000 ten years later. Fleming had discovered penicillin in 1929, and toward the end of the next decade Florey, Chain, Heatley, and Abraham devised methods of producing it in small amounts and found it amazingly effective in treating staphylococcal and streptococcal bloodstream infections. Since England was at this time devoting all her energies to the Second World War, Florey and Heatley came to the United States in 1941 and enlisted the assistance of governmental, industrial, and educational research laboratories. The rapidity with which all agencies tackled the problems of producing and testing penicillin is shown by the fact that in September, 1943, there was sufficient drug for the armed forces of the western allies.

In 1945, total production of penicillin was 12,000 pounds, and the price was $3870 per pound. By 1963, production had increased over 100-fold, and penicillin sold for $56 per pound. The rise in streptomycin production was comparable: 44,000 pounds were sold in 1950 and 870,000 in 1963.

During this time thousands of antibiotics were isolated, and dozens proved to be more or less useful. Waksman listed over 70 newly reported antibiotics from *Streptomyces* species in a two year period (1961–1962). Many new antibiotics are found to be identical with others previously announced, and the majority are too toxic or of too limited effectiveness for practical application.

Production of Penicillin. The mold from which Fleming isolated penicillin was subsequently identified as *Penicillium notatum*. Other strains were later found to yield greater amounts of the antibiotic, and a strain of a different species, *P. chrysogenum,* is now used for commercial production.

Early in World War II penicillin was produced by a surface culture method. Flasks or bottles containing a shallow layer of medium were inoculated with spores and incubated at 24° C. for five to eight days. The penicillin was then harvested from the medium. Strict asepsis was necessary, because contamina-tion by other microorganisms reduced the yield; this may have been caused by the wide spread occurrence of penicillinase-producing bacteria, which inactivate the antibiotic. The surface culture method of manufacturing penicillin was expensive; hundreds of thousands of flasks or bottles were required, and each was inoculated, incubated, and harvested individually.

Submerged culture methods were introduced by 1943 and are now employed almost exclusively. The medium is under constant aeration and agitation, and the mold grows throughout as pellets. Deep tanks with a capacity of several thousand gallons are filled with a culture medium consisting of corn-steep liquor, lactose, glucose, nutrient salts, phenylacetic acid or a derivative, and calcium carbonate as buffer. Corn-steep liquor is an extract obtained during the manufacture of starch and other corn products; it supplies organic nitrogen, minerals, reducing sugar, and lactic acid. Phenylacetic acid and its derivatives are precursors of penicillin and increase the yield of the antibiotic. After fermentation the penicillin is extracted, concentrated, crystallized, dried, and titrated to determine its potency before being bottled and sold.

Assay of Penicillin. The potency of a lot or batch of penicillin is determined by a biologic assay in which the unknown is compared with a standard preparation of crystalline sodium penicillin G. One international unit of penicillin activity is contained in 0.6 µg. of the standard; that is, one mg. of the international standard contains 1667 units of crystalline sodium penicillin G.

The official U. S. Food and Drug Administration cylinder-plate method of assaying penicillin is performed in Petri dishes containing a nutrient agar previously inoculated with a specified strain of *S. aureus* (Fig. 19-4). Stainless steel cylinders open at both ends are placed on the agar and filled with dilutions of standard penicillin and of the unknown sample. The plates are incubated at 37° C. for 16 to 18 hours, and the

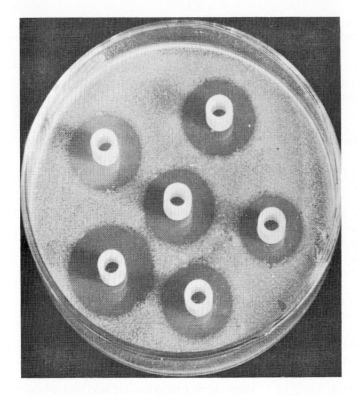

Figure 19-4. Penicillin assay by the agar cup plate method. The agar is inoculated heavily with *Staphylococcus aureus* and poured. Open cups are pressed into place and filled with penicillin solutions. Zones of inhibition appear after a few hours' incubation. (From Grant: Microbiology and Human Progress. New York, Rinehart & Co., Inc., 1953.)

zones of inhibition of bacterial growth are measured. The antibiotic activity of the unknown sample is determined by comparing its zones of inhibition with those of the standard penicillin.

Penicillin is also assayed by a serial dilution method. Dilutions of penicillin are prepared in a liquid medium inoculated with the test organism; the tubes are incubated, and the inhibition of growth is noted. Results with an unknown solution are compared with those produced by a preparation of known strength.

Streptomycin. Streptomycin was discovered in 1943 in Dr. Waksman's laboratory at Rutgers University. It is produced by *Streptomyces griseus,* one of about 150 species in a bacterial genus characterized by moldlike mycelial growth and the formation of conidia. These are primarily saprophytic soil bacteria, particularly active in the decomposition of organic matter.

Streptomycin is produced commer-cially by a submerged culture method in 10,000 to 15,000 gallon tanks. The culture medium contains hydrolyzed protein and sugar. Growth continues at 25° to 30° C. with vigorous aeration until the maximum possible yield of streptomycin has been attained. The mycelium is removed by filtration, and the antibiotic is adsorbed onto activated carbon, eluted, purified, sterilized, dried, and packaged.

Enzymes

Four principal types of microbial enzyme are manufactured for industrial use: amylases, invertase, proteinases, and pectinase. In general, the proper microorganism is cultivated under conditions favorable to enzyme formation, and the enzyme is then extracted and purified by precipitation or other means. Amylase, for example, is often derived from species of *Aspergillus* by the mold-bran process. Wheat bran, moistened with a suitable nutrient solution and sterilized in shallow trays, is inoculated with the mold spores and incubated under optimum temperature and moisture conditions until satisfactory growth has been obtained. The enzyme is then extracted from the bran with a suitable solvent such as alcohol, and is filtered, concentrated or precipitated, and dried. For some purposes mold-bran containing amylase can be dried without extraction, a process that effects a considerable reduction in expense. Amylases are secured from various genera of molds and from a variety of *Bacillus* species.

Amylases are used to hydrolyze starch to dextrins or sugars or both in making adhesives, in preparing materials for sizing, in desizing textiles, in clarifying fruit juices, and in saccharifying starchy solutions for fermentation.

Invertase from the yeast, *Saccharomyces cerevisiae,* is used to hydrolyze sucrose to glucose and fructose in the manufacture of noncrystallizable syrups, as in the production of liquid-centered candies.

Proteinases from *Aspergillus* and *Bacillus* species digest proteins and are used in meat tenderizers, in leather manufacture, in whiskey making, and in clarifying beer.

Pectinases, derived from various species of *Aspergillus,* are used to clarify fruit juices and to ret flax by digesting the cement that holds the fibers together in the plant stem.

Dextrans

Dextrans, which are polymers of glucose that are useful as a blood plasma substitute in combating shock, are formed in considerable quantity by certain capsulated bacteria such as *Leuconostoc mesenteroides.* They are produced when the bacteria grow in a sucrose medium, according to the equation:

$$n \text{ sucrose} = \underset{\text{dextran}}{(\text{glucose})_n} + n \text{ fructose}$$

Dextrans are not produced in a glucose medium. Certain strains of *L. mesenteroides* convert over 35 per cent of the supplied sucrose into dextran that is recoverable by appropriate precipitation. The organism is grown in a sucrose-tryptone-yeast extract broth at pH 6.7 and 25° C. until the reaction falls to pH 4.5. Dextran is then precipitated by the addition of an equal volume of methyl alcohol. Partial hydrolysis with hydrochloric acid yields compounds with a molecular weight of 50,000 to 100,000, which are spray-dried and packaged.

Gibberellins

Gibberellins are plant growth regulators formed by the mold *Fusarium moniliforme.* Diseased rice seedlings infected with this organism grow unusually tall and spindly and are light in color. The responsible mold product has been isolated and is an optically active crystallizable acid with the empirical formula $C_{19}H_{22}O_6$. In small amounts, it is a powerful plant growth stimulant and can be used to hasten maturation and to extend the geographic boundaries within which certain crops can be grown.

Gibberellic acid, the active agent, is produced in aerated cultures in a buffered glucose synthetic medium with NH_4Cl as the source of nitrogen. Cultures are incubated at 25° C. for approximately 65 hours. About 7.5 gm. of crude crystalline product can be obtained from 100 gallons of culture.

Steroid Transformations

Steroids are complex organic compounds with the following basic structure:

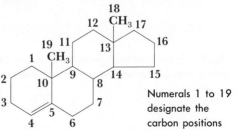

Numerals 1 to 19 designate the carbon positions

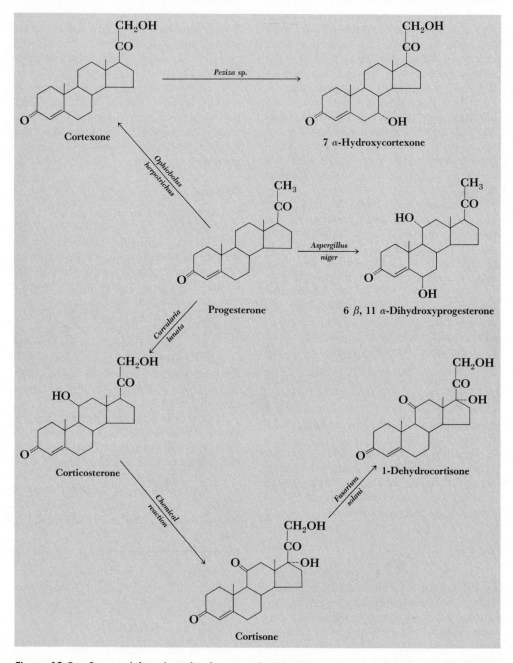

Figure 19-5. Structural formulae of a few steroids. Progesterone occurs naturally; it is transformed into a number of other steroids by enzymes of various fungi.

They are physiologically active substances, normally produced by animals or plants.

The various steroids differ from one another according to the presence and location of small radicals such as $=O$, $-OH$, $-CO \cdot CH_3$, $-CH \cdot CH_2OH$ (Fig. 19-5). About 1950 it was discovered that compounds of a steroid nature from natural sources could be transformed by various fungi into substances of different activity, and an important new branch of research developed: the production and evaluation of steroid drugs.

Steroid transformations differ from the activity usually associated with the manufacture of chemicals by microbial metabolism. Acids, neutral solvents, and most other fermentative or synthetic products are formed in the course of normal metabolic activity, perhaps modified by some change in cultural conditions. Steroids, however, are transformed by the action of one or a very few enzymes—often oxidases or dehydrogenases, which are frequently produced by only a single species of organism—and the reaction is completely separate from the normal metabolic pattern of the organism.

The proper species is cultivated on a sugar medium containing organic or inorganic nitrogen and mineral salts, either pure or in the form of corn-steep liquor, for 17 to 48 hours with aeration and at the optimum temperature for the production of the desired enzyme. The steroid to be transformed is then added to the medium, and further incubation under controlled conditions of pH, temperature, aeration, and agitation, usually for 24 to 48 hours, is allowed. The microbial growth is removed, extracted with a suitable solvent such as chloroform, methylene chloride, or ethylene chloride, and added to the fermentation liquor, which is then also extracted. The product is further purified for use.

Progesterone is normally produced by the corpus luteum of the ovary at ovulation and causes characteristic changes during the latter half of the menstrual cycle. Cortisone and related corticosteroids are active in carbohydrate and protein metabolism: they increase the deposition of glycogen in the liver, cause a marked decrease in circulating lymphocytes and eosinophilic leukocytes and degeneration of the thymus gland, and inhibit the inflammatory response.

Steroid transformations have provided compounds of new or enhanced pharmacologic activity, as well as chemicals from which other useful steroids can be made by further transformations.

Bacterial Toxins (Exotoxins) and Toxoids

Bacterial exotoxins are poisonous proteins secreted by the living cells of certain species. Their toxicity is very great; 1 mg. of tetanus toxin, for example, contains sufficient poison to kill about four million guinea pigs. Fortunately only a few species produce exotoxins; most of these are gram-positive bacteria.

Antigenicity of Toxins and Toxoids. Exotoxins are highly antigenic; that is, they vigorously stimulate the human or animal body to produce antibodies known as antitoxins, which neutralize and destroy the toxic property. Exotoxins are also unstable. They lose toxicity on aging and are gradually converted into toxoids. The transformation into toxoid is accelerated by heat, formaldehyde, and other chemicals. Toxoids retain the antigenic power of the original toxins and, because they lack toxicity, can be used to produce immunity against the corresponding toxins.

Diphtheria and tetanus toxoids are commonly administered to infants as part of their routine immunization during the first year of life; they are often combined in a triple immunizing agent with pertussis (whooping cough) vaccine.

Production of Toxin. Conditions for maximal laboratory production of toxin are frequently critical, and are often not those that favor best growth. Temperature of incubation and the pH and composition of the culture medium are important. The diphtheria organism must be grown aerobically in order to produce toxin, whereas the tetanus, gas gangrene, and botulism bacilli require highly anaerobic conditions.

Manufacture of Toxoid. The proper bacterium is cultivated under optimal conditions until the greatest possible yield of toxin is obtained. The cells are removed and the toxin in the broth is converted into toxoid by treatment with 0.4 to 0.5 per cent formalin until animal tests show that no toxicity remains. This may require a month or more at 37° C. The immunizing power of the toxoid is then determined by inoculating animals and challenging them with potent toxin after an appropriate interval (e.g., two weeks).

Toxoid is partially purified by precipitating the protein from other broth constituents with ammonium sulfate. The protein, redissolved in buffered saline, is known as "fluid toxoid" or "plain toxoid."

Toxoid adsorbed to a precipitate of aluminum hydroxide or aluminum phosphate is preferred in some situations. It is made by adding an aluminum salt to the toxoid solution and precipitating by appropriate chemical treatment. The precipitate contains the toxoid and when suspended in saline is known as "alum precipitated toxoid."

HYDROCARBON FERMENTATION

Hydrocarbons, both aliphatic and aromatic, with the exception of certain compounds of low molecular weight like methane, have generally been considered resistant to microbial attack. Since about 1950 there has been increasing evidence that microorganisms can utilize, or at least degrade, larger hydrocarbons such as those found in petroleum and its products. The central problem for the organism appears to be the transport of a hydrophobic substance to an intracellular site of enzyme

activity. Petroleum and jet fuel are relatively crude mixtures in which emulsifiers may form and assist this process, particularly if traces of water are also present. In consequence, extensive microbial growth produces a slime that clogs fuel lines and causes other trouble. Over 100 species of microorganism have been isolated from such slime and demonstrated to be capable of attacking hydrocarbons. Species of *Pseudomonas* are particularly common among the bacteria.

TEXTILE MICROBIOLOGY

There are two principal aspects of the microbiology of textiles. One is the use of microorganisms in preparing fibers such as flax and hemp. The other is the deterioration of textiles, including cordage and ropes, and the preservation of such materials.

Retting

Fibers of flax and hemp are loosened from the plant stems by retting. The fiber bundles of flax are held just within the outer layers of cells and outside the central pithy and woody layers by an intercellular cement of pectin (Fig. 19-6). Numerous bacteria and molds can digest pectin and permit the fiber

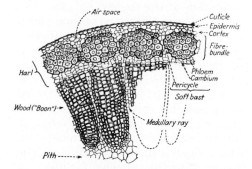

Figure 19-6. Cross section of part of a flax stem showing fiber bundles just inside the outer few layers of cells (diagrammatic). (From Prescott and Dunn: Industrial Microbiology. New York, McGraw-Hill Book Co., Inc., 1959.)

bundles to be separated mechanically from the stems and from each other.

Anaerobic retting is accomplished by immersing the plant stalks in natural or artificial ponds or in tanks of water, where a variety of bacteria including *Clostridium felsineum* and *Cl. pectinovorum* digest the pectin.

An aerobic process known as *dew retting* relies mainly on molds. The plant material is spread in thin layers on the ground and exposed to the elements. Microorganisms from the air, the soil, and the plant itself slowly hydrolyze the pectin, subject to continuous temperature and moisture changes. The fibers obtained by this method are frequently of poor quality and the yield is small.

Tank methods, either aerobic or anaerobic, are more predictable but require close control because overretting may damage the fibers. One tank process requires only 50 hours, whereas dew retting requires several weeks.

Deterioration of Textiles

Textile fibers in common use may be classified as follows:

A. Natural fibers
  1. Plant (principally carbohydrates)
     Examples: cotton, flax, hemp, jute
  2. Animal (principally protein)
     Examples: wool, silk
B. Artificial fibers
  1. Semisynthetic
     Examples: viscose rayon, cellulose acetate
  2. Synthetic
     Examples: Nylon, Orlon, Dacron

Microorganisms weaken and discolor textiles and alter their affinity for dyes. Mildew is the growth of fungi, often noted as a discoloration but actually accompanied by slow loss of strength (Fig. 19-7).

Cotton is composed of cellulose. The microbial flora of raw cotton is that of the soil and may amount to 10,000,000 bacteria and 100,000 molds per gram. Nearly 200 mold species have been found on cotton fabrics. Bacteria are not significant causes of deterioration, because only a few aerobic cellulose-digesting species are known, and they multiply slowly. Many molds, however, can digest cellulose. They need only humid atmosphere and nutrients usually present in a cotton fabric.

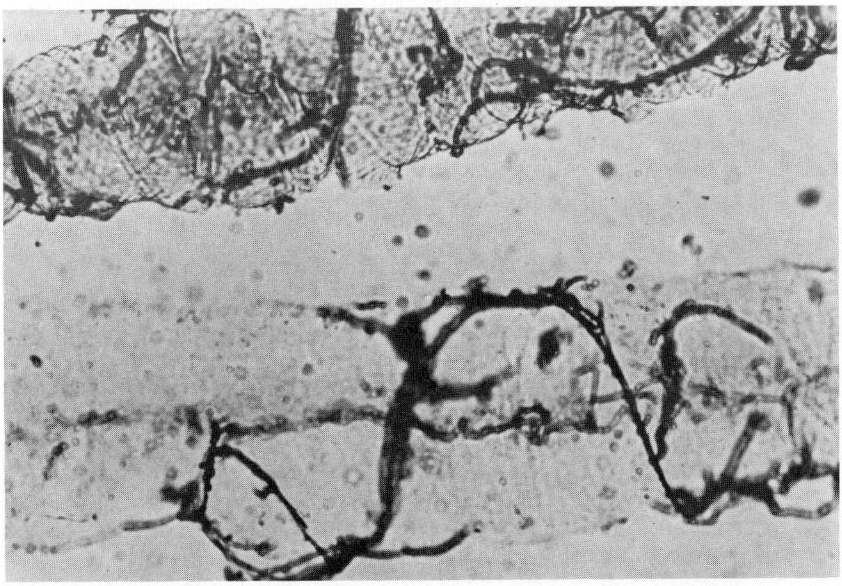

Figure 19-7. Mildewed fiber of cotton. (Photograph by B. Prindle.)

Wool is protein, principally keratin. Microorganisms found on wool include molds, actinomycetes, and true bacteria. Several mold species weaken and discolor wool fabrics; some aerobic spore-forming bacilli cause deterioration, others produce discoloration.

The treatment that a fabric receives during manufacture often affects its susceptibility to deterioration. Starch sizing provides added nutrients for some microorganisms. Bleaching and dyeing, on the other hand, may kill many organisms.

Semisynthetic fibers are partially resistant to deterioration; the resistance of cellulose acetate, for example, is roughly proportional to the degree of acetylation. Synthetic fibers are almost completely unaffected by microorganisms. The natural fibers in mixed fabrics such as cotton-Dacron are, of course, subject to deterioration.

Preservation of Textiles

The only sure method of preventing microbial deterioration of textiles is to maintain the moisture content at less than 8 per cent and the relative humidity less than 75 per cent.

Some materials, such as tents, tarpaulins, fish nets, cordage, and ropes, cannot be kept dry and must therefore be protected by antiseptic chemicals. For centuries sailors have treated ropes with tar to reduce deterioration. Copper compounds are widely used, and a phenolic compound, 2,2'-methylenebis (4-chlorophenol), has been increasingly employed since World War II, when it was used to protect textiles and leather goods for the armed services.

INDUSTRIAL MICROBIOLOGY

SUMMARY

Industrial microbiology comprises the development and control of manufacturing processes in which microorganisms participate. The microorganisms themselves may be the desired product, as in the case of bakers' yeast, or the product may be the chemicals that the microorganisms form as metabolic by-products. The prevention of microbial deterioration of useful materials is another phase of industrial microbiology.

The development of a microbiologic process starts in the laboratory, where strains of organisms and cultural conditions are painstakingly selected. The process is then adapted and modified as necessary for the pilot plant and finally for full scale production.

The manufacture of alcohol in its various forms and of other industrial solvents is a large industry. Basic raw materials include sugars and starches, and their preparation for fermentation varies according to the nature of the responsible microorganism. The fermentation medium, often sterilized to eliminate contaminants that would reduce the yield of desired products, is inoculated heavily, and fermentation is allowed to occur. Then the resulting solution usually must be subjected to purification by physical and chemical treatment such as distillation, precipitation, etc., to separate the useful substances. Further testing is often necessary to ensure a product of satisfactory quality.

Numerous chemicals, such as steroids, not found or rare in nature are produced with microbial assistance.

STUDY QUESTIONS

1. Compare the cultural conditions employed in manufacturing commercial yeast and in brewing. Explain the differences.
2. What are the purposes of the malting and mashing steps in brewing? What changes occur during maturing?
3. Describe the steps in a process by which acetic acid could be made from potatoes by fermentation. Indicate the necessary cultural conditions.
4. Outline a biologic assay procedure used to determine the potency of penicillin.
5. Compare the susceptibility of natural and synthetic fibers to microbial deterioration. Explain.
6. Discuss the role of the microbiologist in industry. What training outside the field of microbiology should he have to be of greatest service?
7. Describe the role of microorganisms in steroid transformation.
8. How would you attempt to secure a culture of an organism capable of digesting a detergent?

SUPPLEMENTARY READING

The large book by Prescott and Dunn contains detailed descriptions of a wide variety of industrial processes for the manufacture of solvents and other chemicals, enzymes, food products, and antibiotics. *Advances in Applied Microbiology* is an annual publication with reviews of many topics of current interest.

Prescott, S. C., and Dunn, C. G.: *Industrial Microbiology,* 3d ed. New York, McGraw-Hill Book Co., Inc., 1959.
Umbreit, W. W. (Ed.): *Advances in Applied Microbiology.* New York, Academic Press, Inc.

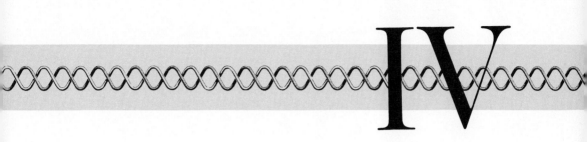

IV

MICROORGANISMS
AND DISEASE

INFECTION AND DISEASE

THE NATURE OF INFECTIOUS DISEASE

Disease is any departure from a state of health, that is, from the typical condition of an individual. *Infectious* diseases are those caused by microorganisms: protozoa, fungi, bacteria, viruses. All other diseases are *noninfectious*.

Infection is the process whereby a microorganism becomes established upon or within an individual and produces injury. Damage to cells or tissues upsets their physicochemical behavior; cellular metabolism and respiration are disturbed, and intermediate metabolic products may accumulate instead of being completely oxidized. The usual signs of disease—malaise, inflammation, fever, pain—call attention to the fact that an infection is in progress. The specific response in a given instance depends on the nature of the infectious agent and on the tissues or physiologic processes it injures or upsets.

Parasitism and Disease Production

Disease as an Accident. Disease is a biologic accident. The cells of a healthy individual are in a state of continuous chemical activity, transforming energy and synthesizing cellular constituents. Interference with vital chemical reactions is fatal.

Normal cellular chemical activity is disturbed by various types of accident. The ability of DNA to direct the formation of normal enzymes can be altered by an accidental variation in its replication or a variation induced by chance exposure to ionizing radiation or a mutagenic chemical. Failure of the supply of essential nutrients, minerals, or vitamins can seriously impair the chemical behavior of body cells, producing deficiency or metabolic disease.

Infection is another kind of accident that may upset the chemistry of a living organism, because most infectious agents possess some degree of parasitic tendency. It has been pointed out pre-

385

viously that parasitism is an association in which one organism lives upon or within another (larger) living organism at the expense of the latter but without compensation for the advantages received. Parasitism is therefore a method of securing food. The specific nutrients required vary from one parasite to another and include individual amino acids, growth factors, vitamins, and nucleotides.

The expression "without compensation for the advantages received" implies possible damage to the host. Damage, if it occurs, is an incidental consequence of the parasitic mode of existence. It is ultimately as harmful to the parasite as to the host, because the most successful parasites are those that cause the least disturbance. Violent host response may result in extermination of the parasite, whereas mild response leads eventually to prolonged association and perhaps commensalism (see page 141).

Treponema pallidum, the cause of

syphilis, and its human host have apparently developed a high degree of compatibility by adaptive modifications during the past several centuries. Early reports described syphilis as an acute disease, but constant association has so modified the host or parasite or both that the disease is usually benign and chronic; a fatal outcome is delayed for many years, and patients frequently die of other, unrelated ailments.

Gradations in Parasitism. Parasitism is quantitative rather than qualitative, but there is great variation among parasitic microorganisms. Moulder divided parasites into four groups according to their behavior *in the living host* (Table 20-1).

Facultative parasites are organisms that live either as saprophytes or as parasites. They can multiply indefinitely outside a living host, but on occasion they enjoy a parasitic existence. *Pseudomonas, Escherichia, Proteus,* and *Clostridium* are often cited as examples. *E. coli* grows luxuriantly in the laboratory,

Table 20-1. Relationship Between Parasitic Habit and Nutritional Requirements of Representative Microorganisms*

Probable Nutritional Requirements During Parasitic Life	Parasitic Habit			
	Facultative Parasites	Obligate Parasites		
		Obligately Extracellular	Facultatively Intracellular	Obligately Intracellular
Simple carbon and energy sources, inorganic nitrogen	*Pseudomonas* *Escherichia*	*S. typhosa* *V. cholerae*		
B vitamins, amino acids, nitrogen bases, etc.	*Clostridium* *Proteus*	*Staphylococcus* *S. dysenteriae* *B. anthracis*		
Complex natural materials: blood, serum, etc.		Trypanosomes *Streptococcus* *D. pneumoniae* *C. diphtheriae* *Leptospira*	*N. gonorrhoeae* *N. meningitidis* *Brucella* *M. tuberculosis*	PPLO *Bartonella*
Unknown; satisfied only within living cells		*T. pallidum*		Viruses Psittacosis group Rickettsiae Malaria parasites

*Modified from Moulder, J. W.: *The Biochemistry of Intracellular Parasitism.* Chicago, The University of Chicago Press, 1962.

even on synthetic media, although its normal habitat is the human or animal body. In its natural environment, it does not produce disease and cannot even be considered parasitic, because its source of food is only the body wastes of the intestinal contents. The same organism, however, occasionally gains access to the kidneys, the bladder, or to subcutaneous tissues and produces infections that are distressing even if not necessarily fatal. In this circumstance it leads a temporarily parasitic existence.

Obligate parasites are organisms that multiply *under natural conditions* only within a living host. Although they may persist for a time in nonliving material in a natural environment, and many can be cultivated indefinitely in laboratory media, they tend to die out in nature when not passed from one host to another. Most unicellular parasites fall into this category, and they are further distinguished according to the character of their relationships with their hosts.

Obligately extracellular parasites multiply only outside body cells, within tissue spaces or body cavities. They cannot invade living cells, and they cease to multiply or are destroyed when ingested by phagocytes.

Facultatively intracellular parasites can multiply either extracellularly or intracellularly within the cytoplasm or nucleus of host cells. Organisms of this kind generally produce severe and prolonged disease, such as gonorrhea, brucellosis, and tuberculosis, and are usually found within phagocytic cells rather than cells of other types. Apparently they are not able to invade host cells actively, but when ingested they find the cellular environment suitable for multiplication.

Obligately intracellular parasites multiply in nature only within living host cells. Many kinds of body cells may be invaded and parasitized, even those without phagocytic properties. Most of these organisms do not grow in nonliving media, for example, viruses, rickettsiae, and malaria parasites.

Table 20-1 indicates also that the nutritional complexity of parasites living *in vivo* correlates well with their parasitic tendency. That is, the facultative parasites require only simple carbon and energy sources and inorganic nitrogen *in vitro* and presumably also in the animal body. Obligate parasites in general require more complex nutrients, together with vitamins, nitrogenous bases, blood or serum; the obligately intracellular parasites can be cultivated only in living host cells, which provide ingredients or conditions not encountered elsewhere (e.g., enzymes, high energy compounds). Noting that in general parasites and host cells are closely similar in chemical and enzymic makeup and in biochemical activity, Moulder concluded that "the unique problem in the multiplication of obligate intracellular parasites . . . is why the intracellular parasites grow so well within suitable host cells and so poorly outside them."

Communicability and the Establishment of Infection

Infectious diseases are subdivided according to the ease with which they are transmitted from one individual to another. *Contagious* or *communicable* diseases are readily transmitted by direct or indirect contact or through the air. Venereal disease, typhoid fever, and the common cold are highly contagious. *Noncontagious* diseases are not readily transmitted from one individual to another of the same species. They are often acquired only by direct inoculation; the living organisms of tetanus must be introduced into the body tissues via a wound. It should be understood that the terms contagious and noncontagious do not describe sharply distinct categories of infectious disease; the communicability of infectious diseases varies continuously from those that are highly contagious to those that rarely, if ever, are transmitted from one individual to another. Many diseases are only moderately or mildly contagious; repeated or constant exposure appears to be necessary for transmission of human tuberculosis.

Factors Determining Infection. Several factors determine the readiness with which infectious disease is transmitted and established in a second individual. Some of these were indicated by Theobald Smith in the following relationship:

$$P = NV/R$$

in which P is the probability that disease will result from a given exposure to a pathogen, N is the number of microorganisms in the infecting dose, V represents their virulence, and R designates the resistance of the host. This expression states that the probability that disease will result from a given exposure to a pathogenic agent depends on the number of organisms and their virulence but varies inversely with the resistance of the host.

Virulence and Pathogenicity. *Virulence* is the capacity of *a given strain* or pure culture of a microbial species to produce disease. The terms virulence and pathogenicity are sometimes loosely used in the same sense. *Pathogenicity* should properly be employed only with reference to the ability of a *group* of organisms (species, genus, etc.) to produce disease. The distinction implies that avirulent strains of pathogenic species may exist; this is, in fact, the case. Avirulent strains of *Mycobacterium tuberculosis, Corynebacterium diphtheriae, Brucella abortus,* and many other species are known.

Virulence and some factors in the transmission of microorganisms and the pathologic response of the host will be discussed in this chapter. The resistance the host offers will be discussed in the next chapter.

VIRULENCE

Virulence, the disease-producing capacity of a microorganism, is attrib-

uted to two factors: toxigenicity and invasiveness. *Toxigenicity* is the ability to produce toxic or poisonous substances, that is, substances that can directly damage host tissues. *Invasiveness* is the capacity of the organism to establish itself within a host. Most non-animal parasites such as bacteria, fungi, and viruses, possess no means of active penetration; entrance into the host body is therefore largely a matter of chance. The invasiveness of these organisms depends on their ability to withstand the shock of initial contact with the host and then to multiply within the host.

Invasiveness

The adaptability of a microorganism to a parasitic existence depends on the production of chemical components, metabolic products, and enzymes that can counteract normal body defenses or assist dissemination from the original site of infection.

Inhibition of Phagocytosis. One of the most important active defenses against infection is *phagocytosis.* Phagocytic cells are present throughout the body. They include certain white blood cells or leukocytes, various wandering small cells within the tissues, and many fixed cells which line the capillaries and are particularly abundant in the liver. The process of phagocytosis is similar to ameboid ingestion; foreign particles are engulfed by the phagocytic cells and are usually digested by intracellular enzymes. Efficient operation of the phagocytic system stops many an infection before it can get started.

Establishment of the parasite is promoted by substances such as *leukocidins,* which kill white blood cells by some mechanism not yet understood; they are produced by some staphylococci, streptococci, and pneumococci. *Coagulase,* produced by pathogenic staphylococci, reacts with the fibrinogen of the host to produce a fibrin clot around the bacterial cells, protecting them against ingestion by phagocytes.

Formation of a fibrin clot around a local staphylococcus infection (e.g., a boil) presumably walls off the infection from neighboring tissues and protects the host against widespread invasion, but it may also protect the staphylococcus against destruction by defensive soluble blood or lymph components.

The presence of *capsules* is associated with virulence of certain bacterial strains. Virulent forms of *Diplococcus pneumoniae, Klebsiella pneumoniae, Bacillus anthracis,* and *Hemophilus influenzae* possess capsules; noncapsulated variants are avirulent. Capsules possess some chemical or physical property that makes them resist phagocytosis. Enzymatic removal of the capsule from a virulent strain of *D. pneumoniae* destroys the virulence of the organism for mice.

Enzymes. Proteolytic and other *enzymes* contribute to the invasiveness of pathogenic bacteria. *Clostridium histolyticum* is actively proteolytic in gangrenous tissue; it digests muscle vigorously and spreads rapidly from the initial site of injury. A similar action has been attributed to hyaluronidase, which hydrolyzes hyaluronic acid, an important constituent of the intercellular cement that binds tissues into their normal structure. This enzyme is produced by some hemolytic streptococci, pneumococci, gas gangrene and other bacteria. Collagenase destroys collagen, an important structural supporting substance in muscle, bone, and cartilage; it is produced particularly by *Cl. perfringens,* one of the gas gangrene bacteria.

Hemolysins are enzymes or toxins that dissolve red blood cells. There are many hemolysins of different properties, and they are produced by nonpathogenic as well as pathogenic bacteria. The hemolysin of *Cl. perfringens* is known to be a lecithinase; it hydrolyses lecithin, a constituent of erythrocytes and of many other body cells. Some hemolysins also possess leukocidin activity. Staphylococci and hemolytic streptococci are among the common pathogens that produce hemolysins.

Streptokinase, formerly called fibrinolysin, is produced by virulent hemolytic streptococci and activates a normal plasma protease that dissolves fibrin clots. Similar enzymes are produced by other species. Hemolytic streptococci also produce streptodornase or deoxyribonuclease, which liquefies purulent exudates and viscous material containing DNA. The detection of streptokinase and streptodornase is of some diagnostic significance, but the importance of these enzymes in virulence is debated. Streptococci are among the most highly invasive bacteria and spread rapidly all over the body from a local infection. One of the first responses of the body to local infection is the formation of a fibrin clot around the area. It may be more than coincidence that pathogenic streptococci are strongly fibrinolytic.

Toxigenicity

Toxins are normal cellular components or metabolic products that damage or interfere with the activity of tissue cells of other animals or plants. They are produced by higher plants (e.g., mushrooms) and animals (e.g., snakes) as well as by microorganisms.

Endotoxins. Bacterial endotoxins are complexes of polysaccharide, protein, and lipid; they comprise part of the cell wall structure and are released by autolysis of the dead cells. Their potency is low: 1 mg. usually contains not more than 10 lethal doses for the mouse. Endotoxins are found in gram-negative bacteria and are present in nonpathogens as well as in pathogens. The endotoxins of *E. coli* and *Serratia marcescens,* for example, are as potent as those of the typhoid and dysentery bacteria. Symptoms observed when these substances are injected into laboratory animals include fever, diarrhea, paralysis of the limbs, disturbed carbohydrate metabolism, and degeneration of blood vessels. All endotoxins produce the same general symptoms, no matter from what species of microorganism they are obtained.

The protein portion of endotoxin is not

essential for toxicity. Most of the lipid can be removed from the remaining lipopolysaccharide without great loss of toxic activity, but preparations completely free from lipid are inactive. There are indications from experiments with germ-free animals that toxicity is a function of repeated interaction of the body with endotoxic material. Animals reared without the usual gram-negative intestinal flora are not normally susceptible to endotoxin, whereas those with typical flora are susceptible. Inasmuch as the intestinal population consists largely of bacteria with endotoxin, it appears likely that "natural antibodies" (see page 403) to them may develop slowly, and when the animal is infected or injected with endotoxic bacteria or material, some sort of generalized shock reaction ensues.

Exotoxins. Exotoxins are soluble protein poisons secreted by the living cells of a few bacteria, plants, and animals. Some of the bacteria are semiparasitic, but the most notorious exotoxin-producing species are saprophytic.

Toxin production by *Cl. botulinum* in foods has already been discussed (page 358). The toxin in affected food resists gastric acids and passes quickly through the stomach wall to the bloodstream.

Cl. tetani multiplies in deep wounds from which oxygen is excluded, utilizing devitalized tissue as source of nutrients. The potent toxin it produces is transported to the central nervous system and induces typical paralysis. This organism is considered a saprophyte because it does not grow in normal living tissue but prefers devitalized, wounded tissue.

Corynebacterium diphtheriae establishes itself within the human upper respiratory tract—throat, nostrils, larynx— but cannot invade the body more deeply. Most of the disease symptoms are attributed to the toxin, which is absorbed through the mucous membranes and distributed over the body by the bloodstream.

Properties of Exotoxins. Exotoxins are extremely powerful. The toxin of *Cl. botulinum* type A is one of the most potent poisons known; 1 mg. of the purified

material contains 31 million lethal doses for the mouse. Most exotoxins are converted to the nontoxic form, toxoid, by aging, heating at 60° C., or treatment with formaldehyde or various other chemicals. Toxoid retains nearly all the immunizing power of exotoxin but lacks poisonous properties; therefore, it can be used with relative impunity for artificial immunization.

Specificity of Exotoxins. Most exotoxins are highly specific with respect to their site and mode of action. *Cl. botulinum* toxin causes paralysis especially of respiratory muscles, apparently by interfering with the release of acetylcholine at the endings of peripheral motor nerves. Tetanus toxin causes a similar paralysis and, in addition, produces spasm of voluntary muscles by stimulating neuromuscular junctions. This toxin has great affinity for brain and spinal cord tissue. Diphtheria exotoxin produces local necrosis, adrenal hemorrhage, paralysis, and degeneration of heart muscles, kidneys, and liver. It seems to interfere with tissue synthesis of cytochrome *b*, which is important in biologic oxidations.

Variations in Invasiveness and Toxigenicity

It is apparent that invasiveness and toxigenicity are separate properties of a microorganism, and each varies independently of the other. A species which is both highly toxigenic and highly invasive will be likely to produce serious disease. Hemolytic streptococci are of this nature and were greatly feared until the advent of sulfonamide drugs and antibiotics. *T. pallidum* is highly invasive but not highly toxigenic; syphilis is not rapidly fatal, but symptoms may appear in any organ. *Cl. botulinum* has no invasiveness whatsoever and yet is highly toxigenic.

TRANSMISSION OF INFECTIOUS DISEASE

Knowledge of the modes of transmission of infectious diseases is important in their control. Most infectious diseases would be eradicated if transmission of their causative agents were completely interrupted.

Portals of Entry

Pathogenic microorganisms gain access to the human or animal body through the respiratory tract, the digestive tract, broken skin, and possibly through unbroken skin. One portal of entry is usually more effective than any other for a given microorganism, because infection is more easily established in specific tissues. The pneumococcus, for example, multiplies luxuriantly in the bronchi and alveoli of the lungs and is usually acquired by the respiratory route. Dysentery bacteria establish themselves only in the intestinal tract and are therefore effectively acquired by the oral route. Some bacteria are versatile and invade the body by several routes, producing a variety of diseases. Hemolytic streptococci, for example, enter by the respiratory route and produce pharyngitis, scarlet fever, or respiratory infections, or they traverse broken skin and produce wound infections, septicemia, erysipelas, etc. The possibility that bacteria may pass through unbroken skin is debated, but the high incidence of laboratory infections by the organisms of brucellosis and tularemia, even among experienced workers, suggests that they may be able to do so.

Routes of Exit

Respiratory pathogens leave the infected patient by the oral or nasal route in saliva and respiratory exudates. Intestinal pathogens are excreted in the feces and possibly in the urine. Microorganisms that cause wound infections are not ordinarily highly contagious, although some can be transmitted by pus or other secretions. It was not uncommon in the days before aseptic surgery for hemolytic streptococci transmitted from a wound by the hands or instruments of the physician to infect a woman in labor and produce fatal puerperal sepsis (childbed fever). The pus from an open venereal sore also transmits infectious agents. Certain pathogens leave a host via insect bites. Mosquitoes, body lice, ticks, and other insects acquire the pathogenic agent in the blood or other ingested material and pass it along to another host, with or without further development in the body of the insect.

Survival Outside the Host

Successful transmission of a microbial cause of disease is accomplished only if the microorganism survives outside the donor long enough to reach another host. This is not much of a problem if the pathogen is not highly parasitic. The typhoid fever organism withstands widely varying conditions of temperature, oxygen, and nutrient supply and can even survive in water or ice for several weeks. It is therefore capable of producing disease many miles away from the individual who excreted it and many weeks later. The bacteria that produce venereal diseases, on the contrary, are highly parasitic; they die quickly if cooled more than a few degrees and fail to multiply unless supplied with complicated foods found in body fluids. These organisms are rarely transmitted by any route other than direct contact.

Agents of Transmission

Agents that transmit microorganisms are conveniently classified as mechanical or biologic.

Mechanical Vectors. Pathogenic organisms are readily transferred from infected to healthy individuals by materials or objects in common use. Hand-to-hand transmission of infectious agents is undoubtedly more frequent than realized. *Thorough* washing removes many microorganisms from the hands.

Fomites. Fomites (objects such as dishes, doorknobs, books, etc.) contaminated by the patient transmit the infection if the pathogen is one that can survive; drying is often a limiting factor.

Cleanliness and disinfection prevent the transmission of disease by these agents.

Infective Droplets. Droplets of saliva or nasal secretions are the usual means of disseminating respiratory pathogens. Infective droplets are aspirated into the air by sneezing, coughing, or even talking. Droplet infection can be reduced by increasing the distance between individuals. The occurrence of *N. meningitidis* in the throats of military personnel quartered in barracks decreases markedly when bunks are spaced 18 inches rather than 6 inches apart. A further decrease results from placing adjacent beds head to foot.

Sputum droplets may be only a few microns in diameter and settle so slowly that the moisture has evaporated by the time the droplet reaches the ground or floor (Table 17-3). Microorganisms in such a droplet are surrounded by a thin film of protective mucus. These organisms become part of the dust and are easily distributed by air currents. Droplets of saliva or nasal secretions constitute a more certain means of transmitting infectious agents than fomites; many cells remain viable and can be readily broadcast over a wide area.

Water, Milk, Foods. Water, milk, and other foods are vehicles for transmission of microorganisms that cause intestinal disease; upper respiratory infections may also be spread by the same agents. The occurrence of a case of intestinal disease means that microorganisms from the excreta of a patient have found their way to the mouth of another individual. Recognition of this fact, unpleasant though it be aesthetically as well as hygienically, stimulated emphasis on community sanitation, and since 1900 the incidence of many intestinal diseases has dropped to the vanishing point in civilized countries.

Biologic Transmission of Infectious Disease. *Insects.* Insects play an active role as primary or intermediate hosts in the transmission of some diseases; they may also have a passive role in the transmission of intestinal pathogens by carrying these organisms upon their bodies or feet. Malaria protozoa develop in mosquitoes as part of their life cycle and are deposited in the human bloodstream when the mosquito feeds. Further stages in the life cycle are completed in man (see page 141). *Pasteurella pestis* is a normal pathogen of rats and is transmitted from rat to rat and from rat to man by the bite of the rat flea. The microorganism multiplies in the digestive tract of the flea and is regurgitated when the flea feeds upon a fresh host. Other diseases transmitted by insects include yellow fever (by the mosquito), Rocky Mountain spotted fever (by ticks), and typhus fever (by lice).

Lower Animals. Lower animals are primary hosts of numerous infectious agents and transmit them by one means or another to man, who serves as a secondary host. Hydrophobia occurs naturally in dogs, foxes, and other species. The virus is transmitted to man by the bite of a rabid animal. Hunters become infected with tularemia bacteria while handling the meat of infected rabbits. The infection begins as a sore or ulcer at the site where the organism penetrates the skin but later spreads and produces a prolonged, debilitating, but not highly fatal generalized infection. The transmission of brucellosis of cattle, goats, and swine, tuberculosis of cattle, and salmonellosis of fowl and rodents to man has already been discussed (see Chap. 18).

Human Carriers. Advances in sanitation and public health have nearly eliminated the transmission of typhoid fever by water and milk, but the typhoid carrier is still a problem, particularly when employed in the food industry. The typhoid carrier harbors *S. typhosa* in his gallbladder or intestines; in either case, the organisms are discharged intermittently in the excreta. They are often found upon the carrier's hands, unless his personal hygiene is unusually good, and are thus transmitted to the food he handles or prepares for others. The intestinal carrier state cannot usually be altered. Carriers are probably more important in the transmission of dysentery than of typhoid fever, because improvements in sanitation have not been accompanied by as great a reduction in dysentery cases.

Human carriers are important in distributing respiratory and upper respiratory infections. Diphtheria patients who have recovered may harbor the pathogen for several months in the nasopharynx and discharge it in infective droplets. The meningococcus is occasionally present in the nasal passages of normal individuals, and the carrier rate may rise to high levels, particularly under crowded conditions of camp or army life. The incidence of pneumococci in the throats of healthy persons is said to be as great as 40 per cent during the winter.

Carriers are undoubtedly more important in transmitting human disease than is realized. It would be interesting to examine a large group of individuals thoroughly to see what pathogens they harbor during the course of a year.

RESPONSES TO INFECTION

Inflammation is the universal response to irritation of any sort—physical, chemical, microbiologic. The five attributes of inflammation—swelling, pain, redness, heat, and loss of function—call attention to the source of irritation, often in time for proper treatment to be instituted.

Local Infection

The course of events following a minor injury such as introduction of a contaminated splinter into the finger will serve to illustrate local inflammation. The physical act of jabbing a splinter into the finger damages or kills some of the tissue cells. The materials of these damaged cells provide an excellent culture medium for the bacteria that were on the splinter or were carried along from the surface of the skin. These organisms multiply and produce further irritation.

Irritated tissues liberate polypeptides and globulin proteins, which cause a series of reactions. Increased permea-

bility of capillaries in the immediate vicinity permits blood plasma to pass into the surrounding tissues and to form a fibrinous clot that inhibits spread of the infectious agent. The number of circulating white blood cells gradually increases, and actively phagocytic polymorphonuclear leukocytes are attracted to the site of infection. The pus that forms is composed largely of these cells, together with plasma and bacteria. Cellular metabolism in the infected area is disturbed as a result of interference with normal circulation, and acids accumulate; temperature control is also disturbed, and there is local fever. Inflamed areas are often warm to the touch.

Most local infections never progress beyond this stage. The infection remains confined, and eventually phagocytes ingest and destroy the infecting microorganisms. The condition of local acidity attracts large leukocytes or macrophages, which replace the polymorphonuclear leukocytes; they dispose of the debris resulting from infection and help repair damaged tissue. A few days later nothing remains but a scar.

Generalized Infections

A local infection sometimes generalizes and spreads to other parts of the body. This can happen if the organisms are unusually virulent, the local defenses unusually weak, or if amateur surgery is attempted before phagocytosis has eliminated all living microorganisms. Some of the bacteria escape from the local, walled-off site in cellular or inflammatory lymph. Lymph from the finger drains into the cubital lymph nodes at the elbow, thence to the axillary nodes in the armpits, and finally into the bloodstream by way of the thoracic duct.

Lymph nodes are composed of single layers of cells separating lymph and blood and function as filters to prevent passage of particulate matter into the blood. Many infections that spread from a local site are stopped at the lymph nodes, because these organs contain phagocytic cells, which can ingest bacteria. Microorganisms may produce secondary inflammation of a lymph node; a well known example is the swollen parotid gland of mumps.

Bacteremia. A particularly virulent organism passes through the lymph node and enters the bloodstream. This produces a temporary *bacteremia,* a condition in which bacteria circulate in the blood but do not damage it and do not multiply.

The R-E System. The blood passes repeatedly through all organs of the body. The spleen, liver, bone marrow and other tissues with highly phagocytic cells constitute the "reticuloendothelial" (R-E) system. Foreign particles of any kind are quickly removed from the blood in its passage through these tissues. Experiments in laboratory animals have demonstrated that millions of bacteria injected into the vein of an animal disappear within a few minutes. Phagocytosis in the R-E system may completely eliminate the pathogen.

Secondary Bacteremia or Septicemia. Occasionally the microorganism is not destroyed and actually multiplies within the R-E system. Reinvasion of the blood then produces secondary bacteremia or even *septicemia,* in which the organisms continue to multiply and damage the blood components. Infection of any or all other organs may occur.

Focal Infection. A local infection from which bacteria continuously or intermittently enter the bloodstream is known as a *focal* infection. Common primary foci of infection are found about the head and throat. Infected teeth or tonsils sometimes provide a constant supply of pathogens, which then infect other organs (e.g., the kidneys). General septicemia with multiple secondary foci of infection is known as *pyemia.*

Physical and Chemical Signs of Infection

The most obvious physical signs of infection are fever and increased pulse rate. Change in the number or percentage of white blood cells is readily detected by simple laboratory procedures.

Leukocytes. The normal individual has between 5000 and 10,000 white blood cells, or leukocytes, per cubic millimeter of blood. The several kinds of leukocytes are classified according to their size (7μ to 20μ), presence and type of granules, shape and size of nucleus, and appearance of cytoplasm. The five principal types are usually present in fairly constant percentages:

	Per Cent
Polymorphonuclear neutrophils	50–70
Basophils	0.5–1.0
Eosinophils	1–5
Lymphocytes	20–30
Monocytes	2–6

The first three types listed are formed in the marrow of the flat bones. Lymphocytes are believed to be formed in lymph nodes, and monocytes are derived from reticulum cells, particularly in the spleen. Leukocytes are short-lived; normally they are replaced within a few hours to four days.

The total number of white blood cells increases in many infectious diseases. *Leukocytosis* is an increase above the normal count; it is usually considered to begin at about 10,000 cells per cubic millimeter. A count of 30,000 or 40,000 represents marked leukocytosis.

A differential count is made by examining stained blood smears and counting the different types of leukocytes, the results being expressed in percentages. An increase in polymorphonuclear neutrophils, designated *neutrophilia,* is characteristic of acute infections by staphylococci, streptococci, and other pus-producing bacteria. *Neutropenia,* a marked decrease in polymorphonuclear neutrophils, occurs in typhoid fever, undulant fever, and influenza. *Lymphocytosis,* an increase in lymphocytes, is typical of whooping cough and mumps. These examples indicate how the blood picture may change as a result of infectious disease and also show one way in which laboratory examinations may assist in diagnosing disease.

Composition of Body Fluids. The chemical composition of the body fluids may change as a result of infection. The concentrations of sugar, protein, chloride, and other substances in the blood increase or decrease in different diseases. Spinal fluid may contain pus cells or abnormal percentages of protein, glucose, and other chemicals. Urine examinations reveal kidney damage. Hemolytic streptococcus infections affect the kidneys almost specifically and increase the excretion of albumin and solid particles known as casts. Protein catabolism is accelerated, and the urine becomes acid and contains a greater amount of nitrogen than normal. Elimination of ketones and diacetic acid is typical of infectious diseases in children.

These and other changes in the physical and chemical make-up of the individual reflect the profound physiologic disturbance caused by infectious disease. Another type of disturbance, leading in some cases to immunity, accompanies recovery from infectious disease. Active immunization is so important that it will be discussed separately in the next chapter, together with other factors that influence resistance to infectious disease.

GNOTOBIOTICS

Before leaving the introductory topic of infection and disease, it may be of interest to consider briefly the situation in *gnotobiotic* (Greek: *gnotos,* known + *bios,* life) animals. These are germ-free animals, deliberately inoculated with one or more known organisms.

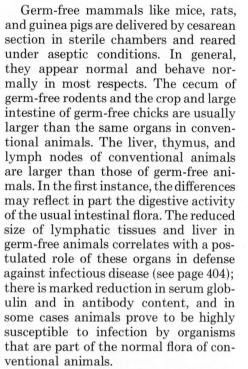

Germ-free mammals like mice, rats, and guinea pigs are delivered by cesarean section in sterile chambers and reared under aseptic conditions. In general, they appear normal and behave normally in most respects. The cecum of germ-free rodents and the crop and large intestine of germ-free chicks are usually larger than the same organs in conventional animals. The liver, thymus, and lymph nodes of conventional animals are larger than those of germ-free animals. In the first instance, the differences may reflect in part the digestive activity of the usual intestinal flora. The reduced size of lymphatic tissues and liver in germ-free animals correlates with a postulated role of these organs in defense against infectious disease (see page 404); there is marked reduction in serum globulin and in antibody content, and in some cases animals prove to be highly susceptible to infection by organisms that are part of the normal flora of conventional animals.

Gnotobiotic studies indicate that two or more species of microorganisms present together in an animal may display cooperative or competitive interaction. For example, one organism may create a condition such as a particular level of pH or oxidation-reduction potential favorable to another, or it may produce a growth factor needed by the other. Or, on the other hand, one may produce a chemical or condition that inhibits the other. The normal microbial flora of conventional animals presents a far more complicated picture, and we are left speculating about the role of the normal population in combating or furthering infectious disease.

INFECTION AND DISEASE

SUMMARY

Infectious disease is a biologic accident; an individual is invaded by a microorganism or poisoned by toxic microbial products. Microorganisms that are parasitic frequently produce disease, because the parasitic mode of existence is usually destructive.

The virulence of a pathogen is a function of its invasiveness (ability to establish itself in a host) and its toxigenicity (ability to produce toxic substances). Some organisms (e.g., *Treponema pallidum*) are highly invasive; others (*Clostridium botulinum*) are highly toxigenic. Species that are both invasive and toxigenic (e.g., *Streptococcus pyogenes*) are especially dangerous.

Successful transmission of infectious agents depends on the mode of exit from an infected individual, the ability of the pathogen to survive outside a host, and the availability of a means of entering a new host. Mechanical and biologic agents assist in effecting the transfer from one individual to another.

Inflammation is a universal response to infection. It not only calls attention to the infectious process but is in itself a defensive reaction. Local infections often resolve spontaneously as a result of phagocytosis. Occasionally microorganisms gain access to the lymph and blood and spread about the body. Lymph nodes become infected, but phagocytosis here or in other body tissues usually overcomes the infectious agent. General infection calls still other defenses into play, and fatal infection is a relatively rare occurrence.

STUDY QUESTIONS

1. Discuss the possibility that there may be nonpathogenic parasites.
2. Name some nonparasitic pathogens.
3. What is the significance of the various terms in the expression: $P = NV/R$?
4. Distinguish between pathogenicity and virulence.
5. Discuss factors that affect virulence. How is the virulence of an organism determined?
6. Discuss invasiveness and various microbial characteristics that enhance it.
7. At one time it was believed that a necklace of asafetida, an ill-smelling plant gum resin, would prevent infection by respiratory pathogens. Why did it apparently do so? Why do diseases spread by infected droplets persist at a high incidence despite advances in sanitation and public health?
8. Describe the responses of the body to a local infection that later generalizes and spreads over the entire body.
9. Is inflammation harmful?
10. Discuss possible roles of the normal body flora in infectious disease.

SUPPLEMENTARY READING

The textbooks by Burrows, Dubos, Smith et al., and Wilson and Miles are imposing volumes, but the student should not be frightened by their bulk. Each contains a section with up-to-date information on the nature of infectious disease, virulence of pathogens, transmission of infectious agents, and body responses. *Mechanisms of Microbial Pathogenicity* and *Microbial Behaviour "In Vivo" and "In Vitro"* are collections of papers presented by world authorities at symposia in London in 1955 and 1964. The first volume contains papers about toxins and other factors that determine the disease-producing power of various bacteria, protozoa, and fungi in man, other animals, and plants. The 1964 volume is concerned with the gap between test tube observations and the true *in vivo* situation when parasites are actually producing disease in the natural host. Moulder discusses parasitism in general and then analyzes the parasitic mechanism of four obligately intracellular parasites.

Burrows, W.: *Textbook of Microbiology,* 18th ed. Philadelphia, W. B. Saunders Co., 1963.

Dubos, R. J., and Hirsch, J. G. (Eds.): *Bacterial and Mycotic Infections of Man,* 4th ed. Philadelphia, J. B. Lippincott Co., 1965.

Moulder, J. W.: *The Biochemistry of Intracellular Parasitism.* Chicago, The University of Chicago Press, 1962.

Smith, D. T., et. al.: *Zinsser Microbiology,* 13th ed. New York, Appleton-Century-Crofts, Inc., 1963.

Society for General Microbiology: *Mechanisms of Microbial Pathogenicity.* Cambridge, Cambridge University Press, 1955.

Society for General Microbiology: *Microbial Behaviour "In Vivo" and "In Vitro."* Cambridge, Cambridge University Press, 1964.

Wilson, G. S., and Miles, A. A.: *Topley and Wilson's Principles of Bacteriology and Immunity,* 4th ed. Baltimore, The Williams & Wilkins Co., 1955.

RESISTANCE AND IMMUNITY

Simultaneously with the evolution of parasitism and the partially related phenomenon of pathogenicity, higher animals may acquire tolerance for their microbial invaders and learn to live with them in reasonable harmony—or they may become completely intolerant and develop means to prevent invasion or to destroy the parasite. In any event, after many generations a balanced state is established. Disease then occurs only when abnormal conditions prevail; for example, when the host is debilitated or encounters an overwhelming number of individual parasites, or when the parasite is unusually virulent.

In this chapter we shall consider the defensive structures and mechanisms with which the host counterbalances the invasive and destructive components or products of pathogenic microorganisms.

Defenses Against Infection. *Natural resistance* is one of three types of protection against infectious disease. It is associated with physical or physiologic conditions characteristic of an individual. It is nonspecific, that is, directed against no particular disease, and varies from time to time in the same individual and from one individual to another.

Nonsusceptibility is absolute protection against particular diseases and is associated with species characteristics. It is therefore basically genetic.

Immunity is directed against specific diseases and varies in degree. It is dependent on antibodies, which are proteins associated with the globulin fraction of blood serum. It is largely an individual characteristic, although strains or even species of animals possess certain antibodies for reasons that are unknown but are assumed to be genetic.

NATURAL RESISTANCE

Natural resistance is attributed to a variety of anatomic and physiologic factors, which vary from one individual to another and also vary within the same individual at different times or under different environmental conditions. Environmental factors are therefore often included in a discussion of natural resistance.

Normal Barriers Against Infection

Mechanical Barriers. Most living forms are surrounded by a covering layer of cells or a membrane of some sort, which separates the organism from its environment. This integument is usually strong and impermeable, except for openings that permit passage of liquids and gases.

Intact skin is an excellent barrier to infection. It is composed of several layers of cells, which constantly slough off from the outside and are replaced from the inside. Even the minute openings of the sweat and sebaceous glands are protected by chemical substances and are not ordinarily invaded by living microorganisms.

The sticky secretion of mucous membranes entraps microorganisms and keeps them from vulnerable organs such as the lungs. Moreover, many mucous surfaces are covered with cilia, whose active motion constantly removes foreign objects.

Few if any microorganisms are able to penetrate healthy, unbroken skin, but physical abrasion and physiologic disturbances induced by abnormal hormone concentrations, malnutrition, etc., occasionally permit microorganisms to enter hair follicles and sebaceous glands, where they multiply and produce local infections.

Chemical Barriers. Extreme acidity or alkalinity inhibits or kills microorganisms. Gastric juice, which may be as acid as pH 2, undoubtedly kills many organisms in water and food and helps to prevent infection. Some bacteria withstand the acidity or are protected by the food with which they are swallowed and establish themselves as intestinal pathogens. These organisms also survive ex-

Table 21-1. Antibacterial Substances from Animal Tissue or Fluid*

Name	Common Source	Chemical Nature	Antibacterial Selectivity
Complement	Serum	Euglobulin-carbohydrate-lipoprotein (?)	Gram negative
Properdin	Serum	Euglobulin	Gram negative
Phagocytin	Leukocytes	Globulin	Gram negative
Lysozyme	Ubiquitous	Small basic protein	Gram positive (chiefly)
β-Lysin	Serum	Protein (?)	Gram positive
Histone	Lymphatics	Small basic protein	Gram positive
Protamine	Sperm	Small basic protein	Gram positive
Tissue polypeptides	Lymphatics	Linear basic peptides	Gram positive
Leukin	Leukocytes	Basic peptides	Gram positive
Plakin	Blood platelets	Peptide (?)	Gram positive
Hematin, mesohematin	Red blood cells	Iron porphyrins	Gram positive
Spermine, spermidine	Pancreas, prostate	Basic polyamines	Gram positive

*Modified from Skarnes and Watson, Bact. Rev., *21*:273–294, 1957.

posure to the strongly alkaline fluid, bile, which enters the intestine in large quantities from the gallbladder.

A number of substances that are antibacterial *in vitro* have been isolated from animal tissues and body fluids (Table 21-1). Their effectiveness in the body is not known in every case.

Complement is a thermolabile (inactivated at 56° C. in 30 minutes) complex of nine or more components present in the sera of most warm-blooded animals. It participates in various serologic reactions (see page 410) and is believed to assist in the destruction of pathogenic organisms under favorable conditions.

Properdin is bactericidal against certain gram-negative bacteria in the presence of complement and Mg++ ions. It has also been implicated in the inactivation of several viruses.

Tears, nasal secretions, and saliva contain lysozyme, an enzyme that dissolves some staphylococci, intestinal streptococci, and possibly other pathogenic bacteria. Sweat is bactericidal for organisms, such as *Escherichia coli, Salmonella typhosa,* and *Streptococcus pyogenes,* that are not normally present on the skin; staphylococci, on the contrary, are resistant. Even the influenza virus is inactivated by skin secretions. The effective substance is probably lactic acid. The reaction of the skin may be as low as pH 5.

Various basic peptides or proteins isolated from lymphatic glands, blood cells, and other tissues appear to kill gram-positive bacteria.

Individual Factors Affecting Resistance

Nutrition. Well nourished individuals tend to resist or recover from infection better than undernourished individuals. Lack of vitamin A decreases resistance to infection, particularly by microorganisms invading the bronchi and upper respiratory passages. Adequate protein in the diet is believed to maintain resistance or immunity or both. Various reports indicate that human populations whose principal dietary staple is animal protein are more resistant to chronic respiratory infection, tuberculosis, etc., than those whose diet is chiefly cereal carbohydrate. The nature of the protein also seems to be important. Rats fed animal protein (casein) are two to three times as resistant to infection by *Salmonella enteritidis* as rats on a plant protein (wheat or soybean) diet.

Paradoxically, virus infections may be enhanced by adequate nutrition. Good health confers no protection against measles, influenza, chickenpox, and smallpox. Undernourished or partially starved mice are more resistant than normal animals to certain encephalitis viruses. Viruses evidently multiply better in healthy cells than in cells damaged by lack of proper nutrients.

Debilitation. General debilitation predisposes to infection by many microbial agents. Chronic disease, infectious or noninfectious, is a debilitating agent. Chronic alcoholism, fatigue, pregnancy, and age also influence the occurrence or severity of infectious disease. Pneumonia is particularly prevalent and severe in infants and in the aged.

Physical Stress. Experimental observations indicate that resistance to infection is correlated with the ability to respond to stress. Rabbits whose body temperatures return to normal promptly after artificial chilling are more resistant than those with a prolonged warming time. Experiments with humans indicate a correlation between the rate of oxygen utilization during exercise and resistance to the common cold.

Temperature and humidity extremes, especially sudden changes of temperature, alter the physiologic state of the nasal mucous membranes and may increase their permeability and susceptibility to invasion by potential pathogens of the normal flora. Fatigue, shock, and oxygen starvation also affect tissue or capillary permeability and increase the likelihood of infection.

Heredity. Heredity is a factor in the response of the individual to infectious agents. Webster, at the Rockefeller Institute, increased and decreased the resistance of mice to *S. enteritidis,* a mouse pathogen, by selective breeding. From normal mice, whose mortality rate was 37 per cent, lines were developed with mortality rates of 85 per cent and 15 per cent.

The resistance of human populations to tuberculosis and syphilis has changed during the last few centuries. Tuberculosis in present civilized populations is usually chronic, but previously unexposed native populations are nearly exterminated by their first contact with the disease. This occurred when tuberculosis was introduced into Tasmania and also in several thousand Kaffirs brought to Ceylon by the Dutch. The few survivors of such an epidemic are more resistant than the majority, and natural selection eventually produces a population in which the disease is chronic and less severe. The physical or physiologic factors responsible for resistance are not known.

Environmental Factors Affecting Resistance

Environmental factors affect the resistance of individuals or of populations only indirectly but should be mentioned because they influence the occurrence of infectious disease.

Climate. Climate determines the distribution of pathogenic microorganisms. Yellow fever and malaria are tropical or subtropical diseases because their mosquito vectors or hosts require a warm climate. Bacillary dysentery is also common in tropical and subtropical areas, but it occurs with some frequency in all climatic regions. It is particularly prevalent in areas of poor sanitation and personal hygiene; climate evidently determines the socioeconomic status of the populations and their state of civilization.

Urbanization. Population density affects the rapidity of transfer of infectious organisms from one individual to another and hence determines the occurrence of epidemics or other outbreaks.

Respiratory infections tend to spread rapidly in heavily populated areas. However, community sanitation, which is developed best in the industrialized areas of the northern and southern temperate zones, has decreased the incidence of intestinal disease almost to the vanishing point.

NONSUSCEPTIBILITY

Nonsusceptibility is absolute protection against specific diseases. It is associated with the species of the host and is inherited in the same sense as other species characteristics. Nonsusceptibility is determined by physiologic and anatomic factors, but in many cases the specific factors are not known.

Man is nonsusceptible to many infectious diseases of animals: chicken cholera, hog cholera, cattle plague, canine distemper. Lower animals are nonsusceptible to many human diseases, including typhoid fever, dysentery, cholera, whooping cough, influenza, measles, mumps, gonorrhea, and syphilis.

Body temperature and diet may contribute to nonsusceptibility. Early experiments demonstrated that frogs and chickens are normally nonsusceptible to anthrax, but frogs inoculated with *Bacillus anthracis* succumbed to the infection when warmed to 35° C., as did chickens artificially cooled from a normal body temperature of about 41° C.

IMMUNITY

Immunity is a specific form of resistance that depends on the presence of antibodies. It varies in degree from one individual to another and may vary during the life of the individual. It occurs in animals but is generally believed not to occur in plants.

Theories of Immunity

The participation of blood components in immunity has long been known, but for several years there were two opposing theories of the mechanism of immunity.

Humoral Theory. According to the humoral theory, soluble substances in the blood serum are responsible for immunity to infectious disease. (Serum is the clear, straw-colored fluid remaining after the cells and fibrin have been removed from blood.) It was observed that bacteria of certain species died when mixed with the serum of animals that had recovered from infection or had been injected with killed bacteria of the same species. Infected animals recovered when injected with immune serum, whereas control animals untreated with serum succumbed. Moreover, bacteria were shown to die and dissolve when injected into an immune animal. The humoral theory was championed by Buchner, Pfeiffer, and others.

Cellular Theory. The cellular theory of immunity was proposed and defended by Metchnikoff. He found by microscopic study of the transparent waterflea, *Daphnia,* that when yeast cells that ordinarily produced a fatal infection were ingested by an ameboid type of body cell, the animal subsequently recovered. When ingestion did not occur, the waterflea succumbed to the infection. Further observations showed that this phenomenon was not limited to *Daphnia,* and that the ameboid cells of other species had the same capacity for ingesting foreign objects, including microorganisms. Metchnikoff postulated that *phagocytosis,* as he called this process, is the mechanism responsible for immunity and recovery from animal disease.

Opsonic Theory. Metchnikoff and the various proponents of the humoral theory debated and defended their respective beliefs for several years. Finally, Wright and Douglas showed in 1903 that both serum and phagocytic cells are important in immunity. Phagocytosis occurs to a limited extent in the absence of serum but is greatly enhanced by a serum component, which they called *opsonin.*

Opsonin is the name applied to antibody as demonstrated by specific phagocytosis. The activity of antibody can be shown in several other ways, and it is often given different names according to the method of demonstration.

Antibodies

An antibody is a modified blood globulin, usually formed in response to an antigenic stimulus, that is capable of combining specifically with the corresponding antigen. Most *antigens* are substances of high molecular weight, either proteins or polysaccharides.

The word "specifically" implies that the antibody can react only with its antigen, but this is not strictly true. The actual reaction sites of both antigen and antibody are small surface areas—about the size of four or five amino acid or monosaccharide residues. Therefore, different antigens that possess similar but not identical reaction sites often react with the same antibody, because reactivity is in part conditioned by a good "fit" between the two substances (Fig. 21-1).

Normal and Immune Blood Proteins. Blood serum contains 6 to 7 per cent protein. More than 30 proteins can be identified in normal serum by precipitation with sodium or ammonium sulfate or with alcohol under controlled conditions, by their electric charges, and by their molecular weights. Two principal fractions are the albumins and the globulins, each comprising about half of the total protein. There are many different globulins, which can be distinguished by their electric charges and molecular weights. Antibodies are among the proteins with the lowest electric charge in animal sera at pH 7 and are found in the so-called gamma globulin fraction. The molecular weight of most antibody globulins is about 160,000.

Antibody globulin and normal globulin differ in only one *known* way, that is, in the ability of antibody to react with its corresponding antigen or hapten.

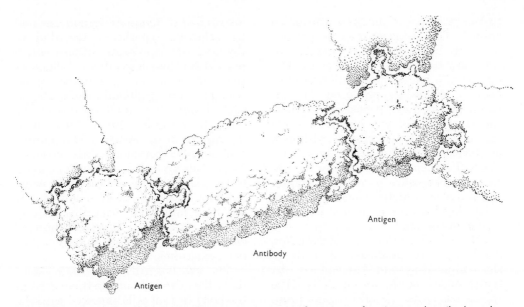

Figure 21-1. "Lock and key" complementary structures of portions of antigen and antibody molecules. The irregularities of the surface structures of the molecules represent chemical radicals (e.g., a benzene ring or an amino acid). Each antibody can combine with two antigen molecules, and each antigen can react with several antibodies. (L. Pauling, Endeavour, Vol. VII, No. 26, 1948.)

They are chemically and physically identical by all other tests. The difference between them is therefore very subtle, and it is generally believed to consist of a slightly different arrangement of groups of atoms, so that the antibody contains structures corresponding in configuration to structures of the antigen. The relationship is like that of a key to a lock or a coin to the die from which it is struck.

Natural Antibodies. Natural antibodies comprise a family of molecules—probably always protein and, in mammals, consisting of globulins—which are found in the body fluids of normal animals and have the ability to react specifically with potentially antigenic substances. They are present in an individual's serum from the time of birth, or shortly thereafter, and persist throughout life. There is no apparent external stimulus for their production. Many animal species possess natural antibodies against human pathogens such as typhoid fever, cholera, and dysentery bacteria. Certain humans possess natural antibodies against the pneumococcus

and the typhoid organism, occasionally in considerable amount. Natural antibodies that react with foreign erythrocytes are present in the blood of various species, and reactions attributed to natural antibodies have been reported with bacterial and animal viruses, fungi, protozoa, and metazoa.

Many human sera contain antibodies that react with erythrocytes of other human individuals. These blood group antibodies or *isohemagglutinins* are under genetic control. They appear within a few months after birth, attain their highest concentration by the age of 10 years, and decrease slowly thereafter.

Antibodies that react with erythrocytes apparently have nothing to do with infectious disease. It is not known whether natural antibacterial antibodies of man and lower animals actually prevent infectious disease. Many investigators doubt that the resistance of lower animals to typhoid fever, cholera, dysentery, and other human diseases can be attributed to natural antibodies.

Immune Antibodies. Immune antibodies appear in the serum in response to the presence of antigens within an animal. The antigens may be present naturally in the course of infection, or they may be injected to induce the formation of a high concentration of antibodies. Antibodies produced in this manner sometimes persist throughout the remainder of the individual's life but usually diminish slowly. Although antibodies disappear, an immunized individual responds more rapidly to subsequent reexposure or reimmunization and produces a higher concentration of antibodies than after the first exposure or immunization.

Site of Formation of Antibodies. Antibodies are produced by cells of the lymphoid system, particularly the lymph nodes and the spleen. Cells of the spleen and other visceral organs probably produce antibody in response to antigens that cause general infection or have been injected intravenously or intraperitoneally. Regional lymph nodes respond first and perhaps solely to local infections or to antigens injected subcutaneously.

The particular cell type from which antibody is derived appears to be the plasma cell. *Plasma cells* are nucleated, and their extensive cytoplasm stains intensely with basic dyes and therefore presumably contains large amounts of RNA, an intermediary in protein synthesis. They are not usually present in peripheral blood but are found in the spleen, lymph nodes, and other locations, especially following antigenic stimulation.

After a first experience with antigen, plasma cells begin to appear in these organs. Further contact with the antigen incites marked lymphoid hyperplasia (multiplication of lymphoid tissue cells) and accelerated replication of plasma cells. There is evidence for the transformation of lymphocytes and reticular cells into plasma cells. Accompanying the increase in plasma cells, antibody production accelerates.

Mechanism of Antibody Formation. There are two major hypotheses of the mechanism of antibody formation: the instructive or template hypothesis and the selective hypothesis. According to the *template hypothesis,* antigen enters protein-synthesizing cells and influences the manner of folding and the spatial configuration of globulin molecules in such a way that small regions of the latter bear the imprint of corresponding regions of the antigen. The imprint consists of a complementary arrangement of atoms and electrostatic charges, which yields a close structural fit when antibody later reacts with antigen. It has been postulated that the reacting radicals of antibody must fit those of antigen with a tolerance of only one or two Angströms.

The *selective hypothesis* states essentially that throughout life there exist in the body certain cells endowed with the inherent ability to react with particular antigens. According to one version of this hypothesis, during embryonic life several thousand cells differentiate, each with different specific reactivity. Those that react with potentially antigenic components of the individual's body are destroyed. The remainder survive and become the precursors of the antibody-producing cells of the immunologically mature individual. They can colonize in the spleen and other lymphoid tissues and produce *clones* of cells with identical antibody-producing capacity and specificity. Upon contact with the appropriate antigen, cells of a given clone are stimulated to proliferate and produce antibody. The nature of the "recognition factor" with which the antigen reacts initially is not known. It has been postulated that circulating natural antibodies are the recognition factors; after encountering and combining with the corresponding antigens, they react with lymphoid cells and incite proliferation, transformation to plasma cells, and antibody production as previously described.

Antigens

Antigens are substances that stimulate the formation of antibodies and that react observably with those antibodies. Most proteins and some polysaccharides are antigenic; lipids are generally not antigenic. Antigens are not necessarily pathogenic; in fact, much experimental work on the nature of antigen-antibody reactions has been done with harmless antigenic substances. The sources of antigenic materials are universal; they are found in all animals, plants, bacteria, viruses, and other microorganisms.

In general it is said that only substances foreign to the injected animal can induce the formation of antibodies. Some exceptional substances, such as thyroglobulin, lens protein of the eye, and spermatozoa, which are normally inaccessible to the blood and lymph, may be antigenic in the same individual when removed from their normal location and injected. Serum proteins can be made antigenic for the donor animal by slight chemical modification (e.g., by addition of iodine, nitrate, or other radicals). Certain human diseases are attributed to the acquisition of antigenicity by normal body components, which undergo chemical modification accompanying aging or other conditions; the altered body constituents induce antibody formation in the same person and provoke a destructive antigen-antibody reaction *in vivo*.

Living organisms of any kind are composed of many antigenic materials. Even bacteria and the smaller forms such as viruses contain several antigenic substances, and animals injected with the whole organisms produce numerous antibodies, each corresponding to a single antigenic component. Bacterial cells are considered mosaics of antigens (Fig. 21-2). Some antigens are peculiar to each species of bacterium, a few are also found in other species. Certain antigens are characteristic of flagella, others of capsules, and still others of the cell bodies. Most antigens have not been identified chemically beyond a determination of their protein or polysaccharide nature, but they can be detected by means of appropriate antibody solutions (antisera). Antigen-antibody reactions will be described in a later section (page 411).

Role of Antibodies in Immunity

Types of Antibodies. An antibody is frequently named according to the method in use at the moment to demonstrate its activity; the same antibody may therefore bear several names. Pneumococcal antiserum, for example, contains antibody that can agglutinate (clump) intact pneumococci and that

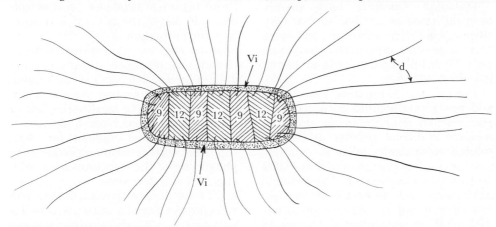

Figure 21-2. Diagrammatic sketch indicating the mosaic-like antigenic structure of a bacterial cell. This organism, *Salmonella typhosa*, possesses a single antigenic component (*d*) in its flagella. Its cell body may contain an "envelope" antigen (*Vi*) and two "somatic" antigens (9 and 12), which are actually part of the cell wall structure. Numeral and letter systems are commonly used to label bacterial cellular antigens.

also can precipitate the capsular polysaccharide of the organisms. If an agglutination test is performed, the antibody is called *agglutinin;* in a precipitation test the same antibody is called *precipitin.*

Antitoxins. Antitoxin is antibody that neutralizes toxin, specifically exotoxin. Exotoxins are neutralized according to the law of multiple proportions by homologous (i.e., corresponding) antitoxin; that is, if one unit of antitoxin neutralizes 100 lethal doses of toxin, 10 units of antitoxin will neutralize 1000 lethal doses. The mechanism of neutralization is not known, but its occurrence is not doubted. Experience during epidemics indicates that individuals possessing a certain small amount of diphtheria antitoxin in their circulating blood are immune from this disease; individuals possessing less antitoxin are likely to acquire diphtheria if exposed.

Cytolysins and Bactericidins. Cytolysins and bactericidal antibodies require the cooperation of the normal serum component, complement, to dissolve or kill bacteria. Complement is not increased by immunization. The effectiveness of cytolytic and bactericidal actions is obvious, but their occurrence is limited to only a few bacterial species.

Opsonins. Opsonins have already been described as antibodies that sensitize certain microorganisms and make them more easily ingested by phagocytic cells. Their full importance is unknown; it is doubtless great.

Precipitins. Precipitins react with and precipitate soluble antigens. This phenomenon occurring *in vivo* probably removes microbial cellular debris and soluble constituents such as capsular substances. The precipitated material is destroyed by phagocytosis. Toxic soluble substances, such as exotoxins, precipitate when mixed in suitable proportions with their corresponding antitoxins *in vitro;* it may be presumed that precipitation also occurs *in vivo.*

Agglutinins. Agglutinins make particulate (cellular) antigens stick together in large masses and settle out like a precipitate. The difference between agglutination and precipitation is that the antigen in agglutination is a particle of microscopic size, whereas a precipitating antigen is in solution.

Agglutination does not necessarily kill the agglutinated organisms, so that the reaction might appear to be of no significance in immunity. However, phagocytosis of clumped bacteria requires little more energy than phagocytosis of a single cell, and the efficiency of phagocytosis is therefore greatly enhanced by previous agglutination, apart from the opsonizing activity of antibody.

Immunizing Effectiveness of Antibodies. Many apparently useless antibodies are produced in the course of infection or artificial immunization with whole bacteria, because the antibody-producing mechanism cannot distinguish between harmful and harmless antigens. Not all the components of a microbial cell are *essential* immunizing antigens. Only antibodies against essential immunizing antigens are necessary for effective immunity, and the nature of these antigens varies according to the microorganism.

Antitoxin appears to be most significant in the case of bacteria that produce exotoxins: diphtheria, tetanus, gas gangrene, scarlet fever, etc. The gas gangrene organism produces 12 exotoxins, but only one of the antitoxins is necessary for protection.

Antibodies for the capsular polysaccharides of pneumococci afford much greater protection against pneumonia than antibodies against the rest of the cell bodies. It will be recalled that encapsulated pneumococci resist phagocytosis. Pneumococcal capsules that have combined with antibody no longer resist phagocytosis; the organisms are readily engulfed and destroyed.

The motile intestinal pathogenic bacteria possess flagellar antigens as well as somatic (i.e., cell body) antigens, but only the somatic antibodies are effective in immunity. Some typhoid fever bacteria possess a special type of somatic component known as the Vi antigen. Vi antibody is essential for a high degree of immunity against Vi strains but offers no additional protection against strains lacking this antigen.

Importance of Phagocytosis. The phagocytic activity of leukocytes is easily demonstrated, but there are actually many other phagocytic cells in the body, some of which are more important in combating infection. The phagocytic systems of the body, commonly designated the reticuloendothelial system (RES), may be outlined briefly as follows:

1. *Cells of reticular and loose connective tissue.* (Reticular cells form the framework of lymph glands, bone marrow, liver, and spleen.)

   A. *Macrophages, including reticular cells.* These cells are actively phagocytic. Most varieties are fixed (i.e., sessile), but histiocytes or clasmatocytes in the loose connective tissue are free or wandering cells.

   B. *Fibroblasts of connective tissue and endothelial cells of blood vessels.* Fibroblasts are structural cells that support and bind tissue together; they are rarely phagocytic. Endothelial cells lining the larger blood vessels and capillaries are also rarely phagocytic.

2. *Free connective tissue and blood cells.* The free connective tissue cells are precursors of macrophages. The blood cells (see page 394), which include many actively phagocytic cells, are the granulocytes (polymorphonuclear neutrophils, eosinophils, and basophils), lymphocytes, and monocytes, in order of presumed decreasing phagocytic activity.

The role of phagocytosis (Fig. 21-3) in prevention of or recovery from infectious disease is more difficult to determine than that of antibodies. Investigators have therefore tended to overemphasize the activities of antibodies and to ignore phagocytosis. Phagocytosis by leukocytes in the absence of opsonizing antibody can be demonstrated upon a "rough" surface, such as filter paper, against which the ameboid cells can trap bacteria or other particles. Phagocytosis occurs *in vivo* in the absence of antibody

when the wandering phagocytic cells "corner" invading microorganisms against tissues or other phagocytic cells. Antibody greatly accelerates phagocytosis by leukocytes. The role of antibody in the activity of *fixed* phagocytic cells is unknown, but the dramatic removal of millions of bacteria per milliliter from the blood, as demonstrated repeatedly, indicates that fixed phagocytes are extremely active and are undoubtedly better guardians against infection than has been appreciated.

Types of Immunity

Natural Immunity. Natural immunity is attributed to natural antibodies, as already mentioned. It is present from birth or shortly thereafter and persists throughout life. Inasmuch as natural antibodies cannot at present be distinguished with assurance from immune antibodies, the importance and even the extent of natural immunity are not known. This would seem to be a valuable field for research.

Acquired Immunity. Acquired immunity is attributed to immune antibodies. If the antibodies are produced by the immunized individual, the result is known as *active acquired immunity*. If preformed antibodies are acquired from the mother at birth or by injection from another individual or animal, the result is called *passive acquired immunity*.

Active Acquired Immunity. The stimulus for antibody production may be a natural infection or a series of injections. Recovery from many infectious diseases is followed by specific immunity: typhoid fever, whooping cough, diphtheria, chickenpox, smallpox, etc. Local infections with *Staphylococcus aureus* (e.g., boils and carbuncles) do not usually create immunity; the infectious agent never gains access to the lymph nodes or to the blood, and hence antibodies are never produced. Reasons for the failure of certain other infectious diseases to produce immunity are less clear. Active immunity, particularly that resulting from infection, is

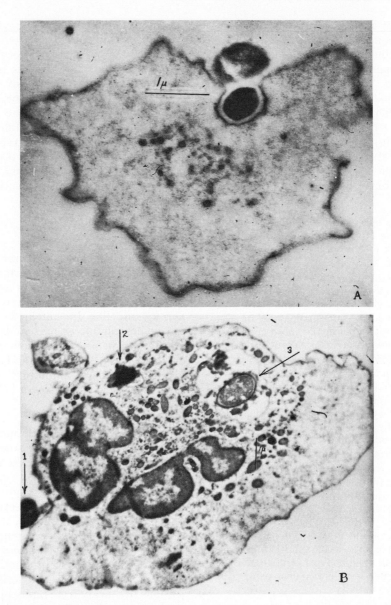

Figure 21-3. Electron photomicrographs of two stages in phagocytosis of staphylococci by poly-morphonuclear neutrophil cells of the blood. A, A deeply stained bacterial cell nearly surrounded by pseudopodia. B, Arrow 1 points to a coccus about to be ingested, arrow 2 indicates a recently ingested bacterial cell, and arrow 3 designates a coccus within a vacuole. (Photographs by J. R. Goodman et al.; A.S.M. LS-354 and -359.)

often of considerable duration and may persist throughout life.

Artificially acquired active immunity is induced by injecting a variety of agents. Sublethal doses of virulent organisms may be introduced by a route favorable

for infection, or larger doses may be given by a route unfavorable for natural infection. The ancient Chinese practice of variolation is an example of the latter. Smallpox virus contained in pustular material from a case of the disease was inoculated into the skin. This virus is normally acquired by the respiratory route; therefore only a mild skin infection was produced, and the individual recovered and was thereafter immune from smallpox. Occasional mishaps, such as frank cases of the disease or concurrent infection with skin bacteria, led to abandonment of this practice, especially when the effectiveness of cowpox vaccine was demonstrated by Jenner in 1796. Immunization with living, virulent microorganisms entails a certain amount of risk and is now usually confined to veterinary practice.

Microorganisms attenuated or weakened by cultivation under unfavorable conditions (e.g., high temperature) or in an unnatural host (e.g., rabies virus transferred through the brains of rabbits and then dried) are often effective immunizing agents and can be used in larger amounts than would be possible with virulent forms. The Sabin poliomyelitis vaccine is composed of living attenuated viruses; it is administered by mouth, the natural infective route.

Killed microorganisms are safer immunizing materials and are used when possible. The standard typhoid-paratyphoid vaccine and pertussis (whooping cough) vaccine are of this type. The Salk vaccine for poliomyelitis consists of virus treated with formalin to inactivate or kill the infective agent.

Bacterial products are used for immunization. Toxoids have already been described. Several laboratories are attempting to isolate the essential immunizing antigens from the typhoid fever, dysentery, and other bacteria. It is hoped that these purified antigens will reduce unpleasant side reactions (sore arm, malaise, etc.) occasionally produced by the routine vaccines.

Artificial immunization or actual infection with one bacterium sometimes induces antibodies and partial immunity against other bacteria possessing some of the same antigens.

The Antibody Response to Artificial Active Immunization. A single injection of antigen is followed by a latent period of several days before antibody appears in detectable amount in the circulating blood. The concentration of antibody rises slowly to a low peak and then diminishes. This is the "primary response" (Fig. 21-4).

A second injection of antigen, several days, weeks, or even months later, induces rapid production of antibody after

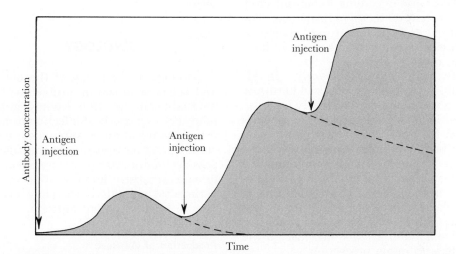

Figure 21-4. Antibody concentration in the blood following one, two, or more injections of antigen. The responses to second and succeeding injections are quicker, steeper, higher, and more persistent.

a shorter latent period; a higher peak is attained and the concentration in the blood decreases more slowly. This is the "secondary response." It can occur even after antibody has completely disappeared from the blood. Additional injections invoke further antibody production within limits: a maximum is eventually reached. The secondary response may also be induced in a previously immunized individual by natural exposure to the homologous infectious agent; antibody is produced rapidly enough to prevent disease.

It should be emphasized that immunity is quantitative rather than qualitative and that no immunization procedure, either natural or artificial, can be guaranteed to produce complete immunity against overwhelming infection. Moreover, artificial immunization with killed or attenuated vaccines is often not as effective as natural immunization by actual infection, and periodic reimmunization or "boosters" may be necessary to maintain a satisfactory protective level of immunity.

Experience with immunization against poliomyelitis and whooping cough underlines the statement that artificial immunization does not always assure complete protection; occasionally, individuals who have received the full course of injections become infected, and a few of these patients die. The vast majority are protected, however, and most of those who become ill have mild cases.

Passive Acquired Immunity. In this state, antibodies are acquired naturally from the mother or artificially by injection. Human babies acquire antibodies from the maternal circulation *in utero.* Antibody molecules traverse the single layer of placental cells separating the maternal and fetal circulations and appear in the blood of the newborn baby. Antibodies acquired in this manner are detectable for only three to six months; active immunization is necessary if the child is to retain protection.

Other animals, such as the cow, have a different mechanism for transferring antibodies from the mother to the offspring. The four layers of cells that separate the maternal and fetal circulations inhibit passage of antibodies, but the colostrum, the first milk delivered after birth of the calf, contains a high concentration of antibodies. These are not digested in the stomach of the newborn calf but pass through the wall of the digestive tract intact and enter the blood.

Artificial passive immunization is the injection of whole blood, plasma, serum, or serum fractions. The injected antibodies are detectable for only a few weeks. Antisera from other animal species are usually used, although the antibodies probably do not persist in the recipient as long as antibodies of the same species. Horses are commonly employed because they produce large quantities of antibody.

Small doses of antiserum or antitoxin provide temporary protection of an individual exposed to an infectious agent or toxin-producing organism. Actual cases of the disease are treated with larger doses. Precautions must be taken in the use of antisera of other species lest allergic reactions and even fatal shock result. Some individuals are naturally sensitive to the proteins of foreign species; others acquire sensitivity by repeated injection of the foreign serum.

SEROLOGY

Serology is the study of the nature and behavior of serum antibodies. The antibody concentration attained in human sera as a result of infection or normal immunization is often not sufficiently great for research or for artificial passive immunization or treatment of disease. Intensive immunization of experimental animals is therefore necessary to produce potent antisera.

Production of Antisera

Rabbits are often used for laboratory production of antisera against bacteria, erythrocytes, protein solutions such as foreign serum or egg albumin, and other materials.

Intravenous, intraperitoneal, and subcutaneous injections may be given. Intravenous inoculation ensures prompt distribution of the antigen to all antibody-producing sites. Dissemination of the antigenic material is slightly slower following intraperitoneal inoculation, but it is somewhat safer. Subcutaneous inoculations are usually safest but provide slow distribution of the antigenic material.

The first injection of a toxic antigen is usually small, and succeeding injections are progressively larger as the animal develops antibodies and can tolerate increased doses. Constant and fairly large quantities of nontoxic antigens may be introduced. Doses are spaced one to four days apart; if they are given every day a rest period is allowed after three or four injections, and inoculations are resumed the following week. Trial titrations are performed at intervals, and when the antibody content of the serum is sufficiently great the needed quantity of blood is taken.

Laboratory animals appear quite insensitive to the techniques of injection and bleeding if properly handled. Rabbits will often sit without restraint on the operator's lap or on a laboratory bench while injections are made and small amounts of blood are taken from an ear vein.

Antigen–Antibody Reactions

Antigen-antibody reactions as customarily demonstrated in the laboratory are two-stage reactions. The first stage is union of antigen and antibody; this is not directly detectable. The second stage is the visible result of antigen-antibody union: agglutination, precipitation, etc.

Union of antigen and antibody is specific; that is, an antibody will combine only with the antigen that invoked its formation or with some other antigens closely related chemically. Most anti-

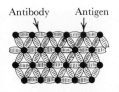

Antibody   Antigen

Figure 21-5. Diagrammatic representation of an antigen-antibody aggregate showing how antigen molecules (or particles) alternate with antibody molecules in a three-dimensional lattice or framework. (From Carpenter: Immunology and Serology, 2d ed. Philadelphia, W. B. Saunders Co., 1965.)

body molecules are believed to be bivalent, that is, capable of combining with two antigen molecules or particles. Antigens are believed to be multivalent and hence can combine with several antibody molecules. Union between antigen and antibody therefore produces a lattice or framework in which antibody molecules alternate with antigen molecules or particles. This is the *lattice* or *framework hypothesis* of antigen-antibody reaction (Fig. 21-5).

Agglutination. Agglutination is the visible second stage result of mixing a particulate or cellular antigen with homologous antiserum. The cells clump together and settle to the bottom of the fluid in the form of flocculent masses, compact granules, or thin sheets. Agitation usually does not redisperse the particles completely. The particles behave as though they are sticky and cling tenaciously together.

Tube agglutination tests are performed in small test tubes. Serial dilutions of serum (1:10, 1:20, 1:40, 1:80, etc.) in saline are prepared, a suspension of the cellular test antigen is added, and the test tubes are incubated. The time and temperature of incubation vary with the antigen-antibody system. After incubation the degree of agglutination in each tube is read (Fig. 21-6). A tube in which all cells are agglutinated is graded + + + +; absence of agglutination is designated −; intermediate reactions, are indicated +, + +, or + + +. The titer of the serum is the

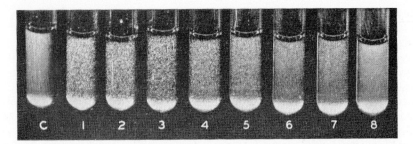

Figure 21-6.   The results of a tube agglutination test. Tube C is a control; it contains bacterial cells in saline, but no antiserum. The remaining tubes contain bacterial cells and increasing dilutions of antiserum. There is agglutination in tubes 1 through 7, but not in tube 8. (From Burrows: Textbook of Microbiology, 18th ed. Philadelphia, W. B. Saunders Co., 1963.)

reciprocal of the greatest dilution causing definite (+) agglutination.

The process of agglutination can be observed microscopically by using very dilute antiserum and a broth culture or saline suspension of the bacteria (Fig. 21-7).

Precipitation.   Solutions of proteins

or certain polysaccharides are used in precipitation tests with appropriate antisera. The antigen is diluted serially, the antiserum is either undiluted or diluted no more than 1:10, because precipitation requires a very high concentration of antibody.

The *ring* or *interfacial test* is a com-

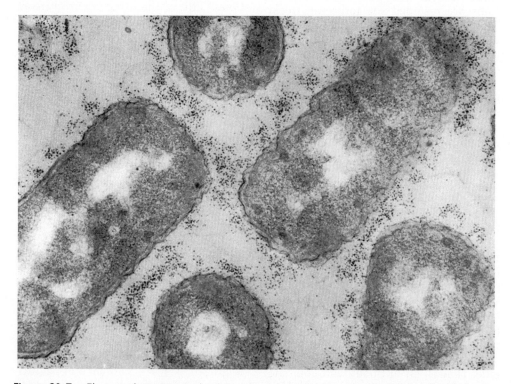

Figure 21-7.   Electron photomicrograph of *E. coli* agglutinated by an antibody labeled with ferritin, an iron-containing compound that is opaque to electrons. The bacterial bodies appear connected by bridges of the ferritin-antibody complex (60,000X). (From Shands, J. Bact., 90:267, 1965.)

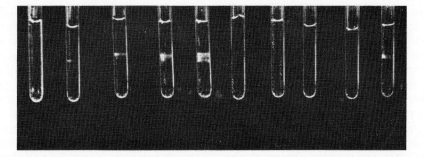

Figure 21-8. The results of a medicolegal precipitation test by the interfacial method. The five tubes on the left contain antihuman serum with upper layers of *decreasing* dilutions of an extract of a blood stain. There is no ring of precipitate in the first tube, but there are increasingly strong zones of precipitate in the next four tubes. The remaining tubes are controls; the last contains known human blood layered over antihuman serum. (From Boyd: Fundamentals of Immunology. New York, Interscience Publishers, Inc., 1956.)

mon method of demonstrating precipitation. A layer of antigen dilution is carefully placed over the antiserum in a very small test tube or capillary. A fine line of precipitate appears at the interface between the two liquids within a few minutes (Fig. 21-8). The titer is expressed as the reciprocal of the greatest antigen dilution yielding a positive result.

The precipitation test is used to identify proteins, and one form of the test is used in the diagnosis of syphilis (e.g., the Kahn test). Protein identification is important in the medicolegal identification of blood stains and body secretions in murder and other criminal acts. Various foods including meats (horse meat in "hamburger," for example) can be identified if appropriate antisera are available.

Neutralization of Toxins. Neutralization of toxicity is determined by experiments with animals. Various quantities of exotoxin are mixed with a constant amount of antitoxin and injected after short incubation to permit chemical union. Neutralization is indicated by survival of the test animal (Table 21-2). The potency of the antitoxin is measured by the amount of toxin it neutralizes and is usually expressed in *units*. A unit is an arbitrary quantity contained in a standard preparation at the National

Table 21-2. Neutralization of Tetanus Toxin by Antitoxin, Tested by Intramuscular Inoculation of Mice

Dose Per Mouse		Death Time (Hours)
Toxin (M.L.D.)*	Antitoxin (Unit)	
200	0.1	Survived
325	0.1	Survived
500	0.1	47
800	0.1	22
1250	0.1	19
2500	0.1	<18

* 1 M.L.D. of tetanus toxin is defined as the least amount that will kill a 20 gm. mouse in 120 hours.

Institutes of Health in Bethesda, Maryland, and at other laboratories throughout the world.

Lysis and Complement Fixation. Lysis or cytolysis may occur when cells that have been *sensitized* by union with their homologous antibodies react with complement. Bacteriolysis, the dissolving of bacteria, is demonstrated most satisfactorily with *Vibrio cholerae* and *S. typhosa*. Hemolysis is the dissolution of erythrocytes; most theoretical studies of lysis have been carried out with hemolysis because the results can be detected readily by macroscopic inspection, whereas bacteriolysis must usually be determined by microscopic examination.

Complement may combine with sensitized antigens and produce no effect detectable by either microscopic or macroscopic examination. If the amount of complement employed in such a preparation is not excessive, the fact that it has combined with the sensitized antigen can be determined by adding another sensitized antigen that does give a visible reaction with complement. Sensitized erythrocytes are usually chosen as the indicator system. Egg albumin and anti-egg albumin serum, for example, mixed in proportions that yield no trace of precipitate, may nevertheless combine with complement to form a three-component complex (Fig. 21-9). Complement is "fixed" in this system and is unable to react with another antigen-antibody system subsequently added, such as erythrocytes sensitized by their homologous antibody (hemolysin). Absence of either the egg albumin or its antibody yields a mixture in which complement is free and lyses the sensitized erythrocytes.

The complement fixation test is very sensitive and detects traces of either antigen or antibody, depending on the manner of setting up the test. It is also used in the Wassermann test for syphilis, in which an antibody-like substance known as *reagin* is the unknown.

Phagocytosis. Phagocytosis *in vitro* can be demonstrated with *S. aureus* and

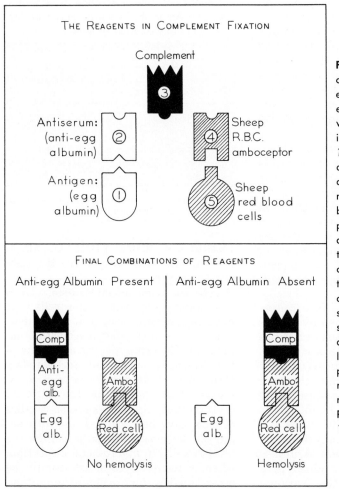

THE REAGENTS IN COMPLEMENT FIXATION

Complement

③

Antiserum: (anti-egg albumin) ②

Sheep R.B.C. amboceptor ④

Antigen: (egg albumin) ①

Sheep red blood cells ⑤

FINAL COMBINATIONS OF REAGENTS

Anti-egg Albumin Present | Anti-egg Albumin Absent

Comp — Anti-egg alb. — Egg alb. — Ambo — Red cell
No hemolysis

Comp — Egg alb. — Ambo — Red cell
Hemolysis

Figure 21-9. The reagents in a complement fixation test with egg albumin as antigen and anti-egg albumin serum. The order in which the reagents are used is indicated by the encircled figures: 1, 2, and 3 are mixed first; after a period of incubation 4 and 5 are added (amboceptor is a name sometimes applied to antibody that participates in complement reactions). If anti-egg albumin antibody is present in the antiserum (2), the three-component aggregate shown in the lower left is formed, and no complement remains to lyse the sensitized R.B.C. If the antiserum does not contain sufficient antibody, the situation in the lower right will obtain; complement will be free to lyse the red cells. (From Carpenter: Immunology and Serology, 2d ed. Philadelphia, W. B. Saunders Co., 1965.)

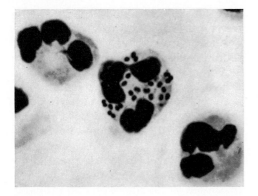

Figure 21-10. Phagocytosis of *Neisseria meningitidis.* The center polymorphonuclear leukocyte has ingested nearly two dozen of the paired cocci (1200X). (From Ruch and Patton: Medical Physiology and Biophysics, 19th ed. Philadelphia, W. B. Saunders Co., 1965.)

human blood. Equal parts of whole blood, bacterial suspension, and antiserum are mixed and incubated at 37° C. for 30 minutes; a smear is then prepared and stained. The average number of bacteria ingested by the polymorphonuclear neutrophils is determined (Fig. 21-10). A measure of the opsonizing activity of immune serum can be obtained by comparing its behavior with that of normal serum.

Hypersensitivity Reactions. Anaphylaxis and allergy can be demonstrated only in a living animal or with living animal tissue.

Anaphylaxis. The guinea pig is the most satisfactory experimental animal for demonstration of anaphylaxis, because it is easily sensitized and shocked. An animal is given a small intraperitoneal injection of a foreign protein such as horse serum or egg albumin. About three weeks later it is injected intravenously with a larger dose of the same antigen. Within a few moments the animal begins to cough, gasps for breath, has convulsions, and dies, often within one or two minutes after injection. A second guinea pig given *repeated* injections of the same antigen becomes "immune"; later reinjection of the antigen is harmless.

Production of anaphylactic shock in the guinea pig requires two injections of antigen separated by a period of about two weeks. The first or sensitizing injection incites production of only a small amount of antibody, and the animal becomes hypersensitive. Most of the antibody is attached to various body cells, and only a low concentration is in the blood.

The second or shocking dose two or three weeks later is larger than the first and is usually injected directly into the bloodstream, where it quickly encounters sensitive cells. The excess antigen reacts with the cellular antibody and damages the cells, which release histamine or a similar substance. The pharmocologic action of histamine in the guinea pig includes the symptoms described above. These symptoms are referable to the contraction of smooth muscle and to capillary dilatation, both induced by histamine.

Passive anaphylactic sensitization is achieved by introduction of serum from a hypersensitive animal or *small amounts* of antiserum from an immune animal. A few hours after injecting the serum, anaphylactic shock can be induced by intravenous injection of the antigen used to prepare the hypersensitive or immune serum.

Anaphylaxis can also be demonstrated *in vitro* by use of smooth muscle from a hypersensitive guinea pig. A strip of uterus or small intestine is suspended from a kymograph needle in a balanced isotonic solution, and antigen is added to the bath. Marked contraction follows within a few seconds. This is the Schultz-Dale test; it has been used to study the nature of antigenicity and the chemical radicals that determine the specificity of antigen-antibody reaction.

Allergy. Allergy is sometimes defined as hypersensitivity occurring naturally in man. There are many familiar manifestations of allergy. Allergy resembles anaphylaxis in many respects. Usually sensitization with the antigenic material precedes establishment of the hypersensitive state.

The antigen is encountered by inhalation, ingestion, or direct contact with the skin, and the type of reaction elicited depends largely on the nature of the antigenic experience. Inhaled substances commonly incite hay fever or asthmatic responses, ingested materials induce gastric distress, contact with poison ivy elicits the typical itching eruption. Urticaria and asthma induced by foods are attributed to antigenic substances in the ingested matter, which reach the skin and bronchi, respectively, via the bloodstream.

Allergy of infection or hypersensitivity of the tuberculin type is of interest in connection with the problem of resistance to certain chronic infectious diseases. An individual infected with *Mycobacterium tuberculosis* becomes hypersensitive to tuberculoproteins. Sensitivity is detected by the tuberculin test; an extract of *M. tuberculosis* injected into the skin incites local inflammation, and edema appears after several hours. The reaction progresses to a maximum between 15 and 48 hours and then slowly fades. A positive tuberculin test occurs in individuals with present or *past* tuberculous infection; it is therefore not necessarily diagnostic of active infection.

Similar delayed but violent inflammation follows injection of *M. tuberculosis* into a tuberculin positive animal. An extensive ulcer develops but soon becomes walled off and heals completely. The same type of response presumably occurs when a tuberculous human is reexposed to the infection and probably constitutes a protective reaction.

Serologic Diagnosis of Infectious Disease

Serologic reactions are important aids in the diagnosis of infectious disease. Antibodies can be detected in the patient's serum, and microorganisms isolated from clinical specimens can be quickly identified by appropriate procedures.

Detection of Antibodies in Patient's Serum. Antibodies usually appear one to two weeks after an infection begins

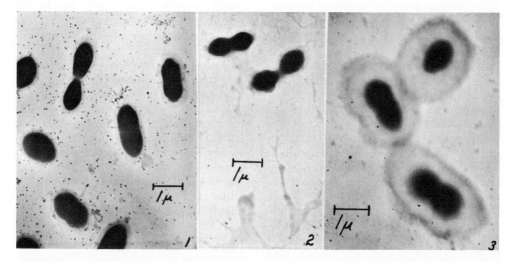

Figure 21-11. Serologic typing of *Diplococcus pneumoniae*. *1, D. pneumoniae*, type 3; the capsules are faintly visible. *2, D. pneumoniae*, type 3, in type 1 antiserum; the cells appear about the same as in *1. 3, D. pneumoniae*, type 1, in type 1 antiserum; homologous antibodies cause marked swelling of the capsule within a few moments. This reaction is specific and can be used for rapid identification of the type of a pneumococcus. (Electron photomicrographs by S. Mudd, F. Heinmets, and T. F. Anderson; A.S.M. LS-27.)

and increase in concentration during several weeks. Laboratory diagnosis by detection of developing antibody is therefore possible in diseases that run a prolonged course (e.g., typhoid and paratyphoid fevers, brucellosis, syphilis).

An appropriate serologic test is performed with a sample of the patient's serum and test antigens consisting of known organisms. It may be suspected, for example, that a patient has one of the enteric fevers. Agglutination tests are prepared by mixing the patient's serum with antigens consisting of suspensions of the typhoid and various paratyphoid bacteria. If the disease is actually typhoid fever, the typhoid bacteria should be agglutinated by high dilutions of the serum.

A high antibody titer usually indicates active infection if the patient's history reveals no previous infection or artificial immunization with the same organism. A second serum specimen should be secured a week or more later, and if this contains a higher titer of antibodies than the first it is almost certain that the patient is infected with the corresponding orga-

nism. Tests with several different antigens are sometimes necessary to determine the cause of disease. Laboratories can prepare their own bacterial test antigens by suspending the organisms from agar slants or broth in saline; certain antigens can be secured from commercial manufacturers.

Agglutination tests are commonly employed to detect bacterial antibodies; phagocytosis tests are also used to a limited extent. Complement fixation is valuable in studying sera of patients with viral disease, and also in the Wassermann test for syphilis.

Identification of Microorganisms. Pure cultures of organisms isolated from patients by the usual methods can be identified by serologic tests with known antisera, usually prepared in rabbits (Fig. 21-11). Serologic procedures are more rapid than most routine cultural and biochemical tests used for identification. They are used for a quick diagnosis to direct the physician toward the treatment most likely to be beneficial, but their results should be confirmed by the other customary tests.

 RESISTANCE AND IMMUNITY

SUMMARY

The processes of infection are opposed by three body defenses. *Natural resistance* is nonspecific and variable; it is attributed to normal mechanical and chemical barriers, proper nutrition and physical vigor, and is indirectly dependent on the climatic and socioeconomic environment. *Nonsusceptibility* is specific and absolute, and depends on genetic factors, in most cases still unknown. *Immunity* is specific but variable, and is always associated with the presence of antibodies.

Antibodies are blood globulins that are so modified in the process of formation that they can react with the substances that stimulated their production, known as antigens. Antigens are proteins or some polysaccharides, normally parts of or derived from cells of plants, animals, or microorganisms. Microbial antigens that enter the body during the course of infection or by artificial inoculation incite a more or less permanent active immunity. Passive immunity, acquired by transfer of antibodies from another individual of the same or a different species, is of short duration but provides temporary protection following exposure to infection.

Antibodies prevent disease or assist in recovery by killing or dissolving microorganisms, promoting phagocytosis, removing microbial debris, and/ or neutralizing certain toxic substances.

Antibodies are demonstrable in the laboratory by agglutination of cellular antigens, precipitation of soluble antigens, neutralization of toxins, sensitization of any antigen so that it can fix complement, enhancement of phagocytosis, and anaphylactic reactivity of a hypersensitive animal. Antigen-antibody reactions are useful in the diagnosis of disease because of their specificity. They can be used to hasten identification of bacteria isolated from a patient, or to detect antibodies in the patient's serum.

STUDY QUESTIONS

1. Discuss the desirable and undesirable effects of urbanization on resistance and immunity against infectious disease.
2. Define serum, vaccine, antibody, antigen.
3. What is gamma globulin? Why is it of interest?
4. How do antibodies assist in the prevention of or recovery from infectious disease?
5. How can one explain the fact that a case of typhoid fever usually confers immunity, whereas furunculosis (crops of boils) does not?
6. What kind of immunity is illustrated by:
    a. The immunity of a newborn baby to diphtheria?
    b. The immunity of a child who has recovered from whooping cough?
    c. The immunity of a person who has received Salk vaccine?
    d. The immunity of a child who has received gamma globulin after exposure to measles?
7. What is meant by the *specificity* of antigen-antibody reactions?
8. What are the functions of the five principal reagents in complement fixation tests?
9. Describe an example of a hypersensitivity reaction that may be beneficial rather than harmful.
10. Discuss the usefulness of serology in the laboratory diagnosis of disease.

SUPPLEMENTARY READING

The textbooks by Burrows, Smith et al., and Wilson and Miles contain sections summarizing the topics of resistance and immunity to infectious disease. Perla and Marmorston's *Natural Resistance and Clinical Medicine* is a large volume surveying in considerable detail the roles of heredity, age, sex, endocrines, blood components, various organs, diet, and climate in resistance.

Several other books deal more specifically with immunology and serology. Raffel's *Immunity, Hypersensitivity, Serology* is a discussion of fundamental aspects of immunity and hypersensitivity, followed by a description of the resistance mechanisms in a dozen specific diseases, and a section on serology. Cushing and Campbell develop the principles of immunology as biologic phenomena. Boyd discusses the general nature of immunity, antigens, antibodies, the antigen-antibody reaction, complement fixation, and hypersensitivity. He also has a chapter on the practical use of immunity and hypersensitivity, and a valuable, long chapter on laboratory and clinical technique. Carpenter follows a traditional pattern in discussing the nature of antigens and antibodies and the various types of reaction between them.

The Burnet book contains a theory of acquired immunity based on the concept of the selection of clones of body cells, each capable of producing a specific antibody. The topic is clearly and logically developed and makes interesting reading, regardless of whether one agrees with the argument.

Boyd, W. C.: *Fundamentals of Immunology,* 3d ed. New York, Interscience Publishers, Inc., 1956.

Burnet, F. M.: *The Clonal Selection Theory of Acquired Immunity.* Nashville, Tenn., Vanderbilt University Press, 1959.

Burrows, W.: *Textbook of Microbiology,* 18th ed. Philadelphia, W. B. Saunders Co., 1963.

Carpenter, P. L.: *Immunology and Serology,* 2d ed. Philadelphia, W. B. Saunders Co., 1965.

Cushing, J. E., and Campbell, D. H.: *Principles of Immunology.* New York, McGraw-Hill Book Co., Inc., 1957.

Perla, D., and Marmorston, J.: *Natural Resistance and Clinical Medicine.* Boston, Little, Brown & Co., 1941.

Raffel, S.: *Immunity, Hypersensitivity, Serology,* 2nd ed. New York, Appleton-Century-Crofts, Inc., 1961.

Smith, D. T., et al.: *Zinsser Microbiology,* 13th ed. New York, Appleton-Century-Crofts, Inc., 1964.

Wilson, G. S., and Miles, A. A.: *Topley and Wilson's Principles of Bacteriology and Immunity,* 5th ed. Baltimore, The Williams & Wilkins Co., 1964.

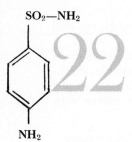

SO$_2$—NH$_2$

NH$_2$

CHEMOTHERAPY

Some of the defenses with which the body opposes infectious disease were described in the preceding chapter. The normal and immune body defenses ordinarily suffice to protect the individual, and he either wards off infection or recovers from it without serious complications. Occasionally, however, additional help is needed. This may take one or more of the following forms: (1) destruction or removal of the causative organism, (2) inhibition of the causative organism, which permits the body to overcome the disease, or (3) stimulation or enhancement of normal defenses.

Destruction or removal of microorganisms is often a matter of disinfection or antisepsis; the chemicals are frequently toxic, and must be used carefully and only externally.

Chemotherapy is the treatment of disease by chemicals that inhibit or kill the infectious agent but do not harm the host in the concentrations employed. Since the composition and physiologic activities of most parasites are fundamentally like those of their hosts, relatively few chemicals are effective without being harmful. This is one aspect of the specificity of chemotherapeutic action.

Specificity is further demonstrated by the selective antimicrobial behavior of chemotherapeutic substances. Chemicals effective against some kinds of organisms are useless against others. This characteristic is attributed to the fact that different chemicals interfere with different physiologic processes and, although all organisms perform much the same basic activities (respiration, synthesis, etc.), they may differ in the individual steps or pathways utilized, as was pointed out in Chapter 12.

Chemotherapeutic agents participate in processes (1) and (2) mentioned above and are administered orally or by injection. Some of the chemicals used kill infectious organisms, but most merely inhibit one or more of their vital activities and retard their rate of multiplication; phagocytosis and other body processes eventually destroy the organisms.

The enhancement and stimulation of normal defenses are illustrated by the administration of antibodies (e.g., pneumococcal antiserum) and by non-

420

specific protein therapy (the injection of foreign proteins that induce a general inflammatory reaction, leukocytosis, and increased liberation of antibody).

DEVELOPMENT OF CHEMOTHERAPY

Synthetic Drugs

Ehrlich. Ehrlich has been called the father of chemotherapy. In 1909 he proposed the use of drugs to attack parasites within a living host and emphasized that a successful chemotherapeutic agent must be selectively toxic for the parasite. He sought repeatedly for a substance that would kill or inhibit trypanosomes and syphilis spirochetes and tested 605 compounds before finding an arsenical, salvarsan, with the desired properties.

Domagk. A quarter century elapsed before the next great advance in chemotherapy. Domagk reported in 1935 that Prontosil produced remarkable cures of streptococcal disease in humans, and it was soon shown that Prontosil breaks down within the tissues to sulfanilamide. This compound competes with p-aminobenzoic acid in the synthesis of folic acid (see page 259), which catalyzes the formation of amino acids. Mammalian tissues are not poisoned by sulfanilamide because animals secure preformed folic acid in their normal diet.

Sulfonamides are essentially bacteriostatic agents, retarding bacterial growth and permitting normal body defenses to combat infection. Failure to appreciate this fact delayed their use in treating disease for nearly a quarter of a century; they were investigated as early as 1912, but showed little bactericidal activity *in vitro* and were discarded.

Antibiotics

The term *antibiosis* was apparently first used by Vuillemin in 1889 to describe the competitive nature of biologic societies in which only the strongest or most fit survive. The same word was applied to microbial antagonism a few years later.

Antagonistic activity among microorganisms had been known for several years. It has long been observed that plate cultures from the soil or air frequently contain "spreaders," whose growth is interrupted or "punctuated" by colonies of other bacteria surrounded by zones in which the spreader is inhibited. The suggestion had been made that products of these inhibitory organisms might be useful for treating disease. Emmerich and Löw in 1899 found that pyocyanase from cultures of *Pseudomonas aeruginosa* was highly bactericidal to many organisms, both gram-positive and gram-negative; unfortunately it is also toxic to animals.

Fleming. Fleming discovered penicillin in 1929. He observed that colonies of a staphylococcus in the vicinity of a contaminating mold on a throat plate gradually dissolved and disappeared. From cultures of the mold he obtained a solution that killed various gram-positive bacteria. The mold was later identified as *Penicillium notatum,* and he named the active principle penicillin.

Fleming continued to study the new antibiotic. Eventually Florey and others at Oxford University succeeded in isolating and purifying it. First yields were minute, and tremendous labor was necessary to produce sufficient material for one patient. The first human trials, in 1941, revealed amazing activity in staphylococcal and streptococcal bacteremias. Its toxicity, both for laboratory animals and for man, was negligible.

Dubos. Dubos discovered a bacterial antibiotic in 1939 as a by-product of his search for an enzyme that would digest the capsules from *Diplococcus pneumoniae.* He isolated a strain of *Bacillus brevis* from a soil culture in which he was attempting to find a capsule-dissolving organism. Cell-free filtrates of cultures of *B. brevis* killed many gram-positive bacteria. The antibiotic principle was called tyrothricin, but it was later shown to contain two crystallizable polypeptides, gramicidin and tyrocidine.

Gramicidin comprises about 20 per cent of tyrothricin. It is active against hemolytic streptococci, pneumococci, tetanus and gas gangrene bacteria. Tyrocidine is active against various gram-positive bacteria *in vitro* but is inactivated by body fluids such as blood and serum and is therefore inactive *in vivo*. Both drugs are toxic when given by injection to experimental animals and can be used in man only by topical application or instillation into certain body cavities.

The discovery of tyrothricin marked the beginning of the "antibiotic age." Despite the limited usefulness of this material, its development stimulated interest in the possibilities of therapeutic substances derived from microorganisms.

Waksman. For several years Waksman and his associates sought for an antibiotic active against gram-negative bacteria; in 1944 they announced the isolation of streptomycin from a soil organism, *Streptomyces griseus.* It was quickly put into production, and within seven years the annual yield was over 165 tons.

Streptomycin is relatively stable, but it is not as harmless as penicillin. It is toxic to the eighth cranial nerve, and continued use may produce dizziness and deafness. No toxic effect is ordinarily seen upon short use.

The Search for Other Antibiotics. Discovery of streptomycin was followed by a widespread search for additional antibiotics, stimulated in part by the development of bacterial strains resistant to penicillin and streptomycin and in part by a desire to find drugs effective against different pathogens. Several thousand antibiotics were discovered and tested; many were potent *in vitro* but toxic to animals, and more than a score were clinically useful and are still manufactured. Some of them are listed in Table 22-1.

THE SULFONAMIDES

The first sulfonamide drug, Prontosil, was a red dye patented by the German dye industry in 1932. Domagk tested it and many other dyes and found Prontosil highly effective against hemolytic streptococci. Animal experiments and finally administration to humans demonstrated that this compound successfully treated the usually fatal streptococcal septicemia or "blood poisoning."

A search immediately began for other derivatives of sulfanilamide that would be more effective or more useful by virtue of different solubilities, excretion rates, and other characteristics. Several thousand compounds were synthesized and tested, and a few proved to be useful: sulfapyridine, sulfathiazole, sulfadiazine, sulfaguanidine, etc. Structural formulas for these and the parent compounds are shown in Figure 22-1.

The active portion of each compound is the aminobenzene ring; the sidechains affect solubility and other accessory properties. Sulfaguanidine, for example, is absorbed more slowly from the intestine than the other compounds and hence is more effective in treating bacillary dysentery. There is little qualitative difference in antibacterial properties among these compounds. In general they are active against streptococci, staphylococci, pneumococci, gonococci, meningococci, plague, and dysentery bacteria, but are relatively ineffective against the typhoid organism and other salmonellae and rickettsiae. They are also useful in urinary infections caused by gram-negative rods and in the prevention of rheumatic fever, bacterial endocarditis, and wound infections.

ANTIBIOTICS

An antibiotic must meet certain requirements in order to be suitable for use in treating human disease: (1) it must possess high antimicrobial activity *in vivo;* (2) it must not produce harmful or undesirable reactions in the patient (that is, it must not be toxic or

Table 22-1. Sources and Properties of Some Common Antibiotics

Antibiotic	Date	Microbial Source	Chemical Nature	Specific Uses
Penicillin	1929	*Penicillium notatum*	Dipeptide (see Fig. 22-2)	Active against gram-positive bacteria, gonococci, meningococci, syphilis spirochetes.
Tyrothricin (gramicidin and tyrocidine)	1939	*Bacillus brevis*	Polypeptides	Active against gram-positive bacteria; local treatment of wounds and upper respiratory infections.
Streptomycin	1944	*Streptomyces griseus*	Basic glucoside (see Fig. 22-3)	Active against tularemia, some *salmonella* and other gram-negative bacteria; treatment of tuberculosis.
Bacitracin	1945	*B. licheniformis*	Polypeptide	Active against gram-positive bacteria; mildly toxic.
Chloramphenicol (Chloromycetin)	1947	*Str. venezuelae*	Nitrobenzene derivative (see Fig. 22-4)	Active against gram-positive and gram-negative bacteria, rickettsiae, large viruses, spirochetes; specific for typhoid fever.
Polymyxin (Aerosporin)	1947	*B. polymyxa*	Polypeptide and fatty acid	Local treatment of mouth, throat, and wound infections; treatment of systemic *pseudomonas* infection.
Chlortetracycline (Aureomycin)	1948	*Str. aureofaciens*	Tetracycline (see Fig. 22-5)	Active against gram-positive and gram-negative bacteria, rickettsiae, large viruses.
Oxytetracycline (Terramycin)	1950	*Str. rimosus*	Tetracycline (see Fig. 22-5)	Active against gram-positive and gram-negative bacteria, rickettsiae.
Nystatin (Mycostatin)	1951	*Str. noursei*		Active against *Candida albicans* and other fungi.
Tetracycline (Achromycin, Tetracyn, Steclin, Polycycline, Panmycin)	1953	Hydrogenation of chlortetracycline	Tetracycline (see Fig. 22-5)	Active against gram-positive and gram-negative bacteria, rickettsiae.

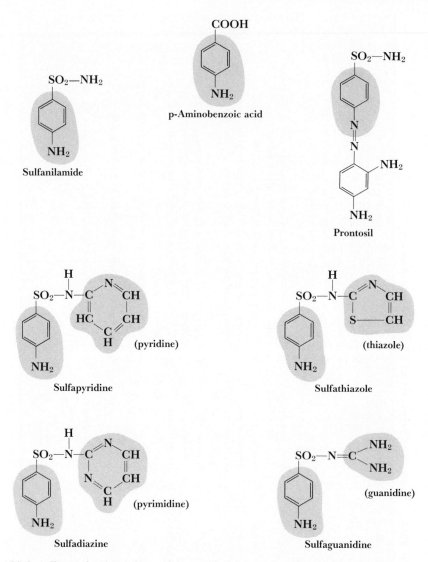

Figure 22-1. Chemical relationships of p-aminobenzoic acid, sulfanilamide, Prontosil, and other common sulfonamides.

hemolytic or produce histamine-like effects or allergic reactions, or precipitate body proteins); (3) it should be soluble in water, saline, and body fluids; (4) it should be stable. Many substances meet some of these requirements, but only a few meet them all. Penicillin and streptomycin are most widely employed; the tetracyclines (Aureomycin, Terramycin, tetracycline) and chloramphenicol are

of next importance, followed by tyrothricin, bacitracin, and polymyxin.

The chemical structures of penicillin, streptomycin, chloramphenicol, and the tetracyclines are shown in Figures 22-2 through 22-5. Many of the other antibiotics are polypeptides. It is obvious that no one type of chemical structure is responsible for antibiosis, and therefore it is not surprising that inhibition or killing is attributed to a variety of mechanisms.

Nature and Uses of Common Antibiotics

Penicillin. There are actually several penicillins (Fig. 22-2), which share a common structure but possess different "R" radicals comprising the second portion of the dipeptide. Penicillins X, G, and V are most active *in vivo*. Penicillin G is considered the most practical and is used more often than the other forms. Penicillin V can be given orally and yields high blood concentrations when absorbed from the intestine. Sodium,

calcium, potassium, and procaine salts are prepared; the potassium and procaine compounds are most common clinically.

Other forms of penicillin are manufactured by a process of microbial alteration of natural penicillins (analogous to steroid transformations discussed on page 375). One such compound, sodium 6-(2,6-dimethoxybenzamido) penicillinate (methicillin, Staphcillin), is of particular interest because the structural alteration gives it unusual resistance to penicillinase, an enzyme responsible for the penicillin resistance of many bacteria.

Penicillin is soluble in water, ethyl

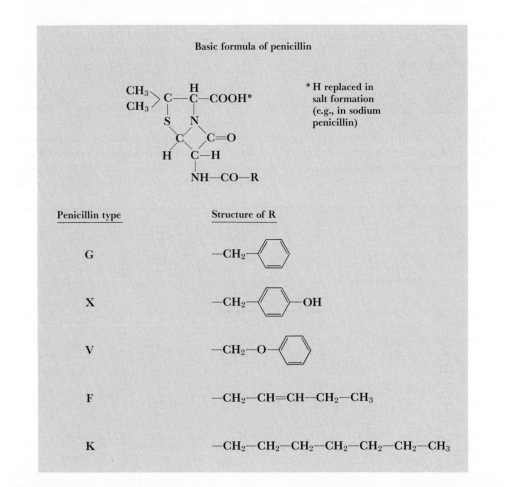

Figure 22-2. Structures of commonly used penicillins. The "R" radical affects the clinical applicability of the compound.

alcohol, ether, and acetone. It is effective in the presence of blood, pus, and body fluids, and is remarkably nontoxic. However, an increasing number of individuals develop allergic hypersensitivity on continued use of the drug; reactions range from urticaria with itching hives and fever to acute, fatal anaphylactic shock.

Crystalline salts of penicillin are stable for several months, particularly when kept cold; aqueous solutions are unstable and must be kept refrigerated. Penicillin is inactivated by heat, alkali, acid (except penicillin V), and penicillinase, produced by many species of bacteria.

Penicillin interferes with the synthesis of cell wall material in sensitive bacteria, apparently by inhibiting the formation of enzymes concerned with assimilation of glutamate: RNA decreases markedly, the synthesis of protein is disturbed, and polypeptide accumulates. The cells become swollen and do not divide. Animal cells are not affected by penicillin because they do not perform the cell-wall synthetic reactions necessary in bacterial cells.

Streptomycin. Streptomycin is a complex three-part basic glucoside (Fig.

22-3). Dihydrostreptomycin is produced from streptomycin by the catalytic hydrogenation of an aldehyde radical. It is not as toxic as streptomycin but has essentially the same antibiotic activity. The toxicity of these compounds results in damage to the eighth cranial nerve and vestibular apparatus; prolonged therapy may cause vertigo, tinnitus, and deafness.

Streptomycin is effective against numerous gram-negative bacteria, some gram-positive bacteria, and the tuberculosis organism. The usefulness of this drug is limited by the readiness with which many bacteria become resistant to it. Susceptibility to streptomycin varies from strain to strain and must be tested in individual cases. Development of resistance is particularly significant in the case of *Mycobacterium tuberculosis,* because treatment of tuberculosis is prolonged. Combination therapy with isonicotinic acid hydrazide (INH) or *p*-aminosalicylic acid (PAS) greatly reduces the opportunity for the appearance of resistant mutants.

Streptomycin appears to interfere with protein synthesis in sensitive bacteria. It has been postulated that the antibiotic becomes associated with the

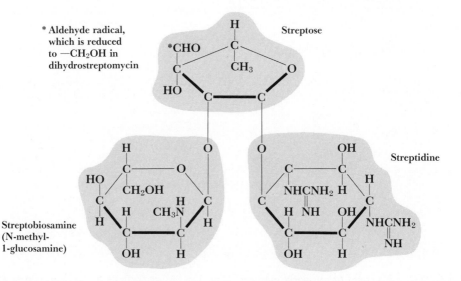

Figure 22-3. Structure of streptomycin.

ribosomes in such a way as to prevent mRNA from attaching to them, thus preventing the synthesis of protein. Streptomycin has also been reported to affect the respiration of sensitive bacteria by inhibiting the oxalacetate-pyruvate condensation reaction.

Chloramphenicol. Chloramphenicol, first isolated from cultures of *Streptomyces venezuelae* and later from cultures of other *Streptomyces* species, is now prepared by synthesis. It is the only antibiotic synthesized on a large scale. This compound is a nitrobenzene derivative.

Chloramphenicol is one of the broad spectrum antibiotics. It is effective against a greater variety of microorganisms than streptomycin or penicillin, including gram-positive and gram-negative bacteria, rickettsiae, and some of the larger viruses. It is particularly effective against the typhoid fever organism and is recommended for treatment of this disease. It is relatively ineffective against bacillary dysentery.

Chloramphenicol inhibits assimilation of ammonia and synthesis of proteins, apparently in part by blocking the synthesis of ribosomes. It is relatively nontoxic and is readily absorbed from the gastrointestinal tract; it can therefore be taken orally. There have, however, been a number of cases of anemia following its use.

Tetracyclines. The tetracyclines include the other important broad spectrum antibiotics, chlortetracycline (Aureomycin), oxytetracycline (Terramycin), and tetracycline. These compounds are very closely related chemically and possess similar antimicrobial properties. They inhibit many gram-positive and gram-negative bacteria and rickettsiae and are relatively nontoxic.

Chlortetracycline presumably inhibits protein synthesis and phosphorylation of mitochondria and adenine nucleotides, a reaction which suggests interference with the Krebs cycle. Oxytetracycline blocks the utilization of RNA reserves that are lost by depolymerization to mononucleotides. It also seems to interfere with the transfer of amino acids from mRNA to polypeptides and hence inhibits protein formation.

Antimicrobial Spectra

Antibiotics are characterized and identified by their antimicrobial spectra. The antimicrobial spectrum is determined by testing the ability of the chemical to inhibit a variety of microorganisms (Table 22-2). Penicillin, for example, inhibits many gram-positive bacteria and very few gram-negative organisms; polymyxin, on the contrary, inhibits a variety of gram-negative bacteria and is practically inactive against gram-positive organisms. Streptomycin, chloramphenicol, and the tetracyclines inhibit most representatives of both groups.

When a new antibiotic is obtained, it is easier to determine its probable identity by testing its ability to inhibit 15 or 20 species of bacteria than by chemical analyses. A substance that inhibits the same organisms as bacitracin, for example, is considered to be identical with bacitracin, or at least to possess no advantage over it as far as inhibitory properties are concerned.

Resistance to Antibiotics

The development of resistance to antibiotics by previously sensitive strains

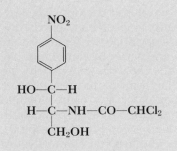

Figure 22-4. Structure of chloramphenicol. This antibiotic is now made synthetically.

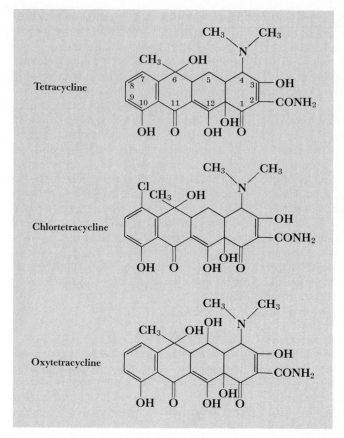

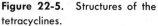

Figure 22-5. Structures of the tetracyclines.

of bacteria was discussed in Chapter 16. It was pointed out that perhaps once in every million or 10 million cell divisions a mutant might appear that is resistant to a given antibiotic. If this mutation occurs in a patient under treatment with the antibiotic, the mutant will possess greater survival value than the patient's normal bacteria and will shortly outnumber them. Further treatment with the same antibiotic will be of no advantage. Moreover, any subsequent cases of the disease arising from exposure to the first patient will be caused by bacteria resistant to the antibiotic.

Since 1945, penicillin-resistant strains of *Staphylococcus aureus* have become widespread. This organism is present on the skin and mucous membranes of many normal individuals and is undoubtedly transferred frequently from one person to another. It is capable of infecting wounds, sinuses, lungs, bones, kidneys—any part of the body. Most *S. aureus* infections were successfully treated by penicillin when the drug was first available. By 1955, however, there had been a tremendous increase in penicillin-resistant staphylococci, particularly in hospitals. Physicians, nurses, and other attendants apparently developed a staphylococcal flora resistant to penicillin, partly by constant association with and use of penicillin, and partly by contamination from patients under treatment with penicillin. The result is that patients entering a hospital for any cause are likely to become infected with penicillin-resistant staphylococci in the hospital. Physicians and hospital administrators recognize that the solution to the problem is no different now than it was a century ago: strict aseptic technique.

Table 22-2. Antimicrobial Spectra of Some Commercially Available Antibiotics* †

Organism	Penicillin	Streptomycin	Chloramphenicol	Tetracyclines	Gramicidin	Bacitracin	Polymyxin
Gram-positive							
Streptococcus pyogenes A	+	+	+	+	+	+	−
Staphylococcus aureus	+	+	+	+	−	±	−
Bacillus subtilis	+	+	+	+	+	−	+
Clostridium perfringens	+	−	±	+	±	±	−
Corynebacterium diphtheriae	+	+	+	+	+	+	−
Mycobacterium tuberculosis	−	+	−		+		
Gram-negative							
Neisseria meningitidis	+	+	+	+	−	+	+
Escherichia coli	−	+	+	+	−	−	+
Salmonella species	−	+	+	+	−	−	+
Pseudomonas species	−	+	−	±	−	−	+
Hemophilus influenzae	+	+	+				+
Brucella species		+	+	+			+

* + = inhibition.

† Adapted from Welch: *Principles and Practice of Antibiotic Therapy.* New York, Medical Encyclopedia, Inc., 1954.

Control of Antibiotic Resistance. The development of antibiotic resistance by pathogens within the body of a patient can be decreased by administering doses of antibiotic large enough to eliminate the infectious agent at once. This is possible only in the case of drugs of little or no toxicity used in patients not allergic to the drug and infected by organisms that do not develop resistant mutants rapidly.

Combined drug therapy also decreases the appearance of resistant organisms. Resistance to different, unrelated antibiotics develops independently. Cells resistant to one antibiotic may arise once in a million cell divisions, and cells resistant to a second antibiotic may also arise once in every million divisions. The probability that a cell resistant to both antibiotics will occur is therefore one in one million million, an almost infinitesimal chance.

The use of antibiotics is obviously not an unmixed blessing. Reliance on antibiotics to control bacterial infection doubtless led some physicians to relax aseptic techniques and to treat various infectious diseases without adequate diagnosis. This practice was often successful before antibiotic-resistant bacteria became common. Moreover, some antibiotics were made available without prescription, and their overuse in treating trivial ailments incited allergic hypersensitivity in many persons. These individuals could not then be given the same agent to treat serious illness without risk of a fatal anaphylactic reaction.

Sensitivity Tests. It is advantageous to test the sensitivity to antibiotics of bacteria isolated from a patient before instituting treatment. The physician can then select the drug that is most likely to be effective in each specific case. There are several types of sensitivity tests. Pure cultures of the isolated organism from the patient are grown in broth containing dilutions of the available antibiotics. Choice of an antibiotic to use in treating the infection is limited to those that inhibit the organism in low concentration (i.e., when highly di-

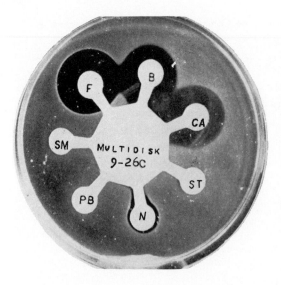

Figure 22-6. Test of the sensitivity of an organism isolated from a patient to various antibiotics and synthetic drugs by means of a filter paper "multidisk." The tip of each arm is impregnated with a chemical, which diffuses into the culture medium. Antibiotics F, B, and CA markedly inhibit the test organism illustrated. (From Microbial Testing for Susceptibility to Chemotherapeutic Agents. Chicago Heights, Ill., Consolidated Laboratories, Inc., 1958.)

luted). This method requires considerable labor and expense, but the results are likely to be significant.

The agar cup plate technique is easier and quicker. Open cylinders of glass, porcelain, or stainless steel are placed on Petri dishes containing an agar medium inoculated with the organism responsible for the patient's infection. The cylinders are filled with dilutions of the antibiotics and incubated for a few hours. The organism is usually most susceptible to the antibiotic that produces the largest zone of inhibition. A simpler modification of the same technique makes use of filter paper disks, either singly or incorporated in a "multidisk" (Fig. 22-6), instead of the cylinders; each disk, impregnated with a different antibiotic or concentration of antibiotic, is placed upon the surface of the inoculated agar and incubated for a few hours. Crude, unpurified clinical specimens (e.g., blood, throat swab) can often be used, and this will save one or two days.

It should be emphasized that the results of sensitivity tests are not always

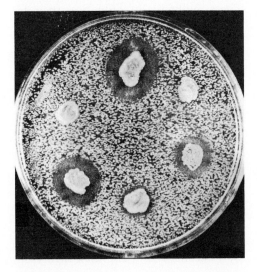

Figure 22-7. Antibiotic-producing bacteria may be found in the human intestine. This plate was inoculated over its surface with one of the dysentery bacteria, and then spot inoculations were made with coliform bacteria picked directly from a stool culture. Four of the six organisms inhibited the dysentery bacteria. The antibiotics produced by coliform organisms are called colicines. (Photograph by S. P. Halbert; A.S.M. LS-215.)

confirmed by clinical experience, and the physician should utilize the laboratory findings only as a guide. Studies of resistance are especially useful in patients undergoing long-term treatment with antibiotics, because the laboratory observations indicate when it is time to shift from one antibiotic to another.

THE FUTURE OF CHEMOTHERAPY

The rapid selection and distribution of resistant mutants of pathogenic bacteria emphasize the need for continued search for antibiotics and synthetic drugs to replace those whose effectiveness declines. Moreover, antibiotics are needed for diseases against which there is no present treatment. Despite the decreasing incidence of tuberculosis and the partial effectiveness of streptomycin and other drugs, another antibiotic that can inhibit or kill *M. tuberculosis* is urgently desired. Additional antibiotics against viruses and fungi are also needed.

Most antibiotics in use today are derived from *Streptomyces* species, a few from molds. Bacteria have not been thoroughly explored as sources of antibiotics. A few substances with antibacterial properties have been isolated from algae and other plants; further investigation in this field might be fruitful.

The developments in chemotherapy have revolutionized the practice of medicine within the past 25 years. The majority of prescriptions today are for substances that were unknown in 1940, and many of these are antibiotics and other chemotherapeutic agents. The next years will see this trend continue as government and private agencies support research directed toward the cure of infectious disease.

CHEMOTHERAPY

SUMMARY

Chemotherapy is the treatment of disease by chemicals that inhibit or kill the infectious agent but do not harm the patient. There are two important classes of chemotherapeutic agents: (1) synthetic drugs, and (2) products of living cells called antibiotics.

Sulfonamides comprise a well known group of synthetic drugs. They complete with *p*-aminobenzoic acid in the synthesis of folic acid, an essential growth factor, and interfere with the formation of amino acids by certain bacteria. Cells inhibited in this manner are readily destroyed by normal body defenses.

Most antibiotics are by-products of microbial metabolism; they inhibit or kill certain other microorganisms. Antibiotics vary in their chemical composition and mode of action. Penicillin, the first and most widely used antibiotic, is active against gram-positive bacteria and the gonorrhea, meningitis, and syphilis organisms. Streptomycin is particularly useful in certain gram-negative bacterial diseases and in tuberculosis. Chloramphenicol and the tetracyclines are *broad spectrum* antibiotics: they are effective against a wide range of gram-positive and gram-negative bacteria, and even against rickettsiae and some large viruses.

Strains of pathogenic organisms resistant to antibiotics may appear as a result of mutation and selection. It is therefore often necessary to test the antibiotic sensitivity of microorganisms from a patient before instituting treatment. The appearance and widespread distribution of penicillin-resistant staphylococci since 1955, even in hospitals, has necessitated reemphasis of aseptic practices in the handling of patients.

STUDY QUESTIONS

1. Some chemotherapeutic agents inhibit pathogenic microorganisms but do not kill them. Explain why this treatment suffices.
2. Does there seem to be any basic similarity in the chemical structures of antibiotics? What are the implications of this fact?
3. Is there a basic chemical structure upon which the antibacterial action of the sulfonamides depends? Explain.
4. What are *broad spectrum* antibiotics? Cite examples and list organisms they inhibit.
5. Discuss the significance of antibiotic-resistant mutants of pathogenic bacteria. How are they detected? How may their rate of appearance be decreased?
6. What are the sources of most of the clinically useful antibiotics?

SUPPLEMENTARY READING

Antibiotics, by Pratt and Dufrenoy, is a discussion of the broad principles of antibiotic action and antibiotic chemotherapy. The production and testing of antibiotics are described, as are the characteristics of some of the important early antibiotics. The book by Welch reviews the antimicrobial activity and pharmacology of the most important antibiotics, and 16 collaborators contribute discussions of specific therapy of a variety of infectious diseases.

Pratt, R., and Dufrenoy, J.: *Antibiotics.* Philadelphia, J. B. Lippincott Co., 1949.
Welch, H.: *Antibiotic Therapy.* New York, Medical Encyclopedia, Inc., 1954.

ECOLOGY OF
INFECTIOUS DISEASE

Ecology is the study of the relationships of living organisms with one another and with their environment. Food is the central theme about which ecology revolves, and the rule is "Eat and avoid being eaten."

THE "CLIMAX" STATE

The Predator-Prey Balance

A natural wild community is a mixed population composed of many plant and animal species growing together. Animals feed on plants and on one another. The predator-prey relationship is a delicately balanced "climax" state characterized by continuous minor fluctuations in population numbers. Increased growth of plants as a result of favorable weather permits the accumulation of an unusually large population of herbivorous animals. Most of these animals are, however, soon eaten by larger carnivores, and the original climax state is reestablished.

The Parasite-Host Balance

At the other end of the biologic scale are parasites. Their activities, often damaging to the host, also lead to a climax state. The evolutionary process by which parasites adapt to their hosts usually deprives them of the power of independent existence. They become dependent on living hosts and die shortly after they kill the host if they do not reach a fresh, susceptible individual. The success of parasitism as a mode of life therefore depends upon the ability of the parasite to secure food without causing too great damage or upon prompt transmission of the parasite to another host, or upon both.

EPIDEMIC VS.
ENDEMIC DISEASE

A parasite introduced into a completely susceptible population or into a new host species in which it can establish itself is likely to spread widely and produce an *epidemic*. The parasite is passed quickly from one individual to another, and soon a large percentage of the host population is infected.

After a certain proportion of the population has become infected, the rate of transmission decreases as the number of uninfected individuals dwindles. The survivors are probably on the average a little more resistant than those who succumb. Moreover, recovered individuals usually possess specific immunity. The parasite persists thereafter in the population at a greatly reduced incidence. Immune individuals sometimes serve as carriers; the organism may produce mild and unrecognized *subclinical* infections in highly resistant individuals or occasional frank cases in the nonresistant. The net result is an *endemic* condition in which the disease is constantly present but in insignificant numbers.

The endemic state is interrupted by epidemics whenever sufficient susceptible and nonimmune individuals accumulate by birth or immigration. Increasing resistance during several generations according to the "survival of the fittest" principle gradually reduces the severity of the disease. At the same time, the parasite may mutate to a form better adapted to the host species and better able to survive. These factors increase the duration of the endemic condition and reduce the frequency of epidemics.

Epidemics of infectious disease, whether in man, lower animals, or plants, are largely the result of interference with the natural distribution of the various species that make up a climax population. A normal tropical rain forest in the East Indies may contain 100 species of trees per acre, together with shrubs and other plants, 30 species of mammals, and other animals. In such a forest there is relatively little opportunity for a parasite to be transmitted from one individual to another of the same species; the climax population consists of many species but few indi-

viduals of each. Disease is either absent or endemic; epidemics are rare.

A natural catastrophe such as a forest fire or deliberate deforestation by man changes the ecologic picture completely. Bare areas are soon invaded by rapidly growing plants and animals, and large populations of a few species are quickly produced. Under these conditions, epidemics of infectious disease can readily occur.

In some East Indian forest areas a rickettsial disease, jungle tsutsugamushi or scrub typhus, has long been endemic. It is transmitted by mites among its natural hosts: voles, shrews, field mice, rats, and other small animals. Deforestation of these areas upsets the normal climax state. Grassy scrub grows quickly, and in this type of vegetation the black rat flourishes. This species is one of the hosts of *Rickettsia tsutsugamushi,* and rapid transfer of the parasite soon causes an epidemic among the rat population, which is also transmitted to man, in whom the mortality is 20 to 40 per cent.

Evolution of Epidemic Disease

There is evidence that many infectious diseases of man and domestic animals have appeared within the few thousand years of recorded history. Prehistoric man lived in caves in small family groups and probably did not congregate in large communities. As in the tropical rain forest, major epidemics were not common. Socialization later occurred, the family group became a tribe, agriculture developed, and eventually urbanization took place. Large populations crowded in small areas provided opportunity for epidemic spread of infectious disease; ancient records indicate that this actually occurred. The widespread distribution of infectious disease initiated the process of selection of resistant individuals. It may be noted in passing that the practice of agriculture—cultivation of plants and animals—disturbs the natural balanced condition in any area and favors the spread of plant and animal diseases.

Factors that Determine the Nature of an Epidemic

The epidemiology of infectious disease depends upon (1) the degree of adaptation of the parasite and host to each other, (2) the ability of the parasite to survive outside the host, and (3) the mode of transfer of the parasite to new host individuals.

Parasite-Host Adaptation. The first contact between a parasite and a new host species or population is likely to be violent, but mutual adaptation eventually occurs. This process may be rapid.

Myxomatosis is a viral infection of rabbits. It is endemic among the wild rabbits of Brazil, where it is transmitted by the bite of contaminated mosquitoes; the virus provokes only slight swellings under the skin and temporary invasion of the blood, and the rabbit is subsequently immune. However, the disease is highly fatal for the European rabbit. Southern Australia is overrun with European rabbits, the descendants of animals imported from England about 1860. Myxomatosis was deliberately introduced into Australian rabbits in 1950 and at first killed 99.5 per cent of the infected animals. Two years later, however, the virus had become attenuated to such an extent that the mortality was only 90 per cent. A similar change in virulence occurred in Europe when the virus entered the wild rabbit population.

Influenza viruses apparently undergo more or less continuous modification. The virus that caused the pandemic of 1918–1919, influenza A, is no longer encountered, but a series of other virus strains followed, one of the latest being the "Asian" influenza of 1957, apparently a variant of influenza A.

Adaptation of man to the syphilis and tuberculosis organisms has already been mentioned; this was apparently a slower process.

Survival of the Parasite. The ability of each species of parasite to survive outside its host is fairly constant, although some changes are to be expected. A parasite that continues the process of adapting to a given host may suffer further loss of independent survival powers; on the other hand, an organism that encounters strenuous environmental conditions between hosts may become increasingly resistant.

Transfer of Parasite. A parasite is usually transferred to a new host individual by the same route. Typhoid fever, dysentery, and cholera bacteria are transmitted by food or water; the common cold and influenza viruses are distributed in airborne droplets from the respiratory tract. Some parasites may be transmitted by more than one vector or route. Myxomatosis is transmitted by mosquitoes in Brazil and Australia but by fleas in Great Britain. Bubonic plague spreads from rat to rat or from rat to man by the rat flea; pneumonic plague, caused by the same microorganism, is transmitted from one man to another by infectious droplets.

EPIDEMIOLOGIC TYPES OF INFECTIOUS DISEASE

The mode of transfer of infectious agents from one host to another and the ability of the agents to survive outside susceptible hosts influence the nature of the epidemics they cause. Moreover, the biologic success of a highly parasitic microorganism is determined by its prompt transfer to a new host after its discharge from or destruction of the preceding host.

The most rapid and certain method of transfer is by direct contact. A number of viruses and highly parasitic bacteria are transmitted in this way (e.g., by venereal contact). Another method of disease transmission that ensures rapid transfer or constant protection and nurture is direct inoculation. Insects and animals deposit microorganisms within susceptible hosts by biting and scratching. Some serve as intermediate or alternate hosts and permit parasites to develop during the interval between leaving one host and entering another. Mechanical injury also provides opportunity for direct inoculation of infectious organisms.

Some parasitic organisms survive for limited periods outside a host if kept moist. Saliva, mucus, and other body secretions temporarily protect against drying. Infective droplets of sputum contain respiratory organisms in viable condition as long as the droplets retain sufficient moisture, and thus can distribute pathogenic organisms widely in large crowds. Hardier and perhaps less highly parasitic forms remain infective even in dried sputum. Microorganisms that are resistant because they are in the spore state or possess capsules or waxy coverings survive in dust.

Physiologically independent microorganisms can live indefinitely apart from a host; they are disseminated by water, food, and other inanimate agents. Human pathogens of this type include organisms that infect the alimentary tract. Many are saprophytic and grow readily upon lifeless laboratory media. They survive for days or weeks in drinking water and multiply to enormous numbers in such foods as milk, cream puffs, and chicken salad.

Diseases Transmitted by Direct Contact

The distribution of organisms transmitted only by direct contact is restricted. Staphylococcal and streptococcal infections of the skin and mucous membranes are usually limited to relatively small groups within institutions where fairly intimate contact occurs. Gonorrhea, syphilis, and other venereal diseases present a special social as well as biologic problem.

Staphylococcal Infections. Staphylococci are among the most widely distributed bacteria associated with the animal kingdom. They are usually present on the skin and in the respiratory tract, and as long as they remain in these locations they do no harm. Many normal individuals harbor pathogenic strains in their nostrils or mouths or upon their skin. These individuals possess some immunity against their own staphylococci or a high degree of resistance in the nature of intact and impermeable skin and mucous membranes. Minute abrasions or a drop in resistance permit the organisms to penetrate into deeper tissues; sometimes, too, they enter via hair follicles or sweat ducts and start infections. The infections usually remain localized, like boils and abscesses, but occasionally they spread to other regions of the body. Recurring boils or furunculosis is a common occurrence. Less frequent are invasion of the bloodstream (septicemia); extension to internal organs, with formation of multiple abscesses; involvement of the bone marrow (osteomyelitis), lungs, brain, and spinal cord —and in fact any organ.

Some strains or species of staphylococcus are more virulent than others. The pathogenic varieties usually share certain characteristics demonstrable by laboratory tests. Most representatives are hemolytic (i.e., capable of dissolving red blood cells), produce coagulase (an enzyme that catalyzes the formation of fibrin clots *in vivo* and *in vitro*), produce a golden pigment, and ferment mannitol. These facts are useful in laboratory detection (Table 23-1) of potentially pathogenic staphylococci but have

Table 23-1. Diagnostic Characteristics That Distinguish Pathogenic from Nonpathogenic Staphylococci

Characteristic	Pathogenic (*S. aureus*)	Nonpathogenic (*S. epidermidis*)
Pigmentation	Golden	White
Coagulase	+	−
Hemolysis on blood agar	+	−
Mannitol fermentation	+	−

little or no known connection with their mechanism of disease production.

S. aureus is the principal pathogenic species and causes the most severe infections. Strains or variants that produce white colonies are designated *S. albus.* Coagulase-negative staphylococci that produce white growth on solid media and fail to ferment mannitol are assigned to a separate species, *S. epidermidis.* These organisms are widespread upon normal skin and mucous membranes and have little pathogenicity.

Staphylococci are gram-positive, spherical cells, 0.5 to 1.0 μ in diameter; they occur singly, in pairs, and in irregular groups or clusters. They grow luxuriantly upon ordinary laboratory media, such as nutrient broth and nutrient agar. They are aerobic and facultatively anaerobic and multiply at any temperature between 10° and 45° C.

Staphylococci are not highly parasitic, although their normal habitat is the human or animal body. Their nutrient requirements are easily satisfied by nonliving organic media or even inorganic media. Disease production is a consequence of formation and liberation of hemolysins, leukocidins, necrotizing or tissue-killing toxins, and probably other chemicals.

It is controversial whether a high degree of immunity against staphylococci can be established. Most staphylococcal infections are local in nature, and the organisms or their products do not gain access to antibody-producing sites. Artificial active immunization by injection of a staphylococcal bacterin (suspension of killed bacteria) may induce some antibody formation, but the antibodies fail to reach the organisms within a local infection in sufficient concentration to inhibit their growth or activity. Even staphylococcal septicemia, which often persists for several weeks, does not induce sufficient antibody to prevent death.

The most effective treatment appears to be antibiotic therapy, preferably guided by laboratory tests to determine the sensitivity of the patient's organisms to the various available drugs. Combinations of antibiotics delay the appearance of resistant forms.

Direct transmission of pathogenic staphylococci from one individual to another is indicated by reports of the widespread distribution of penicillin-resistant strains in hospitals. During the early years of antibiotic therapy, most staphylococci were sensitive to penicillin, and in consequence it was commonly used postoperatively to prevent or counteract surgical infection. Within a few years, however, penicillin-resistant strains became so common upon the skin and mucous membranes of physicians, nurses, and other attendants that the rate of hospital infection rose alarmingly, and organisms isolated from these infections were found to be resistant to penicillin. Numerous studies have shown that patients acquire new strains of resistant staphylococci shortly after admission to a hospital.

Diseases Transmitted by Inoculation

Inoculation by insect or animal bites is about as certain a method of distributing and perpetuating a parasite as direct contact between individual hosts of the same species.

Diseases transmitted by insect bites include some caused by bacteria (bubonic plague), many caused by rickettsiae (typhus fever) and viruses (encephalitis), and a few caused by protozoa (African sleeping sickness). Diseases of man (Table 23-2) and other animals and diseases of plants (aster yellows) are included. In some cases the insect serves as a necessary intermediate host; in others it plays a more passive role.

Insectborne infections often display a seasonal distribution correlated with the life cycle of the vector insect and also a variation that depends on the weather (e.g., dry years vs. damp years). Diseases transmitted by animal bites (hydrophobia), by scratches, or by me-

Table 23-2.   A Few Insectborne Diseases That May Be Transmitted to Man

Disease	Natural Host	Insect Vector or Host
Protozoan diseases		
Malaria	Man	Mosquitoes
African sleeping sickness	Man	Tsetse fly
Bacterial diseases		
Bubonic plague	Rat	Rat flea
Tularemia	Wild rodents, rabbits	Ticks, lice, deer flies
Rickettsial diseases		
Typhus fever	Man	Louse
Rocky Mountain spotted fever	Cattle, sheep, dogs	Ticks
Viral diseases		
Yellow fever	Man, monkeys	Mosquitoes
Encephalitis	Poultry	Mosquitoes

chanical injury (wound infections) occur sporadically rather than in epidemic form.

Insectborne Disease. *Yellow Fever.* Yellow fever was one of the first insectborne viral diseases whose natural history was determined, and although this disease has been practically eradicated in Caribbean areas it is still a major disease in Africa and South America.

Yellow fever is transmitted to man by the bite of a mosquito. The incubation period following the mosquito bite is three to six days. Symptoms include fever, albuminuria, jaundice, and a tendency to hemorrhage from the gums and stomach. There is considerable kidney and liver damage. The disease varies in severity from very mild or even unrecognized cases to those that are rapidly fatal within six to 10 days after onset. Recovery, which occurs in 95 per cent of cases, is accompanied by lifelong immunity.

There are two epidemiologic varieties of yellow fever. The virus in each is the same, and immunity against one variety protects against the other. *Urban yellow fever* is transmitted from man to man by the domestic mosquito, *Aedes aegypti*. The mosquito becomes infected by biting a patient during the first three

days of the disease. Approximately 12 days must then elapse before the mosquito can transmit the infection, but it remains infective throughout the remainder of its life. The virus produces no ill effect in the mosquito, although it multiplies extensively; it is not transmitted by mosquito eggs. *A. aegypti* breeds in small containers of water and hence occurs around human habitations. Urban yellow fever is therefore restricted to localities where (1) the mosquito can breed and (2) a fairly large susceptible human population is found. The existence of permanent strong immunity in recovered patients limits the extent of infected populations.

Jungle yellow fever was discovered when cases of yellow fever were found in areas where *A. aegypti* did not exist. It was learned then that the disease is present in certain wild animals of the forest, particularly monkeys, and that it is transmitted from monkey to monkey by forest-living mosquitoes. Man acquires the infection incidentally and does not constitute part of the normal cycle of transmission. Jungle yellow fever is present in tropical areas of Africa and South America.

There is no specific treatment for

yellow fever. Bed rest and careful nursing are essential. Prevention is attempted by two methods. The first, historically, is control of the mosquito population. This is feasible in the case of *A. aegypti* because of its breeding habits. Elimination of standing water around towns and cities effectively prevents multiplication of the mosquito and interrupts the transmission cycle of the virus. The introduction of DDT and other insecticides has also been of assistance in reducing the mosquito population.

The other approach to prevention of yellow fever is artificial immunization. Two attenuated virus strains are used at present. The French neurotropic virus is a strain that has been adapted to mice and has lost its ability to produce fatal infection in monkeys. The other strain, 17D, has been modified by cultivation in tissue culture to such an extent that it produces little damage. It is grown in chick embryos for the production of vaccine. This material produces fewer untoward reactions than the French vaccine but yields a somewhat lower degree of immunity.

Immunization is the only method available for protecting individuals exposed to jungle yellow fever. It is also the only feasible method of protecting large numbers of individuals in rural areas. Mosquito control is most effective in urban areas.

Mechanical Injury. *Tetanus.* Tetanus is usually acquired by mechanical injury, rarely by other means. The disease is characterized by strong, continuous contractions of the voluntary muscles, often starting locally in the area of an infected wound; usually all the voluntary muscles eventually become involved, and death results from respiratory paralysis. The frequency with which muscles of the jaw are affected during early stages of the disease accounts for its colloquial name, *lockjaw.*

The causative organism, *Clostridium tetani,* is widely distributed on all parts of the earth. It is common in soil and is frequently found in the feces of horses and other animals and occasionally in man. Its spores are highly resistant to desiccation and can survive many years in soil and other contaminated materials (e.g., catgut, garden tools, clothing).

Spores of *Cl. tetani* are so widespread that wounds are likely to be contaminated with them. The fact that relatively few cases of tetanus actually develop, however, indicates that special conditions are necessary for germination and growth. *Cl. tetani* is highly anaerobic, and spores do not germinate in the presence of atmospheric oxygen. Moreover, the organism is not invasive and not parasitic; it lives saprophytically and multiplies only in dead tissue. A deep, dirty wound or a burn provides the necessary devitalized tissue and anaerobic conditions. The presence of other organisms, even aerobic or facultative species, promotes clostridial infection by helping to create anaerobic conditions and by causing further tissue destruction.

The site infected by tetanus bacilli may actually be very small. Disease symptoms, which often involve the whole body, are attributed to the extremely potent exotoxin produced by the organisms within the localized infection. The potency of tetanus toxin is second only to that of *Cl. botulinum* toxin; 1 ml. is sufficient to kill 10 million mice or over three million guinea pigs. It is neurotropic and combines avidly with nerve tissue. This can be demonstrated by mixing a toxin solution with emulsified brain tissue, removing the tissue after a few minutes by centrifugation, and injecting some of the supernatant fluid into mice or guinea pigs; the animals remain healthy.

Cl. tetani is a slender, gram-positive rod that forms terminal, spherical spores of greater diameter than the rod. A sporulated rod therefore looks like a drumstick (Fig. 23-1). The organism grows under strictly anaerobic conditions and produces rhizoid or filamentous, rootlike colonies on blood or other

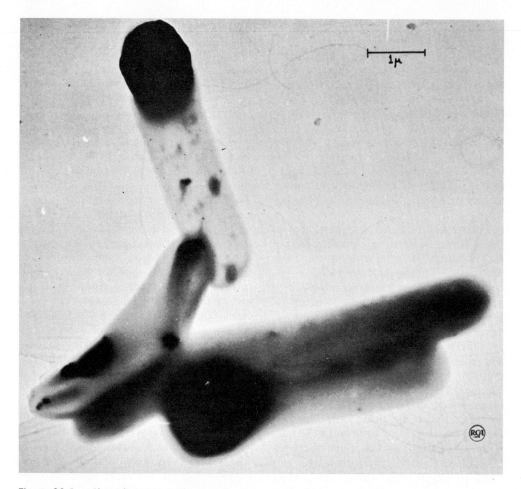

Figure 23-1. *Clostridium tetani.* Electron photomicrograph showing terminal "drumstick" spores. (From Mudd and Anderson, J.A.M.A., 126:561, 1944; A.S.M. LS-63.)

suitable agar media. It can also be cultivated in deep tubes of meat broth containing cooked meat particles and in liquid or semisolid media containing sodium thioglycollate.

The powerful toxin of *Cl. tetani* is easily inactivated by heat (five minutes at 65° C.); treatment with formalin converts the toxin to toxoid, which is nontoxic but highly antigenic. Toxoid is used for artificial immunization of man and animals. It is so completely nontoxic that the equivalent of many lethal doses of toxin may be introduced without harm.

Injection of toxoid is the only means of producing active immunity. Recovery from tetanus infections may occur, but recovered individuals rarely possess sufficient immunity to protect against reinfection, because the actual dose of toxin to which they were subjected is too small. A large enough amount to induce a high degree of immunity would be fatal.

Three injections of toxoid at monthly intervals usually produce satisfactory immunity, and booster inoculations at intervals of three or four years maintain immunity indefinitely. The effectiveness of immunization against tetanus was so convincingly demonstrated during World War II that tetanus toxoid is now combined with diphtheria toxoid and whooping cough bacterin in a triple vaccine for immunization of infants at about the third month of life.

Antitoxin for prevention or treatment of tetanus is prepared in horses. Carefully selected animals are injected, first with toxoid and later with toxin. Increasing doses are given until tests indicate that the animals' blood serum contains a high concentration of antitoxin. Bleeding of each animal is followed by a rest period and further injections to produce more antitoxin. A horse may continue to produce potent antitoxin for years.

The blood collected from the horse, treated with an anticoagulant chemical such as potassium oxalate or sodium citrate, is allowed to stand until the blood cells settle. The supernatant plasma is removed, purified, and tested for its antitoxic potency. Mixtures of various amounts of the antitoxin solution with an official test dose of tetanus toxin are injected subcutaneously into standard (350 gm.) guinea pigs. The unit of tetanus antitoxin in this country is 10 times the least amount necessary to save the life of a guinea pig for 96 hours after inoculation simultaneously with the test dose of toxin. A standard lot of antitoxin is preserved at the National Institutes of Health; the American unit of this particular lot of horse serum antitoxin is 0.00015 gm. Antitoxin is so stable that it can be kept for many years in the dry condition without loss of protective potency.

Antitoxin is useful for temporary protection of individuals believed to be exposed to tetanal infection. The protection decreases rapidly after two weeks. The use of antitoxin to treat tetanus after symptoms are fully developed is usually of little avail, because toxin that has already combined with nerve tissue cannot be neutralized by antitoxin. Patients are sometimes saved by repeated injections of large doses of antitoxin, together with surgical removal of dead tissue, use of drugs to reduce muscle spasms, and other supportive treatment.

Airborne Diseases

Airborne diseases spread widely within a short time. Moreover, transmission of microorganisms through the air is not easily interrupted. Despite the fact that many parasitic organisms die quickly after their discharge from a natural host, they are usually so numerous that enough survivors remain to infect fresh hosts.

There are two chief vehicles for distribution of microorganisms through the air: (1) droplets of sputum, saliva, or other respiratory secretions, and (2) dust.

Infectious Droplets. Nasal and oral secretions are expelled during sneezing, coughing, and talking. Sneezing is a particularly effective means of broadcasting infectious agents, because the explosive discharge of a considerable volume of air atomizes the secretions and ejects them to a distance of several feet. Droplets larger than 0.1 mm. in diameter quickly fall to the ground. Smaller droplets evaporate and leave suspended nuclei containing microorganisms. These minute particles drift about for hours, and the microorganisms they contain remain viable, protected by the residue of evaporated saliva or mucus.

The nostrils and upper respiratory tract contain hairs and sticky mucous surfaces that entrap particulate matter. This mechanism protects the lungs against inhalation of many harmful agents. Large particles (greater than 4 μ in diameter) are usually removed from inhaled air in this manner. Smaller and lighter particles often pass the nasal area and reach and remain in the respiratory tract, including the lungs. Some very small particles are apparently re-exhaled.

Human epidemics of respiratory or upper respiratory infection are common during cold seasons, when people congregate indoors. Transmission of respiratory secretions is enhanced by modern transportation; an individual in the incubation period of influenza, for example, may travel to the other side of the Earth before his symptoms appear. Shortly after Asian influenza was recognized in the Far East in 1957 it was reported in Newport, Rhode Island, and within a few months was widespread across the United States, despite a vigorous program of artificial immunization.

The so called childhood diseases—chickenpox, measles, mumps, scarlet fever, diphtheria—are readily transmitted from person to person by infective droplets of nasal mucus or saliva. The causative organisms are usually present in a population, either harbored by carriers or as causes of subclinical infections. These diseases engender lasting immunity and occur in epidemic form only at intervals of a few years, after a sufficient population of nonimmune individuals accumulates.

Poliomyelitis. Poliomyelitis is usually a mild disease with upper respiratory or gastrointestinal symptoms. It appears to be primarily an infection of the alimentary tract, and most patients do not show symptoms referable to central nervous system involvement. Paralysis is an occasional accident, estimated to occur only once in 100 to 200 actual infections. Despite the widespread distribution of the causative virus in the respiratory and intestinal tracts, the most conspicuous damage is to motor neurons in the ventral horns of the spinal cord and certain parts of the brain.

The poliomyelitis virus (Fig. 23-2) can be found in the patient's pharyngeal secretions and in the feces. Greatest fecal excretion occurs during the first seven to 10 days of infection, but the duration of excretion may be as long as 20 weeks (in volunteers fed attenuated virus).

Man is the only known reservoir and distributor of poliomyelitis virus. He is also the only normal recipient, although it is possible to infect monkeys and other

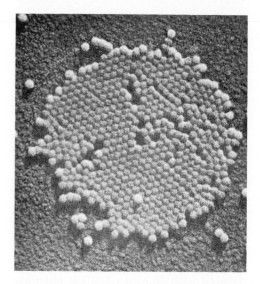

Figure 23-2. Electron photomicrograph of purified poliovirus particles (67,500X). (From Schwerdt et al., Proc. Soc. Exper. Biol. & Med., 86:311, 1954.)

primates in the laboratory, and such infection has actually occurred accidentally.

Despite the discharge of virus in the feces and the fact that it has been detected in sewage, water does not seem to serve as the usual vehicle for transmission of infection. This conclusion is supported by the fact that, whereas public health measures and advances in community sanitation over the past 50 years have almost completely eliminated typhoid fever in the United States, the occurrence of poliomyelitis has been little affected.

Close contact appears to be necessary for transmission of infection from one individual to another. The high incidence of multiple infection within a family and the less frequent transmission of infection to outside individuals indicate that the virus is distributed by pharyngeal secretions.

Immunity against poliomyelitis depends on the presence of antibodies. Administration of human gamma globulin reduces the risk of paralysis if given early enough. These facts justify artificial active immunization.

There are three immunologically distinct types of poliovirus: I (Brunhilde), II (Lansing), and III (Leon). Infection or immunization with one type confers immunity only against its own type. Vaccines for artificial immunization therefore contain all three types.

The Salk vaccine is a mixture of the three viruses, cultivated in monkey kidney tissue and inactivated or killed by formalin. Three properly spaced inoculations induce considerable antibody formation and protection, which is greatly fortified by a booster injection seven to 12 months later. Antibodies persist at least two years after the booster injection; the drop in antibody content of the serum is approximately the same as after clinical paralytic disease. The effectiveness of immunization by the Salk vaccine depends on the number of immunizing injections and other factors. Statistics indicate a reduction in paralytic poliomyelitis of 60 to 70 per cent. However, paralytic and even fatal cases occur in occasional individuals who have received four or more injections of the vaccine.

Some investigators believe that immunization is more effectively accomplished by use of an attenuated, living vaccine given orally. Oral immunization duplicates natural conditions of infection more closely than hypodermic injection and is more easily performed, particularly in young children. The Sabin attenuated vaccine was released in 1960 for use in the United States after field trials in several other countries had demonstrated its effectiveness and safety.

The epidemiology of poliomyelitis resembles that of scarlet fever, diphtheria, measles, and other diseases in which recovery is followed by strong and lasting immunity. There is practically no age distinction in the distribution of cases in previously uninfected populations, and a high percentage of such patients become paralyzed. In populations where the disease has existed for some time, the highest incidence of detected infection is in children over 10 years of age; infections tend to be mild, and there are many abortive and nonparalytic cases for every paralytic case. The average age of infected individuals in urban areas is lower than in rural areas; this fact indicates more rapid dissemination of the virus within a crowded population.

It should be emphasized that any program of artificial immunization markedly reduces the incidence of infection and the opportunities for natural immunization by abortive or subclinical infection. However, occasional cases of frank disease still occur. Immunization of new, nonimmune individuals is therefore necessary, and repeated reimmunization of other individuals may also be required at intervals yet to be determined.

Infective Dust. Infective dust is responsible for transmission of a few human diseases; various pathogens of animals, particularly fowl; and numerous plant pathogens. The psittacosis virus is excreted in the feces of parrots and other pet birds and survives in the dust of cages. Inhalation of the dust transmits the disease to other birds and to man.

Deep-seated fungal infections or systemic mycoses of man, birds, and other animals are acquired by inhalation or ingestion of fungi in soil or dust. Some of these organisms cause diseases of the lung resembling tuberculosis; others produce disease in visceral organs such as the liver. It is of interest that fungi which produce systemic infections are saprophytic and normally live in soil or as accidental residents upon plants. They are usually found only in certain areas, and epidemics are therefore limited geographically. Cases are also usually restricted to agricultural workers.

Numerous plant diseases are caused by partially parasitic fungi and bacteria that survive drying and are distributed by air currents. Epidemics of windborne plant disease are therefore widespread. Tons of bacterial cells or mold spores are scattered over thousands of square miles, and any susceptible plant in the path of the parasite is likely to be infected.

Wheat Rust. Black stem rust of wheat caused by the fungus, *Puccinia graminis,* is found in nearly all parts of the world and affects barley, oats, rye, and certain grasses, as well as wheat. Damage to the wheat crop in the central United States and Canada is extensive despite an active program to combat the infection.

Two hosts are required for the complete life cycle of the fungus (Fig 23-3). The asexual phase occurs on wheat and other grains and grasses. Reddish blisters appear on the stems in late spring, shortly before maturity (Fig. 23-4). These blisters contain fungus mycelium and red spores (uredospores), which are blown to other wheat plants and reproduce the infection. An interval of 10 days is required for the production of a

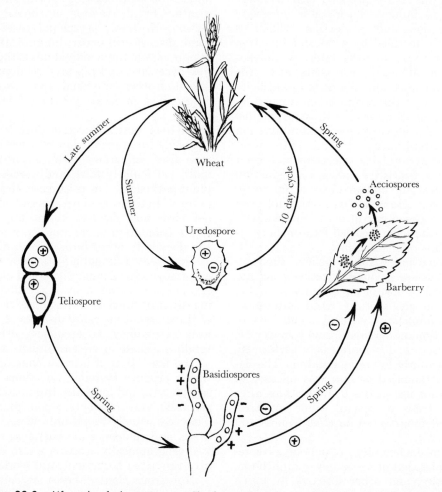

Figure 23-3. Life cycle of wheat stem rust. The fungus *Puccinia graminis* grows on the stems of wheat plants during the late spring and summer, producing uredospores, which are distributed to other plants in a 10 day cycle. Under favorable conditions teliospores are produced. These resist cold weather and survive until the next spring, when they germinate and form sexual basidiospores, which are then carried to the common barberry. Insects effect fertilization of cells of the (+) strain by nuclei from cells of the (−) strain, and aeciospores are liberated. When they are blown to wheat plants they germinate and initiate the summer cycle again.

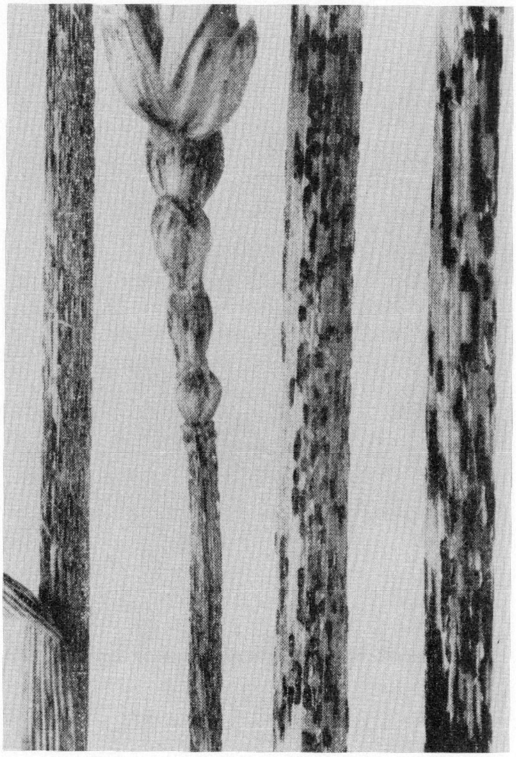

Figure 23-4. Wheat stem rust. The dark, elongated patches on the stems are the blisters, which contain fungus mycelium and spores (3X). (From Weatherwax: Botany, 3d ed. Philadelphia, W. B. Saunders Co., 1956.)

new crop of uredospores. These spores resist drying and may be scattered hundreds of miles by the wind. They are not particularly resistant to cold weather, but under suitable conditions the same mycelium produces a second type of spore (teliospore) in similar blisters; this spore is black or dark brown and the blisters appear black. Teliospores remain dormant over the winter in the straw or on the ground. They germinate in the spring and produce a third type of spore (basidiospore).

Basidiospores are blown about by the wind but do no damage unless they fall upon barberry leaves (Fig. 23-5), where mycelial growth of two different "mating types" is formed. Insects transfer material from one type of mycelium to the opposite type, whereupon fertilization occurs, followed by nuclear division and formation of aeciospores. Aeciospores, when carried by the wind to wheat or other grains or grasses, germinate and produce the mycelium upon

which uredospores are once more formed.

Epidemic spread of wheat stem rust is promoted by several factors: (1) large fields of wheat, such as those found in the central plains of North America from Texas to Canada; (2) mild winters, which permit uredospores to survive; (3) barberry plants on which the sexual cycle can take place; (4) humid or rainy weather in the spring, which favors uredospore germination; (5) vigorous succulent growth of the crop, in which the fungus is most active; and (6) continuous winds to spread the spores.

Wheat rust has been combated by elimination of barberry plants. The first known attempt to control a plant disease by legislation occurred about three centuries ago when officials in Rouen, France, ordered the destruction of barberry bushes. Barberry eradication laws were also enacted in Connecticut, Massachusetts, and Rhode Island between 1726 and 1766. It is of interest in this

Figure 23-5. Wheat stem rust; an infected barberry leaf. Aeciospores produced in these enlarged areas on the lower surface of the leaf are capable of infecting the wheat plant. (From Weatherwax.)

connection that the life cycle of *P. graminis* was not known until about 100 years ago (1865).

Another approach to the problem of eliminating wheat rust is that of breeding resistant varieties of wheat. This has been partially successful, but complete success is hampered by the readiness with which new varieties of the fungus appear. Sexual recombination during the stages in the barberry permits the development of new varieties, some of which possess enhanced survival power even in resistant wheat.

Waterborne and Foodborne Infections

Cases of disease transmitted by water or food are often remote, either in time or space from the source of infection. Many of the microorganisms transmitted by these agents are relatively hardy, and most are only semiparasitic; they may grow within a living host but also multiply readily in nonliving media —both in the laboratory and in foods, and possibly in water. Most pathogens transmitted by water or food cause diseases of the gastrointestinal tract; a few, such as the scarlet fever, diphtheria, and tuberculosis organisms, are also transmitted by infectious droplets through the air and are usually discussed as airborne pathogens.

Epidemics caused by microorganisms spread by water or food are often explosive but are limited in distribution by the nature and extent of the water or food system. The relative hardiness of the organisms that cause typhoid and paratyphoid fevers and dysentery ensures their survival. Contamination of a reservoir, for example, by the excreta of a typhoid fever patient is likely to be followed two weeks later by an outbreak of several hundred cases of the disease, and additional cases appear within the next few weeks until the polluted water is used up or the organisms die.

Dysentery bacteria are a little more exacting in their requirements than the typhoid fever organisms. They are often distributed in food contaminated by carriers or by flies and other insects that have access to the discharges of patients. Bacillary dysentery is usually restricted to institutions, prisons, and camps, rather than occurring in widespread epidemics.

The organisms that cause brucellosis or undulant fever are still more highly parasitic. They are transmitted to man in milk and other dairy products or are acquired by handling meat from infected animals. Cases are therefore limited to persons who use unpasteurized dairy products or work in agriculture.

Typhoid Fever. Typhoid fever is a generalized body infection found only in humans. The usual portal of entry is the mouth, and during the incubation period of 10 to 14 days the causative organism, *Salmonella typhosa,* invades lymphoid tissue of the pharynx or the intestine or both (i.e., the tonsils and Peyer's patches), from which it invades the blood. The organisms are then removed from the blood by cells of the reticuloendothelial system, including the liver, spleen, bone marrow, and mesenteric lymph nodes. Multiplication occurs within these organs, and eventually the bacteria spill over once more into the blood in large numbers.

This bacteremic stage marks the end of the incubation period and the appearance of symptoms of disease: headache, loss of appetite, weakness, diarrhea, fever, and rose spots on the abdomen.

Most of these symptoms are attributed to endotoxins liberated by the bacteria as they undergo autolysis or bacteriolysis. The bacteria also enter the gallbladder, multiply, and are discharged in the bile to the intestine; they therefore appear in the excreta.

Blood cultures usually contain *S. typhosa* during the first week or two of disease, and stool cultures become positive during the second and third weeks. Antibodies also appear in the circulating blood during the second or third week, and at this time the fever often drops.

Antibiotic therapy includes treatment with chloramphenicol. The average mortality is about 10 per cent. Recovery is followed by a slow convalescence requiring several weeks.

Artificial immunization is a widespread practice that is required for all military personnel in the United States and most other countries. The incidence of typhoid fever among soldiers in the field has dropped almost to the vanishing point. Three injections of killed bacteria are given at approximately weekly intervals. Reinoculation two to five years later helps to maintain a high degree of immunity. It should be emphasized that immunization against typhoid fever, like that against most other diseases, is not completely effective; cases occasionally occur in properly immunized individuals during the time they would be expected to be immune.

Epidemic typhoid fever has, until recent years, usually been distributed by polluted water or contaminated milk. Increasing emphasis on sanitation has eliminated most epidemics of these types from civilized countries; water purification and pasteurization of milk have been the responsible developments. The few cases of typhoid fever that occur now are attributed to carriers. These persons are especially dangerous if they work in restaurants, dairies, or other food preparation or food handling establishments.

ECOLOGY OF INFECTIOUS DISEASE

SUMMARY

Epidemics of infectious disease occur when a parasite encounters a susceptible population under conditions that permit its transmission in the viable state from one host individual to another. A large population of susceptible hosts favors epidemic spread of disease. The physical crowding that results from urban civilization and from deliberate cultivation of animals and plants provides the close association necessary for transfer of parasites from one host to another of the same species. In the natural balanced or climax state, individuals of the same species are frequently scattered (except in the case of herd-living animals), and many diseases are endemic rather than epidemic until some external factor upsets the normal balance.

Diseases caused by highly parasitic organisms such as viruses and rickettsiae are transmitted by direct contact or by insect or animal bites. The parasite is not exposed to drying, radiations, or other conditions that might be fatal.

Somewhat hardier organisms survive for limited periods protected by droplets of respiratory secretions, and other resistant forms are distributed in dust.

Many pathogens of poorly parasitic nature, such as the intestinal bacteria, survive and even multiply in food or water. They cause explosive outbreaks or epidemics when ingested by susceptible host populations.

Infectious disease is an accidental consequence of the ecologic rule, "Eat and avoid being eaten." The epidemiology of infectious disease is determined by the various factors that govern the application of this rule: host population density, parasite-host adaptation, survival power and method of transmission of the parasite.

STUDY QUESTIONS

1. What are the conditions under which an epidemic can occur?
2. What becomes of pathogenic microorganisms between epidemics?
3. Discuss the beneficial and harmful aspects of agricultural practices such as cultivation of plants and animals.
4. Describe with examples various factors that determine the speed and extent of epidemic spread of a pathogen.
5. What evidence is there that poliomyelitis is a very widespread disease?
6. Is there any practical method of controlling airborne disease? Explain. Compare with waterborne disease.

SUPPLEMENTARY READING

Burnet's *Natural History of Infectious Disease* is a very readable and stimulating discussion emphasizing the ecologic aspects of infectious disease. A chapter on the evolution of infection and defense is followed by sections on infectious agents, the various defense mechanisms, and the transfer and control of infectious disease. Detailed accounts of many microbial diseases of man and animals—causes, clinical description, laboratory diagnosis, treatment, prevention, epidemiology—are found in the textbooks by Burrows; Dubos; Horsfall; Smith, et al.; and Wilson and Miles. Chester describes the nature and prevention of plant diseases caused by fungi, bacteria, viruses, and nematodes. *The Advance of the Fungi,* by Large, is a fascinating and well written series of historical–biologic sketches in which various fungi play the role of villain.

Burnet, F. M.: *Natural History of Infectious Disease,* 2d ed. Cambridge, Cambridge University Press, 1953.

Burrows, W.: *Textbook of Microbiology,* 18th ed. Philadelphia, W. B. Saunders Co., 1963.

Chester, K. S.: *The Nature and Prevention of Plant Diseases.* Philadelphia, The Blakiston Co., 1942.

Dubos, R. J., and Hirsch, J. G. (Eds.): *Bacterial and Mycotic Infections of Man,* 4th ed. Philadelphia, J. B. Lippincott Co., 1965.

Large, E. C.: *The Advance of the Fungi.* New York, Henry Holt & Co., 1940.

Horsfall, F. L., and Tamm, I. (Eds.): *Viral and Rickettsial Infections of Man,* 4th ed. Philadelphia. J. B. Lippincott Co., 1965.

Smith, D. T., et al.: *Zinsser Microbiology,* 13th ed. New York, Appleton-Century-Crofts, Inc., 1964.

Wilson, G. S., and Miles, A. A.: *Topley and Wilson's Principles of Bacteriology and Immunity,* 4th ed. Baltimore, The Williams & Wilkins Co., 1955.

INDEX

Page numbers of definitions and detailed descriptions are indicated in **boldface** type.

451